Fundamentals of Mathematics
6th Edition

Santa Rosa Junior College
College Skills Department

Arnold R. Steffensen

L. Murphy Johnson
Northern Arizona University

D. Michael Hamm
Brookhaven College

9/4 6:10 - 6:20
meet Rm 610

THOMSON

™

CUSTOM PUBLISHING

Editor: Marc Bove
Publishing Services Supervisor: Donna Brown
Graphic Designer: Krista Pierson
Rights and Permissions Specialist: Kalina Ingham Hintz
Project Coordinator: Mary Snelling
Marketing Manager: Sara L. Hinckley

Thomson Custom Publishing
5191 Natorp Blvd.
Mason, Ohio 45040
USA

For information about our products, contact us:
1-800-355-9983
http://www.thomsoncustom.com

International Headquarters
Thomson Learning
International Division
290 Harbor Drive, 2nd Floor
Stamford, CT 06902-7477
USA

UK/Europe/Middle East/South Africa
Thomson Learning
Berkshire House
168-173 High Holborn
London WCIV 7AA

Asia
Thomson Learning
60 Albert Street, #15-01
Albert Complex
Singapore 189969

Canada
Nelson Thomson Learning
1120 Birchmount Road
Toronto, Ontario MIK 5G4
Canada
United Kingdom

Visit us at www.thomsoncustom.com and learn more about this book and other titles published by Thomson Learning Custom Publishing.

ISBN-13: 978-0-7593-4318-4
ISBN-10: 0-7593-4318-7

The Adaptable Courseware Program consists of products and additions to existing Custom Publishing products that are produced from camera-ready copy. Peer review, class testing, and accuracy are primarily the responsibility of the author(s).

For permission to use material from this text or product, submit a request online at
http://www.thomsonrights.com
Any additional questions about permissions can be submitted by email to thomsonrights@thomson.com

ACKNOWLEDGEMENTS

NCAA NEWS. *Bar graph depicting attendance to NCAA Visitors Center during 1991-1994 and revenue received during that same time period.* From NCAA NEWS. Reprinted with permission from the National Collegiate Athletic Association.

Time Magazine. 1995. *Table titled "Deaths" from January 30, 1995 issue of Time Magazine.* Copyright © 1995 Time Inc. Reprinted by permission.

Time Magazine. 1995. *Table titled "Faith" from January 30, 1995 issue of Time Magazine (Original data from the National Survey of religion and Politics, 1992, University of Akron Survey Research Center).* Copyright © Time Inc. Reprinted by permission.

Time Magazine. 1994. *Table titled "Presidential Batting Averages" from the October 24, 1994 issue of Time Magazine (Original data from Congressional Quarterly).* Copyright © 1994 Time Inc. Reprinted by permission.

Time Magazine. 1995. *Table titled "Housing" from the January 30, 1995 issue of Time Magazine (Original data from the National Association of Realtors).* Copyright © Time Inc. Reprinted by permission.

Time Magazine. 1995. *Tables titled "Spending " "Teachers," and "Income" from the January 30, 1995 issue of Time Magazine.* Copyright © 1995 Time Inc. Reprinted by permission.

Time Magazine. 1994. *Table titled "Jobs Created or Lost" from the October 24, 1994 issue of Time Magazine.* Copyright © 1994 Time Inc. Reprinted by permission.

CONTENTS

PREFACE.. ix

TO THE STUDENT.. xi

PRETEST.. 1

CHAPTER 1   WHOLE NUMBERS

1.1   Place Value and Naming Numbers.................................6
1.2   Adding Whole Numbers..15
1.3   Rounding Whole Numbers and Estimation...................28
1.4   Subtracting Whole Numbers.......................................35
1.5   Multiplying Whole Numbers......................................46
1.6   Properties of Multiplication and Special Products..........56
1.7   Dividing Whole Numbers..66
1.8   More Problem Solving with Whole Numbers.................80
1.9   Primes, Powers, Roots, and Order of Operations............95

Chapter 1 Review...109
Chapter 1 Test..118

CHAPTER 2   MULTIPLYING AND DIVIDING FRACTIONS

2.1   Fractions..122
2.2   Renaming Fractions...129
2.3   Multiplying Fractions..138
2.4   Dividing Fractions..146
2.5   Multiplying and Dividing Mixed Numbers..................153
2.6   More Problem Solving with Fractions.........................161

Chapter 2 Review...166
Chapter 2 Test..171
Cumulative Review: Chapters 1-2.....................................173

CHAPTER 3   ADDING AND SUBTRACTING FRACTIONS

3.1 Adding and Subtracting Like Fractions...176
3.2 Finding Least Common Multiples..181
3.3 Adding and Subtracting Unlike Fractions..187
3.4 Adding and Subtracting Mixed Numbers...194
3.5 Order of Operations and Comparing Fractions.......................................201
3.6 More Problem Solving with Fractions...209

Chapter 3 Review..214
Chapter 3 Test...217
Cumulative Review: Chapters 1-3...219

CHAPTER 4   DECIMALS

4.1 Decimal Fractions and Decimals..222
4.2 Conversions Between Fractions and Decimals...228
4.3 Rounding Decimals and Estimation...237
4.4 Adding and Subtracting Decimals..244
4.5 Multiplying Decimals...255
4.6 Dividing Decimals...265
4.7 Order of Operations and Comparing Decimals.......................................276
4.8 The Calculator..285

Chapter 4 Review..295
Chapter 4 Test...300
Cumulative Review: Chapters 1-4..302

CHAPTER 5 RATIO, PROPORTION, AND MEASUREMENT

5.1 Ratio and Proportion..304
5.2 Rates...313
5.3 The English System of Measurement...318
5.4 Arithmetic of Measurement Numbers..326
5.5 The Metric System of Measurement..334
5.6 Conversions Between Measurement Systems...341

Chapter 5 Review..350
Chapter 5 Test...354
Cumulative Review: Chapters 1-5...355

CHAPTER 6   PERCENT

6.1 Percent and Percent Conversions...358
6.2 Problem Solving with Percent..368
6.3 Tax Problems..380
6.4 Commission and Discount Problems..387

6.5   Interest Problems..393
6.6   Percent Increase and Decrease Problems..400
6.7   Markup and Markdown Problems...409

Chapter 6 Review...415
Chapter 6 Test..420
Cumulative Review: Chapters 1-6...422

CHAPTER 7   INTRODUCTION TO STATISTICS

7.1   Circle Graphs, Bar Graphs, and Pictographs.......................................424
7.2   Broken-Line Graphs and Histograms..435
7.3   Mean, Median, and Mode..445

Chapter 7 Review...455
Chapter 7 Test..460
Cumulative Review: Chapters 1-7...462

Answers to Selected Exercises..463
Applications Index...481
Index..484

PREFACE

Fundamentals of Mathematics, Fifth Edition, is designed to give students a review of the basic skills of mathematics necessary for preparation for the study of algebra. Carefully worded explanations written for the student, detailed examples with parallel practice exercises, abundant exercises of a wide variety, and comprehensive continuous review are hallmarks of the book. The text has been written for maximum instructor flexibility with both core and peripheral topics that can be selected for individual course needs. An annotated instructor's edition, test manual, and computerized test generator are provided for the instructor. Supplements for the student include a set of instructional videotapes and a student's solutions manual written by the authors.

FEATURES

CHAPTER OPENERS now all use real data to illustrate realistic application. Each problem stated in the opener is solved in an example later in the chapter.

STUDENT GUIDEPOSTS specify major topics, rules, and procedures. They are listed at the beginning of each section, and then repeated as the corresponding material is discussed in that section. This feature helps students locate important concepts.

PRACTICE EXERCISES parallel each example and keep students involved with the presentation by allowing them to check their understanding of ideas.

EXAMPLES Nearly 800 examples include detailed, step-by-step solutions and descriptive side comments. A brief descriptive title on each example focuses attention on the concept at hand and aids in review.

NOTES emphasize useful memory devices and provide additional explanation.

EXPLORATION GUIDES consist of problems that involve writing, exploration, or discussion of a particular concept. These provide further emphasis of NCTM standards relative to conceptual understanding and writing exercises.

DEFINITIONS AND RULES are outlined in boxes to stress their importance.

CAUTIONS call students' attention to common mistakes and special problems to avoid.

EXERCISES

As a key feature of the text, more than 7000 exercises are provided. These include many new conceptual and writing exercises that incorporate the use of real data from current literature. Also there are approximately 800 practice exercises and 70 exploration exercises in the margins. All exercises have been reviewed for grading and balance of coverage with emphasis given to practical applications.

End-of-Section Exercises There are two sets of end-of-section exercises. To emphasize that the second set of exercises for each section actually parallels the first set of exercises, the names of these two sets are 'Exercises' and "Parallel Exercises."

Exercises: This set of exercises has work space and all answers are given in the back of the text.

Parallel Exercises: This set matches the exercises given in the first set problem for problem but presented without answers in the back of the text.

Each set of exercises has a "Critical Thinking" section designed to give students an extra challenge or to present problems requiring conceptual understanding, writing skills, or calculator usage. Hints are given for selected exercises in this set.

REVIEW EXERCISES: To provide ample opportunities for review and reinforcement, the text features a variety of review exercises.

FOR REVIEW: These exercises are located at the ends of most of the Exercise sets. They not only encourage continuous review of previously covered material, but also often provide special review preparation for topics covered in the upcoming section.

CHAPTER REVIEW EXERCISES: These are presented at the end of each chapter and are divided into two parts. The problems in Part I are ordered and marked by section for easy reference; those in Part II are not referenced to the source section and are thoroughly mixed to help students prepare for examinations. Answers to all Chapter Review exercises are given at the end of the text.

CUMULATIVE REVIEW EXERCISES: Beginning with Chapter 2, a set of Cumulative Review Exercises concludes each chapter, providing a continuous review of topics previously studied, thereby helping students retain concepts. Answers to all Cumulative Review Exercises are given at the end of the text.

CHAPTER TESTS: Each chapter concludes with a practice test. Answers to Chapter Tests are given at the end of the text.

FINAL REVIEW EXERCISES: These are given at the back of the text, are referenced by chapter, and have answers supplied. They are designed to assist students in preparation for their final exam.

APPLICATIONS: To demonstrate the usefulness and practicality of mathematics, applications are integrated throughout the text, including many that are presented with an accompanying *USA Today* Snapshot of a graph, table, or chart including real data. A special strategy for solving word problems, the ATTACK method, is given in Chapter 10. Relevant applied problems—from such diverse areas as business, engineering, physics, chemistry, agriculture, sports, and recreation—are appropriately labeled and included in chapter introductions, examples, and exercises.

CHAPTER REVIEWS: In addition to including the Chapter Review Exercises and Chapter Tests, the comprehensive Chapter Reviews also include Key Words and Key Concepts. Key Words, listed by section, provide brief definitions. Key Concepts summarize the major points of each section.

SUPPLEMENTS

An extensive supplemental package is available for use with *Fundamentals of Mathematics,* Fifth Edition.

FOR THE INSTRUCTOR

The Annotated Instructor's Edition provides instructors with immediate access to the answers to every exercise in the text, with the exception of the writing exercises. Symbols are used to identify conceptual exercises and writing exercises to assist in making homework assignments.

The Instructor's Test Manual, **written by the authors,** contains a series of ready-to-duplicate tests in an easy-to-use format with all of the answers provided: a Placement Test to help determine which course a student should take, a multiple-choice Pretest for Chapter 1 to help determine where a student should start in this course, six different but equivalent tests for each chapter (four open response and two multiple choice), and two final exams. An extensive exercise bank of additional problems, grouped by section and including writing exercises, are available for in-class quizzes or tests. Section-by-section teaching tips provide suggestions for content implementation that an instructor, tutor, or teaching assistant might find helpful. An appendix on critical reasoning is included and may be used in conjunction with Chapter 8.

A computerized test generator is available in IBM format. The test generator enables instructors to select questions by objective, section, or chapter, or to use a ready-made test for each chapter. The editor enables instructors to edit any preexisting data or to easily create their own questions. The software is algorithm driven, allowing the instructor to regenerate constants while maintaining problem type, providing a nearly unlimited number of available test or quiz items in multiple-choice or open-response formats. The system features printed graphics and accurate mathematics symbols.

FOR THE STUDENT

The Student's Solutions Manual, **written by the authors**, is available for student purchase and contains complete solutions to every exercise in the first set of end-of-section exercises, and to all Practice Exercises, Chapter Review Exercises, Cumulative Review Exercises, Chapter Test questions, and Final Review Exercises.

Videotapes A videotape series is available to accompany *Fundamentals of Mathematics,* Fifth Edition.

TO THE STUDENT

Over the years, we have taught fundamentals of mathematics to many students and have heard comments such as the following on numerous occasions. "I've always been afraid of math and have avoided it as much as possible." 'I have never liked math, but now I have to take it to graduate." "I can't do percent problems!" If you have ever made such a statement, now is the time to think positively and allow us to help you down the path toward success in mathematics. Don't worry about the course as a whole, we will guide you step-by-step, one small step at a time. Here are some general and specific guidelines that are necessary and helpful.

GENERAL GUIDELINES

1. Motivation and dedication are the basic requirements for mastering mathematics. Just as an athlete does not improve without commitment to his or her goal, a mathematics student must be prepared to work hard and spend time studying. Keep up with your assignments. Don't procrastinate and let things slide until the night before your exam. If you need extra help, ask for it right away. In mathematics you will often discover that comprehension of one topic depends on understanding a previous one. If you are behind in your work, you will have more difficulty.

2. Students often have the impression that their homework consists only of the written exercises assigned at the end of a section. Actually, you will take a tremendous step toward success if you recognize that the written homework exercises are only a part of your homework assignment. In reality, your homework should consist of studying your class notes, reading the appropriate section in your text, and finally, testing yourself to see if you really have mastered the material by working the assigned written exercises.

3. Mathematics is not learned by simply watching, listening, or reading; *it is learned by doing.* Use your text, use your pencil, and practice, practice, practice. When your thoughts are organized and written in a neat and orderly manner, you will have taken another giant step toward success. Do not try to take shortcuts, but complete and write out all details. This is especially true when working application problems. Try to pattern your work after the examples presented by your instructor or in the text.

4. The use of a calculator is introduced in Section 4.8. Become familiar with the features of your particular model by consulting the owner's manual. When working problems that involve computing with decimals, a calculator can be a time-saving device. On the other hand, you should not be so dependent on a calculator that you use it to perform simple calculations that might be done mentally. For example, it would probably be ridiculous to use a calculator to find $8 \div 2$, while it would be helpful when finding $7343.84 \div 1.12$. It is important to learn when to use and when not to use your calculator. However, some exercises in the text are specifically designated for calculator use using a calculator symbol.

SPECIFIC GUIDELINES

1. As you begin to study each section, look ahead through the material for a preview of what to expect.

2. Return to the beginning of the section and start reading slowly; study the explanations carefully. The Student Guideposts will help you find important concepts as you progress. Pay close attention to the definitions, rules, and procedures in the colored boxes and try to test yourself by writing out each definition or summarizing each rule or procedure using your own words.

3. Read each example and make sure that you understand each step. The side comments given in color will help you if something is not quite clear.

4. After studying an example, work the parallel Practice Exercise in the margin. This will reinforce what you have read and start the process of practice. Complete solutions to the Practice Exercises are available in the *Student's Solutions Manual.*

5. Periodically you will encounter a Caution. These warn you of common mistakes and special problems that should be avoided.

6. The Notes throughout the text are provided to give you a better understanding of material by providing important information, additional explanation, and useful memory devices.

7. After you finish the material in the body of the section, you need to check your understanding of the concepts and begin to practice, practice, practice! Work all of the exercises assigned by your instructor. Answers to all of the exercises in the first set are provided so you can check your progress. Complete solutions to these as well as to the Practice Exercises, Chapter Review Exercises, Cumulative Review Exercises, Chapter Test questions, and Final Review Exercises are available in the *Student's Solutions Manual.*

8. To help you retain what you have learned and to prepare for topics in the next section, be sure to work the For Review exercises located at the end of most exercise sets.

9. After you have completed all of the sections in the chapter, read the Chapter Review that contains Key Words and Key Concepts. The Chapter Review Exercises provide more practice before you take the Chapter Test.

10. To help you study for your final exam, we have concluded the book with a comprehensive set of Final Review Exercises.

If you follow these guidelines and work closely with your instructor, you will greatly improve your chance of success in mathematics. We wish you the best of luck in your course.

Arnold R. Steffensen
L. Murphy Johnson
D. Michael Hamm

CHAPTER 1 PRETEST

NAME_____   DATE_____ SCORE_____

1.1

1. Give the first three natural numbers.
   (a) 0, 1, 2   (b) 1, 2, 3   (c) 3   (d) none of these

   1. _____b_____

2. Consider the number line. Place the appropriate symbol (< or >) be-tween a and b, a__?__ b.

   ```
   +--+--+--+--+--+--+--+--+--+--+--+-->
   0  1  2  b     6     a    10 11 12
   ```

   (a) $a < b$ (b) $a < b$ (c) neither   (d) none of these

   2. _____d_____

3. Write $400,000 + 6000 + 500 + 3$ in standard notation.
   (a) 465,300   (b) 400,653   (c) 406,503   (d) none of these

   3. _____c_____

4. In the number 65,321,409, what digit represents millions?
   (a) 6   (b) 5   (c) 3   (d) none of these

   4. _____b_____

5. Write 32,502 in expanded notation.
   (a) $30,000 + 2000 + 500 + 2$ (b) $32,000 + 502$
   (c) $30,000 + 5000 + 200 + 20$ (d) none of these

   5. _____a_____

1.2

6. What law of addition is illustrated by $3 + 8 = 8 + 3$?
   (a) associative law   (b) distributive law
   (c) commutative law   (d) none of these

   6. _____a_____

7. What is the missing number? $7 + $__?__$ = 7$
   (a) 14   (b) 7   (c) 0   (d) none of these

   7. _____c_____

Find the following sums.

8.   539
   $+ 46$
   (a) 575 (b) 585
   (c) 493
   (d) none of these

9.   3068
   $+2156$
   (a) 5215 (b) 5225
   (c) 911
   (d) none of these

   8. _____b_____

   9. _____d_____

10. Translate the expression: v increased by 7
    (a) $7v$ (b) $v - 7$ (c) $v + 7$ (d) none of these

    10. _____a_____

11. What law of addition is illustrated by $(2 + 5) + 8 = 2 + (5 + 8)$?
    (a) associative law   (b) distributive law
    (c) commutative law   (d) none of these

    11. _____b_____

1.3

12. Round 24,526 to the nearest thousand.
    (a) 24,000   (b) 25,000   (c) 24,500   (d) none of these

    12. _____b_____

13. Estimate   3459 by rounding to the nearest hundred.
    $+ 375$
    (a) 3800   (b) 4000   (c) 3900   (d) none of these

    13. _____a_____

CHAPTER 1 PRETEST

14. During a two-game championship, 9103 people attended the first game and 10,985 attended the second. First estimate the total attendance, and then find the exact attendance.
    (a) 20,000; 20,088   (b) 19,000; 19,088
    (c) 21,000; 20,988   (d) none of these

14. _____

1.4

15. What is the missing number? $10 - \underline{\quad ? \quad} = 6$
    (a) 0   (b) 3   (c) 6   (d) none of these

15. _____

16. What is the missing number? $\underline{\quad ? \quad} - 0 = 15$
    (a) 25   (b) 15   (c) 30   (d) none of these

16. _____

Find the following differences.

17.   524
    $- \quad 78$
    (a) 446   (b) 456
    (c) 602
    (d) none of these

18.   602
    -327
    (a) 385   (b) 275
    (c) 285
    (d) none of these

17. _____

18. _____

19. Translate the expression: 9 less than m
    (a) $9 - m$ (b) $m - 9$ (c) $9 + m$ (d) none of these

19. _____

1.5

20. Give the first three multiples of 3.
    (a) 0, 3, 6   (b) 3, 6, 9   (c) 0, 6, 12   (d) none of these

20. _____

Find the following products.

21.   56
    $\times 14$
    (a) 774   (b) 764
    (c) 884
    (d) none of these

22.   341
    $\times 105$
    (a) 35,805   (b) 35,705
    (c) 36,805
    (d) none of these

21. _____

22. _____

23. Translate the expression: The product of 4 and n
    (a) $4n$ (b) $4 + n$ (c) $n \div 4$ (d) none of these

23. _____

1.6

24. What law of multiplication is illustrated by $4 \times 7 = 7 \times 4$?
    (a) associative law   (b) distributive law
    (c) commutative law   (d) none of these

24. _____

25. What is the missing number? $8 \times \underline{\quad ? \quad} = 8$
    (a) 1   (b) 8   (c) 16   (d) none of these

25. _____

26. What is the missing number? $5 \times \underline{\quad ? \quad} = 0$
    (a) 25   (b) 5   (c) 0   (d) none of these

26. _____

CHAPTER 1 PRETEST

27. What law of multiplication is illustrated by $(3 \times 5) \times 7 = 3 \times (5 \times 7)$?
    (a) associative law   (b) distributive law
    (c) commutative law   (d) none of these

27. _____

28. Estimate the product 695×207 by rounding to the nearest hundred.
    (a) 120,000   (b) 130,000   (c) 140,000   (d) none of these

28. _____

29. Use the distributive law and the associative law to multiply:
    $2(4x + 5)$
    (a) $8x + 10$ (b) $8x + 5$ (c) $6x + 7$ (d) none of these

29. _____

1.7

30. What is the missing number? $16 \div 2 = \underline{\quad ? \quad}$
    (a) 32   (b) 8   (c) 4   (d) none of these

30. _____

31. What is the missing number? $8 \div \underline{\quad ? \quad} = 2$
    (a) 16   (b) 2   (c) 4   (d) none of these

31. _____

32. What is the missing number? $0 \div 9 = \underline{\quad ? \quad}$
    (a) 0   (b) 9   (c) 1   (d) none of these

32. _____

33. What number cannot be used as a divisor?
    (a) 1   (b) 0   (c) 10   (d) none of these

33. _____

Find the following quotients and remainders.

34. $31\overline{)642}$
    (a) Q:20; R:20   (b) Q:20; R:22
    (c) Q:21; R:9   (d) none of these

34. _____

35. Find the value of the expression: 24 divided by 4
    (a) 2   (b) 28   (c) 12   (d) none of these

35. _____

1.8

Solve.

36. Professor Jordan has three classes with 41, 39, and 17 students, respectively. How many students does Professor Jordan have?
    (a) 97 students   (b) 87 students
    (c) 96 students   (d) none of these

36. _____

37. On the first day of football practice, 145 players reported. After one week, 56 players had been cut or quit the team. How many players were still on the team at the end of that week?
    (a) 99 players   (b) 201 players
    (c) 89 players   (d) none of these

37. _____

38. Jaunita received two checks for her graduation, one for $200 and the other for $250. She used the money to buy a sweater for $48, a skirt for $39, and a book for $18. She kept $50 in cash, and deposited the rest of the money in her savings account. How much did she deposit?
    (a) $395   (b) $295   (c) $345   (d) none of these

38. _____

CHAPTER 1 PRETEST

39. The Allens have three children, and they wish to divide up equally   39. _____
    $9750 between them. How much will each child receive?
    (a) $3225   (b) $3275   (c) $3350   (d) none of these

40. Zach purchased 8 books at $18 each and 3 posters at $5 each. How   40. _____
    much change will he receive if he pays with eight $20-bills?
    (a) $1   (b) $11   (c) $13   (d) none of these

1.9

41. What is the only even prime number?   41. _____
    (a) 4   (b) 10   (c) 2   (d) none of these

42. Write 210 as a product of primes.   42. _____
    (a) $2 \cdot 3 \cdot 5 \cdot 5$ (b) $3 \cdot 5 \cdot 5 \cdot 7$

    (c) $2 \cdot 3 \cdot 3 \cdot 7$ (d) none of these

43. Is 1262 divisible by 3?   43. _____
    (a) yes   (b) no   (c) cannot be determined   (d) none of these

44. What property do numbers that are divisible by 5 have?   44. _____
    (a) The ones digit is 0.   (b) The ones digit is 5.
    (c) The ones digit is either 0 or 5.   (d) none of these

45. Is 25 a perfect square?   45. _____
    (a) yes   (b) no   (c) cannot be determined   (d) none of these

46. What is a square of 4?   46. _____
    (a) 2   (b) 4   (c) 16   (d) none of these

47. What is the square root of 4?   47. _____
    (a) 2   (b) 4   (c) 16   (d) none of these

Perform the indicated operations.

48. $(2+1)^2 - 2^2 + 1^2$ 48. _____
    (a) 0   (b) 3   (c) 6   (d) none of these

49. $2 \cdot 3^2$ 49. _____
    (a) 36   (b) 18   (c) 12   (d) none of these

50. $\sqrt{16} \div 4$ 50. _____
    (a) 1   (b) 2   (c) 4   (d) none of these

CHAPTER o•n•e

WHOLE NUMBERS

Numbers form the basic tools that are used in all of mathematics. However, the idea of a number originated rather late in human history. Many primitive cultures had words for the concepts of *one* and *two*, but numbers past these seemed to be lumped into the concept of *many*. Over the years there have been many different types of *numeration systems*, ways to represent numbers. The system that we use today, the base ten positional Hindo-Arabic system, was refined and introduced by Leonardo Fibonacci of Pisa (1170-1250) during the thirteenth century. It is this system, as it relates to the *whole numbers*, that serves as the starting point for our work. The whole numbers provide a variety of applied problems. The following is an example of the type of problem we can solve using the material found in this chapter. Its solution is given in Example 4 of Section 1.8.

SPACE EXPLORATION The years 1992-93 were busy ones in the exploration of space by space shuttle flights as shown in the table below.

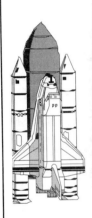

FLIGHT NUMBER	DATE	SHUTTLE NAME	DAYS IN ORBIT	FLIGHT NUMBER	DATE	SHUTTLE NAME	DAYS IN ORBIT
42	1/22/92	Discovery	8	54	1/13/93	Endeavour	6
45	3/24/92	Atlantis	8	56	4/8/93	Discovery	9
49	5/7/92	Endeavour	8	55	4/26/93	Columbia	10
50	6/25/92	Columbia	13	57	6/21/93	Endeavour	10
46	7/31/92	Atlantis	7	51	9/12/93	Discovery	10
47	9/12/92	Endeavour	7	58	10/18/93	Columbia	14
52	10/22/92	Columbia	9	61	12/2/93	Endeavour	11
53	12/2/92	Discovery	7				

Source: U.S. National Aeronautics and Space Administration

(a) Which of the four shuttles spent the most days in orbit during this two-year period?
(b) Which of the four shuttles spent the fewest days in orbit during this two-year period?
(c) Which year was the busiest relative to the total number of days in orbit for all shuttles?
(d) During this two-year period, the Columbia was in orbit how many more days than the Atlantis?

We begin this chapter by discussing the ways that we represent numbers, including the idea of a variable. We then consider the operations of addition, subtraction, multiplication, and division of whole numbers, discuss rounding numbers for use in estimation, and solve a variety of applied problems that involve whole numbers. Finally, we develop the concepts of primes, powers, roots, and the order of operations.

1.1 PLACE VALUE AND NAMING NUMBERS

STUDENT GUIDEPOSTS
1   RECOGNIZING NUMBERS, VARIABLES, AND THE NUMBER LINE
2   ORDERING NUMBERS AND USING INEQUALITY SYMBOLS
3   RECOGNIZING PLACE-VALUE IN OUR NUMBER SYSTEM
4   USING WORD NAMES FOR NUMBERS

1 | NUMBERS, VARIABLES, AND THE NUMBER LINE

The numbers that we learn about first are the **natural** or **counting numbers**. They are used to answer the question "How many?" The symbols or **numerals** representing these numbers are:

$$1, 2, 3, 4, 5, 6, 7, 8, 9, 10, 11,...$$

The three dots are used to show that the pattern continues.

The **whole numbers** are formed by including 0 with the natural numbers. Thus,

$$0, 1, 2, 3, 4, 5, 6, 7, 8, 9, 10, 11$$

are the first twelve whole numbers.

Numbers are actually ideas that exist in our minds. It is helpful to "picture" these ideas using a **number line,** shown in Figure 1.1.

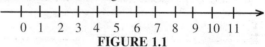

FIGURE 1.1

Every whole number corresponds to a point on a number line. The smallest whole number is 0. There is no largest whole number, since we can keep on extending the number line to the right. The arrowhead points to the direction in which the numbers get larger.

Sometimes we will use a letter such as *a, b, c,* or *x* to represent a number as shown in Example 1. When we do this, the letter is called a **variable.**

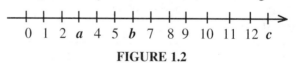

REPRESENTING NUMBERS ON A NUMBER LINE   **EXAMPLE 1**

What numbers are represented by the variables *a, b,* and *c* in Figure 1.2?

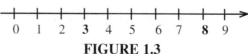

FIGURE 1.2

The variable *a* represents the number 3, *b* represents 6, and *c* represents 13.

2 | ORDERING NUMBERS AND USING INEQUALITY SYMBOLS

The whole numbers occur in a natural **order**. For example, we know that 3 is less than 8, and that 8 is greater than 3. On a number line, 3 is to the left of 8, while 8 is to the right of 3.

FIGURE 1.3

PRACTICE EXERCISE 1

What numbers are represented by *x, y,* and *z* on the number line below?

Answer: *x* represents 5, *y* represents 1, and *z* represents 11.

The symbol < means "is less than." We write "3 is less than 8" as

$$3 < 8.$$

Similarly, the symbol > means "is greater than." Thus, we write "8 is greater than 3" as

$$8 > 3.$$

Notice that $3 < 8$ and $8 > 3$ are two different ways to express the same order relationship between 3 and 8. The symbols < and > are called **inequality symbols.**

ORDER ON A NUMBER LINE

1. If a number a is to the left of another number b on a number line, then a is less than b, and we write $a < b$.
2. If a number a is to the right of another number b on a number line, then a is greater than b, and we write $a > b$.

NOTE When the inequality symbols < and > are used, remember that the symbol points to the smaller of the two numbers. Also, when referring to a number line, it may help to remember that "left" and "less" both begin with the same letter "L", and That The symbol "<" resembles a tilted letter L.

E X A M P L E 2   **ORDERING NUMBERS**

PRACTICE EXERCISE 2

Place the correct symbol (< or >) between the numbers in the given pairs. Use part of a number line if necessary.

(a) 12 $>$ 9

$12 > 9$. Notice that 12 is to the right of 9 on the number line in Figure 1.4. Remember that $12 > 9$ could also be written as $9 < 12$.

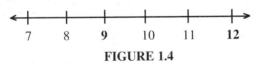

FIGURE 1.4

(b) 0 ____ 42

$0 < 42$. See Figure 1.5.

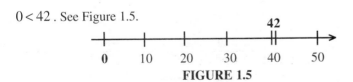

FIGURE 1.5

PRACTICE EXERCISE 2

Place the correct symbol (< or >) between the numbers in the given pairs.

(a) 5 $<$ 15

(b) 106 $>$ 0

Answers: (a) <   (b) >

---

3 PLACE-VALUE NUMBER SYSTEM

The first ten whole numbers,

0, 1, 2, 3, 4, 5, 6, 7, 8, 9,

are called **digits** (from the Latin word *digitus* meaning finger). Any whole number can be written using a combination of these ten digits. For example,

---

EXPLORATION GUIDE

Suppose that a is the three-digit number 3x8, where x is one of the digits. If $a < 368$ and $a > 348$, what digit is x?

5

245 is a three-digit number
3 is a one-digit number
75 is a two-digit number
4280 is a four-digit number.

The value of each digit in a number depends on its place in the number. In other words, our number system is a **place-value system.** For example, the four-digit number

2538,

written above in **standard notation,** is a short form of the **expanded notation**

$$2000 + 500 + 30 + 8,$$

as shown in the following diagram.

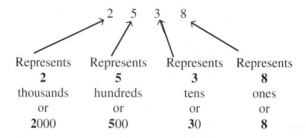

Represents	Represents	Represents	Represents
2	**5**	**3**	**8**
thousands	hundreds	tens	ones
or	or	or	or
2000	**500**	**30**	**8**

PRACTICE EXERCISE 3

Write each number in expanded notation.
(a) 103

$100 + 0 + 3$
$(100 + 3)$

(b) 1030

$1000 + 0 + 30 + 0$
$(1000 + 30)$

WRITING IN EXPANDED NOTATION   **EXAMPLE 3**

Write each number in expanded notation.

(a) 532

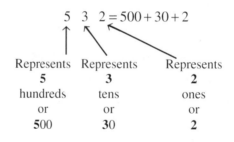

5 3 2 = 500 + 30 + 2

Represents	Represents	Represents
5	**3**	**2**
hundreds	tens	ones
or	or	or
500	**30**	**2**

(b) 5032

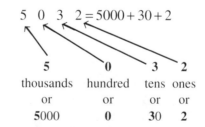

5 0 3 2 = 5000 + 30 + 2

5	**0**	**3**	**2**
thousands	hundred	tens	ones
or	or	or	or
5000	**0**	**30**	**2**

Notice the difference between 5032 and 532 in Examples 3 **(b)** and 3 **(a).** In 5032, 0 represents 0 hundreds while the digit 5 represents 5 thousands. If 0 were not in the hundreds place in 5032, we would read the number as 532. It is clear from this example that 0 is an important **place-holder** in our system.

E X A M P L E
4   **WRITING IN STANDARD NOTATION**

Write each number in standard notation.

(a) $300 + 20 + 8 = 328$

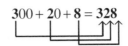

(b) $5000 + 400 + 30 + 9 = 5439$

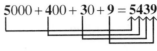

(c) $7000 + 20 = 7020$
   **Notice the zero used in the hundreds place
   and the ones place.**

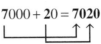

(d) $90,000 + 300 + 1 = 90,301$

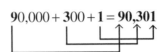

4   **WORD NAMES FOR NUMBERS**

When a number contains more than four digits, commas are used to separate the digits into groups of three, as in the number
$$2,431,897,502,113.$$

Notice that the commas are placed starting at the right. The last group of digits on the left can have one, two, or three digits. Each group of three has a name, as does each digit in the group. These names are given in the following chart.

Trillions			Billions			Millions			Thousands			Units		
hundreds	tens	ones	hundreds	tens	ones	hundreds	tens	ones	hundreds	tens	ones	hundreds	tens	ones
2	,	4	3	1	,	8	9	7	,	5	0	2	,	1	1	3

In words, the preceding number is
two trillion, four hundred thirty-one billion, eight hundred ninety-seven million, five hundred two thousand, one hundred thirteen.

The commas in the word name are in the same place as they are in the standard notation.

> CAUTION   Do not use the word *and* when expressing whole numbers in words. For example, 423,123 is four hundred twenty-three thousand, one hundred twenty-three, *not* four hundred *and* twenty-three thousand, one hundred *and* twenty-three. The word *and* will be used later in Chapter 4 to refer to a decimal point in a number.

E X A M P L E
5   **WRITING WORD NAMES FROM STANDARD
            NOTATION**

Write a word name for each number

(a) 39,205   thirty nine thousand, two hundred five

39,205
↓
Thousand

The word name is: **thirty-nine thousand**, two hundred five. Notice that the word *and* is not written here: ⟶↑

(b) 27,532,141,269

27,532,141,269

Thousand
Million
Billion

The word name is: **twenty-seven billion**, five hundred thirty-two million, one hundred forty-one thousand, two hundred sixty-nine.

(c) 904,000,102,425,000

The word name is nine hundred four trillion, one hundred two million, four hundred twenty-five thousand.

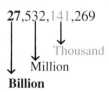

NOTE   Four-digit numbers are usually written without commas. For example, we write 4136 instead of 4,136. However, a number with five or more digits, such as 14,136, should be written with the comma.

(b) 84,000,227

eighty four million, tw hundred twenty seven thousand.

(c) 7,643,000,058

seven trillion, six hundred forty three million, fifty eight thousand

Answers: (a) four hundred thirty-six thousand, one hundred nine
(b) eighty-four million, two hundred twenty-seven   (c) seven billion, six hundred forty-three million, fifty-eight

---

PRACTICE EXERCISE 6

Write each number in standard notation.

(a) Seven thousand, twenty-three   *7,023*

(b) Two hundred eighty-seven million, four hundred five thousand, nine hundred sixty-six   *287,405,966*

(c) Nine trillion, seven hundred fifty thousand, two hundred one   *9,000,000,750,201*

Answers: (a) 7023
(b) 287,405,966
(c) 9,000,000,750,201

PRACTICE EXERCISE 7

Give the value of the digit 7 in each number.
(a) 1,720,458
(b) 65,286,127,003

WRITING STANDARD NOTATION FROM WORD NAMES	EXAMPLE 6

Write each number in standard notation.

(a) **Four** thousand, one hundred thirty-six.

4 136

(b) Four hundred eighty-three billion, two hundred sixty million, five hundred twenty-one thousand, nine hundred ninety-six

Billions	Millions	Thousands	Units
4 8 3,	2 6 0,	5 2 1,	9 9 6

(c) Six trillion, three hundred twenty-four million, five hundred six

6,000,324,000,506

The value of each digit in a number is determined by its place or position.

GIVING THE VALUE OF A DIGIT IN A NUMBER	EXAMPLE 7

Give the value of the digit 4 in each number.

(a) 304,152   **4** thousands
(b) 23,**2**41,309,117   **4** ten millions

(c) 452,000,302,198

(d) 32,922,647

4 hundred billions

4 tens

(c) 97,480,153 *Millin*

(d) 925,703 *7 hundred*

EXAMPLE 8   IDENTIFYING DIGITS BY NAME

In the number 12,345,678 give the digit that represents the following places.

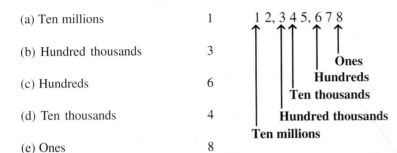

(a) Ten millions   1

(b) Hundred thousands   3

(c) Hundreds   6

(d) Ten thousands   4

(e) Ones   8

1 2, 3 4 5, 6 7 8

Ones
Hundreds
Ten thousands
Hundred thousands
Ten millions

PRACTICE EXERCISE 8

In the number 856,321,409 give the digit that represents the following places.
(a) Hundred millions
(b) Millions
(c) Ten thousands
(d) Thousands
(e) Tens

NOTE   Extremely large numbers, in the billions or larger, are difficult to imagine. For example, traveling day and night at a rate of 55 miles per hour, it would take over 2000 years to travel one billion miles and over 2,000,000 years to travel one trillion miles. Sometimes descriptions like this can help us comprehend very large numbers.

1.1 EXERCISES

Answers to these exercises are given on page 639.

1. What are the numbers 1, 2, 3,... called?
   Counting numbers

2. How are numbers often "pictured" in mathematics?
   using a number line

3. How do we read the symbols $7 > 2$?
   greater than

4. What is the largest three-digit number?
   999

5. What is the smallest two-digit number?
   10

6. What is the largest digit?
   9

7. Is 10 a natural number?
   yes

8. Is 10 a digit? —*no*
   yes

9. What is the smallest whole number?
   0

10. What is the largest whole number?
    there is no largest whole #

Use the given number line to determine what number is represented by each variable in Exercises 11–14.

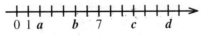

0 1 a   b 7   c   d

11. *a* *2*   12. *b* *5*   13. *c* *10*   14. *d* *13*

Refer to the number line below to place the correct symbol (< or >) between the numbers in Exercises 15–20.

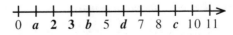

0 *a* 2 3 *b* 5 *d* 7 8 *c* 10 11

15. 2 *<* 3   16. 7 *>* 0   17. *a* *<* 2

18. 7 *<* *c*   19. *d* *>* *a*   20. *b* *<* *d*

Write each number in Exercises 21–26 in expanded notation.

21. 2479

22. 503

23. 207,519

24. 4,127,982

25. 5,000,040

26. 6,020,300,027

Write each number in Exercises 27–32 in standard notation.

27. $500 + 20 + 3$

28. $10,000 + 600 + 20 + 1$

29. $300 + 5$

30. $400,000 + 30,000 + 9000 + 700 + 20 + 1$

31. $6,000,000 + 4000 + 20 + 5$

32. $20,000,000 + 500,000 + 8$

Write a word name for each number in Exercises 33–36.

33. 4219

34. 107,586

35. 93,117

36. 13,219,475

Write each number in Exercises 37–40 in standard notation.

37. Six thousand, seven hundred five

38. Twenty-four thousand, one hundred fifty-nine

39. Three billion, four hundred twenty-seven million, one hundred ninety-three thousand, two hundred

40. Eight hundred twenty-five million, one

Give the value of the digit 5 in each number in Exercises 41–44.

41. 325,076   42. 51,032,299   43. 3,279,005   44. 5,361,291,447

In the number 63,572,189, what digit represents each of the places given in Exercises 45–48?

45. Millions

46. Ten thousands

47. Ten millions

48. Ones

In Exercises 49–50, write the number in the statement in standard notation.

49. **SCIENCE**   The distance around the earth is approximately one billion, five hundred eighty-four million inches.

50. **ECONOMICS**   The U.S. Gross National Product in a recent year exceeded three trillion, six hundred twenty-five billion, one hundred fifty million dollars.

In Exercises 51–52, write a word name for the number in the statement.

51. **PHYSICS**   One light-year, the distance light travels in one year, is approximately 5,879,195,000,000 miles.

52. **GEOGRAPHY**   It has been estimated that about 139,710,000 square kilometers of the earth's surface area is water.

CRITICAL THINKING

Assume that variables a and b represent whole numbers in Exercises 53–56.

53. If $a < b$ is $2 + a < 2 + b$?

54. If $a < 5$ and $5 < b$ is $a < b$?

55. If $a < b$, could we also write $b > a$?

56. If $a < b$ and $b < a$ are both false, what could we conclude?

57. Discuss why we use the terms *natural* or *counting* numbers for 1, 2, 3, 4,.... .

58. Look for articles in newspapers and magazines that refer to very large numbers and write a paragraph describing a way to demonstrate the magnitude of these numbers.

1.1 PARALLEL EXERCISES

Answers to these exercises are not given in the text.

1. What numbers are formed by including 0 with the natural numbers?

2. What is the symbol for a number called?

3. How do we read the symbols $3 < 4$?

4. What is another name for the first ten whole numbers?

5. What is the largest four-digit number?

6. What is the smallest three-digit number?

7. Is 10 a counting number?

8. Is 10 a whole number?

9. What is the smallest natural number?

10. What is the largest natural number?

Use the given number line to determine what number is represented by each variable in Exercises 11–14.

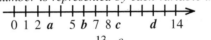

0 1 2 *a* 5 *b* 7 8 *c*   *d* 14

11. *a*   12. *b*   13. *c*   14. *d*

Refer to the number line below to place the correct symbol (< or >) between the numbers in Exercises 15–20.

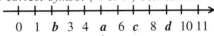

0 1 *b* 3 4 *a* 6 *c* 8 *d* 10 11

15. 4____11   16. 5____0   17. *b*____3

18. 2____*c*   19. *c*____*a*   20. *a*____*d*

Write each number in Exercises 21–26 in expanded notation.

21. 409   22. 21,155   23. 603,114

24. 7,123,321   25. 8,000,200   26. 7,001,050,103

Write each number in Exercises 27–32 in standard notation.

27. $800 + 20 + 7$ 28. $5000 + 800 + 30 + 2$

29. $30,000 + 500 + 40 + 3$ 30. $70,000 + 300$

31. $9,000,000 + 20,000 + 6$ 32. $80,000,000 + 700,000 + 40$

Write a word name for each number in Exercises 33–36.
33. 5143   34. 203,195   35. 65,728   36. 21,205,414

Write each number in Exercises 37–40 in standard notation.
37. Eleven thousand, two hundred twenty-six

38. Ninety-five thousand, six hundred twenty-seven

39. Ten billion, two hundred five million, three hundred forty-seven

40. Seven hundred six million, fifteen

Give the value of the digit 5 in each number in Exercises 41–44
41. 153,040   42. 523,147   43. 27,523   44. 8,146,325,600

In the number 63,572,189 what digit represents each of the places given in Exercises 45–48?
45. Thousands   46. Tens   47. Hundred thousands   48. Hundreds

In Exercises 49–50 write the number in the statement in standard notation.
49. **SCIENCE**   The distance from the earth to the sun is approximately four hundred ninety-one billion, forty million feet.

50. **CONSUMER**   There are over one hundred sixty-five million, five hundred thousand television sets in the United States.

In Exercises 51–52, write a word name for the number in the statement.
51. **CONSUMER**   It has been estimated that motorists in the United States waste over 250,700,000 gallons of gasoline annually just warming up their automobiles.

52. **BUSINESS** A variety store has over 1,570,300 items in its inventory.

 CRITICAL THINKING

Assume that variables a and b represent whole numbers in Exercises 53–56.
53. If $a < b$, is $a + 3 < b + 3$?
54. If $a > 8$, and $8 > b$ is $a > b$?
55. If $a > b$, could we also write $b > a$?
56. If $a < b$ and $a = b$ are both false, what could we conclude?
57. Discuss why we use the term *whole* numbers for 0, 1, 2, 3, ...
58. Write a paragraph discussing why we call our system of numeration a *place-value system*.

GROUP PROJECT

Prior to the development of the numeration system that we use today, there were many other systems used to denote numbers. Investigate some of these other numeration systems (for example, Egyptian numeration, Roman numerals, and the Babylonian system) and prepare a report discussing some of the advantages and disadvantages of each as compared to our present system that is based on the number *ten* and uses the idea of place value. Also discuss why you feel that *ten* became the base number and not the number 7, for example.

1.2 ADDING WHOLE NUMBERS

STUDENT GUIDEPOSTS
1   LEARNING THE BASIC ADDITION FACTS
2   ADDING A ONE-DIGIT NUMBER AND A TWO-DIGIT NUMBER
3   ADDING TWO TWO-DIGIT NUMBERS
4   ADDING TWO MANY-DIGIT NUMBERS
5   RECOGNIZING SOME PROPERTIES OF ADDITION
6   SOLVING APPLICATIONS INVOLVING ADDITION

1   BASIC ADDITION FACTS

Addition of two whole numbers can be thought of as "joining together" or "combining" and counting the result. The two numbers to be added are called **addends,** and the result is their **sum.** The symbol used in addition is the **plus sign, +.** As an example, suppose we add 2 coins and 5 coins. There are 2 coins in one stack and 5 coins in another stack, as in Figure 1.6. The addends are written

$$2 + 5.$$

The sum can be found by counting the total number of coins. When the two stacks are put together, the combined stack contains 7 coins, so

$$2 + 5 = 7.$$

FIGURE 1.6

Addition problems are written either horizontally or vertically.

Horizontal display
$$2 + 5 = 7$$
Addend   Addend   **Sum**

Vertical display
$$
\begin{array}{r}
2 \\
+\, 5 \\
\hline
7
\end{array}
$$
2 ← Addend
+ 5 ← Addend
7 ← **Sum**

Addition can be shown using a number line. To add 2 and 5 on a number line, first move 2 units to the right of 0. From this point, move 5 more units to the right. The net result is a movement of 7 units from 0. Using the number line in Figure 1.7, we have shown that $2 + 5 = 7$.

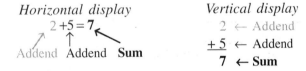

$$2 + 5 = 7$$

FIGURE 1.7

EXAMPLE 1   ADDING TWO WHOLE NUMBERS

Add.

$$4 + 2 = 6 \qquad \text{4 objects + 2 objects results in 6 objects}$$

We could also show this using the number line in Figure 1.8.

PRACTICE EXERCISE 1

Add using a number line.

$$6 + 3$$

Answer: 9

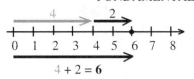

FIGURE 1.8

Finding sums by counting or by using a number line takes time. However, by memorizing the **basic addition facts,** we can find the sum of any two one-digit numbers quickly. These facts, which serve as building blocks for larger sums, are summarized in the table below.

To find $7 + 3$ using the table, start at 7 in the left column and move straight across to the right until you are below the 3 in the top row. You have arrived at the number 10, which is $7 + 3$.

+	0	1	2	3	4	5	6	7	8	9
0	0	1	2	3	4	5	6	7	8	9
1	1	2	3	4	5	6	7	8	9	10
2	2	3	4	5	6	7	8	9	10	11
3	3	4	5	6	7	8	9	10	11	12
4	4	5	6	7	8	9	10	11	12	13
5	5	6	7	8	9	10	11	12	13	14
6	6	7	8	9	10	11	12	13	14	15
7	7	8	9	10	11	12	13	14	15	16
8	8	9	10	11	12	13	14	15	16	17
9	9	10	11	12	13	14	15	16	17	18

Addition Table

When problems are to be solved that involve mathematics, the problems are often stated in words. As a result, we must learn how to translate English statements into mathematical or symbolic statements. For example, consider the statement: *Find the sum of a and b.* If we translate this to symbolic form, we must find $a + b$. In fact, there are numerous ways to indicate sums using English words and phrases. The table below gives several of these.

ENGLISH	*SYMBOLS*
The sum of 4 and 2	$4 + 2$
6 more than 3	$3 + 6$
7 added to x	$x + 7$
y increased by 9	$y + 9$
The sum of m and n	$m + n$
The sum of 3 and 2 is 5	$3 + 2 = 5$

Notice that the word *is* in the last entry in the table translates to the symbol = which is the **equal sign** and is read *equals.*

PRACTICE EXERCISE 2

Use the Addition Table to find the following.

(a) 2 plus 7

(b) 5 increased by 5

FINDING SUMS USING THE ADDITION TABLE   **EXAMPLE 2**

Use the Addition Table to find the following.

(a) The sum of 8 and 4   We must find $8 + 4$. Start at 8 in the left column and move across to below 4. The number is 12. Thus $8 + 4 = 12$.

(b) 8 more than 4   We must find $4 + 8$. Start at 4 in the left column and move across to below 8. Thus $4 + 8 = 12$.

(c) 4 added to 0   We must find $0 + 4$. Start at 0 in the left column and move across to below 4. Thus $0 + 4 = 4$.

It is sometimes necessary to find the sum of three one-digit numbers. We can use a number line as shown in the next example.

EXAMPLE 3   ADDING THREE ONE-DIGIT NUMBERS

Add $3 + 4 + 2$ using a number line.

First move 3 units to the right of 0. From this point (corresponding to 3) move 4 more units to the right arriving at 7. Finally, move two additional units to reach the point that corresponds to 9, as shown in Figure 1.9.

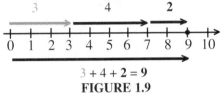

$$3 + 4 + 2 = 9$$
FIGURE 1.9

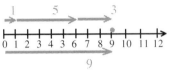
2 ADDING A ONE-DIGIT NUMBER AND A TWO-DIGIT NUMBER

We have now learned the basic facts for adding two one-digit numbers. To add numbers with more digits, these facts are used together with knowledge of the place-value system. To illustrate, suppose we find the following sum.

$$\begin{array}{r} 45 \\ +\ 3 \\ \hline \end{array}$$

Write each addend in expanded notation.

$$45 = 40 + 5 = 4 \textbf{ tens} + 5 \textbf{ ones}$$
$$\underline{\ 3} = \underline{\quad 3} = \underline{\qquad\qquad 3 \textbf{ ones}}$$

Find the sum by adding the ones digits, 5 and 3, and placing the sum with the 4 tens.

$$4 \textbf{ tens} + 5 \textbf{ ones}$$
$$\underline{\qquad\qquad 3 \textbf{ ones}}$$
$$4 \textbf{ tens} + 8 \textbf{ ones} = 48$$

The sum, 48, can be found more directly as shown below using the circled steps.

$$\begin{array}{r} 45 \\ +\ 3 \\ \hline \end{array}$$

② **Bring down tens digit 4** → 48 ← ① **Add ones digits to obtain 8 and place it in the ones position in the sum**

NOTE   To add 45 and 3 as shown above, remember that you will write only the sum, 48. The other remarks shown are used for explanation.

3 | ADDING TWO TWO-DIGIT NUMBERS

Next we find the sum of two two-digit numbers such as the following.

$$35$$
$$+24$$

Remember that

$$35 = 3 \text{ tens} + 5 \text{ ones} \text{ and } 24 = 2 \text{ tens} + 4 \text{ ones}.$$

Find the number of ones in the sum by adding 5 and 4. Then find the number of tens by adding 3 and 2.

$$35 = 3 \textbf{ tens} + 5 \textbf{ ones}$$
$$+24 = 2 \textbf{ tens} + 4 \textbf{ ones}$$
$$5 \textbf{ tens} + 9 \textbf{ ones} = 59$$

The sum can be found more quickly by simply adding the ones digits and then adding the tens digits.

$$35$$
$$+24$$

② Add tens digits to obtain 5 → 59 ← ① Add ones digits to obtain 9

Try to find the following sum in the same way. Adding the ones digits and placing the sum directly below the ones digits in the addends gives

$$27$$
$$+ 65$$
$$\overline{\cancel{12}}.$$ $7 + 5 = 12$

If the tens digits are added, the resulting sum looks strange and is obviously incorrect.

$$27$$
$$+ 65$$
$$\overline{8\cancel{12}}$$ ← **This is not correct**

What have we done wrong? For one thing, most of us would recognize that the sum of 27 and 65 could not possibly be as large a number as 812! In fact, we are forgetting what we know about place value. When we add the 2 and 6, we are adding 2 *tens* and 6 *tens* so that the sum is 8 *tens,* not 8 hundreds, as in 812. This is easier to see if we write the addends in expanded notation.

$$27 = 20 + 7 = 2 \textbf{ tens} + 7 \textbf{ ones}$$
$$+65 = 60 + 5 = 6 \textbf{ tens} + 5 \textbf{ ones}$$
$$8 \textbf{ tens} + 12 \textbf{ ones}$$

Since

$$12 \text{ ones} = 10 \text{ ones} + 2 \text{ ones}$$
$$= 1 \text{ ten} + 2 \text{ ones},$$ **1 ten + 2 ones**

the sum

$$8 \text{ tens} + \textbf{12 ones} = 8 \text{ tens} + \textbf{1 ten} + \textbf{2 ones}$$
$$= 9 \text{ tens} + 2 \text{ ones} = 92.$$

Thus,
$$27$$
$$+ 65$$
$$\overline{92}.$$

The steps shown above are usually shortened by using a process called **carrying.**

$$27$$ $$7$$
$$+65$$ **Add ones and think of** $$+ 5$$
$$\overline{}$$ $$\overline{12}$$

Write 2, the ones digit of this sum, below the ones digits of the addends. Write 1, the tens digit of the sum, above the tens digits of the addends.

```
  ¦  ← Write tens digit in the tens column
 27
+65
────
  2  ← Write ones digit here
```

The number 1 is called a **carry number.** Now add 1, 2, and 6 and write the sum, 9, below the tens digits.

```
  ¦
  27
+ 65
────
  92
```

EXAMPLE 4	ADDING TWO TWO-DIGIT NUMBERS

Find each sum.

(a) ```
      34
     +49
     ────
     ```

The steps to follow are listed below.

① Add ones digits: $4 + 9 = 13$.
② Write 3 under ones digits and carry 1.
③ Add 1, 3, and 4 to obtain 8.

```
  ¦
  34
 +49
 ────
  83
```

(b) ```
      69
     +85
     ────
     ```

Begin as before.

```
  ¦
  69
 +85
 ────
   4     9 + 5 = 14 ; write 4 and carry 1
```

At this point, you must add 1, 6, and 8. Notice that the sum, 15, is really

$$15 \text{ tens} = 10 \text{ tens} + 5 \text{ tens}$$
$$= 1 \text{ hundred} + 5 \text{ tens}. \qquad 10 \text{ tens} = 1 \text{ hundred}$$

Write the 5 under the tens digits of the addends, and the 1 in the hundreds place of the sum.

```
   ¦
   69
 + 85
 ─────
  154
```

4	ADDING TWO MANY-DIGIT NUMBERS

When there are more digits in the addends, continue the process as shown in the next example.

EXAMPLE 5	ADDING TWO THREE-DIGIT NUMBERS

Find the sum.

```
  875
 +398
 ────
```

```
    875
 +  398
 ──────
   1273
```

The completed addition is shown above. Remember to use the following steps.

① Add 5 and 8 to get 13, write 3 and carry 1.

② Add 1, 7, and 9 to get 17, write 7 and carry 1.

③ Add 1, 8, and 3, getting 12. Since

$$12 \text{ hundreds} = 10 \text{ hundreds} + 2 \text{ hundreds}$$
$$= 1 \text{ thousand} + 2 \text{ hundreds} \qquad 10 \text{ hundreds} = 1 \text{ thousand}$$

write the 2 hundreds in the hundreds place and the 1 in the thousands place.

ADDING SEVERAL NUMBERS	EXAMPLE 6

Find the sum. $9369 + 387 + 18 + 538$

$$
\begin{array}{r}
9369 \\
387 \\
18 \\
+538 \\
\hline
10312
\end{array}
$$

① Add 9, 7, 8, and 8; write 2 and carry 3.
② Add 3, 6, 8, 1, and 3; write 1 and carry 2.
③ Add 2, 3, 3, and 5; write 3 and carry 1.
④ Add 1 and 9; write 0 in thousands column and 1 in ten thousands column.

5 | SOME PROPERTIES OF ADDITION

In parts (a) and (b) of Example 2 we saw that changing the order of addition does not change the sum when we discovered that

$$4 + 8 = 8 + 4$$

This property of the number system is true in general.

THE COMMUTATIVE LAW OF ADDITION
If a and b are any two numbers, then $$a + b = b + a.$$ That is, changing the order of addition does not change the sum.

Part (c) of Example 2, showed that

$$0 + 4 = 4.$$

By the commutative law of addition, we also have that

$$4 + 0 = 4.$$

In general, if any number is added to zero or zero is added to any number, the sum is the *identical* number. This is an important property of 0.

ZERO IS THE ADDITIVE IDENTITY
If a is any number, then $$a + 0 = a \text{ and } 0 + a = a.$$ That is, adding zero to any number gives the same identical number for the sum.

Addition is a **binary operation.** This means that only two numbers are added at a time (*bi* means two). Suppose we look again at the problem of adding three numbers. Find the following sum.

$$
\begin{array}{r}
3 \\
5 \\
+2 \\
\hline
\end{array}
$$

Start by adding the top two numbers, 3 and 5. Then add their sum, 8, to 2, to obtain 10. The entire process is usually done mentally, but can be shown in the following way.

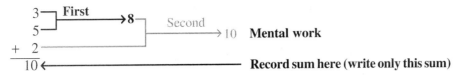

We could also calculate the sum by adding the bottom two numbers, 2 and 5, then adding their sum, 7, to 3 to obtain 10. Again, we can show the technique as follows.

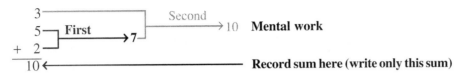

Notice that both cases give the same result.

When the sum is written horizontally, as $3 + 5 + 2$, we use parentheses to show which numbers to add first. In the first case,

$$(3 + 5) + 2 = 8 + 2 = 10.$$

In the second case,

$$3 + (5 + 2) = 3 + 7 = 10.$$

Thus,

$$(3 + 5) + 2 = 3 + (5 + 2).$$

Regrouping the numbers does not change the sum. The same is true for any three whole numbers.

THE ASSOCIATIVE LAW OF ADDITION

If a, b, and c are any three numbers, then

$$(a + b) + c = a + (b + c).$$

That is, the sum of more than two numbers is not changed by the way the numbers are grouped so they can be added two at a time.

We can check addition in one of two ways. One way is to repeat the addition. A second way, which avoids the risk of repeating any error, is to reverse the order of addition. That is, if we added from top to bottom the first time, we check by adding from bottom to top. This method, shown in Example 7, is called the **reverse-order check of addition.**

EXAMPLE 7 REVERSE-ORDER CHECK

Add and check.

(a) Add:
$$
\begin{array}{r}
3 \leftarrow \text{①}\ 3 + 7 = 10 \\
7 \\
\text{②}\ 10 + 8 = 18 \quad +8 \\
\hline
18 \leftarrow
\end{array}
$$

Check
$$
\begin{array}{r}
3 \quad \text{②}\ 15 + 3 = 18 \\
7 \\
+8 \leftarrow \text{①}\ 8 + 7 = 15 \\
\hline
18 \leftarrow
\end{array}
$$

(b) Add, and check in reverse order.
$$
\begin{array}{r}
21 \\
35 \\
+76 \\
\end{array}
$$

The steps used to find the sum are numbered in order. Notice that both the ones column and the tens column are added from the top.

EXPLORATION GUIDE

Sometimes when adding several numbers it helps to look for pairs that add to 10, 20, 30, and so on. This is illustrated below.

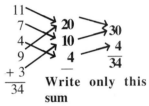

$$
\begin{array}{r}
11 \\
7 \\
4 \\
9 \\
+3 \\
\hline
34
\end{array}
$$

Write only this sum

Explain how the commutative and associative laws of addition are used in this process. Why does adding in this manner simplify the process? Use this technique to add the numbers from 1 to 10.

PRACTICE EXERCISE 7

Add and check.

(a) Add:
$$
\begin{array}{r}
6 \\
2 \\
+9 \\
\end{array}
$$
Check:
$$
\begin{array}{r}
6 \\
2 \\
+9 \\
\end{array}
$$

(b) Add:
$$
\begin{array}{r}
36 \\
51 \\
+89 \\
\end{array}
$$
Check:
$$
\begin{array}{r}
36 \\
51 \\
+89 \\
\end{array}
$$

Answers: (a) 17 (b) 176

④ $1 + 2 = 3$ → $\overset{1}{21}$ ← ① $1 + 5 = 6$

⑤ $3 + 3 = 6$ →   35

⑥ $6 + 7 = 13$ →   76   ← ② $6 + 6 = 12$

⑦ Write 13   → $\overline{132}$ ← ③ Write 2 and carry 1

The steps used to check are numbered in order.

⑥ $12 + 1 = 13$ → $\overset{1}{}$

⑤ $10 + 2 = 12$ →   21   ← ② $11 + 1 = 12$

④ $7 + 3 = 10$ →   35

                             76   ← ① $6 + 5 = 11$

⑦ Write 13   → $\overline{132}$ ← ③ Write 2 and carry 1

6 | APPLICATIONS OF ADDITION

Many problems are solved by adding whole numbers as shown in the next example.

FINDING DISTANCES USING A MAP   EXAMPLE 8

Figure 1.10 shows a sketch of a trail map in a wilderness area. (Note: **mi** is the abbreviation for miles.)

FIGURE 1.10

(a) If Joe hikes from the Miner's Cabin to Trout Lake and on to the Twin Buttes, how far has he hiked?

The distance hiked is the sum of 5 mi and 6 mi. Since

$$5 + 6 = 11$$

Joe hiked 11 mi.

(b) Kelli hiked from Trout Lake to the Hangman's Tree, on to the Twin Buttes, and ended up at the Miner's Cabin. How far did she hike?

Since

$$2 + 3 + 4 = 9$$

Kelli hiked a total of 9 mi.

PRACTICE EXERCISE 8

Refer to Figure 1.10.

(a) A scout troop hiked from the Twin Buttes to Trout Lake and on to the Hangman's Tree. How far did they hike?

(b) Ranger Dave hiked from the Miner's Cabin to the Twin Buttes, on to Trout Lake, and ended the hike at the Hangman's Tree. How far did he hike?

Answers: (a) 8 mi (b) 12 mi

1.2 EXERCISES

Answers to these exercises are given on page 639.

💡 *What addition problems are displayed in Exercises 1–2?*

1.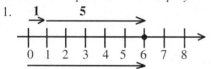

2.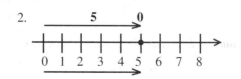

You should be able to complete Exercises 3–47 in 90 seconds or less.

| 3. | 8 +9 | 4. | 0 +2 | 5. | 3 +7 | 6. | 6 +0 | 7. | 2 +4 | 8. | 7 +1 | 9. | 0 +0 |

3. 8
    +9

4. 0
    +2

5. 3
    +7

6. 6
    +0

7. 2
    +4

8. 7
    +1

9. 0
    +0

10. 2
     +5

11. 7
     +7

12. 8
     +2

13. 9
     +0

14. 6
     +5

15. 7
     +8

16. 3
     +4

17. 3
     +0

18. 2
     +7

19. 5
     +9

20. 1
     +3

21. 0
     +4

22. 5
     +7

23. 8
     +1

24. 1
     +6

25. 4
     +0

26. 6
     +9

27. 9
     +2

28. 8
     +5

29. 3
     +5

30. 7
     +9

31. 0
     +3

32. 7
     +6

33. 4
     +7

34. 9
     +3

35. 3
     +1

36. 8
     +6

37. 9
     +9

38. $2 + 8 =$

39. $6 + 3 =$

40. $5 + 5 =$

41. $2 + 6 =$

42. $0 + 9 =$

43. $9 + 1 =$

44. $8 + 0 =$

45. $4 + 3 =$

46. $2 + 3 =$

47. $5 + 2 =$

Find the value of each expression given in Exercises 48–51.

48. The sum of 9 and 4

49. 6 increased by 1

50. 5 more than 4

51. 5 added to 6

52. Translate the following into symbols: The sum of x and z is 47.

Add using a number line in Exercises 53–54.

53. $2 + 3 + 1$

54. $4 + 6 + 3$

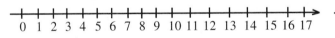

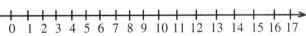

HAULING   *A hauling company has three trucks, one blue, one red, and one white. The blue truck can haul 2 tons of sand, the red one can haul 5 tons of sand, and the white one can haul 8 tons of sand. Use this information in Exercises 55–58.*

55. How many tons can be hauled using the blue truck and the red truck?

56. How many tons can be delivered using the white truck and the red truck?

57. How many tons of sand can be hauled by all three trucks?

58. If a contractor orders 10 tons of sand, which two trucks should be used for the delivery?

Find the sums in Exercises 59–83 and check using the reverse-order method.

59. 42
     + 5

60. $84 + 3$

61. 33
     +22

62. 49
     +35

63. 59
     +76

64. $43 + 79$

65. $\begin{array}{r} 512 \\ +\ 65 \\ \hline \end{array}$

66. $\begin{array}{r} 405 \\ +\ 26 \\ \hline \end{array}$

67. $727 + 73$

68. $\begin{array}{r} 837 \\ +175 \\ \hline \end{array}$

69. $\begin{array}{r} 5824 \\ +1736 \\ \hline \end{array}$

70. $\begin{array}{r} 9999 \\ +1111 \\ \hline \end{array}$

71. $\begin{array}{r} 4002 \\ +3009 \\ \hline \end{array}$

72. $3297 + 816$

73. $\begin{array}{r} 7 \\ 3 \\ +6 \\ \hline \end{array}$

74. $\begin{array}{r} 1 \\ 9 \\ +7 \\ \hline \end{array}$

75. $\begin{array}{r} 31 \\ 46 \\ +72 \\ \hline \end{array}$

76. $85 + 37 + 62$

77. $\begin{array}{r} 456 \\ 767 \\ +318 \\ \hline \end{array}$

78. $\begin{array}{r} 3 \\ 25 \\ 14 \\ +\ 2 \\ \hline \end{array}$

79. $27 + 6 + 9 + 83$

80. $\begin{array}{r} 3 \\ 79 \\ 5 \\ +13 \\ \hline \end{array}$

81. $\begin{array}{r} 615 \\ 203 \\ 970 \\ +341 \\ \hline \end{array}$

82. $\begin{array}{r} 3846 \\ 1092 \\ 637 \\ +\ 4425 \\ \hline \end{array}$

83. $\begin{array}{r} 5298 \\ 6137 \\ 8056 \\ +4321 \\ \hline \end{array}$

Solve each applied problem in Exercises 84–87.

84. **SALES** Wanda Hunt sold 34 cars during November and 27 cars during December. How many cars did she sell for the two months?

85. **TRAVEL** Todd drove 135 miles on the first day of a trip and 467 miles on the second day. How many miles did he drive?

86. **SPORTS** The attendance for the first night of a local sporting event was 379. The second night 413 attended and 505 were present for the final game on the third night. What was the total attendance for the three nights?

87. **BANKING** Janet had a balance of $365 in her checking account before making deposits of $418 and $279. How much did she deposit, and what was her new balance?

CRITICAL THINKING

In Exercises 88–90, complete each statement using the indicated property.

88. Commutative law: $2 + 7 = $ _____

89. Additive identity: $8 + $ ___ $= 8$

90. Associative law: $(2 + 9) + 5 = 2 + $ _____

Suppose that a, b, x, and y represent whole numbers. Use this information in Exercises 91–93.

91. What law is illustrated by $a + x = x + a$?

92. What whole number does $b + 0$ equal?

93. What law is illustrated by $(x + y) + a = x + (y + a)$?

Find each sum in Exercises 94–95.

94. $\begin{array}{l} 6 \text{ ft }\ 2 \text{ in} \\ +5 \text{ ft }\ 4 \text{ in} \\ \hline \end{array}$

95. $\begin{array}{l} 6 \text{ ft }\ 8 \text{ in} \\ +5 \text{ ft }\ 9 \text{ in} \\ \hline \end{array}$

[*Hint:* Remember that 1 ft = 12 in]

🐌96. Burford was asked to add the numbers 43 and 87. (His work is shown below.) Discuss the error he made and explain how he should have added the two numbers.

$$
\begin{array}{r}
43 \\
+\ \ 87 \\
\hline
1210
\end{array}
$$
This is wrong

💡97. What numbers must be placed in the boxes in the following addition problem.

$$
\begin{array}{r}
4\ \square\ 8 \\
+\ 2\ 6\ \square \\
\hline
\square\ 6\ 6
\end{array}
$$

🐌98. Explain why addition is called a *binary operation*.

🐌99. Discuss the commutative law of addition and explain why it is an important property of our number system.

🐌100. Discuss the process of *carrying* when adding whole numbers.

REVIEW OR PREVIEW

101. Write eight trillion, two hundred twenty-five billion, five hundred million, four hundred eighty-six in standard notation.

102. Write 63,247 in expanded notation.

103. Write a word name for 8,275,111.

104. In the number 2,458,769, what digit represents each of the following?
   (a) ten thousands (b) millions (c) thousands (d) tens

💡105. Refer to the given number line to place the correct symbol (< or >) between the numbers in each pair.

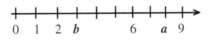

(a) 2____ *a* (b) 6____ *b* (c) *a*____5 (d) *b*____*a*

1.2 PARALLEL EXERCISES

Answers to these exercises are not given in the text.
What addition problems are displayed in Exercises 1–2?

1.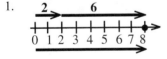

2.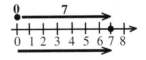

You should be able to complete Exercises 3–47 in 90 seconds or less.

3.	4.	5.	6.	7.	8.	9.
4 +6	3 +4	5 +2	7 +4	9 +3	8 +7	3 +8

10.	11.	12.	13.	14.	15.	16.
9 +5	8 +2	6 +1	3 +5	2 +1	0 +0	4 +3

17.	18.	19.	20.	21.	22.	23.
1 +7	0 +7	2 +5	3 +9	1 +1	0 +3	6 +4

24.	25.	26.	27.	28.	29.	30.
2 +7	1 +8	0 +1	6 +2	9 +7	8 +5	6 +6

| 31. | 4 | 32. | 0 | 33. | 9 | 34. | 2 | 35. | 1 | 36. | 0 | 37. | 5 |
| | +5 | | +6 | | +1 | | +4 | | +3 | | +4 | | +5 |

38. $2 + 9 =$ 39. $1 + 3 =$ 40. $8 + 1 =$ 41. $9 + 2 =$ 42. $7 + 1 =$

43. $3 + 6 =$ 44. $4 + 7 =$ 45. $3 + 7 =$ 46. $0 + 5 =$ 47. $9 + 4 =$

💡 *Find the value of each expression given in Exercises 48–51.*

48. The sum of 1 and 4   49. 4 increased by 9

50. 8 more than 5   51. 7 added to 6

💡 52. Translate the following into symbols: The sum of y and x is 25.

Add using a number line in Exercises 53–54.

53. $4 + 5 + 3$ 54. $5 + 3 + 8$

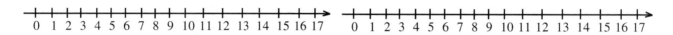

💡 **STORAGE**   *Kim Doane has three boxes for storing cassette tapes, a tan one that holds 5 tapes, a gray one that holds 6 tapes, and a red one that holds 8 tapes. Use this information to solve Exercises 55–58.*

55. How many tapes can Kim store in the tan and gray cases?

56. How many tapes can be stored in the red case and the gray case?

57. How many tapes can Kim store in all three cases?

58. Kim plans to take 13 tapes along on a trip. Which two cases should she use?

Find the sums in Exercises 59–83 and check using the reverse-order method.

| 59. | 32 | 60. | $52 + 7$ | 61. | 63 | 62. | 27 | 63. | 38 |
| | +4 | | | | +18 | | +48 | | +83 |

| 64. | $27 + 87$ | 65. | 392 | 66. | 519 | 67. | $989 + 11$ | 68. | 487 |
| | | | + 12 | | + 91 | | | | +399 |

69.	7904	70.	6329	71.	6195	72.	$4075 + 28$	73.	8
	+2311		+4350		+4805				1
									+5

74.	7	75.	52	76.	$47 + 38 + 91$	77.	806	78.	16
	5		29				359		5
	+2		+14				+461		70
									+19

79.	$4 + 27 + 9 + 41$	80.	52	81.	225	82.	8371	83.	7896
			8		407		5		4327
			63		311		693		5131
			+ 7		+597		+ 12		+ 8454

Solve each applied problem in Exercises 84–87.

84. **EDUCATION**   Professor Williams has 42 students in one history class and 39 students in another. How many tests must she prepare for the two classes?

85. **CHEMISTRY**   A lab assistant poured 585 cubic centimeters of distilled water into a beaker followed by 428 cubic centimeters of alcohol. How much liquid was poured into the beaker? *label answer c.c.*

86. **POLITICS**   Contributions that came in on Wednesday for the campaign of Ann Henry in a local election were $105, $430, and $656. What was the total for the day?

87. **TRAVEL**   The *odometer* on a car indicates how many miles the car has been driven since it was built. Prior to a trip, the odometer on Curt's car read 23,165 miles. He then drove 496 miles one day and 387 miles the next. How many miles did he drive those two days? What was the odometer reading at the end of the second day?

CRITICAL THINKING

In Exercises 88–90, complete each statement using the indicated property.

88. Commutative law: $4 + 9 =$ _____

89. Additive identity: _____ $+ 5 = 5$

90. Associative law: $1 + (3 + 6) =$ _____ $+ 6$

Suppose that a, b, x, and y represent whole numbers. Use this information in Exercises 91–93.

91. What law is illustrated by $b + y = y + b$?

92. What whole number does $0 + x$ equal?

93. What law is illustrated by $(a + b) + y = a + (b + y)$?

Find each sum in Exercises 94–95.

94. $\begin{array}{r} 4 \text{ yd } 1 \text{ ft} \\ +7 \text{ yd } 1 \text{ ft} \\ \hline \end{array}$

95. $\begin{array}{r} 3 \text{ yd } 2 \text{ ft} \\ +5 \text{ yd } 2 \text{ ft} \\ \hline \end{array}$

96. Burford was asked to add the numbers 27 and 35. (His work is shown below.) Discuss the error he made and explain how he should have added the two numbers.

$$\begin{array}{r} 27 \\ + 35 \\ \hline 52 \end{array} \quad \text{This is wrong}$$

97. What numbers must be placed in the boxes in the following addition problem.

$$\begin{array}{r} 5 \square 7 \\ + 1 \ 6 \square \\ \hline \square 9 \ 2 \end{array}$$

98. Explain why 0 is called the *additive identity.*

99. Discuss the associative law of addition and explain why it is important in view of the fact that addition is a binary operation.

100. Discuss how the associative and commutative laws of addition are used in the reverse-order check of addition.

GROUP PROJECT

One of the earliest known calculating machines was invented by the famous mathematician Blaise Pascal (1623-1662). It was a mechanical device using gears that turned wheels showing various numbers. During this same period, logarithms were invented and used to assist in making more complicated arithmetic computations. This theory was applied to a slide rule, which was the predecessor of the modern pocket calculator. In the 1900s, calculators became electrical instead of mechanical, but electricity was used simply to run the various gears in the machine. Thanks to space-age technology, integrated circuits, transistors, and the introduction of the *microprocessor,* a very small processing unit, led to the modern miniature hand calculators we take for granted today. The history of the calculator and the computer is a long and interesting one. Research this topic and write a report on your findings.

1.3 ROUNDING WHOLE NUMBERS AND ESTIMATION

STUDENT GUIDEPOSTS
1   ROUNDING A WHOLE NUMBER
2   USING ROUNDED NUMBERS TO ESTIMATE AND CHECK SUMS

1   ROUNDING A WHOLE NUMBER

In many situations we might use an approximate value of a whole number to obtain an *estimated* answer to a question. For example, suppose we are told that during one working day in a post office, one machine processed 12,780 letters while a second machine processed 9125 letters. If we are asked to determine the total number of letters processed by the two machines, we might approximate the answer in the following way. *Round* 12,780 to 13,000, 9125 to 9000, and quickly find the sum

$$13 \textbf{ thousand} + 9 \textbf{ thousand} = 22 \textbf{ thousand}$$

or

$$13,000 + 9000 = 22,000$$

for an *estimate* of the total number of letters processed. In doing this we are mentally adding two smaller numbers, 9 and 13, to obtain a reasonable approximation of 21,905, the exact sum of 12,780 and 9125.

Numbers may be rounded to the nearest ten, hundred, thousand, ten thousand, and so on. To **round** a number to the nearest ten, use the nearest multiple of ten (0, 10, 20, 30, 40,...) to approximate the given number.

For example, consider rounding 38 to the nearest ten. We may use part of a number line showing the multiples of ten on either side of the given number. The number 38 is between 30 and 40, as shown in Figure 1.11. Since 38 is closer to 40 than 30, we round up to 40. That is, 38 rounded to the nearest ten is 40.

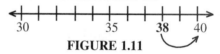

FIGURE 1.11

To round 53 to the nearest ten, consider Figure 1.12. The number 53 is between 50 and 60. Since it is closer to 50, 53 rounded to the nearest ten is 50. What if we wanted to round 25 to the nearest ten? Since 25 is halfway between 20 and 30, we would round down to 20 or round up to 30. When a number is halfway between rounding numbers we will agree to round up. Thus, we will round 25 up to 30 as shown in Figure 1.13.

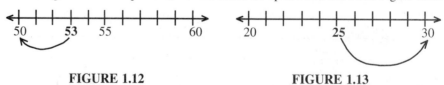

FIGURE 1.12   **FIGURE 1.13**

The following rule allows us to round numbers without using a number line.

TO ROUND A WHOLE NUMBER TO A GIVEN POSITION
1. Identify the digit in that position.
2. If the first digit to the right of that position is 0, 1, 2, 3, or 4, do not change the digit.
3. If the first digit to the right of that position is 5, 6, 7, 8, or 9, increase the digit by 1.
4. *In both cases* replace all digits to the right of that position with zeros, and copy any digits to the left of that position.

| **EXAMPLE 1** | **ROUNDING TO THE NEAREST HUNDRED** |

(a) Round 392 to the nearest hundred.

The digit 3 is in the hundreds position and 9 is the first digit to the right.

Hundreds position
↓
392
↑
First digit to right

(a) Round 541 to the nearest hundred.

Increase 3 by 1 to 4, and replace 9 and 2 with zeros. Thus 400 is the desired rounded number.

(b) Round 6237 to the nearest hundred.

The digit 2 is in the hundreds position and 3 is the first digit to the right.

Hundreds position
↓
62**3**7
↑
First digit to right

(b) Round 1875 to the nearest hundred.

Do not change the 2, and replace 3 and 7 with zeros. Thus 6200 is 6237 rounded to the nearest hundred.

(c) Round 2950 to the nearest hundred.

The 9 is in the hundreds position and 5 is the first digit to the right. Increasing 9 by 1 means that the thousands digit must be increased to 3 and the hundreds digit becomes 0. Thus 2950 to the nearest hundred is 3000.

(c) Round 4950 to the nearest hundred.

Answers: (a) 500 (b) 1900 (c) 5000

| **EXAMPLE 2** | **ROUNDING TO THE NEAREST THOUSAND** |

(a) Round 7283 to the nearest thousand.

The 7 is in the thousands position. Since 2 is the first digit to the right, 7283 rounded to the nearest thousand is 7000.

(a) Round 4423 to the nearest thousand.

(b) Round 26,501 to the nearest thousand.

The 6 is in the thousands position, and 5 is the first digit to the right. Increase 6 to 7 and the rounded number is 27,000.

(b) Round 69,825 to the nearest thousand.

Answers: (a) 4000 (b) 70,000

| **EXAMPLE 3** | **ROUNDING WHOLE NUMBERS** |

(a) Round 4645 to the nearest ten.
There is a 4 in the tens position and 5 is the first digit to the right. Round 4645 to 4650.

(a) Round 9745 to the nearest ten.

(b) Round 4645 to the nearest hundred.

The 6 is in the hundreds position and 4 is the first digit to the right. Leave the 6 and write 4600 for the rounded number.

(b) Round 9745 to the nearest hundred.

Answers: (a) 9750 (b) 9700

> CAUTION   In part **(b)** of Example 3, if 4645 had been rounded to tens before being rounded to hundreds, the final result would have been 4700 instead of 4600. This points out that this method of rounding *cannot* be done in steps; it must be done using the original number, not a rounded number.

2 | USING ROUNDED NUMBERS TO ESTIMATE AND CHECK SUMS

Rounded numbers are used to make quick *estimates* of sums. These estimates may also be used for a quick *check* for significant errors made in addition problems.

ROUNDING TO THE NEAREST TEN

EXAMPLE 4

Estimate the sum by rounding to the nearest ten.

	Rounded to nearest ten
18	**20**
82	**80**
65	**70**
+21	**+ 20**
	190

The estimated sum is 190. The exact sum, which is 186, can be checked by comparing it to the estimate.

ROUNDING TO THE NEAREST HUNDRED

EXAMPLE 5

Estimate the sum by rounding to the nearest hundred.

	Rounded to nearest hundred
425	**400**
607	**600**
587	**600**
+235	**+ 200**
	1800

The estimated sum is 1800. The exact sum, which is 1854, can be checked by comparing it to the estimate.

CAUTION   Using rounded numbers to estimate or check sums provides only a general technique that may not be totally accurate. It should be used with care. For example, in Practice Exercise 5, the estimated sum 2300 differs from the actual sum of 2207 by 93. In part **(a)** of Example 6 an error of 93 causes us to conclude that a mistake was made in addition. In one case, an error of 93 appears acceptable while in the other case it is not. As a result, remember that an *estimate* is an *approximation* not intended to replace actual calculations. Such approximations will help to provide us with some sense of accuracy in our work.

PRACTICE EXERCISE 4

Estimate the sum by rounding to the nearest ten.

```
  94
  48
  25
 +12
```

Answer: The estimated sum is 180 (exact sum is 179).

PRACTICE EXERCISE 5

Estimate the sum by rounding to the nearest hundred.

```
  355
  739
  462
 +651
```

Answer: The estimated sum is 2300 (exact sum is 2207).

EXAMPLE 6   ESTIMATING SUMS BY ROUNDING

Estimate the sum by rounding and use the estimate to check the work shown.

(a) Check by rounding to the nearest ten.

	Rounded to ten
39	**40**
51	**50**
86	**90**
+ 17	**+ 20**
293	**200**

With an estimated sum of 200, we would conclude that the given sum, 293, is incorrect. The correct sum is 193.

(b) Check by rounding to the nearest hundred.

	Rounded to hundred
625	**600**
187	**200**
362	**400**
+ 717	**+ 700**
1691	**1900**

With an estimated sum of 1900, we would probably conclude that the given sum, 1691, is incorrect. The correct sum is 1891. Can you find where the error was made?

Real-life situations often present problems similar to the one in the next example. By using rounded numbers, we can estimate or approximate a solution mentally.

EXAMPLE 7   ESTIMATING IN A BANKING PROBLEM

Harvey has $589 in one savings account and $807 in a second. Without finding the exact total in the two accounts, estimate this total using rounded numbers.

Harvey has $589 in one account. This is about $600, rounding to the nearest hundred. Similarly, he has about $800 in the second account. The total in the two accounts can be estimated by adding $600 and $800.

$$
\begin{array}{r}
600 \\
+ 800 \\
\hline
1400
\end{array}
$$

Thus, Harvey has about $1400 in the two accounts.

> **CAUTION** Do not estimate a sum by adding first and then rounding the answer. This would serve no useful purpose for checking or for getting a "rough" answer.

Estimate the sum by rounding and use your estimate to check the work shown.

(a) Check by rounding to the nearest ten.

$$
\begin{array}{r}
423 \\
165 \\
75 \\
+ 349 \\
\hline
1012
\end{array}
$$

(b) Check by rounding to the nearest hundred.

$$
\begin{array}{r}
835 \\
293 \\
441 \\
+ 752 \\
\hline
2121
\end{array}
$$

Answers: (a) The estimated sum is 1020; the sum appears to be correct. (b) The estimated sum is 2300; the sum appears to be incorrect.

PRACTICE EXERCISE 7

There are 2985 acres on the Walter Ranch and 4120 acres on the Kirk Ranch. Without finding the exact number, estimate the total number of acres on the two ranches.

Answer: 7000 acres (using 3000 and 4000 as the two estimates)

1.3 EXERCISES

Answers to these exercises are given on page 639.

Round each number in Exercises 1–5 to the nearest ten.

1. 33   2. 68   3. 15   4. 625   5. 199

Round each number in Exercises 6–10 to the nearest hundred.

6. 327   7. 372   8. 68   9. 8550   10. 4977

Round each number in Exercises 11–15 to the nearest thousand.

11. 927   12. 9499   13. 9500   14. 23,450   15. 127,456

Estimate each sum in Exercises 16–19 by rounding to the nearest ten. Do not find the exact sum.

16.	23	17.	65	18.	602	19.	1722
	16		91		327		3345
	54		19		455		2471
	+79		+32		+281		+5128

Estimate each sum in Exercises 20–23 by rounding to the nearest hundred. Do not find the exact sum.

20.	329	21.	103	22.	602	23.	1722
	556		75		327		3345
	113		969		455		2471
	+925		+473		+281		+5128

Estimate each sum in Exercises 24–27 by rounding to the nearest thousand. Do not find the exact sum.

24.	4321	25.	6025	26.	19,501	27.	1722
	1530		847		19,499		3345
	2905		9327		38,201		2471
	+3040		+1700		+21,005		+5128

♀*Without finding the exact sum, determine if each sum in Exercises 28–31 seems correct or incorrect.*

28.	72	29.	357	30.	245	31.	2193
	16		125		61		6407
	97		845		193		3356
	+ 33		+ 581		+ 702		+ 409
	218		2308		1201		12,565

Solve each applied problem in Exercises 32–35.

32. **ENVIRONMENT**   A national forest is estimated to have 317,000 fir trees that are at least 40 feet tall. Round the number of trees to the nearest (a) hundred thousand (b) ten thousand.

33. **ECONOMICS**   During the first few weeks of distribution, the latest Harrison Ford movie grossed more than $68,495,240. Round this number to the nearest (a) million (b) ten million.

34. **EDUCATION**   There are 7105 books on the first floor of a university library, and 6898 books on the second floor. Without finding the exact total, estimate the number of books on the two floors.

35. **CONSUMER**   Dr. Morgan purchased a new Buick for $14,958 and a new Honda for $11,141. Without finding the exact total, estimate the amount of money she spent buying these two automobiles.

CRITICAL THINKING

♀36. While doing his homework assignment, Burford was asked to round 2748 to the nearest hundred. He first rounded 2748 to the nearest ten obtaining 2750, and then rounded 2750 to the nearest hundred obtaining an answer of 2800. When he looked at the answer given in the text he found it to be 2700. What was Burford doing wrong?

The following bar graphs appeared in The NCAA News, the Official Publication of the National Collegiate Athletic Association. According to The NCAA News, a total of 63,305 people used the NCAA Visitors Center at Overland Park, Kansas in 1993-94. Also, $456,236 in revenue was taken in through the gift shop, catalog sales and admission fees. Use this information and the graphs below to answer the questions in Exercises 37–40.

37. Could you have determined that the total number of people who used the Visitors Center in 1993-94 was exactly 63,305 just using the bar graph? What would be a reasonable approximation for this total based on the graph alone?

38. What is an approximation for the total attendance in 1992-93?
39. What is an approximation for the total revenue in 1992-93?
40. Find an approximation for the total attendance in the three-year interval shown in the graph.

people
41. Give several reasons why rounded numbers can be very useful in practical situations.

REVIEW OR PREVIEW

42. Write three hundred twenty-one million, one hundred five thousand, six hundred twenty-two in standard notation, then round the result to the nearest million.
43. Write 136,403 in expanded notation.?   44. Write a word name for 39,205,116. thirty-nine million, two

45. In the number 6,258,403, what digit represents each of the following?
   (a) millions   (b) ones   (c) thousands   (d) hundred thousands

1.3 PARALLEL EXERCISES

Answers to these exercises are not given in the text.
Round each number in Exercises 1–5 to the nearest ten.
  1. 47   2. 22   3. 548   4. 195   5. 699
Round each number in Exercises 6–10 to the nearest hundred.
  6. 538   7. 662   8. 059   9. 6850   10. 2195
Round each number in Exercises 11–15 to the nearest thousand.
 11. 4501   12. 4499   13. 2799   14. 8985   15. 135,525
Estimate each sum in Exercises 16–19 by rounding to the nearest ten. Do not find the exact sum.

16.		17.	18.	19.
34	30	75	503	2344
17	20	81	426	1665
65	70	18	545	2582
+88	90	+43	+397	+7138

Estimate each sum in Exercises 20–23 by rounding to the nearest hundred. Do not find the exact sum.

| 20. | 239
665
113
+849 | 21. | 102
875
53
+271 | 22. | 427 *400*
581 *600*
326 *300*
+108 *100* | 23. | 1856
2345
2281
+6195 |

Estimate each sum in Exercises 24–27 by rounding to the nearest thousand. Do not find the exact sum.

| 24. | 6435 *6000*
2505 *3000*
3916 *4000*
+5050 *5000* | 25. | 3175
955
7258
+1900 | 26. | 39,501 *40,000*
39,499 *39,000*
27,208 *27,000*
+41,006 *41,000* | 27. | 4723
2549
3449
+6207 |

💡*Without finding the exact sum, determine if each sum in Exercises 28–31 seems correct or incorrect.*

| 28. | 81
19
48
+ 31
179 | 29. | 445
165
851
+ 558
1999 | 30. | 329
83
294
+ 911
1417 | 31. | 4293
5445
3795
+ 603
14,136 |

Solve each applied problem in Exercises 32–35.

32. **ECONOMICS**   The budget for Warren County for the year is $8,649,000. Round this to the nearest (a) million (b) hundred thousand.

33. **ECONOMICS**   During the first few weeks of distribution, a box-office hit movie grossed more than $45,625,155. Round this number to the nearest (a) million (b) ten million.

34. **INVESTMENT**   Doug Christensen owns 5208 shares of one stock and 7112 shares of another. Without finding the exact total, estimate the number of shares of the two types of stock that he owns.

35. **AERONAUTICS**   A jet is flying at an altitude of 7895 feet and then increases its altitude by 5120 feet. Without finding the exact altitude, estimate its new altitude.

CRITICAL THINKING

💡36. When Burford was asked to round 7245 to the nearest hundred, he first rounded 7245 to the nearest ten obtaining 7250, and then rounded 7250 to the nearest hundred obtaining 7300. Why is Burford's result incorrect?

Refer to the bar graphs given above Exercises 37–40 on page 33 to answer the following.

37. Could you have determined that the total revenue generated was $456,236 just using the bar graph? What would be a reasonable approximation for this total based on the graph alone?

38. What is an approximation for the total attendance in 1991–92?

39. What is an approximation for the total revenue in 1991–92?

40. Find an approximation for the total revenue in the three-year interval shown in the graph.

41. In your own words, describe the method for rounding a whole number to a given position.

GROUP PROJECT

In 1995, Burford was sitting on a bus reading an article in a magazine that said the population of the state of California in that year was 32,398,000. Just at that minute he received a call on his cellular phone telling him that his sister, who lives in San Diego, had twins. A short time later, the man in the seat next to Burford, who was reading the same magazine, remarked that he was surprised that the population of California was 32,398,000. Burford said "You are wrong, the population is 32,398,002!" Does Burford understand the meaning of approximate numbers? Look for other instances where approximate numbers are used and can be misused, and report your findings. For example, is it really 93,000,000 miles from the earth to the sun? Or, is a person exactly 6 feet tall?

1.4 SUBTRACTING WHOLE NUMBERS

STUDENT GUIDEPOSTS

1	LEARNING THE BASIC SUBTRACTION FACTS
2	WORKING WITH RELATED ADDITION AND SUBTRACTION EQUATIONS
3	SUBTRACTING NUMBERS WITH MORE DIGITS
4	BORROWING IN SUBTRACTION PROBLEMS
5	CHECKING SUBTRACTION BY ADDITION

1 BASIC SUBTRACTION FACTS

Subtraction of one whole number from another can be thought of as "removing" or "taking away." For example, suppose we subtract 4 coins from 7 coins. If there are 7 coins in a stack and 4 are removed, 3 coins remain. See Figure 1.14.

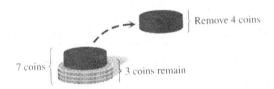

FIGURE 1.14

Subtraction is written with a **minus sign, –,** and can be written either horizontally or vertically.

Horizontal display

Minuend $\nearrow$ **7 − 4 =** 3 $\searrow$ Difference
$\uparrow$
Subtrahend

Vertical display

7 ← **Minuend**
− 4 ← Subtrahend
3 ← Difference

The number being taken away is called the **subtrahend.** The number it is taken from is the **minuend.** The number remaining is the **difference.**

Minuend – Subtrahend = Difference

Subtraction can be shown on a number line. Recall that to find the sum $5 + 2$ using a number line, we move right 5 units from 0 to the point associated with 5 and then move 2 more units to the right to the point 7, as shown in Figure 1.15.

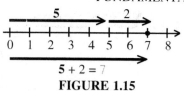

FIGURE 1.15

To find $5 - 2$ using a number line, we start the same way by moving 5 units to the right of 0 to the point 5. We then move 2 units to the *left* of 5 to the point 3. See Figure 1.16. Using a number line we have shown that $5 - 2 = 3$.

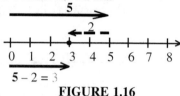

FIGURE 1.16

As was the case with addition, problems involving subtraction are often stated in words and we must be able to translate the English into symbolic statements. For example, consider the statement: *Find the difference of the two numbers a and b.* If we translate this to symbolic form, we must find $a - b$. Some of the other words and phrases to indicate subtraction are given in the table below.

ENGLISH	SYMBOLS
The difference of 4 and 2	$4 - 2$
The difference of x and 5	$x - 5$
7 subtracted from a	$a - 7$
y decreased by 9	$y - 9$
z less 6	$z - 6$
z less than 6	$6 - z$
The difference of m and n is 3	$m - n = 3$

2 | RELATED ADDITION AND SUBTRACTION EQUATIONS

Although we can subtract whole numbers using the "take away" method or the number line, it is better to relate subtraction to addition since we already know the basic addition facts. One way to do this is to use the idea of an **equation,** a statement that two quantities are the same and written using the equal sign =. For example, $5 = 3 + 2$ is an equation as is $5 - 3 = 2$. These two equations are closely *related.* In fact, the first is called the **related addition equation** to the second, and the second is called the **related subtraction equation** to the first. Suppose that we wanted to determine the value of $5 - 3$. We might represent this number using the variable a to obtain $5 - 3 = a$. Consider the related addition equation $5 = 3 + a$. Since we recognize by inspection that the addition equation is true when a is replaced by 2, the subtraction equation is also true when a is 2 so that $5 - 3 = 2$. Thus, we can subtract by using an addition equation. A number that makes an addition equation true, such as 2 when it replaces a in $5 = 3 + a$, is called a **solution** to the equation. When we find such a solution, we are *solving the equation.* In Chapter 10 we will develop a thorough treatment of solving equations, but for now, many simple equations can be solved by inspection.

EXAMPLE 1 — SOLVING EQUATIONS

Solve each equation.

(a) $a + 2 = 6$ To solve this equation we ask: "**What** must be added to 2 to obtain 6?" The answer is 4 since $4 + 2 = 6$. The solution to the equation is 4. That is, $a = 4$.

(b) $5 + x = 12$ To solve this equation we ask: "**What** must be added to 5 to obtain 12?" The answer is 7 since $5 + 7 = 12$. The solution to the equation is 7. That is, $x = 7$.

The next example shows how we can learn to subtract by translating to the related addition equation and solving that equation.

EXAMPLE 2 — USING THE RELATED ADDITION EQUATION

Subtract.

(a) $6 - 2$ If we let $6 - 2 = a$ and change to the related addition equation, $a + 2 = 6$, we recognize that a must be 4. Thus, $6 - 2 = 4$.

(b) $9 - 1$ If we let $9 - 1 = a$, then $a + 1 = 9$, and we recognize that $8 + 1 = 9$, so $a = 8$, Thus, $9 - 1 = 8$.

(c) $7 - 7$ If we let $7 - 7 = a$, then $a + 7 = 7$, and we recognize that $0 + 7 = 7$, so $a = 0$. Thus, $7 - 7 = 0$.

(d) $5 - 0$ If we let $5 - 0 = a$, then $a + 0 = 5$, and we recognize that $5 + 0 = 5$, so $a = 5$. Thus, $5 - 0 = 5$.

With practice, the basic subtraction facts, which come from the basic addition facts, should be easy to remember. Thus, we should be able to do basic subtraction quickly. Example 3 gives more practice using the vertical display.

EXAMPLE 3 — SUBTRACTING USING A VERTICAL DISPLAY

Subtract.

	Subtraction	*Related addition*
(a)	$\begin{array}{r} 9 \\ -\,7 \\ \hline 2 \end{array}$	$\begin{array}{r} 2 \\ +\,7 \\ \hline 9 \end{array}$
(b)	$\begin{array}{r} 5 \\ -\,1 \\ \hline 4 \end{array}$	$\begin{array}{r} 4 \\ +\,1 \\ \hline 5 \end{array}$
(c)	$\begin{array}{r} 4 \\ -\,4 \\ \hline 0 \end{array}$	$\begin{array}{r} 0 \\ +\,4 \\ \hline 4 \end{array}$
(d)	$\begin{array}{r} 3 \\ -\,0 \\ \hline 3 \end{array}$	$\begin{array}{r} 3 \\ +\,0 \\ \hline 3 \end{array}$

3 | SUBTRACTING NUMBERS WITH MORE DIGITS

We now know basic facts of subtraction. To find differences between larger numbers, use the basic facts and the knowledge of place value. For example, find the following difference by writing the numbers in expanded form, then subtracting the ones digits, 8 and 5, and the tens digits, 3 and 2.

$$38 = 30 + 8 = 3 \textbf{ tens} + 8 \textbf{ ones}$$
$$\underline{-25 = 20 + 5 = 2 \textbf{ tens} + 5 \textbf{ ones}}$$
$$1 \textbf{ ten } + 3 \textbf{ ones} = 13$$

The difference, 13, can be found more directly using the two steps shown below.

$$\begin{array}{r} 38 \\ -25 \\ \hline 13 \end{array}$$

② Subtract tens digits to obtain 1 → $\overline{13}$ ← ① Subtract ones digits to obtain 3

The same method works for numbers with more digits as shown in the next example.

PRACTICE EXERCISE 4

Find the difference.

$$\begin{array}{r} 785 \\ -643 \\ \hline \end{array}$$

Answer: 142

SUBTRACTING LARGER NUMBERS

EXAMPLE 4

Find the difference. $\begin{array}{r} 896 \\ -572 \\ \hline \end{array}$

Subtract the ones digits, the tens digits, and the hundreds digits.

$$896 = 8 \textbf{ hundreds} + 9 \textbf{ tens} + 6 \textbf{ ones}$$
$$\underline{-572 = 5 \textbf{ hundreds} + 7 \textbf{ tens} + 2 \textbf{ ones}}$$
$$324 \quad 3 \textbf{ hundreds} + 2 \textbf{ tens} + 4 \textbf{ ones} = 324$$

4 | BORROWING IN SUBTRACTION PROBLEMS

You probably noticed that in Example 4 only subtraction of one-digit numbers was needed. We now look at problems which require subtraction of a one-digit number from a two-digit number. The notion of place value plays an important part in this process. Consider the following problem.

$$\begin{array}{r} 63 \\ -48 \\ \hline \end{array}$$

We quickly see that the ones digit 8 cannot be subtracted from the ones digit 3. The difficulty can be removed by "borrowing" ten ones from the tens column in 63. That is,

$$63 = \textbf{6 tens} + 3 \text{ ones}$$
$$= \textbf{5 tens} + \textbf{1 ten} + 3 \text{ ones} \qquad 6 \text{ tens} = 5 \text{ tens} + 1 \text{ ten}$$
$$= 5 \text{ tens} + \textbf{10 ones} + \textbf{3 ones} \qquad 1 \text{ ten} = 10 \text{ ones}$$
$$= 5 \text{ tens} + 13 \text{ ones}.$$

Thus,

$$63 = 6 \text{ tens} + 3 \text{ ones} = 5 \text{ tens} + 13 \text{ ones}$$
$$\underline{-48 = 4 \text{ tens} + 8 \text{ ones} = 4 \text{ tens} + 8 \text{ ones}}$$
$$15 \qquad\qquad\qquad 1 \text{ tens} + 5 \text{ ones} = 15.$$

We usually write the problem in shortened form as follows.

$$\overset{513}{\cancel{6}\cancel{3}}$$
$$\underline{-48}$$
$$15$$

Borrow 1 ten from 6 tens, change 6 to 5 and 3 to 13

Subtract corresponding columns. 13 − 8 is 5, 5 − 4 is 1

> **NOTE**   Borrowing in a subtraction problem is the reverse of carrying in an addition problem.

EXAMPLE 5 — BORROWING IN A SUBTRACTION PROBLEM

PRACTICE EXERCISE 5

Find the difference.

$$529$$
$$\underline{-365}$$

Find the difference.

$$638$$
$$\underline{-491}$$

$$\overset{4\ 12}{\cancel{5}\cancel{2}9}$$
$$\underline{-365}$$
$$164$$

Subtract 5 from 9 to obtain 4. Since 2 − 6 is not a whole number, borrow 1 hundred from 5, change 5 to 4 and 2 to 12.
Subtract 6 from 12 and 3 from 4

Answer: 147

Sometimes we need to borrow more than once in the same problem. This is illustrated in the next example.

EXAMPLE 6 — BORROWING SEVERAL TIMES

PRACTICE EXERCISE 6

Find each difference.

Find each difference.

(a) $\begin{array}{r}723\\-475\end{array}$

(a) $\begin{array}{r}425\\-187\end{array}$

$$\overset{1\ 13}{7\ \cancel{2}\ \cancel{3}}$$
$$\underline{-4\ 7\ 5}$$
$$8$$

Borrow 1 ten from 2, change 2 to 1 and 3 to 13

Subtract 5 from 13

$$\overset{11}{\overset{6\ 1\ 13}{\cancel{7}\ \cancel{2}\ \cancel{3}}}$$
$$\underline{-4\ 7\ 5}$$
$$4\ 8$$

Since 1 − 7 is not a whole number, borrow 1 hundred from 7, change 7 to 6 and 1 to 11
Subtract 7 from 11

$$\overset{11}{\overset{6\ \cancel{1}13}{\cancel{7}\ \cancel{2}\ \cancel{3}}}$$
$$\underline{-47\ 5}$$
$$24\ 8$$

Subtract 4 from 6

(b) $\begin{array}{r}6312\\-4795\end{array}$

(b) $\begin{array}{r}7436\\-2697\end{array}$

$$\overset{0\,12}{6\ 3\ \cancel{1}\ \cancel{2}}$$
$$\underline{-4\ 7\ 9\ 5}$$
$$7$$

Borrow 1 ten from 1, change 1 to 0 and 2 to 12

Subtract 5 from 12

$$\overset{10}{\overset{2\,\cancel{0}12}{6\cancel{3}\cancel{1}\cancel{2}}}$$
$$\underline{-4795}$$
$$17$$

Since 0 − 9 is not a whole number, borrow 1 hundred from 3, change 3 to 2 and 0 to 10
Subtract 9 from 10

$$\overset{12\,10}{\overset{5\ \cancel{2}\cancel{0}12}{\cancel{6}\ \cancel{3}\ \cancel{1}\ \cancel{2}}}$$
$$\underline{-4\ 7\ 9\ 5}$$
$$1\ 5\ 1\ 7$$

Since 2 − 7 is not a whole number, borrow 1 thousand from 6, change 6 to 5 and 2 to 12
Subtract 7 from 12 and 4 from 5

Answers: (a) 238 (b) 4739

When there is a zero in a position from which we must borrow, we borrow across that position. This is shown in the next example.

PRACTICE
EXERCISE 7

Find each difference.

(a)   502
    −267

(b)   6007
    −2659

Answers: (a) 235 (b) 3348

BORROWING ACROSS A ZERO   **EXAMPLE 7**

Find each difference.

(a)   605
    −238

$$
\begin{array}{r}
\overset{5\ 10}{\cancel{6}\ \cancel{0}\ 5} \\
-2\ 3\ 8
\end{array}
$$
We must borrow 1 ten, but since 605 has no tens, we must first borrow 1 hundred (10 tens) from 6. Change 6 to 5 and 0 to 10.

$$
\begin{array}{r}
\overset{9}{\overset{5\ \cancel{10}15}{\cancel{6}\ \cancel{0}\ \cancel{5}}} \\
-2\ 3\ 8 \\
\hline
3\ 6\ 7
\end{array}
$$
Now borrow 1 ten from 10, change 10 to 9 and 5 to 15

Subtract 8 from 15, 3 from 9, and 2 from 5

(b)   2003
    − 895

$$
\begin{array}{r}
\overset{1\ 10}{\cancel{2}\ \cancel{0}\ 0\ 3} \\
-8\ 9\ 5
\end{array}
$$
We must borrow 1 ten, but there are no tens, so we try to borrow 1 hundred. Since there are no hundreds, we must first borrow 1 thousand. Change 2 to 1 and 0 (the hundreds digit) to 10.

$$
\begin{array}{r}
\overset{9}{\overset{1\ \cancel{10}}{\cancel{2}\ \cancel{0}\ 0\ 3}} \\
-\ 8\ 9\ 5
\end{array}
$$
Next, change 10 (hundreds) to 9 and 0 (tens) to 10

$$
\begin{array}{r}
\overset{9\ 9}{\overset{1\ \cancel{10}\cancel{10}13}{\cancel{2}\ \cancel{0}\ \cancel{0}\ 3}} \\
-\ 8\ 9\ 5
\end{array}
$$
Change 10 (tens) to 9 and 3 (ones) to 13

$$
\begin{array}{r}
\overset{9\ 9}{\overset{1\ \cancel{10}\cancel{10}13}{\cancel{2}\ \cancel{0}\ \cancel{0}\ \cancel{3}}} \\
-\ 8\ 9\ 5 \\
\hline
1\ 1\ 0\ 8
\end{array}
$$
Subtract 5 from 13, 9 from 9, 8 from 9, and bring down the 1

EXPLORATION
GUIDE

Discuss what is meant by the statement: *Although the operation of addition of whole numbers is both commutative and associative, the operation of subtraction is neither commutative nor associative.*

5 | CHECKING SUBTRACTION BY ADDITION

Subtraction can be checked in one of two ways. If we check by repeating the subtraction step by step, chances are that any error made the first time will be repeated. Since it is better to check work using a different process, we use the related addition sentence.

$$7 - 3 = 4 \text{ is true since } 4 + 3 = 7.$$

This example can be generalized.

TO CHECK A SUBTRACTION PROBLEM

The subtraction problem $a - b = c$ is correct if $c + b = a$. That is, if the sum of the difference c and the subtrahend b is equal to the minuend a, then a subtraction problem is correct.

The format to follow when checking a subtraction problem is illustrated in the following example.

EXAMPLE 8	CHECKING SUBTRACTION BY ADDITION

Check each subtraction problem.

$$\begin{array}{r} 629 \\ -342 \\ \hline 287 \end{array}$$

(a)

These must be equal
$$\begin{array}{r} 629 \\ 342 \\ \hline 287 \leftarrow \\ \textbf{629} \leftarrow \\ \hline \end{array}$$
Add these and place sum below dashed line

The dashed line can be thought of as the line for the addition

problem
$$\begin{array}{r} 342 \\ + \ 287 \\ \hline 629. \end{array}$$

(b)
$$\begin{array}{r} 4030 \\ -2376 \\ \hline 1664 \end{array}$$

$$\begin{array}{r} 4030 \\ -2376 \leftarrow \\ \hline 1664 \\ \textbf{4040} \\ \hline \end{array}$$
Since these are not equal, the problem is incorrect. The difference should be 1654.

PRACTICE EXERCISE 8

Check each subtraction problem.

(a)
$$\begin{array}{r} 847 \\ -269 \\ \hline 578 \end{array}$$

(b)
$$\begin{array}{r} 6701 \\ -4985 \\ \hline 1726 \end{array}$$

Answers: (a) Since 269 + 578 = 847, the subtraction is correct. (b) Since 4985 + 1726 = 6711 ≠ 6701, the subtraction is incorrect.

EXAMPLE 9	SUBTRACTING IN A BANKING PROBLEM

Peggy has $883 in her checking account and writes a check for $209. First estimate the number of dollars left in her account, and then find the exact amount.

Since $883 is about $900 and $209 is about $200 (rounding to the nearest 100), estimate the number of dollars left in the account by subtracting 200 from 900.

$$\left.\begin{array}{r} 900 \\ -200 \\ \hline 700 \end{array}\right\} \text{ Mental work}$$

Peggy has about $700 left in the account. To find the exact amount, subtract 209 from 883.

$$\begin{array}{r} 883 \\ -209 \\ \hline 674 \end{array}$$

The exact amount left in her account is $674.

PRACTICE EXERCISE 9

Phil Mortensen owned 3105 cattle and sold 1970 of them. First estimate the number of cattle he still owned, and then find the exact number.

Answer: Estimated number: 1000 cattle; exact number: 1135 cattle

---

1.4 EXERCISES

Answers to these exercises are given on page 640.

💡*What subtraction problem is displayed in Exercises 1–2?*

1.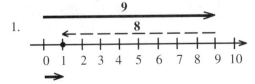

2.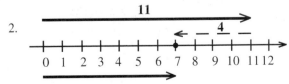

You should be able to complete Exercises 3–47 in two minutes or less.

3. 6   4. 5   5. 2   6. 9   7. 8   8. 7   9. 9
    -4 -1 -1 -6 -5 -0 -2

10. 9   11. 8   12. 7   13. 7   14. 5   15. 6   16. 9
    -4 -2 -1 -4 -4 -2 -8

17. 3   18. 1   19. 5   20. 8   21. 12   22. 10   23. 13
    -0 -1 -2 -4 -8 -4 -5

24. 15   25. 10   26. 17   27. 11   28. 14   29. 10   30. 12
    -8 -2 -9 -5 -7 -1 -4

31. 10   32. 18   33. 16   34. 13   35. 11   36. 15   37. 11
    -6 -9 -9 -6 -2 -7 -8

38. $14 - 6 =$ 39. $10 - 5 =$ 40. $12 - 7 =$

41. $11 - 6 =$ 42. $15 - 9 =$ 43. $10 - 8 =$

44. $11 - 3 =$ 45. $13 - 9 =$ 46. $12 - 5 =$

47. $16 - 8 =$

Find the value of each expression given in Exercises 48–51.

48. The difference of 12 and 9   49. 18 less 9

50. 13 decreased by 8   51. 3 less than 12

52. Translate the following into symbols: The difference of *a* and *v* is 21.

Solve each applied problem in Exercises 53–54.

53. **RECREATION**   Kathy had 9 kittens and gave away   54. **CONSUMER**   Greg has $14 in his wallet. If he buys
     4 of them. How many kittens did she have left?   a book for $6, how much money will he have left?

Find each difference in Exercises 55–66.

55. 63   56. 57   57. 983   58. 634
    -21 -36 -365 -519

59. 205   60. 603   61. 300   62. 400
    -173 -381 -215 -260

63. 6973   64. 3005   65. 4315   66. 38,000
    -4325 -1624 -2549 $-23,999$

Check each subtraction problem in Exercises 67–71.

67.	96 −23	68.	425 −132	69.	325 −279	70.	4392 −1782	71.	8002 −4293
	73		293		156		2610		4709

Find each difference and check your work in Exercises 72–76.

72.	423 −105	73.	700 −268	74.	302 − 78	75.	7562 −3157	76.	6006 −1991

Solve each applied problem in Exercises 77–80.

77. **ECONOMICS**   The High-Tech Computer company sells a Model II computer. The Model III came out last month with a price increase. First estimate the increase in price, and then find the exact increase.

Model II $1389   Model III $1605

78. **PUBLISHING**   A new printing press can print 5890 brochures in one day, while an older model can print only 2995 brochures each day. First estimate the difference in the number of brochures per day, and then find the exact difference.

79. **SALES**   At the close of business on Wednesday a large camera warehouse in New York had 1206 of their most popular cameras in stock. On Thursday they sold 319 cameras, on Friday 474 cameras went out, and on Saturday 184 cameras were sold.
    (a) How many cameras were sold during the last three days of the week?
    (b) How many cameras were still in stock for the opening of the next business day?

80. **TRAVEL**   At the end of a three-day trip, the odometer on Walter's car read 36,297 miles. Suppose he drove 426 miles, 298 miles, and 512 miles on the three days.
    (a) What was the total number of miles driven on the three-day trip?
    (b) What was the odometer reading prior to the trip?

CRITICAL THINKING

In Exercises 81–86, n represents a whole number. Find n by writing the related addition or subtraction equation.

81. $n - 5 = 9$ 82. $n + 5 = 9$ 83. $n - 1 = 6$
84. $n - 0 = 3$ 85. $n - n = 0$ 86. $n + 5 = 2$

In Exercises 87–90, perform the operations in parentheses first.

87. $(3 + 2) - 4$ 88. $(8 + 6) - (9 + 1)$
89. $(8 - 5) + 3$ 90. $(6 - 2) - (9 - 8)$

91. Discuss the process of *borrowing* when subtracting whole numbers. Why is *borrowing* in subtraction sometimes called the reverse of *carrying* in addition?

REVIEW OR PREVIEW

92. Estimate the sum by rounding to the nearest (a) ten (b) hundred (c) thousand.

    2351
    4932
    +6145

💡*Without finding the exact sum, determine if each sum in Exercises 93–95 seems correct or incorrect.*

93. 19
     38
     52
   + 87
   ─────
    176

94. 491
     650
     125
   + 749
   ─────
    2015

95. 2395
      841
       89
   + 153
   ──────
     3478

1.4 PARALLEL EXERCISES

Answers to these exercises are not given in the text.

💡*What subtraction problem is displayed in Exercises 1–2?*

1.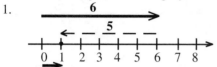

2.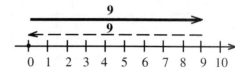

You should be able to complete Exercises 3–47 in two minutes or less.

3. 10   4. 13   5. 2   6. 16   7. 14   8. 0   9. 1
   − 1   − 4   −0   − 7   − 9   −0   −0

10. 16   11. 6   12. 6   13. 4   14. 9   15. 8   16. 12
    − 8   −1   −2   −2   −0   −5   − 9

17. 7   18. 5   19. 5   20. 7   21. 12   22. 11   23. 16
    −3   −2   −3   −4   − 6   − 5   − 9

24. 11   25. 5   26. 9   27. 10   28. 14   29. 4   30. 10
    − 6   −1   −8   − 5   − 7   −0   − 6

31. 6   32. 6   33. 9   34. 17   35. 11   36. 13   37. 10
    −4   −3   −1   − 8   − 8   − 6   − 7

38. $9 - 4 =$ 39. $7 - 6 =$ 40. $15 - 8 =$
41. $12 - 3 =$ 42. $17 - 9 =$ 43. $3 - 1 =$
44. $7 - 7 =$ 45. $6 - 6 =$ 46. $8 - 3 =$
47. $7 - 0 =$

Find the value of each expression given in Exercises 48–51.
48. The difference of 14 and 5   49. 12 less 4
50. 2 decreased by 2   51. 6 less than 15
52. Translate the following into symbols: The difference of c and w is 17.

Solve each applied problem in Exercises 53–54.
53. **SHIPPING** A delivery truck contains 17 cartons. At the first stop, 6 cartons are left off. How many cartons remain on the truck?
54. **RECREATION** Wendy has 13 cassette tapes in a tan storage case and 7 cassette tapes in a blue case. How many more tapes are in the tan case than the blue case?

55. 45   56. 84   57. 581   58. 511
    −13   −43   −124   −208

59. 430
    −319

60. 270
    −115

61. 600
    −103

62. 500
    −128

63. 3728
    −1154

64. 6005
    − 251

65. 25,132
    −14,627

66. 42,135
    −11,329

Check each subtraction problem in Exercises 67–71.

67. 46
    −38
    ___
    18

68. 407
    −229
    ___
    178

69. 700
    −296
    ___
    504

70. 3075
    − 346
    ___
    2729

71. 5040
    −2504
    ___
    3546

Find each difference and check your work in Exercises 72–76.

72. 208
    −129

73. 601
    −392

74. 7302
    − 488

75. 4700
    −1308

76. 8000
    −6989

Solve each applied problem in Exercises 77–80.

77. **TRAVEL** A motor home will travel 402 miles on one 30-gallon tank of gasoline, while a Blazer can travel 595 miles on the same amount of gasoline. First estimate the difference in miles traveled, and then find the exact difference.

30 gal
402 mi

30 gal
595 mi

78. **ENVIRONMENT** In a meadow a technician counted 3105 individual plants of a particular type. The next year there were 6970 of these plants. Estimate the increase in the number of plants, and then find the exact increase.

79. **CONSUMER** Lisa Kamins bought a new compact car for a base price of $7890. The options that she selected came to an additional $1955.
    (a) What was the total price of the new car including the options?
    (b) If Lisa made a down payment of $950, how much of the total did she need to borrow?

80. **BUSINESS** A salesperson has a monthly expense account of $550. Suppose the amount already spent this month includes $125 for gasoline, $210 for food, and $86 for the telephone.
    (a) What is the total spent thus far this month?
    (b) What is the balance remaining in the expense account?

CRITICAL THINKING

In Exercises 81–86, n represents a whole number. Find n by writing the related addition or subtraction equation.

81. $n - 3 = 8$

82. $n + 2 = 11$

83. $n - 2 = 6$

84. $n - 0 = 4$

85. $n + 0 = n$

86. $n + 7 = 6$

In Exercises 87–90, perform the operations in parentheses first.

87. $(6 + 3) - 4$

88. $(5 + 6) - (9 + 2)$

89. $(7 - 5) + 6$

90. $(8 - 5) - (7 - 6)$

91. We say that *subtraction is defined in terms of addition using the related addition equation.* Explain what is meant by this statement.

Many of the terms that we use in mathematics have a similar meaning outside of mathematics, and some do not. For example, when comparing the ages of two children, we might say that the *difference* in their ages is 2 years. In this sense, the 2 comes from subtracting the age of the younger child from the age of the older one. That is, the term *difference* actually means the result of a subtraction problem. Investigate some of the other terms we have considered (such as *sum, subtrahend, minuend, digit,* etc.) and write a report giving the derivation of these words.

1.5 MULTIPLYING WHOLE NUMBERS

STUDENT GUIDEPOSTS
1 LEARNING THE BASIC MULTIPLICATION FACTS
2 MULTIPLYING A TWO-DIGIT NUMBER BY A ONE-DIGIT NUMBER
3 MULTIPLYING A MANY-DIGIT NUMBER BY A ONE-DIGIT NUMBER
4 MULTIPLYING A NUMBER BY A MANY-DIGIT NUMBER
5 SOLVING APPLICATIONS INVOLVING MULTIPLYING WHOLE NUMBERS

1   **BASIC MULTIPLICATION FACTS**

In Section 1.4 we saw that subtraction is closely related to addition. Similarly, multiplication can be thought of as an extension of addition. For example, suppose we want to find the cost of four pieces of 5¢ candy. One way would be to find the sum

$$5+5+5+5 = 20.$$

Because repeated sums like this occur frequently, we should look for a shorter method for finding them. This shorter method is called **multiplication.** In our example, we are finding the sum of four 5s, or,

4 times 5.

The symbol $\times$, called the **multiplication sign** or **times sign,** means "times" in multiplication statements. The two numbers being multiplied are called **factors** (sometimes the **multiplier** and the **multiplicand**) and the result is called their **product.** Thus, in

$$4 \times 5 = 20,$$

4 and 5 are the factors (4 is the multiplier and the multiplicand is 5) whose product is 20. We can picture the product 4×5 as in Figure 1.17.

EXPLORATION GUIDE

Since multiplication is simply an extension of addition, we might argue: *If we know how to add whole numbers, there is no reason to learn how to multiply whole numbers.* Discuss the meaning of this statement, and give reasons why this argument is probably not valid.

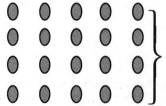

4 groups each having 5 objects results in **4 × 5** or **20** objects

FIGURE 1.17

Remember that in 4×5, 4 tells us the number of 5s that must be added together to obtain 20. That is,

$$4 \times 5 = \underbrace{5+5+5+5}_{\text{Four 5s}} = 20.$$

Multiplication problems are written either horizontally or vertically.

Horizontal display
$$\mathbf{4 \times 5 = 20}$$
$$\underset{\textbf{Factors}}{\nwarrow \nearrow} \quad \underset{\textbf{Product}}{\uparrow}$$

Vertical display
$$\begin{array}{r} 5 \\ \times 4 \\ \hline 20 \end{array}$$
$\leftarrow$ **Factors**
$\leftarrow$ Product

Several other symbols or notations are used in multiplication. In place of the times symbol, ✕, a raised dot is often used. For example,

$$4 \cdot 5 = 20 \qquad \text{is the same as} \qquad 4 \times 5 = 20.$$

Also, parentheses can be used around one or both of the factors with the multiplication signs ✕ and · left out.

$$(4)(5) = 20 \quad \text{or} \quad 4(5) = 20 \quad \text{or} \quad (4)5 = 20$$

The multiplication sign ✕ is avoided when variables are used since it can be confused with the variable x. In fact, when we use variables, we often indicate multiplication without using any symbol at all. For example, $2 \cdot x$ is written as $2x$ and $x \cdot y$ as xy. As with the other operations, there are many ways to indicate multiplication in English. The statement "Find the product of a and b." translates to ab. The table below gives several other translations.

ENGLISH	SYMBOLS
The product of 4 and 2	4×2 or $4 \cdot 2$ or $(4)(2)$ ~~also~~ [4][3]
The product of 2 and 4	2×4 or $2 \cdot 4$ or $(2)(4)$
The product of 3 and y	$3y$
The product of m and n	mn
7 times x	$7x$
twice y	$2y$
The product of a and c is 35	$ac = 35$ ~~letters side by side = multiply~~

EXAMPLE 1	MULTIPLYING BY REPEATED ADDITION	PRACTICE EXERCISE 1

Multiply.

(a) $3 \times 2 = \underbrace{2+2+2}_{\text{Three 2s}} = 6$

$$\begin{array}{r} 2 \\ \times 3 \\ \hline 6 \end{array}$$

(b) $4 \cdot 6 = \underbrace{6+6+6+6}_{\text{Four 6s}} = 24$

$$\begin{array}{r} 6 \\ \times 4 \\ \hline 24 \end{array}$$

Multiply.

(a) $6 \times 3 =$

$3+3+3+3+3+3 = \underline{\quad}$

(b) $5 \times 7 =$

$7+7+7+7+7 = \underline{\quad}$

Answers: (a)18   (b) 35

Finding products by repeated addition takes time. By memorizing certain basic facts, we can find the product of any two one-digit numbers quickly. These facts are summarized in a Multiplication Table below. To find 8×3 using the table, start at 8 in the left column and move straight across to the right until you are below the 3 in the top row. You have arrived at the number 24 which is 8×3.

×	0	1	2	3	4	5	6	7	8	9
0	0	0	0	0	0	0	0	0	0	0
1	0	1	2	3	4	5	6	7	8	9
2	0	2	4	6	8	10	12	14	16	18
3	0	3	6	9	12	15	18	21	24	27
4	0	4	8	12	16	20	24	28	32	36
5	0	5	10	15	20	25	30	35	40	45
6	0	6	12	18	24	30	36	42	48	54
7	0	7	14	21	28	35	42	49	56	63
8	0	8	16	24	32	40	48	56	64	72
9	0	9	18	27	36	45	54	63	72	81

Multiplication Table

The multiplication table can be used to solve some basic equations. Remember that a solution to an equation is a number that makes the equation true. For example, consider the equation

$$5x = 30.$$

The solution to this equation is the number that when multiplied by 5 gives a product of 30. So, starting at 5 in the left column and looking across to the right until we locate 30, we see that it occurs under the 6 in the top row. Therefore, we know that the solution must be $x = 6$.

PRACTICE EXERCISE 2

Solve each equation.

(a) $7z = 21$

(b) $63 = 7x$

Answers: (a) 3   (b) 9

SOLVING EQUATIONS   **EXAMPLE 2**

Solve each equation.

(a) $3y = 18$ The solution to $3y = 18$ is 6 since $3 \cdot \mathbf{6} = 18$.

(b) $12 = 6a$ The solution to $12 = 6a$ is 2 since $12 = 6 \cdot \mathbf{2}$.

A **multiple** of a number is the product of the number and a whole number. To find the multiples of a number, simply multiply it by each of the whole numbers, beginning with zero.

PRACTICE EXERCISE 3

(a) List the multiples of 3.

(b) List the multiples of 10.

Answers: (a) 0, 3, 6, 9, 12,...
(b) 0, 10, 20, 30, 40,...

FINDING MULTIPLES OF A NUMBER   **EXAMPLE 3**

(a) **Multiples of 2**

$0 \times 2 = \mathbf{0}$

$1 \times 2 = \mathbf{2}$

$2 \times 2 = \mathbf{4}$

$3 \times 2 = \mathbf{6}$

$4 \times 2 = \mathbf{8}$

$\vdots$

(b) **Multiples of 5**

$0 \times 5 = \mathbf{0}$

$1 \times 5 = \mathbf{5}$

$2 \times 5 = \mathbf{10}$

$3 \times 5 = \mathbf{15}$

$4 \times 5 = \mathbf{20}$

$\vdots$

NOTE   In the Multiplication Table, the numbers in any row are multiples of the number at the left of that row. Also, the numbers in any column are multiples of the number at the top of that column.

2 | MULTIPLYING A TWO-DIGIT NUMBER BY A ONE-DIGIT NUMBER

The Multiplication Table includes all products of two one-digit numbers. We now consider the product of a one-digit number and a two-digit number, for example, 2×43. We know that

$$2 \times 43 = \underbrace{43 + 43}_{\textbf{Two 43s}} = 86.$$

In expanded form,

$$2 \times \textbf{43} = 2 \times (\textbf{40} + \textbf{3}) = 2 \times (\textbf{4 tens} + \textbf{3 ones})$$

$$= (4 \text{ tens} + 3 \text{ ones}) + (4 \text{ tens} + 3 \text{ ones})$$

$$= 4 \text{ tens} + 4 \text{ tens} + 3 \text{ ones} + 3 \text{ ones}$$

$$= 8 \text{ tens} + 6 \text{ ones} = 86 \cdot$$

There is a simpler way to find the product as shown in the following two steps.

② **Multiply 4, the tens digit in 43, by 2 and write the result in the tens column** ⟶
$$\begin{array}{r} 43 \\ \times\ 2 \\ \hline 86 \end{array}$$
⟵ ① **Multiply 3, the ones digit in 43, by 2 and write the result in the ones column**

EXAMPLE 4	MULTIPLYING A TWO-DIGIT NUMBER BY A ONE-DIGIT NUMBER

Find the product.
$$\begin{array}{r} 32 \\ \times\ 3 \\ \hline \end{array}$$

② **9 is the product of 3 and the tens digit in 32** ⟶
$$\begin{array}{r} 32 \\ \times\ 3 \\ \hline 96 \end{array}$$
⟵ ① **6 is the product of 3 and ones digit in 32**

PRACTICE EXERCISE 4

Find the product.
$$\begin{array}{r} 34 \\ \times\ 2 \\ \hline \end{array}$$

Answer: 68

3 | MULTIPLYING A MANY-DIGIT NUMBER BY A ONE-DIGIT NUMBER

The procedure shown above can be extended to some products of one-digit numbers and many-digit numbers.

EXAMPLE 5	MULTIPLYING A THREE-DIGIT NUMBER BY A ONE-DIGIT NUMBER

Find the product.
$$\begin{array}{r} 423 \\ \times\ 2 \\ \hline \end{array}$$

PRACTICE EXERCISE 5

Find the product.
$$\begin{array}{r} 341 \\ \times\ 2 \\ \hline \end{array}$$

③ Multiply 4, the hundreds digit in
423, by 2 and write the result
in the hundreds column ⟶

$$\begin{array}{r} 423 \\ \times\,2 \\ \hline 846 \end{array}$$ ⟵

① Multiply 3, the ones digit
in 423, by 2 and write the
result in the ones column

② Multiply 2, the tens digit in 423, by 2 and
write the result in the tens column

Answer: 682

In the example above, each individual step resulted in a one-digit number. In some problems, such as 2×73, individual steps may give 2-digit numbers.

$$\begin{array}{r} 73 \\ \times\,2 \\ \hline 146 \end{array}$$

② Multiply tens digit, 7, by
2 and write result 14 here

① Multiply ones digit, 3, by 2
and write result 6 here

In this example, the final product resulted in a two-digit number. We now consider problems in which a two-digit number occurs sooner, for example, 2×38. Using expanded notation,

$$2 \times 38 = 2(30 + 8) = 2(\mathbf{3\ tens + 8\ ones})$$

$$= (3\ tens + 8\ ones) + (3\ tens + 8\ ones)$$

$$= 6\ tens + \mathbf{16\ ones}$$

$$= 6\ tens + \mathbf{10\ ones + 6\ ones}$$

$$= 6\ tens + 1\ tens + 6\ ones \qquad \text{10 ones = 1 ten}$$

$$= 7\ tens + 6\ ones = 76$$

There is a simpler way to find this product. First, multiply 2 times the ones digit, 8, and obtain 16. Write 6 in the ones place and, to remember that 1 ten must still be recorded, that is, carry a 1 above the tens digit in 38.

$$\begin{array}{r} 1 \\ 38 \\ \times 2 \\ \hline 6 \end{array}$$

Next, multiplying 2 times 3, the tens digit, gives 6 which stands for 6 tens. These 6 tens added to the 1 ten carried earlier gives 7 tens. Put the 7 in the tens place.

$$\begin{array}{r} 1 \\ 38 \\ \times 2 \\ \hline 76 \end{array}$$

PRACTICE EXERCISE 6

Find the products.

(a) $\begin{array}{r} 75 \\ \times 8 \\ \hline \end{array}$

(b) $\begin{array}{r} 3056 \\ \times 4 \\ \hline \end{array}$

EXAMPLE 6	**MULTIPLYING USING REMINDER NUMBERS**

Find the products.

(a) $\begin{array}{r} 96 \\ \times 7 \\ \hline \end{array}$

$$\begin{array}{r} \overset{4}{9}6 \\ \times 7 \\ \hline 672 \end{array}$$

① $7 \times 6 = 42$; record 2, carry the 4
② $7 \times 9 = 63; 63 + 4 = 67;$
   67 tens $= 60$ tens $+ 7$ tens $= 6$ hundreds $+ 7$ tens
③ Record 7 in tens column and 6 in hundreds column

(b) $\begin{array}{r} 2905 \\ \times 5 \\ \hline \end{array}$

$$\begin{array}{r} {\scriptstyle 4\ \ 2} \\ 2905 \\ \times 5 \\ \hline 14,525 \end{array}$$

① $5 \times 5 = 25$; record 5, carry the 2
② $5 \times 0 = 0$; $0 + 2 = 2$; record 2
③ $5 \times 9 = 45$; record 5, carry the 4
④ $5 \times 2 = 10$; $10 + 4 = 14$; record 14

Answers: (a) 600 (b) 12,224

4 | MULTIPLYING A NUMBER BY A MANY-DIGIT NUMBER

Earlier in this section, we found the product $2 \times 43 = 86$. Suppose we attempt to multiply 43×2. We first multiply the ones digits to obtain 6.

$$\begin{array}{r} 2 \\ \times 43 \\ \hline \mathbf{6} \end{array}$$

Next we multiply 4 times 2. Remember that in 43, 4 represents 4 tens. Thus, we are actually multiplying $(4 \text{ tens}) \times 2 = 8 \text{ tens} = 80$. We show this by writing 80 below 6.

$$\begin{array}{r} 2 \\ \times 43 \\ \hline 6 \\ \mathbf{80} \end{array}$$

We draw a line below 80 and add the 8 tens and 6 ones.

$$\begin{array}{r} 2 \\ \times 43 \\ \hline 6 \\ 80 \\ \hline 86 \end{array}$$ 6 First product
    80 Second product
    86 Sum of first and second products

Let us summarize what we have learned.

TO MULTIPLY A NUMBER BY A MANY-DIGIT NUMBER

1. Find the first product in exactly the same way as when multiplying a many-digit number by a one-digit number.
2. To form the second product, place a 0 in the ones column, multiply the multiplicand by the tens digit in the multiplier. Place the result to the left of 0.
3. If the multiplier has three or more digits, a third product is formed by placing zeros in the ones and tens columns and multiplying the multiplicand by the appropriate digit. This process is continued for more digits.
4. Add all products to find the final product.

EXAMPLE 7   MULTIPLYING BY A TWO-DIGIT NUMBER

Find the product.

$$\begin{array}{r} 78 \\ \times 96 \\ \hline \end{array}$$

$$\begin{array}{r} {\scriptstyle 7} \\ {\scriptstyle \not 5} \\ 78 \\ \times 96 \\ \hline 468 \\ 7020 \\ \hline 7488 \end{array}$$

① First product: $6 \times 78 = 468$
② Second product: Place 0 in the ones column with $9 \times 78 = 702$ to the left of 0
③ Add first and second products

PRACTICE EXERCISE 7

Find the product.

$$\begin{array}{r} 69 \\ \times 87 \\ \hline \end{array}$$

Answer: 6003

Notice that the first reminder number, 4, written when finding 6×8, was crossed out when the second reminder number, 7, was written.

Multiplying a number by a 3-digit number uses the same approach.

PRACTICE EXERCISE 8

Find the products.

(a)   437
    ×516

(b)   835
    ×209

Answers: (a) 225,492
(b) 174,515

MULTIPLYING BY A THREE-DIGIT NUMBER   **EXAMPLE 8**

Find the products.

(a)   325
    ×618

The first two rows of this product are found the same way as in previous examples. The third row has two 0s to the right with 6×325 to the left.

```
        13
        ƶ̶ƴ̶
       325
     × 618
     ──────
      2600    First product: 8 × 325
      3250    Second product: 0 with 1 × 325
    195000    Third product: 00 with 6 × 325
    ──────
    200850    The desired product is the sum of the three products
```

(b)   647
    ×305

```
        12
        ƶ̶ƶ̶
       647
     × 305
     ──────
      3235    5 × 647
      0000    0 with 0 × 647
    194100    00 with 3 × 647
    ──────
    197335    Add products
```

Since the second row does not affect the sum, we can save time by omitting it from our work. Thus, we would show the product in the following way.

```
       647
     × 305
     ──────
      3235
    194100
    ──────
    197335    Keep 00 with 3 × 647
```

NOTE   With practice, and by paying close attention to the columns in the products, we may omit the extra zeros shown to the right in each row. For example, we might write the product in Example 8(a) in the following form.

```
       325
     × 618
     ──────
      2600
       325
      1950
     ──────
    200850
```

5 | APPLICATIONS OF MULTIPLYING WHOLE NUMBERS

Some real-life applied problems involve multiplying whole numbers.

EXAMPLE 9   SOLVING A PROBLEM IN EDUCATION

There are 32 mathematics classes with 25 students enrolled in each. What is the total number of students in these classes?

The word *total* in this problem seems to indicate an addition problem. In fact, this is true. One way to solve the problem is to add $25 + 25 + 25 + ... + 25$ where there are 32 twenty-fives in this sum. Of course since multiplication is a shortcut for finding such sums (or totals), we will solve the problem by multiplying 32 and 25.

$$
\begin{array}{r}
32 \\
\times 25 \\
\hline
160 \\
640 \\
\hline
800
\end{array}
$$

Thus, there are 800 students in the 32 classes.

PRACTICE EXERCISE 9

There are 52 weeks in a year. How many weeks are there in 8 years?

Answer: 416 weeks

1.5 EXERCISES

Answers to these exercises are given on page 640.

💡*Consider the multiplication problem* $5 \times 8 = 40$ *and answer each question in Exercises 1–3.*

1. What is 5 called?   2. What is 8 called?   3. What is 40 called?

💡4. The numbers 0, 3, 6, 9, 12, and 15 are all multiples of what number?

You should be able to complete Exercises 5–54 in 90 seconds or less.

5. $\begin{array}{r}0\\ \times 0\end{array}$	6. $\begin{array}{r}7\\ \times 1\end{array}$	7. $\begin{array}{r}2\\ \times 4\end{array}$	8. $\begin{array}{r}6\\ \times 0\end{array}$	9. $\begin{array}{r}3\\ \times 7\end{array}$	10. $\begin{array}{r}0\\ \times 2\end{array}$	11. $\begin{array}{r}8\\ \times 9\end{array}$	12. $\begin{array}{r}5\\ \times 4\end{array}$	13. $\begin{array}{r}3\\ \times 8\end{array}$	14. $\begin{array}{r}3\\ \times 6\end{array}$
15. $\begin{array}{r}2\\ \times 5\end{array}$	16. $\begin{array}{r}2\\ \times 9\end{array}$	17. $\begin{array}{r}3\\ \times 3\end{array}$	18. $\begin{array}{r}1\\ \times 2\end{array}$	19. $\begin{array}{r}0\\ \times 7\end{array}$	20. $\begin{array}{r}1\\ \times 5\end{array}$	21. $\begin{array}{r}6\\ \times 7\end{array}$	22. $\begin{array}{r}8\\ \times 3\end{array}$	23. $\begin{array}{r}8\\ \times 1\end{array}$	24. $\begin{array}{r}5\\ \times 7\end{array}$
25. $\begin{array}{r}6\\ \times 8\end{array}$	26. $\begin{array}{r}7\\ \times 2\end{array}$	27. $\begin{array}{r}7\\ \times 9\end{array}$	28. $\begin{array}{r}3\\ \times 5\end{array}$	29. $\begin{array}{r}8\\ \times 5\end{array}$	30. $\begin{array}{r}9\\ \times 2\end{array}$	31. $\begin{array}{r}6\\ \times 9\end{array}$	32. $\begin{array}{r}4\\ \times 0\end{array}$	33. $\begin{array}{r}1\\ \times 6\end{array}$	34. $\begin{array}{r}1\\ \times 7\end{array}$
35. $\begin{array}{r}4\\ \times 7\end{array}$	36. $\begin{array}{r}7\\ \times 6\end{array}$	37. $\begin{array}{r}0\\ \times 3\end{array}$	38. $\begin{array}{r}8\\ \times 4\end{array}$	39. $\begin{array}{r}8\\ \times 7\end{array}$	40. $\begin{array}{r}5\\ \times 0\end{array}$	41. $\begin{array}{r}1\\ \times 1\end{array}$	42. $\begin{array}{r}4\\ \times 9\end{array}$	43. $\begin{array}{r}0\\ \times 5\end{array}$	44. $\begin{array}{r}6\\ \times 2\end{array}$
45. $\begin{array}{r}9\\ \times 1\end{array}$	46. $\begin{array}{r}2\\ \times 0\end{array}$	47. $\begin{array}{r}0\\ \times 6\end{array}$	48. $\begin{array}{r}9\\ \times 5\end{array}$	49. $\begin{array}{r}9\\ \times 4\end{array}$	50. $\begin{array}{r}3\\ \times 2\end{array}$	51. $\begin{array}{r}5\\ \times 3\end{array}$	52. $\begin{array}{r}1\\ \times 8\end{array}$	53. $\begin{array}{r}4\\ \times 4\end{array}$	54. $\begin{array}{r}9\\ \times 8\end{array}$

💡*Find the value of or translate each expression in Exercises 55–58.*

55. The product of 7 and 4

56. 9 times a

57. The product of d and a

58. twice w

Solve each equation in Exercises 59–64.

59. $2x = 14$

60. $6y = 6$

61. $9z = 36$

62. $15 = 3x$

63. $81 = 9c$

64. $12 = 4m$

Find each product in Exercises 65–84.

65. 25
     ×2

66. 22
     ×3

67. 36
     ×2

68. 53
     ×3

69. 93
     ×3

70. 503
     ×3

71. 527
     ×3

72. 287
     ×8

73. 700
     ×3

74. 5003
     ×3

75. 9325
     ×4

76. 43
     ×12

77. 33
     ×22

78. 73
     ×45

79. 37
     ×40

80. 80
     ×80

81. 603
     ×42

82. 839
     ×42

83. 803
     ×601

84. 900
     ×900

Solve each applied problem in Exercises 85–87.

85. **HEALTH**   Playing tennis burns up 230 calories every hour. How many calories would be burned up by a player in a match taking 4 hours?

86. **TIME MEASUREMENT**   There are 365 days in a year. How many days are there in 5 years?

87. **HYDROLOGY**   A water tank contains 50,000 gallons of water. When opened, an outlet valve will release 40 gallons of water every minute.

(a) How many gallons of water will be released in 48 minutes?

(b) How many gallons of water remain in the tank after 48 minutes?

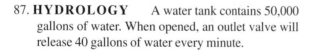

CRITICAL THINKING

Find the products in Exercises 88–90.

88.   6000
    × 200

89.   4006
    × 6004

90.   7000
    × 5000

 91. When told to find the product of 36 and 21, Burford obtained 66 for the answer. Can you discover what he did wrong to obtain this? Write a paragraph explaining the correct way to find the product.

92. Consider the lists of multiples of 2, multiples of 7, and multiples of 14. Discuss the relationship between these three lists.

93. **COMMUNICATIONS**   A communications satellite travels 31,200 miles in one orbit of the earth. If the satellite makes 6 orbits per day, how many miles will it travel in 1 year? [Use 365 days for 1 year.]

REVIEW OR PREVIEW

Exercises 94–99 will help you prepare for the next section. Perform operations inside parentheses first.

94. Find $5 + 3$.

95. Find 2×5.

96. Find 2×3.

97. Find $2 \times (5 + 3)$.

98. Find $(2 \times 5) + (2 \times 3)$.

99. Compare the results of Exercises 91 and 92. What do you discover?

1.5 PARALLEL EXERCISES

Answers to these exercises are not given in the text.

💡*Consider the multiplication problem* $7 \times 9 = 63$ *and answer each question in Exercises 1–3.*

1. What is 63 called?

2. What is 9 called?

3. What is 7 called?

💡4. The numbers 0, 7, 14, 21, 28, and 35 are all multiples of what number?

You should be able to complete Exercises 5–54 in 90 seconds or less.

5. $8 \cdot 1 =$ 6. $9 \cdot 2 =$ 7. $2 \cdot 0 =$ 8. $8 \cdot 8 =$ 9. $7 \cdot 9 =$

10. $6 \cdot 1 =$ 11. $4 \cdot 2 =$ 12. $3 \cdot 5 =$ 13. $6 \cdot 7 =$ 14. $9 \cdot 9 =$

15. $2 \cdot 6 =$ 16. $7 \cdot 7 =$ 17. $6 \cdot 9 =$ 18. $7 \cdot 2 =$ 19. $4 \cdot 1 =$

20. $0 \cdot 2 =$ 21. $9 \cdot 8 =$ 22. $7 \cdot 1 =$ 23. $6 \cdot 8 =$ 24. $9 \cdot 5 =$

25. $0 \cdot 0 =$ 26. $3 \cdot 4 =$ 27. $4 \cdot 0 =$ 28. $1 \cdot 8 =$ 29. $0 \cdot 6 =$

30. $5 \cdot 0 =$ 31. $5 \cdot 5 =$ 32. $6 \cdot 3 =$ 33. $1 \cdot 2 =$ 34. $0 \cdot 7 =$

35. $0 \cdot 8 =$ 36. $8 \cdot 9 =$ 37. $0 \cdot 5 =$ 38. $5 \cdot 7 =$ 39. $9 \cdot 3 =$

40. $0 \cdot 4 =$ 41. $1 \cdot 7 =$ 42. $7 \cdot 4 =$ 43. $3 \cdot 2 =$ 44. $3 \cdot 0 =$

45. $8 \cdot 6 =$ 46. $6 \cdot 5 =$ 47. $5 \cdot 8 =$ 48. $0 \cdot 3 =$ 49. $9 \cdot 7 =$

50. $5 \cdot 9 =$ 51. $3 \cdot 7 =$ 52. $6 \cdot 4 =$ 53. $9 \cdot 0 =$ 54. $4 \cdot 8 =$

💡*Find the value of or translate each expression in Exercises 55–58.*

55. The product of 6 and 7

56. 5 times b

57. The product of a and d

58. twice p

Solve each equation in Exercises 59–64.

59. $2y = 10$

60. $8x = 8$

61. $9b = 45$

62. $15 = 5w$

63. $27 = 3v$

64. $64 = 8n$

Find each product in Exercises 65–84.

65. $\begin{array}{r} 13 \\ \times 3 \\ \hline \end{array}$

66. $\begin{array}{r} 41 \\ \times 2 \\ \hline \end{array}$

67. $\begin{array}{r} 18 \\ \times 3 \\ \hline \end{array}$

68. $\begin{array}{r} 61 \\ \times 7 \\ \hline \end{array}$

69. $\begin{array}{r} 231 \\ \times 3 \\ \hline \end{array}$

70. $\begin{array}{r} 223 \\ \times 4 \\ \hline \end{array}$

71. $\begin{array}{r} 783 \\ \times 5 \\ \hline \end{array}$

72. $\begin{array}{r} 656 \\ \times 9 \\ \hline \end{array}$

73. $\begin{array}{r} 979 \\ \times 2 \\ \hline \end{array}$

74. $\begin{array}{r} 6257 \\ \times 2 \\ \hline \end{array}$

75. $\begin{array}{r} 6987 \\ \times 1 \\ \hline \end{array}$

76. $\begin{array}{r} 52 \\ \times 11 \\ \hline \end{array}$

77. $\begin{array}{r} 64 \\ \times 15 \\ \hline \end{array}$

78. $\begin{array}{r} 83 \\ \times 92 \\ \hline \end{array}$

79. $\begin{array}{r} 70 \\ \times 38 \\ \hline \end{array}$

80. $\begin{array}{r} 40 \\ \times 99 \\ \hline \end{array}$

81. $\begin{array}{r} 748 \\ \times 19 \\ \hline \end{array}$

82. $\begin{array}{r} 554 \\ \times 78 \\ \hline \end{array}$

83. $\begin{array}{r} 387 \\ \times 430 \\ \hline \end{array}$

84. $\begin{array}{r} 954 \\ \times 702 \\ \hline \end{array}$

Solve each applied problem in Exercises 85–87.

85. **POLITICS**   A petition to get Sarah Devoney on the ballot for student president has 25 signatures on each of 32 pages. How many signatures were collected?

86. **EDUCATION**   With 12 points for each question and 135 questions on a 3-hour final exam, how many points were possible?

87. **MANUFACTURING**   The manufacturer of woodburning stoves has 247 stoves in stock. The company can make 12 stoves each day.

(a) How many stoves can be made in 25 days?

(b) Assuming no stoves are sold out of stock, how many stoves will be in stock 25 days from now?

CRITICAL THINKING

Find the products in Exercises 88–90.

88. 5000
     $\underline{\times\ 200}$
     1000000

89. 2003
     $\underline{\times\ 3002}$

90. 4000
     $\underline{\times\ 9000}$

91. When told to find the product of 24 and 13, Burford obtained 46 for the answer. Can you discover what he did wrong to obtain this? Write a paragraph explaining the correct way to find the product.

92. Consider the lists of multiples of 3, multiples of 5, and multiples of 15. Discuss the relationship between these three lists.

93. **EDUCATION**   If your teacher assigns the multiples of 4 in 1.5 Exercises, which problems should you work?

GROUP PROJECT

The number 9 has a lot of interesting properties. Consider what happens when you add the digits of the first ten multiples of 9? Also, consider a multiple of 9 and reverse the digits. What kind of number do you obtain? Investigate other peculiar properties of 9 and write a report about your discoveries.

1.6 PROPERTIES OF MULTIPLICATION AND SPECIAL PRODUCTS

STUDENT GUIDEPOSTS
1   RECOGNIZING THE COMMUTATIVE LAW OF MULTIPLICATION
2   USING THE REVERSE-ORDER CHECK OF MULTIPLICATION
3   RECOGNIZING THE ASSOCIATIVE LAW OF MULTIPLICATION
4   USING THE DISTRIBUTIVE LAW
5   MULTIPLYING BY 10, 100, OR 1000
6   USING ROUNDED NUMBERS TO ESTIMATE AND CHECK PRODUCTS

1   COMMUTATIVE LAW OF MULTIPLICATION

You have probably noticed that changing the order of multiplication does not change the product. For example, 4×6 and 6×4 are both 24. From a visual standpoint, consider a page with 4 rows, each containing 6 objects, as shown in Figure 1.18(a). When the page is turned as in Figure 1.18(b), the result has 6 rows, each containing 4 objects. Since the number of objects remains the same, $4 \times 6 = 6 \times 4$. This demonstrates an important property of multiplication.

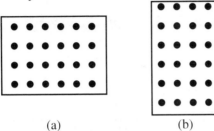

(a)   (b)

FIGURE 1.18

THE COMMUTATIVE LAW OF MULTIPLICATION

If a and b are any two numbers, then

$$ab = ba.$$

That is, changing the order of multiplication does not change the product.

EXAMPLE 1   RECOGNIZING THE COMMUTATIVE LAW

Multiply.

(a) $3 \times 5 = \underbrace{5 + 5 + 5}_{\textbf{Three 5s}} = 15$

(b) $5 \times 3 = \underbrace{3 + 3 + 3 + 3 + 3}_{\textbf{Five 3s}} = 15$

Notice that $3 \times 5 = 5 \times 3$.

(c) $(4)(0) = \underbrace{0 + 0 + 0 + 0}_{\textbf{Four 0s}} = 0$

Since we know that $(0)(4) = (4)(0)$ by the commutative law, and since $(4)(0) = 0$, we have that $(0)(4) = 0$.

(d) $7 \cdot 1 = \underbrace{1 + 1 + 1 + 1 + 1 + 1 + 1}_{\textbf{Seven 1s}} = 7$

(e) $1 \cdot 7 = \underset{\textbf{One 7}}{\downarrow} 7$

Notice that $7 \cdot 1 = 1 \cdot 7 = 7$

In Example 1(c), we saw that multiplying 4 times 0 or 0 times 4 resulted in 0 for the product. This is true in general.

PRACTICE EXERCISE 1

Multiply.

(a) 7×2

(b) 2×7

(c) $(12)(0)$

(d) $5 \cdot 1$

(e) $1 \cdot 5$

Answers: (a)14 (b)14 (c) 0 (d) 5 (e) 5

ZERO PROPERTY OF MULTIPLICATION

If *a* is any number, then

$$a \cdot 0 = 0 \text{ and } 0 \cdot a = 0.$$

That is, multiplying any number by 0 gives 0 for the product.

Also, from Example 1 (d) and (e), we saw that multiplying 7 by 1 or multiplying 1 by 7 gives 7 for the product. In general, if any number is multiplied by 1 or 1 is multiplied by any number, the product is the *identical* number.

ONE IS THE MULTIPLICATIVE IDENTITY

If *a* is any number, then

$$a \cdot 1 = a \text{ and } 1 \cdot a = a.$$

That is, multiplying any number by 1 gives the identical number for the product.

2 | REVERSE-ORDER CHECK OF MULTIPLICATION

One method for checking our work in a multiplication problem would be to repeat the process. However, in doing this, we are likely to repeat any error that might have been made the first time. A better method to use is based on the commutative law of multiplication, which guarantees that changing the order of multiplication does not change the product. Suppose we have found the following product:

$$\begin{array}{r} 23 \\ \times 47 \\ \hline 161 \\ 92 \\ \hline 1081 \end{array}$$

To check our work, we interchange the multiplier and the multiplicand and find the new product:

$$\begin{array}{r} 47 \\ \times 23 \\ \hline 141 \\ 94 \\ \hline 1081 \end{array}$$

Because we know that 47×23 is the same as 23×47, the answers should be equal. This check is the **reverse-order check of multiplication.**

USING THE REVERSE-ORDER CHECK	EXAMPLE 2

Find the product of 329 and 54. Check your work using the reverse-order check.

Multiply: 329   Check: 54   Factors are inter-
          $\times$54 $\times$329   changed
          ‾‾‾‾   ‾‾‾‾
          1316   486
          1645   108
          ‾‾‾‾‾   162
          17766   ‾‾‾‾‾
                                17766

The check on the right may look strange. We usually write the number with more digits above the one with fewer digits in a multiplication problem. However, this example shows that the multiplication method works either way.

PRACTICE EXERCISE 2

Find the product of 457 and 35. Check your work using the reverse order check.

457   Check: 35
$\times$35 $\times$457

Answer: 15,995

3 | ASSOCIATIVE LAW OF MULTIPLICATION

Multiplication, like addition, is a binary operation (that is, we multiply two numbers at a time). To find the product of three or more numbers, we can multiply in steps. For example, consider the product $3 \times 2 \times 5$. We can first multiply 3×2, then multiply the result by 5.

$$(\mathbf{3 \times 2}) \times 5 = \mathbf{6} \times 5 = 30$$

Or we can multiply 2×5 first, then multiply the result by 3.

$$3 \times (\mathbf{2 \times 5}) = 3 \times \mathbf{10} = 30$$

The parentheses show which products are found first. The same result is obtained regardless of how the factors are grouped. That is,

$$(\mathbf{3 \times 2}) \times 5 = 3 \times (\mathbf{2 \times 5}),$$

which is an example of an important property of multiplication.

ASSOCIATIVE LAW OF MULTIPLICATION

If a, b, and c are any three numbers, then

$$(\mathbf{ab})\mathbf{c} = \mathbf{a}(\mathbf{bc}).$$

That is, the product of more than two numbers is not changed by the way that the numbers are grouped so they can be multiplied two at a time.

NOTE Because of the commutative and associative laws of multiplication, when you multiply two or more numbers, the order of the numbers or the grouping of the numbers does not affect the product.

EXPLORATION GUIDE

Suppose we wish to find the following product.

$$2 \times 5 \times 6 \times 8$$

Remember that multiplication is a binary operation, which means that we only multiply two numbers at a time. Show that the product of the four numbers given above is equal to 480, and justify each of your steps using one of the properties of multiplication.

4 | DISTRIBUTIVE LAW

An important relationship between multiplication and addition is shown in the following problem.

$$3 \times (\mathbf{4 + 5}) = 3 \times \mathbf{9} \qquad \text{Operate within parentheses first}$$
$$= 27 \qquad \text{Find the product of 3 and 9. 27}$$

Next, find the following.

$$(3 \times 4) + (3 \times 5) = \mathbf{12 + 15} \qquad \text{Operate within the parentheses first}$$
$$= 27 \qquad \text{Find the sum of 12 and 15, 27}$$

As a result, $\quad \mathbf{3 \times (4 + 5) = (3 \times 4) + (3 \times 5)}.$

In a sense, the expression to the right of the equal sign is formed by "distributing" multiplication by 3 over the sum of 4 and 5. That is why this property is called the **distributive law** of multiplication over addition.

THE DISTRIBUTIVE LAW

If a, b, and c be any three numbers, then

$$a(b + c) = ab + ac.$$

NOTE   The multiplication procedure in Section 1.5 actually involves repeated use of the distributive law. Consider

$$3 \times 42 = 3 \times (40 + 2) \qquad \textbf{Expanded notation}$$
$$= (3 \times 40) + (3 \times 2) \quad \textbf{Distributive law}$$
$$= 120 + 6 \qquad\qquad \textbf{Multiply (withinarentheses)}$$
$$= 126 \qquad\qquad\quad \textbf{Add}$$

Notice that when the problem is written vertically, 3×2 is found in the first row and 3×40 in the second row.

$$
\begin{array}{r}
42 \\
\times 3 \\
\hline
6 \\
120 \\
\hline
126
\end{array}
$$

$$
\begin{array}{l}
(3 \times 2) \\
+ (3 \times 40) \\
\hline
(3 \times 40) + (3 \times 2)
\end{array}
$$

The distributive law is also used on expressions that involve variables, and is sometimes used together with the associative law of multiplication. This is illustrated in the next example.

<table>
<tr><td>

PRACTICE EXERCISE 3

Multiply.

(a) $6(y + 5)$

(b) $3(8 + 4z)$

Answers: (a) $6y + 30$
(b) $24 + 12z$

</td><td>

USING THE DISTRIBUTIVE LAW   **EXAMPLE 3**

Multiply.

(a) $4(x + 3) = 4x + 4 \cdot 3$ Distributive law
$$= 4x + 12$$

(b) $2(3a + 7) = 2(3a) + 2 \cdot 7$ Distributive law
$$= (2 \cdot 3)a + 2 \cdot 7 \qquad \text{Associative law}$$
$$= 6a + 14$$

</td></tr>
</table>

5 | MULTIPLYING BY 10, 100, OR 1000

Multiplication problems involving the numbers 10, 100, and 1000 occur frequently. Recall that **multiples of 10** are numbers such as

10, 20, 30, 40, 50.

Multiples of 100 include

100, 200, 300, 400, 500, and so on,

while **multiples of 1000** include

1000, 2000, 3000, 4000, 5000, and so on.

Products that involve multiples of 10, 100, or 1000 can be found quickly by using the following rule.

TO MULTIPLY A NUMBER
1.   by **10,** attach **one 0** at the end of the number,
2.   by **100,** attach **two 0s** at the end of the number,
3.   by **1000,** attach **three 0s** at the end of the number.

E X A M P L E 4   **MULTIPLYING BY 10, 100, OR 1000**

Find each product.

(a) $10 \cdot 5 = 50$ Attach one 0 to 5

(b) $10 \cdot 435 = 4350$ Attach one 0 to 435

(c) $100 \cdot 4 = 400$ Attach two 0s to 4

(d) $100 \cdot 497 = 49{,}700$ Attach two 0s to 497

(e) $1000 \cdot 9 = 9000$ Attach three 0s to 9

(f) $1000 \cdot 138 = 138{,}000$ Attach three 0s to 138

When multiplying two multiples of 10, 100, or 1000, similar shortcuts are possible.

E X A M P L E 5   **MULTIPLYING WITH MULTIPLES OF 10, 100, OR 1000**

Find each product.

(a)   40   Multiply $7 \cdot 4$ and attach two (the total number
     $\times 70$ of zeros in the factors) zeros
    ———
    2800

(b)   700   Multiply $9 \cdot 7$ and attach three zeros $(2 + 1 = 3)$
     $\times 90$
    ———
   63000

In each case, the total number of zeros attached to the product is the sum of the zeros in the factors.

6   **USING ROUNDED NUMBERS TO ESTIMATE AND CHECK PRODUCTS**

Earlier in this section we used the reverse-order method to check a multiplication problem. The obvious drawback of this technique is that it takes just as long to check as to find the original product. For this reason, it is helpful to have another method. Rounded approximations for the factors can be used for **estimating products** and discovering any major errors.

E X A M P L E 6   **CHECKING MULTIPLICATION BY ESTIMATING**

Find the product of 476 and 31; then check your work by estimating the product.

Multiply: 476   Check: 500   476 rounds to 500
        $\times 31$ $\times 30$ 31 rounds to 30
      ———   ———
      476   15000
    1428
    ———
   14756

PRACTICE EXERCISE 4

Find each product.

(a) $8 \cdot 10$

(b) $648 \cdot 10$

(c) $3 \cdot 100$

(d) $476 \cdot 100$

(e) $7 \cdot 1000$

(f) $929 \cdot 1000$

Answers: (a) 80   (b) 6480
(c) 300 (d) 47,600   (e) 7000
(f) 929,000

PRACTICE EXERCISE 5

Find each product.

(a)   400
   $\times 700$

(b)   9000
   $\times 400$

Answers: (a) 280,000
(b) 3,600,000

PRACTICE EXERCISE 6

Find the product of 295 and 42; then check your work by estimating the product.

Answer: Rounding 295 to 300 and 42 to 40, the estimated product is
$40 \cdot 300 = 12{,}000$ (the actual product is 12,390).

Since 15,000 is "close" to 14,756, we would assume that no major error has been made.

NOTE   When rounding numbers to find estimated products, round all fourdigit numbers to the nearest thousand, all three-digit numbers to the nearest hundred, and all two-digit numbers to the nearest ten.

Rounded numbers can also be used to estimate solutions to applied problems.

PRACTICE EXERCISE 7

If one piece of pie has 205 calories, without finding the exact number, estimate the number of calories in 89 pieces.

Answer: 18,000 calories (using 200×90)

ESTIMATING A PRODUCT IN AN APPLIED PROBLEM   EXAMPLE 7

There are 4985 students in a school, and each spent $41 for athletic fees. Without finding the exact amount, estimate the total amount of money spent on athletic fees by these students.

Since 4985 is about 5000 and $41 is about $40, we can estimate the total by multiplying 5000 by 40.

$$\left.\begin{array}{r} 5000 \\ 40 \\ \hline 200000 \end{array}\right\} \quad \text{Mental work}$$

Thus, about $200,000 was spent on these fees.

1.6 EXERCISES

Answers to these exercises are given on page 640.

1. The fact that $2 \times 7 = 7 \times 2$ illustrates what law of multiplication?

2. The number 1 times any number always gives what number for the product?

3. Use the associative law of multiplication to complete the following: $(3 \times 5) \times 7 = \underline{\quad}$.

4. Use the distributive law to complete the following: $4 \times (5 + 7) = \underline{\quad}$.

5. (a) Evaluate $7 \times (2 + 9)$. (b) Evaluate $(7 \times 2) + (7 \times 9)$. (c) Why are your answers to (a) and (b) the same?

6. (a) Evaluate $9 \times (3 \times 5)$. (b) Evaluate $(9 \times 3) \times 5$. (c) Why are your answers to (a) and (b) the same?

7. (a) Evaluate 8×11. (b) Evaluate 11×8. (c) Why are your answers to (a) and (b) the same?

8. The number 0 times any number always gives what number for the product?

In Exercises 9–11, find the product and check using the reverse-order check.

9. $\begin{array}{r} 47 \\ \times 19 \\ \hline \end{array}$

10. $\begin{array}{r} 161 \\ \times 37 \\ \hline \end{array}$

11. $\begin{array}{r} 545 \\ \times 139 \\ \hline \end{array}$

Find each product in Exercises 12–26.

12. $10 \cdot 9$ 13. $42 \cdot 10$ 14. $387 \cdot 10$ 15. $7 \cdot 100$ 16. $100 \cdot 77$

17. $100 \cdot 427$ 18. $1000 \cdot 5$ 19. $1000 \cdot 42$ 20. $78 \cdot 1000$ 21. $1000 \cdot 529$

22. $\begin{array}{r} 70 \\ \times 60 \\ \hline \end{array}$ 23. $\begin{array}{r} 800 \\ \times 400 \\ \hline \end{array}$ 24. $\begin{array}{r} 700 \\ \times 20 \\ \hline \end{array}$ 25. $\begin{array}{r} 6000 \\ \times\ 30 \\ \hline \end{array}$ 26. $\begin{array}{r} 7000 \\ \times 500 \\ \hline \end{array}$

Check by estimating each product in Exercises 27–29.

27. $\begin{array}{r} 78 \\ \times 21 \\ \hline 78 \\ 156 \\ \hline 1638 \end{array}$ 28. $\begin{array}{r} 409 \\ \times 38 \\ \hline 3272 \\ 1227 \\ \hline 15542 \end{array}$ 29. $\begin{array}{r} 813 \\ \times 491 \\ \hline 813 \\ 7317 \\ 3252 \\ \hline 499183 \end{array}$

Use the distributive law and multiply in Exercises 30–32.

30. $5(x + 3)$ 31. $4(y + 7)$ 32. $9(4 + z)$

Use the distributive law and the associative law to multiply in Exercises 33–35.

33. $2(3a + 1)$ 34. $7(5z + 7)$ 35. $6(3 + 2m)$

Solve each applied problem in Exercises 36–39.

36. **LIBRARY SCIENCE**   There are 29 volumes in a set of reference books, and each volume has 995 pages. Without finding the exact number, estimate the total number of pages in the set.

37. **BUSINESS**   A store had 103 customers on Saturday, and the average amount spent by each was $289. Without finding the exact amount, estimate the total receipts for Saturday.

38. **ENVIRONMENT**   In a study of the Colorado river Greg McRill collected 105 fish per day for 42 days. Without finding the exact number, estimate the number of fish involved in the study.

39. **RECREATION**   A merry-go-round in a traveling carnival makes 11 revolutions a minute. Without finding the exact number, estimate the number of revolutions made in 103 minutes.

CRITICAL THINKING

Let a, b, and c be any three whole numbers. Complete each statement in Exercises 40–43.

40. Associative law: $a(bc) = $ _____

41. Commutative law: $cb = $ _____

42. Distributive law: $a(b + c) = $ _____

43. $a \cdot 1 = $ ___ and $a \cdot 0 = $ ___

Audio Video Entertainment Systems distributes Cassette Players (CP), Compact Disk Players (CDP), and Video Cassette Recorders (VCR) to electronics dealers in the western United States. The graph below shows the number of each that was sold and distributed during a recent month. Use this information in Exercises 44–47.

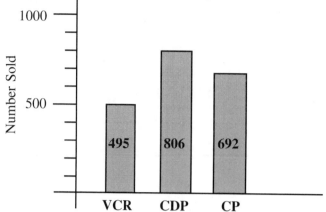

44. What was the total number of units sold during the month?
45. If the actual number of each unit sold was not given, could you approximate the number from the graph? How close would your approximation be? Using these approximations, about how many audio units (CDs and CDPs) were sold during the month?
46. If the VCRs sold for $198, approximately how much revenue was earned on the sale of VCRs? What was the actual revenue?
47. If the CPs sold for $99, approximately how much revenue was earned on the sale of CPs? What was the actual revenue?

48. In your own words, and using complete sentences, describe the commutative law of multiplication and explain why this property is important.
49. Discuss some of the important properties of the number 0 relative to addition and multiplication. Use complete sentences.
50. Discuss the distributive law of multiplication over addition. Give an example to show that multiplication can also be *distributed* over subtraction.

REVIEW OR PREVIEW

Find each product in Exercises 51–53. Check your work using the reverse-order check.

51. 253
    ×41

52. 621
    ×113

53. 785
    ×243

1.6 PARALLEL EXERCISES

Answers to these exercises are not given in the text.

1. Use the commutative law of multiplication to complete the following: $9 \times 5 =$ _____ .
2. The number 0 times any number always gives what number for the product?
3. Use the associative law of multiplication to complete the following: $2 \times (4 \times 9) =$ _____ .
4. Use the distributive law to complete the following: $(2 \times 5) + (2 \times 8) =$ _____ .
5. (a) Evaluate $10 \times (2 + 3)$. (b) Evaluate $(10 \times 2) + (10 \times 3)$. (c) Why are your answers to (a) and (b) the same?
6. (a) Evaluate $3 \times (4 \times 10)$. (b) Evaluate $(3 \times 4) \times 10$. (c) Why are your answers to (a) and (b) the same?

7. (a) Evaluate 12×4. (b) Evaluate 4×12. (c) Why are your answers to (a) and (b) the same?

8. Any number times 1 always gives what number for the product?

In Exercises 9–11, find the product and check using the reverse-order check.

9.   83   10.   452   11.   893
    ×48   ×12   ×452

Find each product in Exercises 12–26.

12. $10 \cdot 5$ 13. $71 \cdot 10$ 14. $593 \cdot 10$ 15. $100 \cdot 8$ 16. $43 \cdot 100$

17. $100 \cdot 645$ 18. $1000 \cdot 3$ 19. $1000 \cdot 57$ 20. $84 \cdot 1000$ 21. $259 \cdot 1000$

22.   70   23.   400   24.   500   25.   9000   26.   8000
     ×40   ×700   ×30   ×40   ×400

Check by estimating each product in Exercises 27–29.

27.   61   28.   678   29.   290
       ×88   ×51   ×603
     ─────   ─────   ─────
       488   678   870
       488   3390   1740
     ─────   ─────   ─────
      4368   34578   18270

Use the distributive law and multiply in Exercises 30–32.

30. $8(x + 2)$ 31. $3(y + 9)$ 32. $9(2 + z)$

Use the distributive law and the associative law to multiply in Exercises 33–35.

33. $4(2a + 1)$ 34. $5(6z + 2)$ 35. $7(7 + 2m)$

Solve each applied problem in Exercises 36–39.

36. **SALES**   During the sales season Don Cole worked 51 hours a week for 39 weeks. Without finding the exact number, estimate the number of hours Don worked during this period.

37. **BUSINESS**   A drug store has 7958 bottles of pills in its inventory. If the average number of pills per bottle is 98, approximately how many pills are in the store? [Do not find the exact number.]

38. **CONSTRUCTION**   A block layer can lay 46 cinder blocks an hour. Estimate the number of blocks that can be laid in a 52-hour workweek. [Do not find the exact number.]

39. **DATA PROCESSING**   Diane can type 85 words a minute. Estimate the number of words that she can type in 7 hours. [Do not find the actual number of words. Use the fact that 7 hours is 420 minutes.]

CRITICAL THINKING

Let a, b, and c be any three whole numbers. Complete each statement in Exercises 40–43.

40. Associative law: $(bc)a =$ _____

41. Commutative law: $ba =$ _____

42. Distributive law: $cb + ca =$ _____

43. $1 \cdot b =$ ___ and $0 \cdot b =$ ___

Refer to the bar graph given above Exercises 44–47 to answer the following questions

44. What was the total number of audio systems (CPs and CDPs) sold during the month?

45. If the actual number of each unit sold was not given, could you approximate the number from the graph? How close would your approximation be? Using these approximations, about how many total units were sold during the month?

46. If the CDPs sold for $149, approximately how much revenue was earned on the sale of CDPs? What was the actual revenue?

47. Approximately how much revenue was earned on the sale of all three units during the month? What was the actual revenue? (Each VCR: 198; CDP: $149; CP: $99.)

48. In your own words, and using complete sentences, describe the associative law of multiplication and explain why this property is important.

49. Discuss some of the important properties of the number 1 relative to multiplication. Use complete sentences.

50. Write a paragraph describing the method used to multiply a whole number by 10, 100, or 1000, and explain how multiplying multiples of 10, 100, or 1000 can be used to obtain approximate answers to given multiplication problems.

GROUP PROJECT

Burford was overheard to say "I don't need to know anything about the properties like the commutative and associative laws or the distributive law, I just need to know how to operate with numbers and find answers." Collect some examples and write a report that will illustrate to Burford that he is mistaken, and that to really understand and work with mathematics, one must know the *rules of the game,* in this case the properties of our number system, and be able to use them.

1.7 DIVIDING WHOLE NUMBERS

STUDENT GUIDEPOSTS
1   LEARNING THE BASIC DIVISION FACTS
2   USING SPECIAL PROPERTIES OF DIVISION
3   DIVIDING BY A ONE-DIGIT NUMBER
4   DIVIDING BY A TWO-DIGIT NUMBER
5   DIVIDING BY A THREE-DIGIT NUMBER
6   CHECKING DIVISION

1 | BASIC DIVISION FACTS

The final arithmetic operation we study is division. Recall that multiplication can be thought of as repeated addition. Similarly, division can be thought of as repeated subtraction.

The word *division* means "separation into parts." Consider dividing 15 by 3. We use ÷ as the **division symbol** and write $15 \div 3$,
(read "15 divided by 3"). In the example, 15, the number being divided, is called the **dividend,** and 3, the dividing number, is the **divisor.** Suppose we have 15 objects and separate or divide them into 3 equal parts. As shown in Figure 1.19, each equal part has 5 objects in it.

$$
\begin{array}{ccccc}
0 & 0 & 0 & 0 & 0 \\
0 & 0 & 0 & 0 & 0 \\
0 & 0 & 0 & 0 & 0 \\
\end{array}
$$

15 objects
divided into **3 groups**
each having **5** objects

FIGURE 1.19

We write $15 \div 3 = 5$, and call 5 the **quotient** of 15 and 3.

We could also look at the problem as repeated subtraction. That is, $15 \div 3$ could be thought of as the number of times 3 can be subtracted from 15 until zero remains.

$$
\begin{array}{rl}
15 & \\
-\ 3 & \text{First subtraction of } 3 \\
\hline
12 & \\
-\ 3 & \text{Second subtraction of } 3 \\
\hline
9 & \\
-\ 3 & \text{Third subtraction of } 3 \\
\hline
6 & \\
-\ 3 & \text{Fourth subtraction of } 3 \\
\hline
3 & \\
-\ 3 & \text{Fifth subtraction of } 3 \\
\hline
0 & \\
\end{array}
$$

We have subtracted 3 from 15 a total of 5 times. That is, $15 \div 3 = 5$. The three ways to write a division problem are illustrated by

$$15 \div 3 = 5, \quad \frac{15}{3} = 5, \quad \text{and} \quad 3\overline{)15}^{\,5}.$$

The notation $\frac{15}{3}$ will be used extensively in Chapters 2 and 3 on fractions. The horizontal line is called a **fraction bar.** The notation $3\overline{)15}$ is used primarily in the long division problems found in this chapter. In words, the division forms are:

$$\text{dividend} \div \text{divisor} = \text{quotient} \qquad \frac{\text{dividend}}{\text{divisor}} = \text{quotient} \qquad \text{divisor}\overline{)\text{dividend}}^{\,\text{quotient}}$$

EXAMPLE 1   DIVIDING BY REPEATED SUBTRACTION

Find the quotient $20 \div 5$ by repeated subtraction.

Since 5 can be subtracted from 20 four times,

$$20 \div 5 = 4.$$

$$
\begin{array}{rl}
20 & \\
-\ 5 & \text{First subtraction} \\
\hline
15 & \\
-\ 5 & \text{Second subtraction} \\
\hline
10 & \\
-\ 5 & \text{Third subtraction} \\
\hline
5 & \\
-\ 5 & \text{Fourth subtraction} \\
\hline
0 & \\
\end{array}
$$

Find the quotient by repeated subtraction.

$$\frac{30}{6}$$

Answer: 5; 6 can be subtracted 5 times

In Section 1.3 we considered the related subtraction equation and related addition equation. Similar to these are the **related division equation** and **related multiplication equation.** Notice that

$$20 \div 5 = 4 \qquad \text{Division equation}$$

and

$$5 \times 4 = 20 \qquad \text{Multiplication equation}$$

are very closely related. That is, for a given division equation, there is a related multiplication equation, and conversely, for a given multiplication equation, there is a related division equation. This gives us an important principle of division that allows us to divide by considering a multiplication problem.

THE BASIC PRINCIPLE OF DIVISION

Let a, b, and c be numbers. For every division equation

$$a \div b = c \qquad \textbf{dividend} \div \textbf{divisor} = \textbf{quotient}$$

there is a related multiplication equation

$$b \cdot c = a \qquad \textbf{dividend} \cdot \textbf{divisor} = \textbf{quotient}$$

and conversely.

NOTE To obtain a related multiplication equation for a division problem, move the divisor to the other side of the equal sign and multiply.

PRACTICE EXERCISE 2

Give a related multiplication equation for each division equation.

(a) $25 \div 5 = 5$

(b) $6\overline{)42}^{\,7}$

Answers: (a) $5 \times 5 = 25$
(b) $6 \times 7 = 42$

FINDING THE RELATED MULTIPLICATION EQUATION

EXAMPLE 2

Give a related multiplication equation for each division equation.

(a) $14 \div 7 = 2$

Since 14 is the dividend, 7 the divisor, and 2 the quotient, a related multiplication equation is $7 \times 2 = 14$.

Notice that by the commutative law, $2 \times 7 = 14$ is also a related multiplication equation.

(b) $\dfrac{36}{4} = 9$

A related multiplication equation is $4 \times 9 = 36$.

Using the basic multiplication facts that we have learned, we can understand the basic division facts. When we know these facts completely, it will not be necessary to think in terms of the related multiplication equation.

PRACTICE EXERCISE 3

Divide.

(a) $36 \div 9$

(b) $49 \div 7$

(c) $8\overline{)72}$

(d) $\dfrac{48}{6}$

Answers: (a) 4 (b) 7 (c) 9
(d) 8

USING THE BASIC DIVISION (MULTIPLICATION) FACTS

EXAMPLE 3

Divide.

(a) $18 \div 3 = 6$ This is true since $6 \times 3 = 18$

(b) $35 \div 7 = 5$ This is true since $5 \times 7 = 35$

(c) $8\overline{)64}^{\,8}$ This is true since $8 \times 8 = 64$

(d) $\dfrac{54}{9} = 6$ This is true since $6 \times 9 = 54$

As with the other operations, there are many ways to talk about division in English. Consider the statement: *Find the quotient of a and b.* If we translate to symbolic form, we must find $a \div b$, $\dfrac{a}{b}$, or $b\overline{)a}$ Some other translations are included in the table below.

ENGLISH	*SYMBOLS*
The quotient of x and 2	$x \div 2$ or $\dfrac{x}{2}$ or $2\overline{)x}$
The quotient of 2 and x	$2 \div x$ or $\dfrac{2}{x}$ or $x\overline{)2}$
3 divided by z	$3 \div z$ or $\dfrac{3}{z}$ or $z\overline{)3}$
The ratio of a to b	$a \div b$ or $\dfrac{a}{b}$ or $b\overline{)a}$
The quotient of 35 and m is 7	$35 \div m = 7$ or $\dfrac{35}{m} = 7$ or $m\overline{)35}^{\,7}$

2 | SPECIAL PROPERTIES OF DIVISION

The basic principle of division is helpful for special division problems. In particular,

$$8 \div 8 = 1 \qquad \text{since} \qquad 8 \cdot 1 = 8$$

$$\frac{12}{12} = 1 \qquad \text{since} \qquad 12 \cdot 1 = 12$$

$$35\overline{)35}^{\,1} \qquad \text{since} \qquad 35 \cdot 1 = 35.$$

In general, we have the following.

DIVIDING A NONZERO WHOLE NUMBER BY ITSELF

If a is any nonzero number, then

$$a \div a = 1 \quad \text{or} \quad \frac{a}{a} = 1$$

That is, any nonzero number divided by itself is always 1.

Also,

$$5 \div 1 = 5 \qquad \text{since} \qquad 1 \cdot 5 = 5$$

$$\frac{9}{1} = 9 \qquad \text{since} \qquad 1 \cdot 9 = 9$$

$$1\overline{)13}^{\,13} \qquad \text{since} \qquad 1 \cdot 13 = 13.$$

These are examples of the following.

DIVIDING A WHOLE NUMBER BY 1

If a is any number, then

$$a \div 1 = a \quad \text{or} \quad \frac{a}{1} = a$$

That is, any number divided by 1 is always that same number.

When we divide 6 by 2, we see that

$$6 \div 2 = 3 \qquad \text{means that} \qquad 2 \cdot 3 = 6.$$

Suppose we try to divide 6 by 0 in the same manner. Let's use a for the quotient.

$$6 \div 0 = a \qquad \text{means that} \qquad 0 \cdot a = 6.$$

Then a must represent what number? Suppose a is 6, then

$$a \cdot 0 = \mathbf{6} \cdot 0 = 0, \ not \, 6.$$

What if a is 0? Then

$$a \cdot 0 = \mathbf{0} \cdot 0 = 0, \ not \, 6.$$

What if a is 2? Then

$$a \cdot 0 = \mathbf{2} \cdot 0 = 0, \ not \ 6.$$

In fact, what if a is *any number?* Then

$$a \cdot 0 = (\textbf{any number}) \cdot 0 = 0, \ not \ 6.$$

Since there is no number we can use for a to make $a \cdot 0$ equal to 6, we conclude that 0 cannot be used as a divisor of 6, or for that matter, as a divisor of any number.

DIVISION BY ZERO

Division by zero is undefined. That is, if x is any number, then

$$x \div 0 \quad \text{or} \quad \frac{x}{0} \quad \text{or} \quad 0\overline{)x} \text{ is undefined.}$$

We agree never to divide any number by 0.

Although division *by* zero is impossible, zero can be *divided by* any whole number (except 0). For example,

$$0 \div 3 = 0 \qquad \text{since} \qquad 3 \cdot 0 = 0$$

$$\frac{0}{12} = 0 \qquad \text{since} \qquad 12 \cdot 0 = 0$$

$$9\overline{)\overset{0}{0}} \qquad \text{since} \qquad 9 \cdot 0 = 0.$$

In general, we have the following.

DIVIDING ZERO BY ANY NONZERO WHOLE NUMBER

Let x be any nonzero whole number. Then

$$0 \div x = 0 \quad \text{or} \quad \frac{0}{x} = 0 \quad \text{or} \quad x\overline{)\overset{0}{0}}.$$

That is, 0 divided by any nonzero number is always 0.

---

3 | DIVIDING BY A ONE-DIGIT NUMBER

The basic division facts allow us to divide special two-digit numbers by one-digit numbers. We now consider more general problems like the one below. If we try to find the quotient

$$86 \div 2$$

by repeated subtraction, we will have to subtract 2 a great number of times. We can shorten the process by subtracting many 2s at once, as follows.

$$
\begin{array}{rl}
86 & \\
\underline{-20} & \text{Ten 2s subtracted} \\
66 & \\
\underline{-20} & \text{Ten more 2s subtracted} \\
46 & \\
\underline{-20} & \text{Ten more 2s subtracted} \\
26 & \\
\underline{-20} & \text{Ten more 2s subtracted} \\
6 & \\
\underline{-\ 6} & \text{Subtract three 2s} \\
0 &
\end{array}
$$

EXPLORATION GUIDE

We have discovered several properties of division in this section. However, unlike multiplication, we have that: *Division is neither commutative nor associative.* Discuss the meaning of this statement and give examples to show that it is true.

The total number of 2s subtracted is

$$10 + 10 + 10 + 10 + 3 = 43.$$

As a result, we see that

$$86 \div 2 = 43 \quad \text{or} \quad 2\overline{)86}^{\,43}.$$

In the previous display, we see that if the tens digit, 8, is divided by 2, we obtain the tens digit, 4, of the quotient. Similarly, dividing the ones digit, 6, by 2, we obtain the ones digit, 3, of the quotient.

$$8 \div 2 = 4 \longrightarrow \mathbf{43} \longleftarrow 3 = 6 \div 2$$
$$2\overline{)86}$$

When dividing the tens digit and the ones digit, we use basic division facts.

EXAMPLE 4 — DIVIDING BY A ONE-DIGIT NUMBER

Find the quotient. $3\overline{)96}$

$$
\begin{array}{l}
 3 = 9 \div 3 \quad \text{(tens digit)} \\
\mathbf{32} \longleftarrow 2 = 6 \div 3 \quad \text{(ones digit)} \\
3\overline{)96}
\end{array}
$$

Divide tens digit first, then divide ones digit.

In Example 4, the quotient in each step was a basic division fact. We next consider problems in which this is not the case. For example, suppose we find the quotient

$$3\overline{)48}.$$

First we use repeated subtraction.

$$
\begin{array}{rl}
48 & \\
\underline{-30} & \text{Subtract ten 3s} \\
18 & \\
\underline{-18} & \text{Subtract six 3s} \\
0 &
\end{array}
$$

Adding 10 and 6 gives the quotient, 16. Had we written the problem as before, we would have

$$3\overline{)48}^{\,16}.$$

PRACTICE EXERCISE 4

Find the quotient.

$$3\overline{)690}$$

Answer: 230

Since $4 \div 3$ is not a basic division fact, we must find this quotient in several steps.

① **Find the largest number less than 4 which is divisible by 3. This number is 3, and $3 \div 3 = 1$. Place 1 above the 4.**

$$\begin{array}{r} 1 \\ 3\overline{)48} \end{array}$$

② **Multiply 1 times 3 and place the product below 4.**

③ **Draw a line below 3 and subtract 3 from 4 to obtain 1.**

$$\begin{array}{r} 1 \\ 3\overline{)48} \\ \underline{3} \\ 1 \end{array}$$

④ **Bring down the eight.**

⑤ **Divide 18 by 3 and place the quotient, 6, to the right of 1.**

$$\begin{array}{r} 16 \\ 3\overline{)48} \\ \underline{3} \\ 18 \end{array}$$

⑥ **Multiply 6 times 3 and place the result below 18.**

⑦ **Draw a line below 18 and subtract obtaining 0.**

$$\begin{array}{r} 16 \\ 3\overline{)48} \\ \underline{3} \\ 18 \\ \underline{18} \\ 0 \end{array}$$

In the second step, the 1 in the quotient stands for 1 ten, so the product 1×3 represents 3 tens or 30. Compare this to the result of repeated subtraction.

When we divided 48 by 3 above, the final difference, 0, is called the **remainder.** In general, the remainder can be any number less than the divisor.

PRACTICE EXERCISE 5

Find the quotient.

$$3\overline{)473}$$

Answer: 157 R2

OBTAINING A NONZERO REMAINDER   EXAMPLE 5

Find the quotient. Follow the numbered steps.

$$4\overline{)537}$$

⑤ $12 \div 4 = 3$

① $4 \div 4 = 1 \longrightarrow$ 134 $\longleftarrow$ ⑨ $16 \div 4 = 4$
                                       $4\overline{)537}$
② $1 \times 4 = 4 \longrightarrow$ $\underline{4}$
③ $5 - 4 = 1 \longrightarrow$ 13 $\longleftarrow$ ④ **Bring down 3**
⑥ $3 \times 4 = 12 \longrightarrow$ $\underline{12}$
⑦ $13 - 12 = 1 \longrightarrow$ 17 $\longleftarrow$ ⑧ **Bring down 7**
⑩ $4 \times 4 = 16 \longrightarrow$ $\underline{16}$
                                       1   $\longleftarrow$ ⑪ $17 - 16 = 1$ (remainder)

> **NOTE** If you obtain a remainder that is greater than or equal to the divisor, you have made a mistake. In the final division step, the divisor went into the dividend more times. Remember that your remainder must always be less than the divisor.

In many cases the first digit of the dividend is less than the divisor.

PRACTICE EXERCISE 6

Find the quotient.

$$6\overline{)656}$$

DIVIDING INTO THE FIRST TWO DIGITS   EXAMPLE 6

Find the quotient. $3\overline{)263}$

Since there is no number less than or equal to 2 which is divisible by 3, use the first *two* digits of the dividend in the first step. Find the largest number less than or equal to 26 which is divisible by 3. That number, 24, when divided by 3 gives a quotient of 8. Place 8 above 6 and continue.

① $24 \div 3 = 8$ ⟶ ⑤ $24 \div 3 = 7$

$$\begin{array}{r} 87 \\ 3\overline{)263} \end{array}$$

② $8 \times 3 = 24$ ⟶ 24

③ $26 - 24 = 2$ ⟶ 23 ⟵ ④ Bring down 3

⑥ $7 \times 3 = 21$ ⟶ 21

2 ⟵ ⑦ $23 - 21 = 2$ **(remainder)**

The answer can be written 87 R2 where R stands for *remainder*.

It is easy to extend the process to dividends with more than three digits.

Answer: 109 R2

EXAMPLE 7 DIVIDING A FOUR-DIGIT NUMBER

**PRACTICE
EXERCISE 7**

Find each quotient.

Find each quotient.

(a) $5\overline{)3825}$

(a) $2\overline{)4056}$

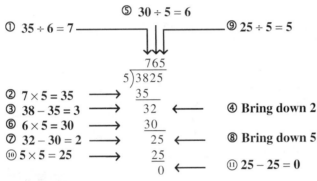

⑤ $30 \div 5 = 6$

① $35 \div 6 = 7$ ⟶ ⑨ $25 \div 5 = 5$

$$\begin{array}{r} 765 \\ 5\overline{)3825} \end{array}$$

② $7 \times 5 = 35$ ⟶ 35

③ $38 - 35 = 3$ ⟶ 32 ⟵ ④ Bring down 2

⑥ $6 \times 5 = 30$ ⟶ 30

⑦ $32 - 30 = 2$ ⟶ 25 ⟵ ⑧ Bring down 5

⑩ $5 \times 5 = 25$ ⟶ 25

0 ⟵ ⑪ $25 - 25 = 0$

(b) $7\overline{)3528}$

(b) $8\overline{)4824}$

$$\begin{array}{r} 504 \\ 7\overline{)3528} \\ 35 \\ \hline 028 \\ 28 \\ \hline 0 \end{array}$$ Since 7 cannot divide 2, bring down 8 and write 0 above 2

Answers: (a) 2028 (b) 603

CAUTION   If you forget to write the digit 0 in a quotient, such as in Example 7(b), your answer will be wrong. Remember that 0 is an important placeholder in our number system.

4 DIVIDING BY A TWO-DIGIT NUMBER

Finding quotients when the divisor has more than one digit is a bit more challenging. Consider

$$25\overline{)825}.$$

The quotient can be found directly using what we have learned about dividing by one-digit numbers. We first decide which of the first few digits of the dividend (825) make a number greater than or equal to the divisor (25). In our example, that number is 82. The largest number less than 82 which is divisible by 25 is 75. The quotient, 3, is placed above the last digit in 82.

$$\overset{3}{25\overline{)825}} \qquad 82 \geq 25 \text{ and } 75 \div 25 = 3$$

Next multiply 3×25, place the result below 82 and subtract. The difference is 7. Bring down 5.

$$\overset{33}{25\overline{)825}} \\ \underline{75} \\ 75$$

Finally divide 75 by 25. The quotient is 3 which is placed above 5. Multiply 3×25, place the product below 75, and subtract to obtain 0.

$$\overset{33}{25\overline{)825}} \\ \underline{75} \\ 75 \\ \underline{75} \\ 0$$

Dividing by a two-digit number involves the use of estimation as we try to find each digit in the quotient. For example, suppose we want to find the quotient $960 \div 42$. We might start by looking at the first digits in 960 and 42 and asking

What number less than or equal to 9 can be divided by 4?

Since $8 \leq 9$, and $8 \div 4 = 2$, we try 2. This technique, while not foolproof, gives us a starting point, as shown in the next example.

<table>
<tr><td>**PRACTICE EXERCISE 8**</td><td>**DIVIDING BY A TWO-DIGIT NUMBER**</td><td>**E X A M P L E 8**</td></tr>
</table>

Find the quotient.

$$41\overline{)861}$$

Find the quotient.

$$32\overline{)739}$$

The number less than or equal to 7 which is divisible by 3 is 6, and since $6 \div 3 = 2$, begin by placing 2 above 3 in 739.

$$
\begin{array}{ll}
① \ 6 \div 3 = 2 \longrightarrow 2 & \\
 & 32\overline{)739} \\
② \ 2 \times 32 = 64 \longrightarrow \underline{64} & \\
③ \ 73 - 64 = 9 \longrightarrow 99 & \longleftarrow \ ④ \text{ Bring down 9}
\end{array}
$$

To divide 99 by 32, find the largest number less than or equal to 9 which is divisible by 3. That number is 9 and $9 \div 3 = 3$. Thus, place 3 above 9 in 739 and proceed as before.

$$
\begin{array}{ll}
 & \overset{23}{32\overline{)739}} \\
 & \underline{64} \\
 & 99 \\
3 \times 32 = 96 \longrightarrow & \underline{96} \\
 & 3 \quad \longleftarrow \ 99 - 96 = 3 \ \text{(remainder)}
\end{array}
$$

The answer is 23 R3.

5 | DIVIDING BY A THREE-DIGIT NUMBER

An **algorithm** is a procedure or method used to perform a certain task. The algorithm for finding quotients that we have shown involves "trial-and-error." Sometimes estimating can make "trial-and-error" faster. The number of trials that you make before finding the desired quotient will decrease with practice.

This algorithm can be used to find quotients involving three-digit divisors.

EXAMPLE 9 | DIVIDING BY A THREE-DIGIT NUMBER

Find the quotient.

$$562\overline{)116527}$$

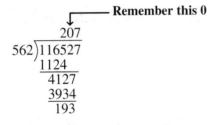

— 412 cannot be divided by 562

10 ÷ 5 = 2

207 ← 35 ÷ 5 = 7

$$\begin{array}{r} 207 \\ 562\overline{)116527} \\ \underline{1124} \\ 412 \\ \underline{000} \\ 4127 \\ \underline{3934} \\ 193 \end{array}$$

The work can be shortened by bringing down the next digit, 7, when we realize that 412 cannot be divided by 562. But be sure to place 0 in the quotient.

— Remember this 0

$$\begin{array}{r} 207 \\ 562\overline{)116527} \\ \underline{1124} \\ 4127 \\ \underline{3934} \\ 193 \end{array}$$

6 | CHECKING DIVISION

As with other arithmetic operations, there should be a way to check if a quotient is correct. Consider the following division problem.

$$\begin{array}{r} 6 \longleftarrow \textbf{Quotient} \\ \textbf{Divisor} \rightarrow 4\overline{)25} \longleftarrow \textbf{Dividend} \\ \underline{24} \\ 1 \longleftarrow \textbf{Remainder} \end{array}$$

Observe that

$$(6 \times 4) + 1 = 25$$

$$24 \quad + 1 = 25.$$

PRACTICE EXERCISE 9

Find the quotient.

$$451\overline{)93808}$$

Answer: 208

This relationship is true in general and provides a check for division.

CHECK FOR DIVISION

In any division problem

(quotient × divisor) + remainder = dividend.

The final example in this section illustrates how rounded numbers can be used to find approximate solutions to applied division problems.

PRACTICE EXERCISE 10

There are 1092 weeks in 21 years. First find the approximate number of weeks in one year; then find the exact number.

Answer: Approximate number is 50 (using $1000 \div 20$); exact number is 52 (using $1092 \div 21$)

ESTIMATING IN A DIVISION APPLICATION   **EXAMPLE 10**

Manuel wants to divide 117 pieces of candy among 9 children. First find the approximate number each will receive; and then find the exact number.

Since 117 is about 120 and 9 is about 10, we can mentally divide 120 by 10 to obtain approximately 12 pieces for each. To find the exact number, divide 117 by 9. The quotient is 13, so each child receives exactly 13 pieces.

1.7 EXERCISES

Answers to these exercises are given on page 641.

1. Consider the division problem $6 \div 2 = 3$. (a) What is 6 called? (b) What is 2 called? (c) What is 3 called?

2. In any division problem, the product of the divisor and the quotient is equal to what number?

3. If a is any whole number, $a \div 1 = \underline{\quad}$.

4. If a is any whole number except 0, $0 \div a = \underline{\quad}$.

You should be able to complete Exercises 5–49 in 90 seconds or less. Find each quotient.

5. $18 \div 2 =$ 6. $28 \div 4 =$ 7. $30 \div 6 =$ 8. $16 \div 4 =$ 9. $8 \div 4 =$

10. $5\overline{)25}$ 11. $2\overline{)2}$ 12. $6\overline{)18}$ 13. $2\overline{)6}$ 14. $8\overline{)72}$

15. $9 \div 1 =$ 16. $27 \div 9 =$ 17. $16 \div 8 =$ 18. $7 \div 7 =$ 19. $0 \div 8 =$

20. $\dfrac{12}{6} =$ 21. $\dfrac{1}{1} =$ 22. $\dfrac{36}{9} =$ 23. $\dfrac{42}{6} =$ 24. $\dfrac{24}{4} =$

25. $5 \div 5 =$ 26. $18 \div 9 =$ 27. $16 \div 2 =$ 28. $45 \div 5 =$ 29. $48 \div 6 =$

30. $3\overline{)15}$ 31. $2\overline{)12}$ 32. $5\overline{)40}$ 33. $5\overline{)0}$ 34. $4\overline{)36}$

35. $6 \div 1 =$ 36. $24 \div 3 =$ 37. $64 \div 8 =$ 38. $63 \div 7 =$ 39. $20 \div 5 =$

40. $\dfrac{0}{1} =$ 41. $\dfrac{48}{8} =$ 42. $\dfrac{54}{6} =$ 43. $\dfrac{0}{2} =$ 44. $\dfrac{8}{8} =$

45. $24 \div 8 =$ 46. $6 \div 3 =$ 47. $36 \div 6 =$ 48. $21 \div 3 =$ 49. $35 \div 5 =$

Find the value of or translate each expression in Exercises 50–53.

50. The quotient of 12 and 4

51. The quotient of 7 and y

52. p divided by 8

53. The ratio of v to 9

54. Translate the following into symbols: The quotient of a and 5 is 7.

Find each quotient in Exercises 55–69.

55. $2\overline{)46}$ 56. $2\overline{)446}$ 57. $4\overline{)408}$ 58. $2\overline{)58}$ 59. $5\overline{)90}$

60. $3\overline{)438}$ 61. $3\overline{)225}$ 62. $6\overline{)546}$ 63. $5\overline{)905}$ 64. $5\overline{)545}$

65. $4\overline{)4076}$ 66. $2\overline{)6054}$ 67. $4\overline{)2836}$ 68. $32\overline{)672}$ 69. $28\overline{)1316}$

Find each quotient and remainder in Exercises 70–73. Check your answer.

70. $7\overline{)67}$ 71. $6\overline{)714}$ 72. $42\overline{)737}$ 73. $466\overline{)10736}$

Solve each applied problem in Exercises 74–75.

74. **BUSINESS** For a shipment of 9 computer programs the bill was $1782. First find the approximate cost of each program, and then find the exact cost.

75. **DIET** There are 4011 calories in 21 candy bars. First find the approximate number of calories in each bar, and then find the exact number.

CRITICAL THINKING

💡*Let n represent a whole number. In Exercises 76–79, solve each equation for n by writing the related multiplication or related division equation.*

76. $n \div 5 = 6$ 77. $8n = 24$ 78. $\dfrac{n}{7} = 5$ 79. $6n = 42$

💡*Assume that a, b, and c represent whole numbers in Exercises 80–82. Complete each statement or answer the question.*

80. If a is not zero, $a \div a =$ ___

81. If a is not zero, $\dfrac{0}{a} =$ ___

82. Are $a \div b$ and $b \div a$ the same?

83. What can be concluded from the results of Exercise 82?

🖋84. Explain the statement: *Division can be defined as repeated subtraction.*

🖋85. Explain why we agree never to divide a whole number by 0, that is, why division by zero is undefined.

🖋86. Explain what is wrong with Burford's work in the division problem given below. What is the correct answer?

$$
\begin{array}{r}
69 \\
4\overline{)2436} \\
\underline{24} \\
036 \\
\underline{36} \\
0
\end{array}
$$

REVIEW OR PREVIEW

Find each product in Exercises 87–89.

87.   500
      ×30

88.   600
      ×900

89.   4000
      × 20

Check by estimating each product in Exercises 90–91.

90.   92
      ×19
      828
       92
      1748

91.   743
      ×102
      1486
       743
      8916

1.7 PARALLEL EXERCISES

Answers to these exercises are not given in the text.

1. Consider the division problem $54 \div 9 = 6.$ (a) What is 6 called? (b) What is 9 called? (c) What is 54 called?

2. In any division problem, the dividend is equal to the product of the quotient and what number?

3. Any nonzero whole number divided by itself is equal to what number?

4. What whole number can never be used as a divisor?

You should be able to complete Exercises 5–49 in 90 seconds or less. Find each quotient.

5. $\dfrac{20}{4} =$ 6. $\dfrac{48}{6} =$ 7. $\dfrac{12}{4} =$ 8. $\dfrac{24}{4} =$ 9. $\dfrac{28}{7} =$

10. $16 \div 4 =$ 11. $56 \div 7 =$ 12. $6 \div 2 =$ 13. $4 \div 2 =$ 14. $7 \div 7 =$

15. $\dfrac{0}{5} =$ 16. $\dfrac{12}{3} =$ 17. $\dfrac{63}{7} =$ 18. $\dfrac{4}{4} =$ 19. $\dfrac{0}{2} =$

20. $5\overline{)15}$ 21. $2\overline{)16}$ 22. $9\overline{)63}$ 23. $9\overline{)36}$ 24. $7\overline{)49}$

25. $\dfrac{27}{3} =$ 26. $\dfrac{35}{5} =$ 27. $\dfrac{30}{5} =$ 28. $\dfrac{9}{3} =$ 29. $\dfrac{21}{3} =$

30. $6 \div 3 =$ 31. $18 \div 3 =$ 32. $42 \div 7 =$ 33. $24 \div 8 =$ 34. $0 \div 9 =$

35. $\dfrac{32}{4} =$ 36. $\dfrac{1}{1} =$ 37. $\dfrac{0}{7} =$ 38. $\dfrac{18}{9} =$ 39. $\dfrac{35}{7} =$

40. $1\overline{)0}$ 41. $9\overline{)72}$ 42. $1\overline{)6}$ 43. $3\overline{)15}$ 44. $1\overline{)3}$

45. $\dfrac{9}{1} =$ 46. $\dfrac{56}{8} =$ 47. $\dfrac{25}{5} =$ 48. $\dfrac{9}{9} =$ 49. $\dfrac{18}{2} =$

Find the value of each expression in Exercises 50–53.

50. The quotient of 16 and 8

51. The quotient of 3 and y

52. p divided by 5

53. The ratio of v to 7

54. Translate the following into symbols: The quotient of a and 6 is 4.

Find each quotient in Exercises 55–64.

55. $2\overline{)64}$ 56. $3\overline{)639}$ 57. $3\overline{)609}$ 58. $3\overline{)84}$ 59. $6\overline{)84}$

60. $4\overline{)712}$ 61. $4\overline{)384}$ 62. $2\overline{)134}$ 63. $3\overline{)327}$ 64. $4\overline{)208}$

Find each quotient in Exercises 65–69.

65. $6\overline{)6066}$ 66. $3\overline{)6309}$ 67. $8\overline{)4064}$ 68. $45\overline{)720}$ 69. $67\overline{)3484}$

Find each quotient and remainder in Exercises 70–73. Check your answer.

70. $9\overline{)93}$ 71. $23\overline{)1081}$ 72. $67\overline{)5728}$ 73. $342\overline{)68742}$

Solve each applied problem in Exercises 74–75.

74. **BUSINESS**   For 11 light fixtures the bill is $396. First find the approximate cost of each fixture and then find the exact cost.

75. **EXERCISE SCIENCE**   A man's heart beats 2016 times during an exercise period of 21 minutes. First find the approximate number of beats per minute, and then find the actual number (which in this case is also really an approximation).

 CRITICAL THINKING

Let n represent a whole number. In Exercises 76–79, solve each equation for n by writing the related multiplication or related division equation.

76. $n \div 3 = 8$ 77. $5n = 45$ 78. $\dfrac{n}{4} = 3$ 79. $9n = 36$

Assume that a, b, and c represent whole numbers in Exercises 80–82. Complete each statement or answer the question.

80. $\dfrac{a}{1} = $ ____

81. What does $a \div 0$ equal?

82. Are $(a \div b) \div c$ and $a \div (b \div c)$ the same?

83. What can be concluded from the results of Exercise 82?

84. Suppose we are given a division equation. Discuss what is meant by the *related multiplication equation* and why it is important.

85. Explain why 0 divided by any whole number (other than 0 itself) is always 0. Why is 0 excluded in this case?

86. Explain what is wrong with Burford's work in the division problem given below. What is the correct answer?

$$\begin{array}{r} 13 \\ 32\overline{)451} \\ 32 \\ \hline 131 \\ 96 \\ \hline 35 \end{array}$$

GROUP PROJECT

Division problems, and especially approximating division, occur frequently in the *real world*. Almost daily we must solve simple problems by finding or approximating a quotient. For example, suppose you are having a birthday party for your daughter and 22 children will be attending, including your daughter. You go to WalMart and discover that packets of party hats contain 6 hats. How many packets will you need to purchase to make sure every child has a hat? The actual quotient and remainder in this case are not really important since it is impossible to purchase a part of a packet. Thus, when we approximate the number of packets needed, we can see that we will need to buy 4 of them, and we will have 2 left over. All of our calculations in this case are performed mentally. Collect a number of other examples where division or approximating division occur in real life and report your findings.

1.8 MORE PROBLEM SOLVING WITH WHOLE NUMBERS

STUDENT GUIDEPOSTS	
1	USING A PROBLEM-SOLVING METHOD
2	USING THE TOTAL-VALUE RELATIONSHIP
3	FINDING THE AREA OF A RECTANGLE
4	SOLVING BUSINESS APPLICATIONS
5	CALCULATING MILES PER GALLON
6	USING UNIT PRICING

1 A PROBLEM-SOLVING METHOD

In previous sections we have solved a variety of applied problems that involve finding sums, differences, products, and quotients of whole numbers. This section contains numerous other types of applications. We begin by outlining a sequence of problem-solving steps that should be followed.

TO SOLVE AN APPLIED PROBLEM

1. Read the problem several times to be certain you understand what is being asked. Draw a picture whenever possible.
2. Identify what is given and what must be found, then make a plan of attack.
3. Solve, using your plan and the given information.
4. Ask yourself if your answer is reasonable. If it is, check your work. If not, return to Step 1.

NOTE   Deciding if an answer is reasonable is important and can help you avoid making errors. For example, suppose the problem asks for the price of a new car. If you obtain an answer of $200, your answer is clearly unreasonable, and you should begin again.

PRACTICE EXERCISE 1

At a recent concert, ticket prices were $7 for adults, $4 for students between 12 and 20 years of age, and $2 for children 12 years and younger. Becky is 13 years old and her sister Cindy is 9. If their parents take them to the concert, how much will the four of them pay?

Answer: $20

SOLVING A BANKING APPLICATION   EXAMPLE 1

Carlos has two passbook savings accounts, one with $2350 and the other with $1745. He also has three certificates of deposit with values of $5000, $2500, and $1250. What is the total of these cash assets?

$$\begin{array}{r} 2350 \\ 1745 \\ 5000 \\ 2500 \\ +1250 \\ \hline 12845 \end{array}$$

After reading the problem several times, we see that the key word in this problem is *total*, which refers to addition. We must add the amounts in the five different accounts as shown to the right.

This appears to be a reasonable total in view of the value of each account, and it does check using the reverse-order method. Thus, Carlos has $12,845 in cash assets.

SOLVING A SPORTS APPLICATION   EXAMPLE 2

The players' scores in a recent basketball game are shown in the table. What was the team score?

The team score is the sum of the individual player's points. Suppose we add the players points and get 538.

First time

21
17
12
10
8
7
3
3
―――
538   **Incorrect**

Player	Points
Hudson	21
Betton	17
Herman	12
Williams	10
Ingram	8
Hurd	7
Payne	7
Spencer	3
Rodriguez	3

Second time

21
17
12
10
8
7
3
3
――
88   **Correct**

Since 538 is unreasonable for the score of a team in a basketball game, reread the problem. Again it is clear that the nine numbers must be added. In adding a second time, the error is found. The actual sum is 88, which does check.

EXAMPLE 3 — READING A MAP

Figure 1.20 shows a sketch of a map of part of the western United States.

(a) How far is it from Denver to Phoenix through Albuquerque?

From Denver to Albuquerque is 419 mi, and from Albuquerque to Phoenix is 469 mi. Find the following sum.

$$\begin{array}{r} 419 \\ +469 \\ \hline 888 \end{array}$$

FIGURE 1.20

Since this is reasonable, and does check, it is 888 mi from Denver to Phoenix through Albuquerque.

(b) Is it shorter to go from Los Angeles to Salt Lake City through San Francisco or through Phoenix?

The distance from Los Angeles to Salt Lake City through San Francisco is found by adding 401 and 751. The distance from Los Angeles to Salt Lake City through Phoenix is found by adding 471 and 641.

$$\begin{array}{r} 401 \\ + 751 \\ \hline 1152 \end{array}$$ Through San Francisco $$\begin{array}{r} 471 \\ + 641 \\ \hline 1112 \end{array}$$ Through Phoenix

Since these sums appear reasonable, and do check, it is shorter to go by way of Phoenix.

(c) The Jacksons, who live in Los Angeles, plan a trip to Denver for their summer vacation. Going, they will take the southern route through Phoenix and Albuquerque. They plan to return through Salt Lake City and San Francisco. How far will they travel?

Add the six numbers 471, 469, 419, 495, 751, and 401. The total, 3006, seems reasonable and does check. Thus, the family will travel 3006 mi on their vacation.

$$
\begin{array}{r}
471 \\
469 \\
419 \\
495 \\
751 \\
+ \ 401 \\
\hline
3006
\end{array}
$$

The next example solve the applied problem given in the chapter introduction.

| PRACTICE EXERCISE 4 | SOLVING A SPACE EXPLORATION APPLICATION | EXAMPLE 4 |

Use the table in Example 4 to answer the following questions.

The years 1992-93 were busy ones in the exploration of space by space shuttle flights as shown in the table below.

FLIGHT NUMBER	DATE	SHUTTLE NAME	DAYS IN ORBIT	FLIGHT NUMBER	DATE	SHUTTLE NAME	DAYS IN ORBIT
42	1/22/92	Discovery	8	54	1/13/93	Endeavour	6
45	3/24/92	Atlantis	8	56	4/8/93	Discovery	9
49	5/7/92	Endeavour	8	55	4/26/93	Columbia	10
50	6/25/92	Columbia	13	57	6/21/93	Endeavour	10
46	7/31/92	Atlantis	7	51	9/12/93	Discovery	10
47	9/12/92	Endeavour	7	58	10/18/93	Columbia	14
52	10/22/92	Columbia	9	61	12/2/93	Endeavour	11
53	12/2/92	Discovery	7				

Source: U.S. National Aeronautics and Space Administration

(a) Which of the four shuttles spent the most days in orbit in 1992?

(a) Which of the four shuttles spent the most days in orbit during this two-year period?

We begin by reading the problem carefully and by getting familiar with the information presented in the table. Next we form a plan of attack. Since we must determine which shuttle spent the most days in orbit, we will find the number of days each spent in orbit during the period. From the table we can see that the total number of days in orbit for each shuttle is:

Discovery: $8 + 7 + 9 + 10 = 34$ days

Atlantis: $8 + 7 = 15$ days

Endeavour: $8 + 7 + 6 + 10 + 11 = 42$ days

Columbia: $13 + 9 + 10 + 14 = 46$ days

Thus, the Columbia spent the most days in orbit, 46 days. This answer seems reasonable in view of the information in the table.

(b) Which of the four shuttles spent the fewest days in orbit in 1992?

(b) Which of the four shuttles spent the fewest days in orbit during this two-year period?

From our work in part (a), we can see that the Atlantis spent the fewest days in orbit, 15 days.

(c) During 1993, how many more days was the Endeavour in orbit than the Discovery?

(c) Which year was the busiest relative to the total number of days in orbit for all shuttles?

Since the first column of the table relates to 1992 and the second column relates to 1993, we must add the numbers of days in orbit in each column as shown below:

1992: $8 + 8 + 8 + 13 + 7 + 7 + 9 + 7 = 67$ days

1993: $6 + 9 + 10 + 10 + 10 + 14 + 11 = 70$ days

Thus, 1993 was the busier year with the shuttles in orbit a total of 70 days.

(d) During this two-year period, the Columbia was in orbit how many more days than the Atlantis?

Again, with our work in part (a), we see that the Columbia was in orbit 46 days and the Atlantis was in orbit only 15 days. To find how many more days the Columbia was in orbit, we must subtract.

$$46 - 15 = 31 \text{ days}$$

Thus, the Columbia was in orbit 31 more days than the Atlantis during the two-year period.

EXAMPLE 5 **SOLVING A GEOGRAPHY APPLICATION**

The height of Mount Everest is twenty-nine thousand, twenty-eight feet, and the height of Mount McKinley is twenty thousand, three hundred twenty feet. How much higher is Mount Everest than Mount McKinley?

First visualize the problem as shown in Figure 1.21.

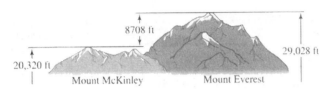

FIGURE 1.21

Subtract 20,320 (the height of Mount McKinley) from 29,028 (the height of Mount Everest).

$$\begin{array}{r} 810 \\ 2\cancel{9}\cancel{0}28 \\ -20320 \\ \hline 8708 \end{array}$$

This difference is certainly reasonable, and it checks. Thus, Mount Everest is 8708 ft higher than Mount McKinley.

EXAMPLE 6 **MAKING PAYMENTS ON A PURCHASE**

Kenny Boskett purchased a personal computer from his uncle to be used in his dorm room at college. The purchase price of the computer was $1100, and his uncle agreed to let Kenny pay $80 down and the rest in equal monthly payments for one year. How much were Kenny's monthly payments if he is not being charged any interest?

Because Kenny paid $80 down, the difference $1100 - \$80 = \$1020$ is the amount he has to pay over 12 months ($1 \text{ year} = 12 \text{ months}$). To find the amount paid each month, divide 1020 by 12.

$$\begin{array}{r} 85 \\ 12\overline{)1020} \\ \underline{96} \\ 60 \\ \underline{60} \\ 0 \end{array}$$
Check:
$$\begin{array}{r} 85 \\ \times 12 \\ \hline 170 \\ 85 \\ \hline 1020 \end{array}$$
and
$$\begin{array}{r} 1020 \\ + \ 80 \\ \hline 1100 \end{array}$$

Since this amount seems reasonable and does check, Kenny's monthly payment is $85.

(d) During 1993, how many more days was the Columbia in orbit than the Atlantis?

Answers: (a) Columbia (22 days) (b) The Discovery, Atlantis, and Endeavour are tied with 15 days. (c) 8 days (d) 24 days (The Columbia was in orbit 24 days, but the Atlantis was not in orbit in 1993.)

PRACTICE EXERCISE 5

The height of Pike's Peak is fourteen thousand, one hundred ten feet, and the height of Long's Peak is fourteen thousand, two hundred fifty-six feet. How much higher is Long's Peak than Pike's Peak?

Answer: 146 feet

PRACTICE EXERCISE 6

Lennie purchased four new tires for his car. If each tire cost $75 and the tax on the purchase of the four was $12, what was the total cost of the tires? If the dealer agreed to let him pay for the tires in 3 equal monthly payments, how much does he pay each month?

Answer: $312; $104

1 | THE TOTAL-VALUE RELATIONSHIP

A basic principle used in many applied problems involves finding a *total value*. The total value of a quantity made up of a number of identical parts is the value per part multiplied by the number of parts.

(total value) = (value per part) · (number of parts).

For example, if you have 35 dimes, the total value of these coins is given by:

(total value of 35 dimes) = (value of 1 dime) · (number of dimes)

$$= (10¢) \cdot (35)$$
$$= 350¢.$$

We use this principle in the next example.

PRACTICE EXERCISE 7

Lucy had a job babysitting which paid $3 per hour. How much was she paid for sitting a total of 14 hours?

| FINDING TOTAL VALUE IN A BUSINESS PROBLEM | E X A M P L E 7 |

During a sale on men's sweaters, the owner of the Sweater Shoppe sold 43 sweaters at $18 a sweater. How much money did he take in during the sale?

For **1** sweater sold, he receives $18 \cdot \mathbf{1} = \$18$.

For **2** sweaters sold, he receives $18 \cdot \mathbf{2} = \$36$.

For **3** sweaters sold, he receives $18 \cdot \mathbf{3} = \$54$.

For **43** sweaters sold,

(total value of 43 sweaters sold) = (value per sweater) · (number of sweaters)

$$\$774 = \$18 \cdot \mathbf{43}.$$

That is, we multiply 18 by 43 to obtain $774. Since $774 seems reasonable (40 sweaters at $20 each would bring in $800; so 774 appears to check), the store owner took in $774 during the sale.

Answer: $42

3 | AREA OF A RECTANGLE

The formula for finding the area of a rectangle, a four-sided figure with opposite sides equal and four right angles, has many applications involving multiplication.

AREA OF A RECTANGLE
The area of a rectangle is given by the formula
Area = (length) · (width).

The rectangle in Figure 1.22 has area given by

$$\text{Area} = (\text{length}) \cdot (\text{width}).$$
$$= 3 \cdot 2$$
$$= 6.$$

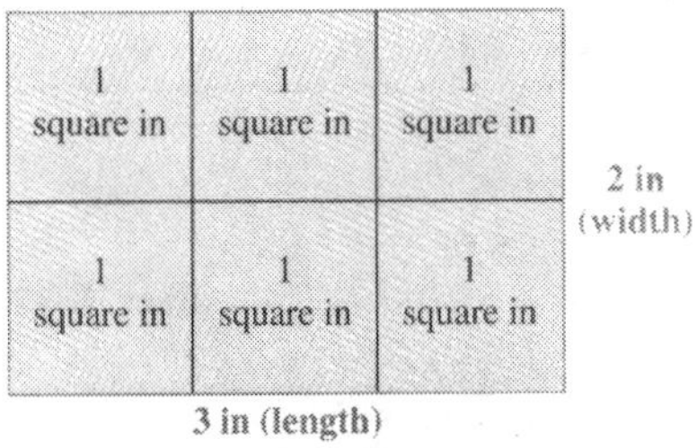

| 1 square in | 1 square in | 1 square in |
| 1 square in | 1 square in | 1 square in |

2 in (width)

3 in (length)

FIGURE 1.22

Since the rectangle contains 6 squares which have 1 inch sides, the measure of the area of the rectangle is given in square inches (sometimes abbreviated **sq in**). Thus, the rectangle has area 6 sq in. Had the sides of the rectangle been 3 ft and 2 ft, the area would have been 6 sq ft.

| **E X A M P L E 8** | **FINDING AREA AND PERIMETER** |

A room is 4 yd wide and 5 yd long (**yd** is the abbreviation for yards).

(a) Find the floor area of the room.

In many word problems, it is helpful to make a sketch that describes the situation. A sketch of the floor of the room is shown in Figure 1.23. The area of the floor is

$$\text{Area} = \textbf{(length)} \cdot (\text{width})$$
$$= \textbf{5} \cdot 4 = 20 \text{ sq yd.}$$

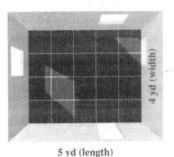

4 yd (width)

5 yd (length)

FIGURE 1.23

(b) Find the perimeter of the room.

The **perimeter** is the distance around the room found by adding the lengths of its sides. Thus, the perimeter is

$$\textbf{5} + \textbf{5} + \textbf{4} + \textbf{4} = 18 \text{ yd.}$$

(c) If carpet costs $16 a square yard, how much would it cost to carpet the room?

One square yard of carpet costs $16. Then the total cost of 20 sq yd at $16 a yard, which is the number of units times the price per unit, is

$$20 \cdot 16 = \$320.$$

4 | BUSINESS APPLICATIONS

Many applications of multiplication can be found in business. Forms such as invoices, shipping orders, packing slips, and purchase orders use multiplication. A sample purchase order is shown in the next example.

EXAMPLE 9 | COMPLETING A PURCHASE ORDER

Complete the purchase order in Figure 1.24.

PRACTICE EXERCISE 9

Complete the purchase order.

Quantity	Description	Unit Price	Amount
12	Shirts	$14	(a)
36	Pair socks	$ 4	(b)
50	Pair slacks	$24	(c)
25	Belts	$13	(d)
	TOTAL		(e)

NORTHERN PENNSYLVANIA UNIVERSITY
General Stores

Customer's Order No. __11937-Q__   Date __Mar. 20__ 19 _98_

Name____ Mathematics Department

Address____ Box 5717   MAT 115

Sold by A.S.	Cash	C.O.D.	Charge	On Acct. ✓	Mdse.	Retd.	Paid Out

Quantity	Description	Unit Price	Amount
50 reams	Multi-purpose Paper	$2	*$100*
6 cans	Duplicating Fluid	$3	*18*
3	Staplers	$4	*12*
8 pkg	Writing Pads	$3	*24*
1	Paper Trimmer	$42	*42*
		TOTAL	*$196*

Rec'd.by _____

FIGURE 1.24

To complete this form, compute the numbers that go into the Amount column. The price of each ream of Multi-purpose Paper is $2 so the cost of 50 reams is $50 \times \$2$, which is **$100.** Enter this cost in the Amount column. Compute and enter the remaining costs the same way as shown in color.

Find the total cost of all items by adding the separate costs in the Amount column $(100 + 18 + 12 + 24 + 42)$. Enter this sum, **$196**, next to TOTAL as shown.

Answers: (a) $168 (b) $144 (c) $1200 (d) $325 (e) $1837

> **NOTE**   Read an applied problem carefully and be aware that a given problem might involve more than one arithmetic operation. In Example 9, for instance, to complete the purchase order we first find five products and then find their sum.

5 | CALCULATING MILES PER GALLON

In the next example we provide a formula for finding the number of miles that a vehicle can be driven using one gallon of gasoline.

EXAMPLE 10	CALCULATING MILES PER GALLON

In order to check the gas mileage on his car, Mike noted that the odometer reading was 18,432 when he filled the tank with gas. At 18,696 he refilled the tank with 11 gallons of gas. What was his mileage per gallon?

The miles per gallon (mpg) is found by:

$$\text{mpg} = \frac{\textbf{number of miles driven}}{\textbf{number of gallons used}}$$

To find the number of miles driven, subtract odometer readings.

$$\begin{array}{r} 18696 \\ -\ 18432 \\ \hline 264 \end{array} \quad \text{Miles driven}$$

Thus,

$$\text{mpg} = \frac{264}{11} = 24.$$

Since 24 mpg seems reasonable and does check ($24 \times 11 = 264$ and $18,432 + 264 = 18,696$), Mike is getting 24 miles per gallon of gas.

On a recent trip, Sharon traveled from El Paso, Texas, to Cheyenne, Wyoming, a distance of 750 miles, and returned to El Paso. If she used a total of 75 gallons of gas on the trip, how many miles per gallon did she get?

Answer: 20 mpg

6 | UNIT PRICING

The wise shopper has learned to compare prices by determining *unit prices.* For example, if a can of beans weighs 15 oz (**oz** stands for ounces) and costs 45¢, the

$$\textbf{unit price} = \frac{\textbf{Price}}{\textbf{No. units}} = \frac{45¢}{15\ \text{oz}} = 3¢ \text{ per ounce.}$$

If a different brand of beans sells for 52¢ but weighs 13 oz, then

$$\text{unit price} = \frac{\text{Price}}{\text{No. units}} = \frac{52¢}{13\ \text{oz}} = 4¢ \text{ per ounce.}$$

Assuming equal quality of the products, the first can is clearly the better buy. Unit pricing gives us excellent examples of division problems.

EXPLORATION GUIDE

From past experience Burford formed the conclusion that it is always wise to buy items in large quantities. As a result, he purchased a 100-pound bag of dog food for $8.00 (800¢) instead of buying four 25-pound bags of the same food for $1.75 (175¢) per bag. Is Burford truly a wise shopper? Explain using the concept of *unit pricing.*

1.8 EXERCISES

Answers to these exercises are given on page 641.

Solve each applied problem in Exercises 1–6.

1. **RECREATION**   A rock festival had 1379 in attendance the first day, 2811 the second day, and 3281 on the final day. What was the total attendance during the three days?

2. **BUSINESS**   During a special week-day promotion the Movie House rented 237 movies on Monday, 184 movies on Tuesday, 301 movies on Wednesday, and 479 movies on Thursday. How many movies were rented during the promotion?

3. **CONSTRUCTION** The room shown below is in the shape of a rectangle that is 15 feet long and 12 feet wide. How many feet of baseboard would be required to go all the way around the room?

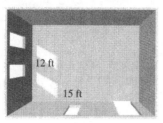

12 ft

15 ft

4. **GEOMETRY** A table has a top in the shape of a triangle with dimensions as shown in the figure below. What is the perimeter, the distance around, the triangle?

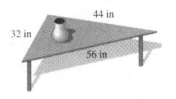

44 in

32 in

56 in

5. **RECREATION** A bowler rolled games of 179, 203, and 188. What was her total for the three game series?

6. **SPORTS** Jim Tecu's scorecard for playing the front nine holes of golf is shown here. How many shots did Jim take on the front nine?

Hole	1	2	3	4	5	6	7	8	9
Score	3	5	6	4	4	5	4	3	5

Exercises 7–8 refer to the map of Lake Powell shown below.

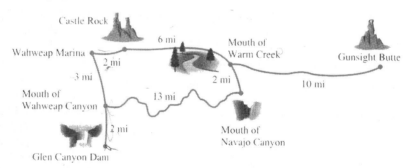

Castle Rock

Wahweap Marina

6 mi

Mouth of Warm Creek

Gunsight Butte

2 mi

3 mi

Mouth of Wahweap Canyon

13 mi

2 mi

10 mi

2 mi

Mouth of Navajo Canyon

Glen Canyon Dam

7. **TRAVEL** Which distance is greater, Castle Rock to Gunsight Butte, or Glen Canyon Dam to the mouth of the Navajo Canyon? How much greater?

8. **TRAVEL** What distance is traveled by a boat that leaves Wahweap Marina and makes a circular trip past the mouths of Wahweap Canyon, Navajo Canyon, and Warm Creek and returns to the marina by way of Castle Rock?

Exercises 9–10 refer to the information given in the following table.

Game Statistics

Home Team			Visiting Team		
Player	Points	Fouls	Player	Points	Fouls
Hanaki	25	4	Kirk	18	3
Bonnett	19	3	Mutter	18	2
Condon	13	0	Westmoreland	15	4
Bell	7	5	Anderson	9	1
Walter	6	2	Ratliff	7	2
Meyer	3	1	Romero	1	3
Shaff	0	5	Thoreson	1	0

9. **SPORTS** How many points were scored by the home team?

10. **SPORTS** How many fouls were committed by the home team?

11. **MINING** The Henderson mine in western Arizona is 6483 ft deep. The Lupine mine in southern Colorado is 3976 ft deep. How much deeper is the Henderson mine?

12. **TRAVEL** Before leaving on a trip, Luisa noticed that the odometer reading on her car was 38,427. When she returned home from the trip, the reading was 41,003. How many miles did she drive?

13. **BANKING** At the beginning of June, Mr. Hernandez had a balance of $625 in his checking account. During the month he made deposits of $300 and $235. He wrote checks for $23, $18, $113, $410, and $32. What was his balance at the end of the month?

14. **CONSUMER** On a shopping trip Sue Thompson bought a sweater for $76, some shoes for $59, a book for $27, and a camera for $162. If she paid by check and had $350 in her account at the start of the trip, how much was left in the account.

Exercises 15–16 refer to the map.

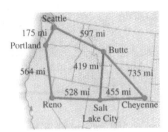

15. **TRAVEL** What is the shortest route from Salt Lake City to Seattle? How much shorter is it than the next shortest route?

16. **TRAVEL** The Hardy family, who live in Portland, plan a trip to Cheyenne on their summer vacation. How much shorter is it to go through Butte than through Reno?

17. **TRANSPORTATION** A bulk tanker contains 1478 gallons of gasoline. Three deliveries are made, one of 230 gallons, a second of 435 gallons, and the third of 170 gallons. How much gasoline remains in the tanker?

18. **BUSINESS** Sales at Darrell's Men's Wear were $1245 on Friday. If this is $305 more than on Thursday, and $785 less than on Saturday, what were the sales on Thursday? On Saturday?

19. **TRAVEL** A compact car has a 12-gallon gas tank and can travel 29 miles on one gallon of gas. How far can it travel on a full tank?

20. **BUSINESS** The *margin of profit* when an item is sold is the list price of the item less the cost of the item. During a recent clearance sale, a store owner sold a bedroom set at cost, for $1150. If she had sold the set at its list price, $1595, what would the margin of profit have been?

21. **TIME MEASUREMENT** There are 365 days in a year.
(a) How many days are there in 5 years?
(b) How many hours are there in a year? [1 day = 24 hours]
(c) How many hours are there in 5 years?

22. **GEOMETRY** A rectangular vegetable garden is 14 m wide and 26 m long (m stands for meter).
(a) What is the area of the garden?
(b) What is the perimeter of the garden?

23. **RECREATION** Suppose that 225 lift tickets are sold per day at the Sugar Loaf Ski Area.
(a) How many tickets are sold in a 14-day period?
(b) If each ticket costs $7, how much money is taken in during a 14-day period?

24. **BUSINESS** Marty's Men's Shop pays $52 each for sweaters, $43 each for jeans, and $26 each for shirts. What would it be billed for 6 sweaters, 8 pair of jeans, and 10 shirts?

25. **CONSUMER** Barbara wants to put a rectangular mirror measuring 8 ft by 5 ft on the wall of her living room. If a mirror costs $3 a square foot, how much will the mirror cost?

26. **CONSUMER** A rectangular room measures 9 yd long and 5 yd wide. How much will it cost to carpet the room over a foam pad if carpet costs $20 a sq yd, padding costs $2 a sq yd, and installation costs are included in the price of carpet and padding?

27. **CONSUMER** A sketch of the floor plan of a family room is shown in the figure. Mr. Kirk plans to cover the floor with vinyl floor covering costing $9 a sq yd. How much will it cost to complete the job?
[*Hint:* Divide the floor plan into two rectangular areas.]

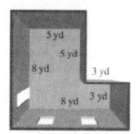

5 yd

9 yd

28. **BUSINESS** Complete the following purchase order.

Quantity	Description	Unit Price	Amount
3	Back Packs	$90	(a) _____
1	Tent	140	(b) _____
4	Sleeping Bags	110	(c) _____
4	Ground Pads	15	(d) _____
1	Pack Stove	20	(e) ____
8	Complete Meals	7	(f) _____
	TOTAL		(g) _____

29. **HOME MORTGAGE** Sam and Carolyn have a home mortgage that requires a monthly payment of $520 for 30 years.
    (a) How many monthly payments must they make over the 30-year period?
    (b) How much will they have paid in total at the end of 30 years?

30. **SPORTS** A domed football stadium is divided into 20 sections of seats. Suppose that 5 sections each seat 400 spectators, 8 sections each seat 1200 spectators, and the remaining sections each seat 950 spectators.
    (a) What is the seating capacity of the dome?
    (b) If every seat is sold for the championship game, and the price of each ticket is $5, how much money is taken in for the game?

31. **WORD PROCESSING** Lowell can type 85 words per minute. How long will it take him to type 21,760 words?

32. **GAS MILEAGE** At the start of a trip, Mr. Creighten's odometer read 24,273. When he returned from the trip, it read 25,561. If he used 56 gallons of gas, what was his gas mileage?

33. **BUSINESS** The Small Appliance Place has $1200 to use on an order of portable mixers. If each mixer costs $21, how many can be ordered? How much of the $1200 will be left after the order?

34. **CONSUMER** Which is the better buy, a 12-lb bag of dog food selling for $3.72 (372¢) or a 9-lb bag of dog food selling for $2.88 (288¢)?

35. **EDUCATION** The enrollment at a university is 12,100 students. If the faculty numbers 550, what is the number of students per teacher?

36. **INVESTMENT** Kent Merrill has $13,250 to invest in the stock market. If Allgood stock is now selling for $125, how many shares of this stock could he buy?

37. **GEOGRAPHY** Bridal Veil Falls is 1957 feet high. Niagara Falls is 193 feet high. How much higher is Bridal Veil Falls than Niagara Falls?

38. **GAS MILEAGE** A Buick Park Avenue gets 30 mpg during highway travel. How many gallons of gas would be required for a highway trip of 2610 miles?

39. **MONTHLY PAYMENTS** Lupe purchased a computer system from a friend for $1500 by paying $300 down and the rest in equal monthly payments over a period of 24 months (no interest was charged). How much were her monthly payments?

 CRITICAL THINKING

40. **CHEMISTRY** How many 3-cubic-centimeter samples can be drawn from a container holding 52 cubic centimeters of a saline solution? How much will be left in the container after the samples are drawn?

41. **DIET** A dog is on a special diet and must be fed exactly 12 ounces of food twice a day. How many cans of food will be required to feed the dog for one week if each can contains 16 ounces of food?

42. **TRAVEL** A map has a scale of 40 miles to the inch. How far apart in the real world are two cities that appear 12 inches apart on the map? How far apart on the map will two cities appear if they are actually 320 miles apart?

43. **RECREATION** Let n represent the number of people at a concert. If tickets were sold for $11 each and $2816 was collected, find n.

44. **CONSUMER** Let n represent the number of shirts that Sherman bought. The shirts cost $16 each. If he paid a total of $68 for the shirts plus a $20 pair of pants, find n.

45. In your own words, outline the four-step approach to problem solving and explain why approximation is very useful.

46. Discuss the formula for finding the area of a rectangle and explain why the units of measure for area are called *square units*.

REVIEW OR PREVIEW

Find each quotient in Exercises 47–49 and check your answer.

47. $8\overline{)1880}$

48. $37\overline{)7750}$

49. $259\overline{)107744}$

Exercises 50–51 will help you prepare for the next section.

50. List the multiples of 2 between 1 and 15.

51. List the multiples of 3 between 1 and 20.

1.8 PARALLEL EXERCISES

Answers to these exercises are not given in the text.

Solve each applied problem in Exercises 1–6.

1. **EDUCATION**   Jay Beckenstein had scores of 92, 86, 95, and 89 on four math tests. What is his total number of points for these tests?

2. **SPORTS**   Curt Reynolds has been pitching for five seasons. The first year he had 212 strikeouts, the second 279 strikeouts, 256 the third, 312 the fourth, and 327 the fifth year. What was Curt's total strikeouts for the five seasons?

3. **AGRICULTURE**   A field is in the shape of a square, which is a rectangle with four equal sides. If one side of the square field is 212 meters, how many meters of fencing are required to go all the way around the field?

4. **GEOMETRY**   Peggy has a garden in the shape shown below. If she plans to put a fence around the garden, how many feet of fencing will she need?

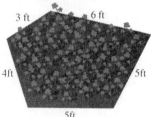

5. **EDUCATION**   Enrollments in the five colleges of a university are: Arts and Science, 3810; Business, 1608; Education, 1425; Engineering, 865; and Forestry, 239. What is the total university enrollment?

6. **POLITICS**   The votes for each of the four candidates in an election are given in the table below. What is the total number of votes cast?

Watts	Horn	Guy	Bond
1234	1712	1544	1399

In Exercises 7–8, use the map of Lake Powell on page 88.

7. **TRAVEL**   What is the shortest distance from the Mouth of Wahweap Canyon to the Mouth of Warm Creek?

8. **TRAVEL**   What is the distance traveled by a boat that leaves Glen Canyon Dam and sails to Gunsight Butte past the Mouth of Wahweap Canyon, Wahweap Marina, Castle Rock, and the Mouth of Warm Creek?

In Exercises 9–10, use the table given above Exercise 9.

9. **SPORTS**   How many points were scored by the visiting team?

10. **SPORTS**   How many fouls were committed by the visiting team?

11. **RECREATION**   On a TV quiz show the winner for the day had 953 points. If her opponent had 894 points how many more points did the winner have?

12. **CONSUMER**   Ms. Balushi has a subcompact car and a luxury sedan. She figures that over the period of one year, it will cost $735 to drive the luxury sedan to work while only $265 to drive the subcompact car. How much can she save by driving the subcompact car?

13. **BANKING**   At the beginning of the month, Mr. Lopez had a balance of $735 in his checking account. If he made deposits of $400 and $375, and wrote checks for $87, $180, $112, $415, and $7 during the month, what was his balance at the end of the month?

14. **CONSUMER** Barb bought a textbook for $74 and a calculator for $17. If the tax on these two purchases totals $5, how much change will she receive if she pays with a check for $100?

Exercises 15–16 refer to the following backpacker's trail map.

15. **RECREATION** What is the shortest hike from Blue Lake to the beaver ponds?

16. **RECREATION** What is the shortest hike from the waterfall to the cabin?

17. **BUSINESS** Lori bought a car for $3800. If she spent $625 on repairs and then sold it for $5100, how much money did she make on the deal?

18. **SALARY** Rob earns $724 a week. If he has $98 withheld for federal taxes, $43 withheld for Social Security taxes, and $140 withheld and deposited in his credit union, what is his net take-home pay each week?

19. **TRAVEL** A boat has a 45-gallon gas tank. If the boat can travel 4 miles on one gallon of gas, how far can it go on a full tank of gas?

20. **BUSINESS** During a sale on CB radios, Chuck sold 18 radios at $78 each. How much money did he take in?

21. **TIME MEASUREMENT** There are 365 days in a year.
    (a) How many days are there in 7 years?
    (b) How many hours are there in 7 years?
    (c) How many minutes are there in 7 years?

22. **GEOMETRY** A room is 12 ft wide and 15 ft long.
    (a) Find the floor area of the room.
    (b) Find the perimeter of the room.
    (c) If carpet costs $2 a sq ft, how much would it cost to carpet the room?

23. **BUSINESS** Suppose that 120 tickets are sold per day to see *The Mummy* at The Tourist Trap.
    (a) How many tickets are sold in a 30-day period?
    (b) If each ticket costs $4, how much money is taken in during a 30-day period?

24. **SALES** During a one hour period on Saturday, the Fashion Shop sold 4 dresses for $189 each, 6 pairs of shoes for $83 each, and 5 sweaters for $72 each. What was the total revenue (amount of money taken in) on these sales?

25. **CONSUMER** The flat roof of a mobile home measures 60 ft long and 15 ft wide. If it costs $2 a square foot to put sealer on the roof, how much will the seal job cost?

26. **CONSUMER** A rectangular patio measures 30 ft long by 12 ft wide. How much will it cost to put outdoor carpeting on the patio if carpet costs $3 a square foot and installation costs are $1 a square foot?

27. **CONSUMER** A sketch of the floor plan of the first floor in the Andrews'
home is shown in the figure. How much will it cost to lay carpeting, costing $20
a square yard, over padding, costing $3 a square yard, over the entire floor?

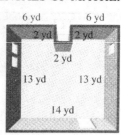

28. **BUSINESS** Complete the following purchase order.

Quantity	Description	Unit Price	Amount
120	Dress Shirts	$17	(a) _____
85	Ties	8	(b) _____
36	Suits	170	(c) _____
24	Belts	13	(d) _____
	TOTAL		(e) _____

29. **HOME MORTGAGE** The Orlandos have a house mortgage which requires a monthly payment of $480 for 25
years.
   (a) How many monthly payments must they make over the 25-year period?
   (b) How much will they have paid in total at the end of 25 years?

30. **SPORTS** A basketball arena is divided into 16 sections of seats. Suppose that 8 sections each seat 300 spectators, 4
sections will each seat 420 spectators, and the remaining sections will each seat 565 spectators.
   (a) What is the seating capacity of the arena?
   (b) If every seat is sold for $4 each, how much money will the athletic department take in?

31. **CONSTRUCTION** Kelly Construction Company has 3416 tiles on the construction site to cover a floor. If each row
that is put down requires 56 tiles, how many rows can be finished before the next shipment of tiles comes in?

32. **GAS MILEAGE** When Anita filled the gas tank on her car before leaving on a trip, she observed that the odometer
reading was 27,154. When she returned from the trip, she refilled the tank and noted that the odometer reading was then
27,518. If she purchased 14 gallons of gas, what was her mileage per gallon?

33. **BUSINESS** There is $150 left in the budget to purchase pens. If each box of pens costs $18, how many boxes can be
ordered? How much will be left of the $150 after the pens are purchased?

34. **CONSUMER** Which is a better buy, a 9-lb bag of kitty litter selling for 99¢ or a 13-lb bag selling for $1.30 (130¢)?

35. **EDUCATION** The enrollment at a community college is 18,200 students. If the faculty number 728, what is the
number of students per teacher?

36. **FINANCE** Bob Carlton has $256,000 to invest in lots in a development project. If each lot costs $32,000, how many
lots can he purchase?

37. **BANKING** Bob had $387 in his savings account. If he withdrew $175, how much was left in the account?

38. **GAS MILEAGE** A Toyota gets 26 mpg. How many gallons would it take to make a 2444-mile trip?

39. **MONTHLY PAYMENTS** Dyane purchased a used car from a friend for $1500 by paying $150 down and the rest in
equal monthly payments over a period of 18 months (no interest was charged). How much were her monthly payments?

CRITICAL THINKING

40. **RECREATION** The total cost of a party was $1020. The bill is to be divided equally among eighteen people. To avoid the use of change, Jean Sharp agreed to pay her share plus any dollars left over after the bill was divided. How much did Jean have to pay?

41. **NUTRITION** After surgery, Gerri must build up her strength by taking 10 ounces of a special vitamin supplement three times a day. If the supplement comes in 24 ounce cans, how many cans must Gerri purchase for a two-week supply?

42. **TRAVEL** A map has a scale of 15 miles to the inch. How far apart in the real world are two National Parks that appear 7 inches apart on the map? How far apart on the map will two parks appear if they are actually 195 miles apart?

43. **SALES** Let n represent the number of cars a dealer had available for sale one month. If she sold 60 during the month and had 120 left on the lot, find n.

44. **EDUCATION** Sharon Noble now has a total of 674 points in a history course. Let n represent the number of points she had before making 90 on the last test. Find n.

45. Explain how to calculate gas mileage in miles per gallon.

46. Discuss the notion of *unit pricing* and give reasons why knowledge of unit prices can be beneficial to a consumer.

GROUP PROJECT

Constructing meaningful application problems can be quite a challenge. Design problems that have the following answers:

(a) 24 minutes (b) 7 miles (c) $535 (d) 6 boys and 9 girls (e) 64 sq mi (f) 40 ounces

Consider your problems carefully to see whether you can improve them relative to interest and content. Then present them to the class for additional criticism.

1.9 PRIMES, POWERS, ROOTS, AND ORDER OF OPERATIONS

STUDENT GUIDEPOSTS

1 FINDING DIVISORS OF A WHOLE NUMBER
2 RECOGNIZING PRIME AND COMPOSITE NUMBERS
3 USING DIVISIBILITY TESTS
4 FINDING POWERS OF A NUMBER
5 FINDING PERFECT SQUARES AND SQUARE ROOTS
6 USING ORDER OF OPERATIONS

1 DIVISORS OF A WHOLE NUMBER

In this section we consider several topics related to multiplication and division of whole numbers. A **multiple** of a whole number is the product of the number and some other whole number. For example, some multiples of 3 are

$$0 = 3 \times 0, \quad 3 = 3 \times 1, \quad 6 = 3 \times 2, \quad 9 = 3 \times 3, \quad 12 = 3 \times 4 \,.$$

Another way of saying the same thing (if we exclude zero) is that one number is a **divisor** or **factor** of a second if the second is a multiple of the first. For example,

$$6 = 3 \times 2$$

6 is a multiple of both 3 and 2   3 and 2 are both divisors or factors of 6

**PRACTICE
EXERCISE 1**

Show that 1, 2, 5, 10, 25, and 50 are all divisors of 50.

Answer: Since $1 \times 50 = 50$, $2 \times 25 = 50$, and $5 \times 10 = 50$, 50 is a multiple of each number, which means each of the numbers is a divisor of 50.

FINDING DIVISORS OF A NUMBER   **EXAMPLE 1**

Show that 1, 2, 3, 4, 6, 8, 12, and 24 are all divisors (factors) of 24.

Since 24 is a multiple of each of these numbers, as shown below,

$$1 \times 24 = 24 \qquad 2 \times 12 = 24 \qquad 3 \times 8 = 24 \qquad 4 \times 6 = 24$$

each is a divisor of 24.

In Example 1, notice that 1, 2, 3, 4, 6, 8, 12, and 24 all divide 24 evenly; that is, the remainder is zero. This is true in general.

DIVISOR OF A NUMBER

One number is a divisor of another if division results in a remainder of zero.

NOTE   To find the divisors of a number such as 15, we would need to divide 15 by each of the numbers less or equal to 15: 1, 2, 3, 4, 5, 6, 7, 8, 9, 10, 11, 12, 13, 14, and 15, and look at the remainders. This process would show that the only divisors of 15 are 1, 3, 5, and 15, since dividing 15 by these numbers, and only these numbers, results in a remainder of 0. Actually, there is no need to try 8, 9, 10, 11, 12, 13, and 14 since they are greater than half of 15.

---

2   PRIME AND COMPOSITE NUMBERS

Certain natural numbers have only two divisors, 1 and the number itself. For example, the only divisors of 7 are 1 and 7.

PRIME NUMBERS

A natural number that has *exactly two different* divisors (factors), 1 and itself, is called a **prime number.**

RECOGNIZING PRIME NUMBERS   **EXAMPLE 5**

Are the following numbers prime?

(a) 1 is *not* prime since 1 can only be written as $1 = 1 \times 1$. Thus, 1 does not have two *different* divisors.

(b) 2 is prime. The only divisors of 2 are 1 and $(2 = 1 \times 2)$. Thus, 2 is the first prime number.

(c) 4 is *not* prime since $4 = 2 \times 2$.

**PRACTICE
EXERCISE 2**

Are the following numbers prime?
(a) 3

(b) 5

(c) 9

Answers: (a) 3 is prime. (b) 5 is prime. (c) 9 is not prime since $9 = 3 \times 3$.

COMPOSITE NUMBERS

A natural number greater than 1 that is not a prime is a **composite number.**

NOTE   Every composite number can be written as a product of two natural numbers *other than* the number itself and 1.

EXAMPLE 3   RECOGNIZING COMPOSITE NUMBERS

Show that the following numbers are composite.

(a) 4 is composite since $4 = 2 \times 2$.

(b) 8 is composite since $8 = 2 \times 4$.

(c) 9 is composite since $9 = 3 \times 3$.

NOTE   The number 1 is neither prime nor composite. It is the only natural number with this property.

Every composite number can be written as a product of primes. In Example 3, 4 was written as 2×2 and 9 as 3×3. Although 8 was written as 2×4, we could also write 8 as $2 \times 2 \times 2$. In all cases, the composite number has been written as a product of prime factors, called the **prime factorization** of the number.

PRIME FACTORIZATION OF A COMPOSITE NUMBER

Each composite number can be written as a product of primes, and except for the order in which the primes are written, this factorization is the only one possible.

Although we know that a composite number can be expressed as a product of primes, we do not yet have a good way to find these prime factors. The best way is to try to divide the number by each of the primes

2, 3, 5, 7, 11, 13, 17, 19, 23, ...,

starting with 2 and continuing in order of size as long as necessary. When a remainder is zero, the prime is a factor of the number. The process is repeated using the new quotient as the dividend. For example, to find the prime factors of 60, start by dividing 60 by 2.

$$60 \div 2 = 30, \qquad \text{so} \qquad 60 = 2 \cdot 30$$

Now try possible prime divisors of 30, starting again with 2.

$$30 \div 2 = 15, \qquad \text{so} \qquad 60 = 2 \cdot \mathbf{30} = 2 \cdot \mathbf{2 \cdot 15}$$

Next look for prime divisors of 15. Since the remainder when 15 is divided by 2 is 1, not zero, move on to the next prime, 3.

$$15 \div 3 = 5 \qquad \text{so} \qquad 60 = 2 \cdot 2 \cdot \mathbf{15} = 2 \cdot 2 \cdot \mathbf{3 \cdot 5}$$

Since all factors listed (2, 2, 3, and 5) are prime, we say the prime factorization of 60 is $2 \cdot 2 \cdot 3 \cdot 5$.

EXPLORATION GUIDE

The problem of identifying prime numbers has intrigued mathematicians for many years. One way to discover the primes up to some number, 100 for example, is to list all the counting numbers from 2 through 100. We know that 2 is prime, but all the other multiples of 2 must be composite. Circle the 2 and cross out all the remaining multiples of 2 in the list. Since 3 is prime, circle 3 and cross out all the remaining multiples of 3. Continue this process, and when you are finished, only the primes between 2 and 100 will remain in your list. This method, attributed to the Greek astronomer Eratosthenes (about 276-192 B.C.) is called the **Sieve of Eratosthenes.** Explain why this method works, and use it to obtain all the primes that are less than 100.

One way to display the prime factorization of 60 shown above is to use a *factor tree* like the following.

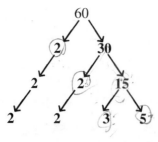

Divide 60 by 2, write down 2 and the quotient, 30

Divide 30 by 2: on the next row, write both 2s and the new quotient, 15

2 does not divide 15, so try the next larger prime, 3

These are the prime factors

This process can be continued for larger numbers. Multiplying the numbers across each row of the factor tree gives the original number, with the bottom row giving the prime factors.

Another technique that can be used to obtain the same prime factorization of 60 is shown below.

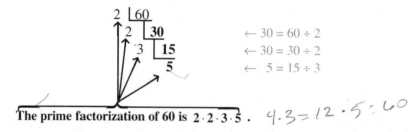

$$\leftarrow 30 = 60 \div 2$$
$$\leftarrow 30 = 30 \div 2$$
$$\leftarrow 5 = 15 \div 3$$

The prime factorization of 60 is $2 \cdot 2 \cdot 3 \cdot 5$. $4 \cdot 3 = 12 \cdot 5 = 60$

The information given in light type in the previous display is used for explanation and would not be written if you use this technique.

**PRACTICE
EXERCISE 4**

Find the prime factors of each number.

(a) 20

(b) 120

(c) 490

FINDING PRIME FACTORIZATIONS   **E X A M P L E
4**

Find the prime factors of each number.

(a) 28

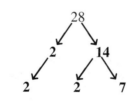

$$28 \div 2 = 14$$

$$28 = 2 \cdot 2 \cdot 7$$

(b) 182

$$182 \div 2 = 91, \ 2, 3, \text{ and } 5 \text{ do not divide } 91$$

$$182 = 2 \cdot 7 \cdot 13$$

(c) 825

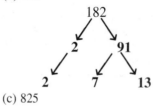

3 is the smallest prime that divides 825

$$825 = 3 \cdot 5 \cdot 5 \cdot 11$$

Alternatively, we find the same prime factorization using the following.

$$\begin{array}{r|l} 3 & 825 \\ \hline 5 & \mathbf{275} \\ \hline 5 & \mathbf{55} \\ \hline & \mathbf{11} \end{array}$$

$\leftarrow 275 = 825 \div 3$
$\leftarrow 55 = 275 \div 5$
$\leftarrow 11 = 55 \div 5$

Again we obtain $825 = 3 \cdot 5 \cdot 5 \cdot 11$.

(d)

$$\begin{array}{r|l} 5 & 3185 \\ \hline 7 & 637 \\ \hline 7 & 91 \\ \hline & 13 \end{array}$$

Thus, $3185 = 5 \cdot 7 \cdot 7 \cdot 13$.

(d) 3003

Answers: (a) $20 = 2 \cdot 2 \cdot 5$
(b) $120 = 2 \cdot 2 \cdot 2 \cdot 3 \cdot 5$
(c) $490 = 2 \cdot 5 \cdot 7 \cdot 7$
(d) $3003 = 3 \cdot 7 \cdot 11 \cdot 13$

3 | DIVISIBILITY TESTS

To find out whether a given number (prime or composite) is a divisor of another without actually dividing, we can use simple tests called *divisibility tests*. We shall give tests for the numbers

2, 3, 5, and 10.

DIVISIBILITY TESTS

1. A number is *divisible by 2* if its ones digit is 0, 2, 4, 6, or 8.
2. A number is *divisible by 3* if the sum of its digits is divisible by 3.
3. A number is *divisible by 5* if its ones digit is 0 or 5.
4. A number is *divisible by 10* if its ones digit is 0.

EXAMPLE 5   TESTING DIVISIBILITY BY 2

Are the following numbers divisible by 2?

(a) 23**5** is not divisible by 2 since the ones digit is 5.

(b) 428**4** is divisible by 2 since the ones digit is 4.

Numbers divisible by 2 are called **even numbers.** The first ten even whole numbers are 0, 2, 4, 6, 8, 10, 12, 14, 16, and 18. Numbers that are not even, such as 1, 3, 5, 7, 9, 11, and 13, are called **odd numbers.**

EXAMPLE 6   TESTING DIVISIBILITY BY 3

Are the following numbers divisible by 3?

(a) 24 is divisible by 3 since $\mathbf{2 + 4 = 6}$ and 6 is divisible by 3.

(b) 3241 is not divisible by 3 since $\mathbf{3 + 2 + 4 + 1 = 10}$ and 10 is not divisible by 3.

Since the sum of the digits of a number is smaller than the original number, it is easier to find out if the sum is divisible by 3.

PRACTICE EXERCISE 5

Are the following numbers divisible by 2?
(a) 350
(b) 3273

Answers: (a) Yes; its ones digit is 0. (b) No; its ones digit is 3 and not 0, 2, 4, 6, or 8.

PRACTICE EXERCISE 6

Are the following numbers divisible by 3?
(a) 73

(b) 6594

Answers: (a) No; $7 + 3 = 10$, and 10 is not divisible by 3.
(b) Yes; $6 + 5 + 9 + 4 = 24$, and 24 is divisible by 3.

NOTE   For a number to be divisible by 6, it must be divisible by both 2 and 3, since $6 = 2 \times 3$. Thus, a divisibility test for 6 is a combination of the tests for 2 and 3.

TESTING DIVISIBILITY BY 5   EXAMPLE 7

Are the following numbers divisible by 5?

(a) 32**0** is divisible by 5 since the ones digit is 0.

(b) 430**4** is not divisible by 5 since the ones digit is 4.

TESTING DIVISIBILITY BY 10   EXAMPLE 8

Are the following numbers divisible by 10?

(a) 24**0** is divisible by 10 since its ones digit is 0.

(b) 325,36**1** is not divisible by 10 since its ones digit is 1, not 0.

4   POWERS OF A NUMBER

Often we are asked to multiply the same number by itself several times. For example, the number 64 expressed as a product of primes is

$$64 = 2 \cdot 2 \cdot 2 \cdot 2 \cdot 2 \cdot 2$$

Such expanded products can be abbreviated by using *exponents*. We write

2^6 for $2 \cdot 2 \cdot 2 \cdot 2 \cdot 2 \cdot 2$

Base   **Exponent**   Six 2s

The expression 2^6, read "2 to the sixth," is called the **sixth power** of 2; 6 is an **exponent,** and 2 is the **base.** An exponent tells how many times a base is used as a factor. Suppose we find the first five powers of 2.

The **first power** of 2 is 2^1 or 2.

The **second power** of 2, also read "two **squared,**" is $2^2 = 2 \cdot 2 = 4$.

The **third power** of 2, also read "two **cubed,**" is $2^3 = 2 \cdot 2 \cdot 2 = 8$.

The **fourth power** of 2 is $2^4 = 2 \cdot 2 \cdot 2 \cdot 2 = 16$.

The **fifth power** of 2 is $2^5 = 2 \cdot 2 \cdot 2 \cdot 2 \cdot 2 = 32$.

EVALUATING NUMBERS HAVING EXPONENTS   EXAMPLE 9

Find the value by writing without exponents.

(a) 5^3 We have $5^3 = 5 \cdot 5 \cdot 5 = 125$.   The base is 5, the exponent is 3

(b) 4^5 We have $4^5 = 4 \cdot 4 \cdot 4 \cdot 4 \cdot 4 = 1024$.

| EXAMPLE 10 | WRITING NUMBERS USING EXPONENTS |

Write each product using exponents.

(a) $6 \cdot 6 \cdot 6 \cdot 6$ Since there are four 6s, the base is 6 and the exponent is 4. Thus, $6 \cdot 6 \cdot 6 \cdot 6 = 6^4$.

(b) $10 \cdot 10 \cdot 10$ There are three 10s, so we have 10^3.

Write each product using exponents.
(a) $5 \cdot 5 \cdot 5 \cdot 5 \cdot 5 \cdot 5$
(b) $100 \cdot 100 \cdot 100 \cdot 100$

Answers: (a) 5^6 (b) 100^4

| EXAMPLE 11 | PRIME FACTORIZATION USING EXPONENTS |

Write the prime factorization for each number using exponents.

(a) 100   Using a factor tree, we have $100 = 2 \cdot 2 \cdot 5 \cdot 5$. Using exponents, $2 \cdot 2$ becomes 2^2 and $5 \cdot 5$ becomes 5^2. Thus, $100 = 2^2 \cdot 5^2$.

(b) 540   Using a factor tree, we have $540 = 2 \cdot 2 \cdot 3 \cdot 3 \cdot 3 \cdot 5$. Using exponents, $540 = 2^2 \cdot 3^3 \cdot 5$.

Write the prime factorization for each number using exponents.
(a) 1323
(b) 2200

Answers: (a) $3^3 \cdot 7^2$
(b) $2^3 \cdot 5^2 \cdot 11$

| EXAMPLE 12 | EVALUATING PRODUCTS HAVING EXPONENTS |

Find the value of each product.

$$(a) \ 2^5 \cdot 5^2 = \underbrace{2 \cdot 2 \cdot 2 \cdot 2 \cdot 2}_{} \cdot \underbrace{5 \cdot 5}_{}$$
$$= \quad 32 \quad \cdot \quad 25$$
$$= 800$$

$$(b) \ 2 \cdot 3^4 \cdot 7^2 = 2 \cdot \underbrace{3 \cdot 3 \cdot 3 \cdot 3}_{} \cdot \underbrace{7 \cdot 7}_{}$$
$$= 2 \cdot \quad 81 \quad \cdot 49$$
$$= 7938$$

| 5 | PERFECT SQUARES AND SQUARE ROOTS |

The opposite of finding powers is taking *roots*. For example, we know that the square of 3 is 9, $3^2 = 9$. We call 3 a *square root* of 9, and 9 is called a *perfect square*. That is,

┌─ **9 is the square of 3,**
│   **making 9 a perfect square**
$3^2 = 9.$

3 is a square root of 9 ─┘

PERFECT SQUARES AND SQUARE ROOTS

When a whole number is squared, the result is a **perfect square.** The number which is being squared is a **square root** of the perfect square.

| EXAMPLE 13 | FINDING SQUARE ROOTS |

Find the square root of each number.

(a) 25   Since $25 = 5^2$, 5 is a square root of 25.

(b) 64   Since $64 = 8^2$, 8 is a square root of 64.

(c) 0   Since $0 = 0^2$, 0 is a square root of 0.

Find the square root of each number.
(a) 16
(b) 81
(c) 1
Answers: (a) 4 (b) 9 (c) 1

> **NOTE**   Remember that to find the square root of a number, you must ask: "What number squared (multiplied by itself) is equal to the given number?"

The symbol $\sqrt{}$, called a **radical,** means "square root." For example, $\sqrt{25}$ is read "the square root of 25." Similarly, $\sqrt{64}$ is read "the square root of 64." By Example 13 we see that

$$\sqrt{25} = 5 \qquad \text{and} \qquad \sqrt{64} = 8.$$

> **CAUTION**   Do not confuse the terms *square* and *square root.* For example,
>
> $$4 \text{ is a square root of 16}$$
> $$\downarrow$$
> $$16 = 4^2.$$
> $$16 \text{ is the square of 4}$$

PRACTICE EXERCISE 14

Find each square root.

(a) $\sqrt{36}$

(b) $\sqrt{144}$

Answers: (a) 6 (not 6^2) (b) 12

Perfect square	Whole number square root
0	$\sqrt{0} = 0$
1	$\sqrt{1} = 1$
4	$\sqrt{4} = 2$
9	$\sqrt{9} = 3$
16	$\sqrt{16} = 4$
25	$\sqrt{25} = 5$
36	$\sqrt{36} = 6$
49	$\sqrt{49} = 7$
64	$\sqrt{64} = 8$
81	$\sqrt{81} = 9$
100	$\sqrt{100} = 10$
121	$\sqrt{121} = 11$
144	$\sqrt{144} = 12$
169	$\sqrt{169} = 13$
196	$\sqrt{196} = 14$
225	$\sqrt{225} = 15$

FINDING SQUARE ROOTS   E X A M P L E 14

Find each square root.

(a) $\sqrt{9}$ Since $9 = 3^2$, $\sqrt{9} = 3$.

(b) $\sqrt{100}$ Since $100 = 10^2$, $\sqrt{100} = 10$.

> **CAUTION**   A common mistake is to say that $\sqrt{9} = 3^2$. Notice that $3^2 = 9$ so that $\sqrt{9}$ is just 3, *not* 3^2.

The first sixteen perfect squares and their whole number square roots are listed in the table in the margin.

6 | ORDER OF OPERATIONS

Some problems involve several operations. For example, when we checked a division problem such as

$$\begin{array}{r} 4 \\ 6\overline{)25} \\ \underline{24} \\ 1 \end{array}$$

we wrote $(6 \times 4) + 1 = 24 + 1 = 25$. The parentheses show that 6 and 4 are multiplied first, and then the product is added to 1. If we had omitted the parentheses and written

$$6 \times 4 + 1,$$

there could be some confusion about the *order* of operations. Should we multiply 6×4 first and then add 1, or should we add $4 + 1$ first, and then multiply the sum by 6 to obtain $6 \cdot 5 = 30$? The parentheses were necessary to avoid this confusion. Another way to eliminate this problem is to agree on a definite **order of operations** when addition, subtraction, multiplication, division, finding powers, and taking roots occur in a problem.

ORDER OF OPERATIONS

1. Find all powers and square roots, in any order, first.
2. Multiply and divide, in order, from left to right.
3. Add and subtract, in order, from left to right.

EXAMPLE 15 — USING ORDER OF OPERATIONS

Perform the indicated operations.

(a) $2 + 3 \cdot 4$

$$2 + 3 \cdot 4 = 2 + 12 \quad \text{Multiply first}$$
$$= 14 \quad \text{Then add}$$

(b) $5 \cdot 6 - 12 \div 4$

$$5 \cdot 6 - 12 \div 4 = 30 - 3 \quad \text{Multiply and divide first}$$
$$= 27 \quad \text{Then subtract}$$

(c) $\sqrt{64} - 2^3$

$$\sqrt{64} - 2^3 = 8 - 8 \quad \text{Take root and cube first}$$
$$= 0 \quad \text{Then subtract}$$

(d) $4^2 \div 2 + \sqrt{9} - 1$

$$4^2 \div 2 + \sqrt{9} - 1 = 16 \div 2 + 3 - 1 \quad \text{Find power and root first}$$
$$= 8 + 3 - 1 \quad \text{Divide next}$$
$$= 11 - 1 \quad \text{Add next}$$
$$= 10 \quad \text{Subtract last}$$

PRACTICE EXERCISE 15

Perform the indicated operations.

(a) $5 \cdot 7 - 10$

(b) $18 \div 3 + 2 \cdot 4$

(c) $5^2 - \sqrt{36}$

(d) $\sqrt{81} + 6^2 \div 9 - 2$

Answers: (a) 25 (b) 14 (c) 19 (d) 11

When parentheses are used, they affect the order of operations.

EVALUATING USING PARENTHESES

Always operate within parentheses first. Then follow the standard order of operations.

EXAMPLE 16 — OPERATIONS INVOLVING PARENTHESES

Perform the indicated operations.

(a) $(5 - 1) \cdot 3 + 7$

$$(5 - 1) \cdot 3 + 7 = 4 \cdot 3 + 7 \quad \text{Subtract inside parentheses first}$$
$$= 12 + 7 \quad \text{Multiply before adding}$$
$$= 19$$

(b) $\sqrt{9}(6 \div 2) + 5^2$

$$\sqrt{9}(6 \div 2) + 5^2 = \sqrt{9}(3) + 5^2 \quad \text{Divide inside the parentheses first}$$
$$= 3 \cdot 3 + 25 \quad \text{Take root and square next}$$
$$= 9 + 25 \quad \text{Multiply before adding}$$
$$= 34$$

(c) $(3 \cdot 5)^2$

$$(3 \cdot 5)^2 = (15)^2 \quad \text{Multiply inside parentheses first}$$
$$= 225 \quad \text{Then square}$$

PRACTICE EXERCISE 16

Perform the indicated operations.

(a) $2(6 + 1) - 3$

(b) $3^2 - \sqrt{4}(10 \div 5)$

(c) $(2 \cdot 7)^2$

(d) $2 \cdot 7^2$

(d) $3 \cdot 5^2$

$$3 \cdot 5^2 = 3 \cdot 25 \qquad \text{Square first}$$
$$= 75 \qquad \text{Then multiply}$$

(e) $(1+4)^3$

(e) $(2+3)^3$

$$(2+3)^3 = (5)^3 \qquad \text{Add inside parentheses first}$$
$$= 125 \qquad \text{Then cube}$$

(f) $1^3 + 4^3$

(f) $2^3 + 3^3$

$$2^3 + 3^3 = 8 + 27 \qquad \text{Cube first}$$
$$= 35 \qquad \text{Then add}$$

Answers: (a) 11 (b) 5
(c) 196 (d) 98
(e) 125 (f) 65

CAUTION   Parts (c) and (d) in Example 16 show that

$$3 \cdot 5^2 \neq (3 \cdot 5)^2,$$

and parts (e) and (f) show that

$$(2+3)^3 \neq 2^3 + 3^3.$$

A common mistake when working with exponents is to assume that expressions like those above are equal. Remember to evaluate within parentheses before finding a power.

1.9 EXERCISES
Answers to these exercises are given on page 641.

Answer true or false in Exercises 1–3. If the answer is false, explain why.

1.   Since $15 = 3 \times 5$, 15 is a multiple of both 3 and 5.

2.   A natural number with exactly two different divisors, 1 and itself, is called a composite number.

3.   The only even prime number is 2.

Find all the divisors of each number in Exercises 4–6.

4.   18   5.   28   6.   56

Find the first ten multiples of each number in Exercises 7–9.

7.   4   8.   7   9.   100

Find the prime factorization of each number in Exercises 10–18.

10. 55   11. 65   12. 78

13. 169   14. 294   15. 429

16. 693   17. 1300   18. 5100

Determine whether each number in Exercises 19–24 is prime or composite.

19. 13   20. 27   21. 31

22. 49
23. 51
24. 97

Use the following numbers to answer the questions in Exercises 25–28.
120, 126, 240, 147, 130, 104, 70, 135, 72, 110, 88, 4125

25. Which numbers are divisible by 2?

26. Which numbers are divisible by 3?

27. Which numbers are divisible by 5?

28. Which numbers are divisible by 10?

29. Consider the number 3^4. (a) What is the number 4 called? (b) What is the number 3 called? (c) What power of 3 is this?

30. What is the second power of a number called?

31. When parentheses are not used, which operation is performed first, addition or multiplication?

Find the value of each expression in Exercises 32–34 by writing without exponents.
32. 2^8
33. 10^4
34. 8^3

Write each product in Exercises 35–37 using exponents.
35. $3 \cdot 3 \cdot 3 \cdot 3$
36. $9 \cdot 9 \cdot 9 \cdot 9 \cdot 9$
37. $4 \cdot 4 \cdot 4 \cdot 4 \cdot 4 \cdot 4$

Find the prime factorization of each number in Exercises 38–40 using exponents.
38. 252
39. 2646
40. 4400

Evaluate each product in Exercises 41–43 without using exponents.
41. $2 \cdot 3^3 \cdot 11$
42. $3^2 \cdot 5^2 \cdot 7^2$
43. $3 \cdot 5^3 \cdot 13^2$

Find the square root of each number in Exercises 44–46.
44. 49
45. 100
46. 121

Find the square of each number in Exercises 47–49.
47. 49
48. 100
49. 121

Find each square root in Exercises 50–52.
50. $\sqrt{16}$
51. $\sqrt{1}$
52. $\sqrt{169}$

Perform the indicated operations in Exercises 53–76.
53. $3 + 9 - 5$
54. $14 \div 7 - 1$
55. $4 - 8 \div 2 + 1$

56. $7 + 2 \cdot 3 - 4$
57. $36 \div 6 - 3 \cdot 2$
58. $5 + 2^2$

59. $\sqrt{25} - 2^2$
60. $5^2 - \sqrt{49}$
61. $3^2 + 5 - \sqrt{4} + 1$

62. $\sqrt{25} + 15 - 2^2 \cdot 5$
63. $2^5 - \sqrt{100} + 7$
64. $2^3 \div \sqrt{16} + 3$

65. $(9 - 2) \cdot 3 + 4$ 2
66. $(2 + 3) \div 5 - 0$
67. $6 + 2(5 - 3)$

68. $(5 + 1) \cdot (4 - 2) - 3$
69. $\sqrt{4}(9 \div 3) + 2^3$
70. $2(\sqrt{4} \div 2) - 2$

71. $(3 \cdot 7)^2$
72. $3 \cdot 7^2$
73. $3^2 \cdot 7^2$

74. $(3 + 7)^2$
75. $3^2 + 7^2$
76. $2(3 + 7)^2$

CRITICAL THINKING

77. Outline the steps that you would follow in finding the prime factorization of a large number such as 13,650. What is the prime factorization?

78. Outline the steps that you would follow in evaluating a complex expression such as $\sqrt{1+8} \cdot \sqrt{6-2} + (5-2)^2 \div 3$.

79. Explain how the terms *multiple, divisor,* and *factor* are related and give an example to illustrate this relationship.

80. Without actually dividing, determine if 1782 is divisible by 6 and explain your method.

81. Explain why we use exponents to write certain products.

82. What is meant by finding the *prime factorization* of a number? Does a number have more than one such factorization?

83. Explain why every number that is divisible by 10 is also divisible by 5. If a number is divisible by 5 is it necessarily divisible by 10? Explain.

84. Burford's work simplifying an expression is shown below. What is he doing wrong? What is the correct simplification?

$$14 - 6 \div 2 + 1$$
$$= 8 \div 2 + 1$$
$$= 4 + 1$$
$$= 5$$

REVIEW AND PREVIEW

Solve each applied problem in Exercises 85–93.

85. **RECREATION** For an antique car rally Brad Rogers drove 3 times as far as he had in the previous rally. If he drove 321 miles during this rally, how far had he driven at the previous one?

86. **MONTHLY PAYMENTS** Burford purchased a TV from his roommate for $614. He paid $50 down and the rest in equal monthly payments over a period of one year. If no interest was charged, what were his monthly payments?

87. **CONSUMER** A hall measures 2 yd wide by 10 yd long, and a living room measures 12 yd long by 7 yd wide. If it costs $20 a square yard for carpeting, how much will it cost to carpet the hall and living room?

88. **MORTGAGE PAYMENTS** The Connors have a second mortgage which requires a monthly payment of $200 for 12 years.
    (a) How many monthly payments must they make over the 12-year period?
    (b) How much will they have paid in total at the end of 12 years?

89. **TRAVEL** A map is drawn to scale but the number of miles to the inch is not given. If the distance between two cities is 280 miles and they are 8 inches apart on the map, what is the scale of the map in miles per inch?

90. **CONSUMER** Ed Moura has only $20 bills in his wallet. If he buys 3 pairs of shoes at $42 each, how many bills must he use? How much change will he receive?

91. **RECREATION** An auditorium used for concerts is divided into three sections. There are 20 rows, each with 12 seats, in the first section. The second section consists of 30 rows, each with 18 seats. The third section has the same number of seats as the first section. How many seats are in the auditorium?

92. **CONSUMER** A student pays $120 a month for rent and $75 a month for food during the 9-month school year.
    (a) How much does she spend on rent?
    (b) How much does she spend on food?
    (c) How much does she spend on rent and food together?

93. **RECREATION**   A truck weighs 4845 pounds
    when empty. When it is loaded with a camper, it
    weighs 7525 pounds. What is the weight of the
    · camper?

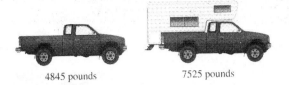

4845 pounds   7525 pounds

1.9 PARALLEL EXERCISES

Answers to these exercises are not given in the text.

Answer true or false in Exercises 1–3. If the answer is false, explain why.

1. Since $12 = 2 \times 6$, 2 and 6 are divisors of 12.
2. The multiples of 2 are odd numbers.
3. The only natural number which is neither prime nor composite is 1.

Find all divisors of each number in Exercises 4–6.

4. 21   5. 36   6. 54

Find the first ten multiples of each number in Exercises 7–9.

7. 3   8. 6   9. 1000

Find the prime factorization of each number in Exercises 10–18.

10. 66   11. 82   12. 96
13. 273   14. 630   15. 945
16. 1750   17. 1050   18. 5610

Determine whether each number in Exercises 19–24 is prime or composite.

19. 17   20. 26   21. 31
22. 55   23. 63   24. 213

Use the following numbers to answer the questions in Exercises 25–28.
815, 150, 156, 42, 784, 125, 343, 90, 210, 66, 56, 3280

25. Which numbers are divisible by 2?   26. Which numbers are divisible by 3?

27. Which numbers are divisible by 5?   28. Which numbers are divisible by 10?

29. Consider the number 5^4. (a) What is the number 5 called? (b) What is the number 4 called? (c) What power of 5 is this?

30. What is the third power of a number called?

31. When parentheses are not used, which operation is performed first, subtraction or division?

Find the value of each expression in Exercises 32–34 by writing without exponents.

32. 3^5 33. 5^3 34. 10^5

Write each product in Exercises 35–37 using exponents.

35. $2 \cdot 2 \cdot 2$ 36. $5 \cdot 5 \cdot 5 \cdot 5 \cdot 5 \cdot 5 \cdot 5$ 37. $8 \cdot 8 \cdot 8 \cdot 8$

Find the prime factorization of each number in Exercises 38–40 using exponents.

38. 270   39. 1008   40. 11,880

Evaluate each product in Exercises 41–43 without using exponents.

41. $2^2 \cdot 3 \cdot 13$ 42. $3^2 \cdot 5^3 \cdot 7$ 43. $3 \cdot 7^2 \cdot 13^2$

Find the square root of each number in Exercises 44–46.

44. 36   45. 81   46. 144

Find the square of each number in Exercises 47–49.

47. 36   48. 81   49. 144

Find each square root in Exercises 50–52.

50. $\sqrt{64}$ 51. $\sqrt{169}$ 52. $\sqrt{225}$

Perform the indicated operations in Exercises 53–76.

53. $5 + 8 - 3$ 54. $18 \div 9 - 1$ 55. $6 - 12 \div 4 + 7$

56. $9 + 3 \cdot 5 - 7$ 57. $49 \div 7 - 2 \cdot 2$ 58. $\sqrt{25} + 75$

59. $\sqrt{81} - 2^3$ 60. $6^2 - \sqrt{121}$ 61. $4^2 + 3 - \sqrt{9} + 2$

62. $\sqrt{49} + 5 - 2^3 \cdot 3$ 63. $2^6 - \sqrt{144} + 5$ 64. $3^2 \div \sqrt{9} + 1$

65. $(8 - 4) \cdot 2 + 6$ 66. $(3 + 1) \div 2 - 0$ 67. $5 + 2(7 - 3)$

68. $(2 + 3) \cdot (6 - 1) - 2$ 69. $\sqrt{25}(6 \div 2) + 3^2$ 70. $3(\sqrt{16} \div 2) - 6$

71. $(2 \cdot 11)^2$ 72. $2 \cdot 11^2$ 73. $2^2 \cdot 11^2$

74. $(2 + 6)^2$ 75. $2^2 + 6^2$ 76. $3(2 + 6)^2$

CRITICAL THINKING

✎77. Outline the steps that you would follow in finding the prime factorization of a large number such as 17,199. What is the prime factorization?

✎78. Outline the steps that you would follow in evaluating a complex expression such as $\left(4^2 - 3^2\right) \div 7 + \left(\sqrt{25} - \sqrt{4}\right)$.

✎79. What is the relationship between a *prime* number and a *composite* number? What is the only counting number that is neither prime nor composite? Give reasons why primes are important.

✎80. Give several reasons for understanding and using the tests for divisibility.

✎81. Discuss the difference between the terms *square* and *square root*.

✎82. Summarize the order of operations, explain why it is important to have an agreed upon order, and discuss how the use of parentheses affects the order of operations when evaluating a numerical expression.

✎83. Explain why a number that is divisible by 4 must also be divisible by 2? If a number is divisible by 2 is it necessarily divisible by 4? Explain.

💡84. Burford's work simplifying an expression is shown below. What is he doing wrong? What is the correct simplification?

$$5 - 2^2 + 4$$
$$= 3^2 + 4$$
$$= 9 + 4$$
$$= 13$$

GROUP PROJECT

Prime numbers have fascinated mathematicians for many years. Questions like "Is there a largest prime number?" or "How many primes are there?" have now been answered. There is no largest prime, and there are infinitely many prime numbers. While it is known that there are infinitely many primes, no one has yet determined a way to generate them. Primes that differ by 2 are called *twin primes*. For example, 3 and 5, 5 and 7, and 11 and 13 are twin primes. One of the classic unsolved problems in mathematics involves twin primes. Are there infinitely many twin primes? No one as of yet has been able to answer this question. Can you find a pair of twin primes between 15 and 25? Between 50 and 75? Between 75 and 100? Between 105 and 110? Investigate some of the other interesting properties of prime numbers and report your discoveries to the class.

CHAPTER 1 REVIEW

KEY WORDS

 1.1

- The **natural** or **counting numbers** are 1, 2, 3, 4, ...
- The **whole numbers** are the natural numbers together with zero: 0, 1, 2, 3, ...
- A **numeral** is a symbol used to represent a number.
- A **number line** is used to "picture" numbers.
- A letter that is used to represent a number is called a **variable.**
- The first ten whole numbers, 0, 1, 2, 3, 4, 5, 6, 7, 8, and 9, are also called **digits.**
- Our number system is a **place-value system** because the value of each digit depends on its place or position in a numeral.

1.2

- Two numbers to be added are called **addends** and the result is called their **sum.**
- Addition is a **binary operation,** which means that only *two* numbers are added at a time.

1.3

- Numbers can be **rounded** or approximated by numbers to the nearest ten, hundred, thousand, and so on.

1.4

- In a subtraction problem, the number being take away is called the **subtrahend,** the number it is taken from is the **minuend,** and the result is the **difference.** That is,

      minuend – subtrahend = difference.

- An **equation** is a statement that two quantities are the same, and is written using an equal sign =.
- A number that makes an equation true when the number replaces the variable in the equation is called a **solution** to the equation.
- The **related addition** equation to $7 - 3 = 4$, for example, is $4 + 3 = 7$.
- Similarly, the **related subtraction equation** to $4 + 3 = 7$, for example, is either $7 - 3 = 4$ or $7 - 4 = 3$.

1.5

- In a **multiplication** problem, such as $2 \times 4 = 8$, $\times$ is called the **multiplication sign** or **times sign,** 2 and 4 are **factors,** 2 is the **multiplier,** 4 is the **multiplicand,** and 8 is the **product.**
- A **multiple** of a number is the product of the number and a whole number.

1.7

- In a division problem, such as $12 \div 3 = 4$, $\div$ is called the **division symbol,** 12 is the **dividend,** 3 is the **divisor,** and 4 is the **quotient.**
- The final difference in a division problem is called the **remainder,** a number that is less than the divisor.
- Let *a, b,* and *c* be numbers. For every division equation $a \div b = c$ there is a **related multiplication equation** $b \cdot c = a$, and conversely for a **related division equation.**
- An **algorithm** is a method or procedure used to perform a certain task.

1.9

- One number is a **divisor** of a second if the second is a multiple of the first.
- A **prime number** is a natural number that has exactly two different divisors, 1 and itself.
- A **composite number** is a natural number greater than 1 that is not prime.
- An **even number** is divisible by 2. Remember that 0 is an even number.
- A number that is not even is called an **odd number.**
- In the expression 3^5, 5 is called the **exponent,** 3 is called the **base,** and 3^5 is called the **fifth power** of 3.
- The second power of a number is called the **square** of the number.
- The third power of a number is called the **cube** of the number.
- When a whole number is squared, the result is called a **perfect square** and the number being squared is a **square root** of the perfect square.
- The symbol $\sqrt{}$ is called a **radical** and is used to indicate square roots.

KEY CONCEPTS

 1.1

1. The whole numbers occur in a natural order. If one whole number is to the left of a second whole number on a number line, it is *less than* the second. The symbol < represents "less than," and > represents "greater than."

2. The number 4379, written in standard notation, is a short form of expanded notation

$$4000 + 300 + 70 + 9.$$

3. Zero is used as a place-holder to show the difference between numbers such as 5032 and 532.

4. Write numbers such as 123 as "one hundred twenty-three" and *not* as "one hundred *and* twenty-three."

1.2

1. The *sum* of two numbers can be thought of as the number of objects in a combined collection.

2. Addition problems may be written either horizontally or vertically.

3. Changing the order of addition does not change the sum by the commutative law. That is, if a and b are numbers, $a + b = b + a$.

4. Adding 0 to any number gives the same number as the sum since 0 is the additive identity. That is, if a is any number, $a + 0 = a$ and $0 + a = a$.

5. Regrouping sums does not change the sum by the associative law. That is, if a, b, and c are numbers, $(a + b) + c = a + (b + c)$.

6. The process of addition can be shortened by the carrying procedure.

7. Addition can be checked by the reverse-order method or by estimation.

1.3

Rounded numbers can be used to estimate sums.

1.4

1. The *difference* of two numbers can be thought of as the number of objects which remain when objects are removed or taken away from a collection.

2. Subtraction can be defined by using the related addition equation and the basic addition facts.

3. Borrowing in subtraction problems is the reverse of carrying in addition problems.

4. Subtraction can be checked by adding the difference to the subtrahend.

1.5

1. When two whole numbers are multiplied, the multiplier shows the number of times the multiplicand is used as an addend. For example,

$$4 \times 3 = \underbrace{3 + 3 + 3 + 3}$$
Four 3s in the sum

2. When multiplying a many-digit number by a one-digit number, write down the ones digit and add the tens digit to the next product.

3. When multiplying by a many-digit number, remember to use zeros as placeholders or else to move each new product over one more place to the left.

4. To check a multiplication problem, interchange the factors and find the new product (the reverse-order check).

1.6

1. By the commutative law, changing the order of multiplication does not change the product. That is, if a and b are numbers, then $ab = ba$.

2. Multiplying any number by 0 gives 0 for the product. That is, if a is any number, $a \cdot 0 = 0$ and $0 \cdot a = 0$.

3. Multiplying any number by 1 gives the identical number for the product since 1 is the multiplicative identity. That is, if a is any number, then $a \cdot 1 = a$ and $1 \cdot a = a$.

4. By the associative law, regrouping the factors in a multiplication problem does not change the product. That is, if a, b, and c are numbers, then $(ab)c = a(bc)$.

5. The distributive law is an important property relating multiplication and addition. If a, b, and c are numbers, then $a(b + c) = ab + ac$.

1.7

1. A related multiplication equation for $10 \div 2 = 5$ is $2 \cdot 5 = 10$. Division can be defined in terms of multiplication using the related multiplication equation and the basic multiplication facts.

2. Any nonzero number divided by itself is always 1. That is, if a is a nonzero number, then $a \div a = 1$.

3. Any number divided by 1 is always that same number. That is, if a is any number, $a \div 1 = a$.

4. Division by 0 is undefined. That is, if a is any number, $a \div 0$ is not defined.

5. Zero divided by any nonzero number is always 0. That is, if a is not zero, then $0 \div a = 0$.

6. A division problem can be checked by using (quotient × divisor) + remainder = dividend.

KEY CONCEPTS

🔑 1.8

1. When working an applied problem, make a plan of attack and identify what is given and what must be found. A picture or sketch may be helpful. Always make sure that any answer you obtain seems reasonable before checking your answer in the words of the problem.

2. (total value) = (value per part) · (number of parts)

3. The area of a rectangle is given by the formula

$$\text{Area} = (\text{length}) \cdot (\text{width}).$$

4. Miles per gallon (mpg) is found by

$$\text{mpg} = \frac{\text{number of miles driven}}{\text{number of gallons used}}.$$

🔑 1.9

1. Each composite number can be written as a product of primes called the prime factorization of the number. A factor tree or the continuous division method is useful in finding these primes.

2. Do not confuse the terms square and square root. For example,

4 is the **square root** of 16

16 is the **square** of 4.

3. Operations should be performed in the following order.
   (a) Operate within parentheses.
   (b) Evaluate powers and roots.
   (c) Multiply and divide from left to right.
   (d) Add and subtract from left to right.

CHAPTER 1 REVIEW EXERCISES

PART I

Answers to these exercises are given on page 642.

1.1

💡1. What is the symbol for a number called?

💡2. Give the first five natural numbers.

💡3. Give the first five whole numbers.

💡4. What are the ten digits?

💡5. Why is the number system called a place-value system?

Answer Exercises 6–11 using the given number line.

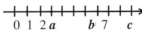

0 1 2 *a*   *b* 7 *c*

6. What number is represented by the variable *a*?

7. What number is represented by the variable *c*?

Place the correct symbol (< or >) between the given numbers, remembering that a, b, and c are from the number line above.

8. 2 _____ 7

9. *b* _____ *a*

10. *b* _____ *c*

11. *a* _____ *c*

12. Write 13,247,165 in expanded notation.

13. Write $400,000 + 3000 + 400 + 5$ in standard notation.

14. Write a word name for 27,405,036.

In the number 145,237,098 what digit represents each of the following places?

15. Millions

16. Hundreds

17. Ten thousands

18. Ones

1.2

💡19. Consider the addition problem $7 + 3 = 10$.
   (a) What are 7 and 3 called?   (b) What is 10 called?   (c) What is the symbol + called?

💡20. Complete the statement using the commutative law of addition. $5 + 4 =$ _____

💡21. When a given number is added to 0, what is the sum?

Find each sum in Exercises 22–24 and check your work.

22. $\begin{array}{r} 457 \\ +168 \\ \hline \end{array}$

23. $\begin{array}{r} 5678 \\ +8765 \\ \hline \end{array}$

24. $\begin{array}{r} 5654 \\ 327 \\ +4032 \\ \hline \end{array}$

Translate each expression in Exercises 25-26.

25. 9 more than x

26. y increased by 20

💡27. Why is the operation of addition called a binary operation?

💡28. What is the name of the law illustrated by $(3 + 2) + 7 = 3 + (2 + 7)$?

1.3

Round each number in Exercises 29–31 to the nearest ten.

29. 73

30. 285

31. 4176

Round each number in Exercises 32–34 to the nearest hundred.

32. 451

33. 83

34. 2550

Round each number in Exercises 35–37 to the nearest thousand.

35. 7350

36. 875

37. 12,627

💡38. Estimate the sum by rounding to the nearest ten.

$$\begin{array}{r} 1657 \\ 2349 \\ + \ 836 \\ \hline 492 \end{array}$$

💡 39. Estimate the sum by rounding to the nearest hundred.

$$\begin{array}{r} 1657 \\ 2349 \\ + \ 836 \\ \hline \end{array}$$

40. **RECREATION**   A rock concert took in $351,360 the first night and $420,150 the second night. First estimate the total receipts, and then find the exact total taken in on the two nights.

1.4

💡41. Consider the subtraction problem $54 - 23 = 31$. (a) What is the number 54 called? (b) What is the number 23 called? (c) What is the number 31 called? (d) What is the symbol "−" called?

Find each difference in Exercises 42–44 and check your work.

42. $\begin{array}{r} 3406 \\ -139 \\ \hline 277 \end{array}$

43. $\begin{array}{r} 352 \\ - \ 87 \\ \hline \end{array}$

44. $\begin{array}{r} 56307 \\ -2187 \\ \hline 320 \end{array}$

Find the value of or translate each expression in Exercises 45–46.

45. 7 decreased by z

46. 8 less than 19

1.5

💡47. Consider the multiplication problem $7 \times 9 = 63$. (a) What is 7 called? (b) What is 9 called? (c) What is 63 called?

💡48. The numbers 0, 4, 8, 12, 16, and 20 are the first six multiples of what number?

Find each product in Exercises 49–53 and check using the reverse-order check.

49. 4398
    ×7

50. 723
    ×31

51. 479
    ×628

52. 4039
    ×705

53. 6493
    ×3000

54. Translate the expression: 6 times m

55. Solve the equation: $4x = 40$

1.6

56. The fact that $2 \cdot x = x \cdot 2$ illustrates what law of multiplication?

57. Use the distributive law and the associative law to multiply: $3(2w + 7)$

Check by estimating the product given in Exercises 58–59.

58.   86
      ×31
       86
      258
     ‾‾‾‾
     2666

59.   307
     ×513
      921
      307
     1835
    ‾‾‾‾‾‾
    187491

1.7

60. Consider the division problem $12 \div 4 = 3$.
    (a) What is 12 called?
    (b) What is 4 called?
    (c) What is 3 called?

61. What is the related multiplication sentence for $12 \div 4 = 3$?

Complete each statement in Exercises 62–65.

62. $5 \div 5 =$ _____

63. $5 \div 1 =$ _____

64. $0 \div 5 =$ _____

65. $5 \div 0 =$ _____

Find each quotient in Exercises 66–67 and check your work.

66. $7\overline{)6531}$

67. $47\overline{)1252}$

Translate each expression in Exercises 68-69.

68. The quotient of y and 5

69. 3 divided by w

1.8

Solve each applied problem in Exercises 70–78.

70. **BUSINESS** The Mortensen Tool Company had an increase in profits of $6732 over last year. If profits last year were $39,529, how much did the company make this year?

71. **CONSUMER** It costs Ms. Spinelli $735 to drive her car to work during the year. If she carpools with two others, it only costs $278 a year. How much can she save by forming a carpool?

72. **BANKING** At the beginning of the month, Sid had a balance of $693 in his checking account. During the month he made deposits of $450 and $580. He wrote checks for $137, $320, $18, $5, and $79. What was his balance at the end of the month?

73. **INVESTMENT** The Bonnetts bought a house for $55,280. After making several improvements which totaled $4375, they sold the house for $66,900. How much profit did they make on the sale?

74. **RECREATION** Bill Bass has $3360 in an account for his recreation for the year. If he has one trip planned that will require $1200, how much can he spend per month on regular entertainment?

75. **SPORTS** A nine-man softball team wins a tournament and receives a prize of $1000. They agree to split the prize money evenly (in dollars) with the remainder to be given to the captain. How much does the captain receive?

76. **AGRICULTURE** A farm has the dimensions given in the figure below. How many meters of fencing are needed to put a fence completely around the farm?

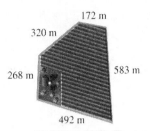

77. **CONSUMER** Dick wants to carpet his dining and living rooms with carpet selling for $18 a square yard. A sketch of the floor plan of the rooms is shown in the figure. How much will the carpet cost?
[Hint: Draw a line dividing the area into two rectangles.]

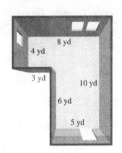

78. **CONSUMER** Assuming equal quality, which is the better buy, a 12-oz box of cat food for 84¢ or a 13-oz box of food for 78¢?

79. **BUSINESS** A hardware store sells 35 snow blowers at $329 each and 40 chain saws at $289 each.
   (a) How much money does the store take in on the sale of snow blowers?
   (b) How much money does the store take in on the sale of chain saws?
   (c) How much money does the store take in on the sale of both snow blowers and chain saws?

1.9

80. What do we call a natural number that has exactly two different divisors, 1 and itself?

81. What is a number called if it is greater than 1 and not prime?

82. What is the only natural number which is neither prime nor composite?

83. What do we call a natural number that is divisible by 2?

84. How many even prime numbers are there?

85. Find all divisors of 105.

86. Find the first five multiples of 13.

Find the prime factorization of each number in Exercises 87–89.
87. 112

88 1089

89. 2730

Use the numbers 140, 273, 105, *and* 150 *to answer the questions in Exercises 90–93.*
90. Which numbers are divisible by 2?

91 Which numbers are divisible by 3?

92. Which numbers are divisible by 5?

93. Which numbers are divisible by 10?

94. Is 50 a perfect square?

95. What is the square of 9?

96. What is the square root of 9?

97. Evaluate 6^3 without using an exponent.

98. Write $5 \cdot 5 \cdot 5 \cdot 5 \cdot 5 \cdot 5$ using an exponent.

99. Evaluate $2^3 \cdot 11^2$ without using exponents.

100. Find the prime factorization of 11,000 using exponents.

Find each square root in Exercises 101–102.

101. $\sqrt{81}$

102. $\sqrt{144}$

Perform the indicated operations in Exercises 103–108.

103. $2 - 1 + 3$ 104. $3 - 8 \div 4 + 2$ 105. $\sqrt{36} - 2$

106. $(7 - 3) \cdot 2 + 1$ 107. $(5 \cdot 4)^2$ 108. $5 \cdot 4^2$

PART II

💡*In a recent survey taken for the **MOUNTAIN CAMPUS NEWS,** published by Northern Arizona University, people were asked to give their primary reason for visiting the Grand Canyon National Park. Many went simply to sightsee, while others were interested in outdoor activities such as hiking, camping or running the Colorado River. The results of this survey are presented in the graph below. Use it to answer the questions in Exercises 109–112.*

Reasons to Visit the Grand Canyon

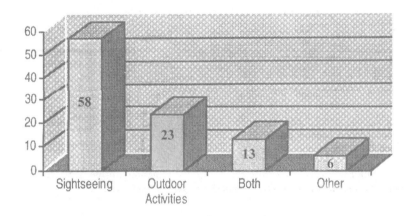

109. How many people went to sightsee or for outdoor activities or for both of these reasons?

110. How many more people went to sightsee than for outdoor activities?

111. How many people went for reasons other than sightseeing?

112. How many people were questioned in this survey?

Solve each applied problem in Exercises 113–114.

113. **SEARCH AND RESCUE**   The Harper county sheriff has 228 searchers to divide into groups of 12 each to look for a child lost in the forest. First find the approximate number of groups that she can form, and then find the exact number.

114. **POPULATION**   An average of 10,990 people live in each of 11 counties. First estimate the number of people living in these counties; then find the actual number based on these figures.

Perform the indicated operations in Exercises 115–126.

115. $\begin{array}{r} 623 \\ \times 8 \\ \hline \end{array}$ 116. $\begin{array}{r} 347 \\ 206 \\ +493 \\ \hline \end{array}$ 117. $43\overline{)1204}$ 118. $\begin{array}{r} 35{,}001 \\ -7296 \\ \hline \end{array}$

119. $28 \div 1$ 120. $0 \div 28$ 121. $28 \div 28$ 122. $8 - 5 + 6 - 2$

123. $\sqrt{81} - 2^2$ 124. $(4 - 2) \cdot 6 - 3$ 125. $3^2 \cdot 2^3$ 126. $(3 \cdot 2)^4$

💡127. What is the square of 16?

💡128. What is the square root of 16?

💡129. Is 4311 divisible by 3?

💡130. Find the prime factorization of 3234.

💡131.What is the name of the law illustrated by $5 + 11 = 11 + 5$?

💡132.We know that $8 + 0 = 8$. What is 0 called in this sentence?

133. Round 4351 to the nearest (a) ten (b) hundred (c) thousand.

134. Estimate the following sum by rounding to the nearest hundred.

$$2641$$
$$375$$
$$\underline{+1529}$$

Translate each expression in Exercises 135–138.

135. The quotient of 9 and n

136. 8 more than x

137. 11 decreased by w

138. Twice y

139. Find the area and perimeter of the rectangle with length 45 m and width 17 m.

140. Solve the equation $5x = 10$.

141. Place the appropriate symbol (< or >) between the given numbers. 9 _____ 0

142. Estimate the following difference by rounding to the nearest hundred.

$$6317$$
$$\underline{-4250}$$

143. Check by estimating the product.

$$91$$
$$\underline{\times 48}$$
$$728$$
$$\underline{364}$$
$$4368$$

144. Estimate the following product by rounding to the nearest hundred.

$$708$$
$$\underline{\times 489}$$

Solve each applied problem in Exercises 145–150.

145. **INCOME TAX** Peter's monthly gross earnings are \$2875. Suppose that \$320 are taken out for federal income tax, \$54 for state income tax, and \$75 for an IRA.
(a) What is the total taken out of his gross pay for these three items?
(b) What is Peter's take-home pay?

146. **CONSUMER** It takes 130 kilowatt-hours of electricity to operate a stereo for a year, 510 kilowatt-hours to operate a TV for a year, and 4225 kilowatt-hours to operate a spa for a year.
(a) How many kilowatt-hours are required to operate all three for a year?
(b) How many more kilowatt-hours are required to operate the spa than the other two together?

147. **SOCIAL SECURITY** The Shipps are retired and receive a Social Security payment of $491 each month. Next month they will receive an increase in benefits to $689 per month. First estimate the increase, and then find the actual increase.

148. **SPORTS** During the month of November, a basketball player scored 22, 18, 11, 27, and 13 points in five games. First estimate the total points scored in these five games, and then find the exact number of points.

149. **EDUCATION** The total enrollment in the four classes (freshmen, sophomores, juniors, and seniors) at State University is 8227. If there are 2436 freshmen, 2107 sophomores, and 1939 juniors, how many seniors are there in attendance?

150. **FARMING** On Monday, the hens at the Chicken Farm laid 4942 eggs, and on Tuesday they laid 4802 eggs. How many 12-egg cartons will be needed to hold the eggs laid on these two days?

CHAPTER 1 TEST

Answers to these exercises are given on page 643.

1. Answer *true* or *false*. The symbol < is read "is greater than."

   1. _____

2. Name the law of addition illustrated by: $(2+3)+7 = 2+(3+7)$

   2. _____

3. Consider the number line below. Place the correct symbol (< or >) between *a* and *b*, *a* __?__ *b*.

   3. _____

   ```
   <--+--+--+--+--+--+--+--+--+--+-->
      0  1  a     4           b
   ```

4. Write $300,000 + 80,000 + 400 + 7$ in standard notation.

   4. _____

5. Give the value of the digit 4 in the number 348,106.

   5. _____

6. In the number 39,725,184 which digit represents tens?

   6. _____

Find the following sums.

7. 427
   +88

8. 5139
   +4108

   7. _____

   8. _____

9. Translate the expression: 30 more than *w*

   9. _____

10. Estimate   8142   by rounding to the nearest hundred.
    650
    + 99

    10. _____

11. Bill Ewing has a pickup and a subcompact car. He figures that over the period of one year, it will cost $887 to drive the pickup to work while only $403 to drive the subcompact car. Without finding the exact savings, estimate the amount that Bill can save by driving the car.

    11. _____

Find the following differences.

12. 427
    −78

13. 502
    −295

    12. _____

    13. _____

14. Translate the expression: 5 less *m*

    14. _____

15. A bulk tanker contains 1985 gallons of fuel. Three deliveries are made, one of 295 gallons, a second of 310 gallons, and the third of 105 gallons. Without finding the exact amount, estimate the amount of fuel that remains in the tanker after the deliveries.

    15. _____

Find the following products.

16. 329
    × 4

17. 4037
    ×209

    16. _____

    17. _____

18. Solve the equation: $3x = 15$

    18. _____

19. Find the product. $100 \cdot 895$

    19. _____

CHAPTER 1 TEST

20. A car dealer has 51 cars on a lot, and each is valued at $11,150. Without finding the exact amount, estimate the total value of the cars on the lot.

20._____

Find the following quotients (and remainders).

21. $5\overline{)1180}$ 22. $23\overline{)3556}$

21._____
22._____

23. Find the value of: The quotient of 22 and 11

23._____

24. Adam Bryer bought 31 boxes of candy at a cost of $154. Find the approximate cost of 1 box of candy.

24._____

Complete the following.

25. $15 \div 15 = \underline{\ \ ?\ \ }$

25._____

26. $0 \div 15 = \underline{\ \ ?\ \ }$

26._____

27. $a \div 1 = \underline{\ \ ?\ \ }$

27._____

28. $a \div 0 = \underline{\ \ ?\ \ }$

28._____

29. Explain when a number is divisible by 3.

29._____
_____

30. Write the prime factorization of 350.

30._____

31. What is the square root of 25?

31._____

32. What is the square of 25?

32._____

Perform the indicated operations.

33. $(8 - 2) \div 3 + 7$

33._____

34. $\sqrt{49} + 5 - 2^2$

34._____

35. $(2 \cdot 3)^3$

35._____

36. $2 \cdot 3^3$

36._____

Solve.

37. Wanda bought 3 coats for $130 each, 6 shirts for $27 each, and 5 books for $14 each during a sale. How much did she spend for these items?

37._____

38. Dick wants to put carpeting costing $30 a square yard on the floor in his bedroom. If the room measures 5 yd long and 4 yd wide, how much will the carpeting cost?

38._____

39. A map has a scale of 45 miles to the inch. If two cities are actually 360 miles apart, how far apart are they on the map?

39._____

40. What length of fence is required to go all the way around a pasture that is in the shape of a rectangle which is 479 feet long and 358 feet wide?

40._____

41. Is the product of any two whole numbers always bigger than their sum?

41._____

CHAPTER *t·w·o*

MULTIPLYING AND DIVIDING FRACTIONS

The statement "God made the whole numbers, all the rest is the work of man" has been attributed to the famous mathematician Leopold Kronecker (1823-1891). Accepting this, in the present chapter we begin to consider some of the numbers that can be thought of as *the work of man*. When some whole numbers are divided by others, the quotient is again a whole number. For example, $6 \div 2 = 3$ and $20 \div 5 = 4$. In many cases, however, a whole number divided by another whole number *is not* a whole number. For example, $1 \div 2$ and $3 \div 8$ are not whole numbers. The concept of a *fraction* gives us a way to interpret quotients like these. Fractions are also used to indicate parts of various objects. This is illustrated in the following applied problem which is solved in Example 8 of Section 2.2.

SPORTS There have been seven U.S. professional boxers who have knocked out their opponent in a world title match in less than 90 seconds of the first round. They are listed below with the year the fight took place and the number of seconds their match lasted.

Boxer	Year	Time
Al McCoy	1914	45 seconds
Bobby Czyz	1986	61 seconds
Michael Dokes	1982	63 seconds
Tony Canzoneri	1930	66 seconds
Marvin Hagler	1982	67 seconds
Terry McGovern	1899	75 seconds
Al Hostak	1939	81 seconds

Source: Guiness Book of World Records

The length of one round in a boxing match is 180 seconds (3 minutes). What fraction of the first round was required for Al McCoy to knockout his opponent?

We begin this chapter by developing the concept of a fraction and introducing the ways that we can rename fractions that are equal. Next we consider the operations of multiplication and division of fractions. We then discuss the concept of a mixed number, learn how to multiply and divide mixed numbers, and finally, solve numerous applications that involve fractions and mixed numbers.

2.1 INTRODUCTION TO FRACTIONS

STUDENT GUIDEPOSTS
1   DEFINING FRACTIONS
2   CONSIDERING PROPER AND IMPROPER FRACTIONS
3   SUMMARIZING TYPES OF FRACTIONS

1   FRACTIONS

In the first chapter we looked at whole numbers. Whole numbers are used to name "whole" or entire quantities such as 3 (whole) miles, 15 (whole) dollars, or 1 (whole) day. At times, however, we may be interested in parts of a single quantity such as part of a mile, part of a dollar, or part of a day. For this, we use *fractions*.

DEFINITION OF FRACTION
A **fraction** is a number of the form $$\dfrac{a}{b}$$ (also written a/b) where a and b are whole numbers and b is not zero.

We will extend this definition of fractions in Chapter 9, where the values a and b will include positive or negative whole numbers, known as integers.

Suppose we have a bar like the one in Figure 2.1.

FIGURE 2.1

This bar may be thought of as a piece of wood, a stick of butter, a bar of candy, or any similar quantity. If the bar is divided into two equal parts, each of the parts is called a **half** of the whole bar. See Figure 2.2. This quotient is a new number, called *one half,* and is written

$$\frac{1}{2}.$$

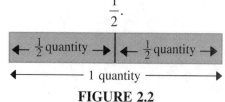

FIGURE 2.2

If we divide the bar into three equal parts as in Figure 2.3, each part is a **third** of the whole. The quotient

$$\frac{1}{3}$$

is a new number called *one third.* If the bar were a bar of candy to be split equally among 3 children, each child would receive $\frac{1}{3}$ bar. If there were 2 girls and 1 boy, the girls would receive 2 of the 3 equal parts, that is, *two thirds* of the bar. The first two shaded parts in Figure 2.3 corresponds to $\frac{2}{3}$. The number $\frac{2}{3}$, read "2 over 3" or "2 divided by 3," is a quotient of two whole numbers, 2 and 3.

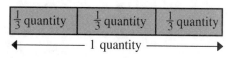

FIGURE 2.3

Any quotient of two whole numbers is called a **fraction.** The top number (the dividend) is called the **numerator** of the fraction, while the bottom number (the divisor) is called the **denominator.** In our example with the candy bar, we would have the following.

Numerator ⟶ $\frac{2}{3}$ ⟵ Number of parts the girls received
Denominator ⟶ ⟵ Bar divided into 3 equal parts

EXAMPLE 1 — FINDING A FRACTION OF A WHOLE

Leftover pie is to be divided into equal parts and served to 5 boys and 1 girl. The pie shown in Figure 2.4 has been divided into 6 equal parts $(5 + 1 = 6)$. Each part is a **sixth** of the pie, and each child receives $\frac{1}{6}$ of the pie. Since there are 5 boys, they will

receive   Numerator ⟶ 5 ⟵ Number of parts the boys receive
           Denominator ⟶ 6 ⟵ Number of equal parts of pie

of the pie. The leftover blueberry pie corresponds to this fraction, while the cherry part, $\frac{1}{6}$, corresponds to the part received by the girl.

FIGURE 2.4

EXAMPLE 2 — FINDING A FRACTION OF A WHOLE

The square in Figure 2.5 is divided into equal parts. What fraction of the square is shaded dark?

There are 4 equal parts with 3 of them shaded dark. Thus, the fraction of the square shaded dark is *three fourths,* written $\frac{3}{4}$.

FIGURE 2.5

2 — PROPER AND IMPROPER FRACTIONS

All the fractions that we have considered thus far have been *proper fractions.* A **proper fraction** is one whose numerator is less than its denominator. For example,

$$\frac{1}{2}, \frac{1}{3}, \frac{2}{3}, \frac{5}{6}, \frac{3}{4}, \frac{32}{67}, \frac{101}{102}$$

are all proper fractions. Each of these proper fractions have a value less than one.

Some fractions are not proper fractions. For example, consider the bar in Figure 2.6 that is divided into five equal parts. All five parts are shaded. In this case, the fraction of the bar which is shaded is *five fifths,* or $\frac{5}{5}$. But since the whole bar is shaded ,

$$1 = \frac{5}{5}. \quad \text{One whole = five fifths}$$

FIGURE 2.6

This agrees with what we have learned about division of whole numbers. Recall that any whole number except zero divided by itself is 1.

PRACTICE EXERCISE 1

A man divided his land as shown in the figure. If his daughter got the lightly shaded portion, what fraction of the land did she get?

Answer: $\frac{5}{8}$

PRACTICE EXERCISE 2

The dark part of the lot shown was used for a building. What fraction of the lot was used?

Answer: $\frac{1}{3}$

$$\frac{2}{2} = 1, \quad \frac{3}{3} = 1, \quad \frac{4}{4} = 1, \quad \frac{25}{25} = 1$$

The fractions above are special types of improper fractions. An **improper fraction** is one whose numerator is greater than or equal to its denominator. Other examples of improper fractions are:

$$\frac{3}{2}, \quad \frac{5}{4}, \quad \frac{7}{3}, \quad \frac{12}{12}, \quad \frac{9}{3}, \quad \frac{8}{7}.$$

Each of these improper fractions has a value greater than or equal to one. Consider the fraction $\frac{4}{3}$, read *four thirds*. Let us use as a unit the bar divided into 3 equal parts in Figure 2.7.

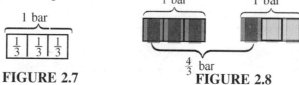

FIGURE 2.7   **FIGURE 2.8**

The question is, what fraction of the bar in Figure 2.7 is shaded dark in Figure 2.8? Four of the thirds are shaded dark, so that the dark shaded region represents $\frac{4}{3}$.

$$\frac{4}{3} \quad \begin{array}{l} \longleftarrow \quad \textbf{Number of parts shaded dark} \\ \longleftarrow \quad \textbf{Number of parts in } \textit{one } \textbf{unit} \end{array}$$

CAUTION NOTICE THAT THE UNIT IN FIGURE 2.7 IS ONE BAR DIVIDED INTO *THIRDS*. THUS THE FRACTION SHADED DARK IS
$$\frac{4}{3} \quad \text{NOT} \quad \frac{4}{6}.$$

USING AN IMPROPER FRACTION   EXAMPLE 3

Consider the bar in Figure 2.9 as one whole unit.

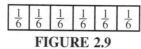

FIGURE 2.9

What fraction of the bar shown in Figure 2.9 is shaded dark in Figure 2.10? What fraction is shaded light?

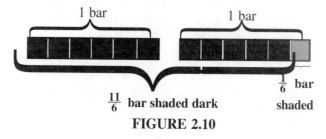

$\frac{11}{6}$ bar shaded dark $\frac{1}{6}$ bar shaded

FIGURE 2.10

Since each bar has been divided into 6 equal parts and 11 of the parts are shaded dark, this shaded portion corresponds to $\frac{11}{6}$. The light shaded part represents $\frac{1}{6}$.

Shaded dark: $\frac{11}{6}$ $\begin{array}{l} \longleftarrow \quad \textbf{Number of parts shaded dark} \\ \longleftarrow \quad \textbf{Number of parts in } \textit{one } \textbf{bar} \end{array}$

Shaded light: $\frac{1}{6}$ $\begin{array}{l} \longleftarrow \quad \textbf{Number of parts shaded light} \\ \longleftarrow \quad \textbf{Number of parts in } \textit{one } \textbf{bar} \end{array}$

PRACTICE EXERCISE 3

What fraction of the figure is shaded dark?

Answer: $\frac{5}{4}$

We have seen that the whole number 1 can be written as a fraction such as $\frac{3}{3}$. Other whole numbers can also be written as fractions. For example,

$$\frac{4}{2} = 2, \quad \frac{6}{2} = 3, \quad \frac{8}{2} = 4.$$

In each case, if the numerator is divided by the denominator, the result is a whole number. The whole number 0 can also be represented by a fraction. For example,

$$\frac{0}{5} \text{ corresponds to 0.}$$

We can interpret $\frac{0}{5}$ as dividing an object into 5 equal parts and taking none of them.

3 | TYPES OF FRACTIONS

We now summarize what we have learned about fractions below.

TYPES OF FRACTIONS

Proper fractions: $\frac{a}{b}$ where $a < b$ (b is not 0)

$\frac{4}{9}$ Numerator less than denominator

$\frac{0}{9} = 0$ Whole number zero

Improper fractions: $\frac{a}{b}$ where $a \geq b$ (b is not 0)

$\frac{9}{4}$ Numerator greater than denominator

$\frac{4}{4} = 1$ Numerator equals denominator; whole number one

$\frac{12}{4} = 3$ Whole number 3

EXAMPLE 4   FINDING A FRACTION OF A NUMBER OF OBJECTS

A dozen bottles of soda were taken to a picnic. If seven bottles were drunk, what fractional part was left?

Note that 7 of the 12 bottles are empty and 5 are full ($12 - 7 = 5$). Thus, $\frac{5}{12}$ of the original amount was left.

PRACTICE EXERCISE 4

Wendy Reed made two dozen cookies. Her son Paul ate 13 of them before dinner. What fraction of the cookies was left?

Answer: $\frac{11}{24}$

2.1 EXERCISES

Answers to these exercises are given on page 643.

Give the numerator and the denominator of each fraction in Exercises 1–4.

1. $1\frac{5}{7}$ 2. $\frac{11}{4}$ 3. $\frac{0}{8}$ 4. $\frac{12}{12}$

What fractional part of each figure is shaded in Exercises 5–13?

5.

6.

7.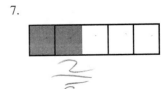

8.

9.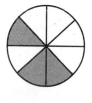

10.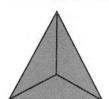

11.

12.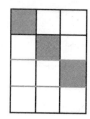

13.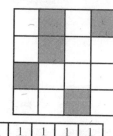

14. The bar 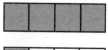 represents one whole unit. What fraction of the unit is shaded below? Consider the whole figure. There is one answer, and it is an improper fraction.

15. The figure 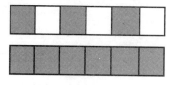 represents one whole unit. What fraction of the unit is shaded below? Consider the whole figure. There is one answer, and it is an improper fraction.

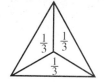

16. The circle represents one whole unit. What fraction of the unit is shaded below?

17. The triangle 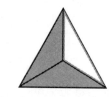 represents one whole unit. What fraction of the unit is shaded below?

 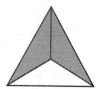

18. The numerator of the fraction $\frac{4}{7}$ stands for how many of the equal parts of a whole?

Solve each applied problem in Exercises 19–22.

19. **EDUCATION** Don Morales got 47 out of 50 points on a test.
    (a) What fractional part of the points did he get?
    (b) What fractional part of the points did he miss?

20. **SPORTS** A baseball player gets 4 hits in 9 times at bat during a double header. The number of hits is what fraction of his total at bats?

21. **CONSUMER** Two pies are each cut into 6 pieces, and each of 7 people eats one piece.
    (a) What fractional part of one pie was eaten?
    (b) What fractional part of one pie was not eaten?

22. **CONSUMER** A student received $300 from home. She spent $30 for books, $75 for a bicycle, $40 for utilities, and put the rest into savings. What fractional part of the $300 went for (a) books? (b) the bicycle? (c) utilities? (d) savings?

In Exercises 23–26, express each fraction as a whole number.

23. $\frac{12}{3}$ 4

24. $\frac{0}{5}$

25. $\frac{43}{43}$

26. $\frac{26}{13}$

CRITICAL THINKING

Let a and b represent natural numbers with $a > b$. *Tell which of the fractions in Exercises 27–28 are proper and which are improper.*

27. $\frac{b}{a}$

28. $\frac{a+b}{a-b}$

29. **ECONOMICS**   If the national debt of the United States were to be paid by individuals, the amount owed by each person would be found by dividing the debt by the population. Thus, the numerator of the fraction would be the debt and the denominator the population. Would this be a proper fraction or an improper fraction?

$$\frac{debt.}{popul.}$$

30. Discuss the applications of *proper fractions.*

REVIEW OR PREVIEW

In Section 2.2 we will discuss renaming fractions. Can you think of a simplified name for the fractions in Exercises 31–34.

31. $\frac{2}{4}$

32. $\frac{3}{6}$ $= \frac{1}{2}$

33. $\frac{2}{6}$

34. $\frac{10}{4}$

2.1 PARALLEL EXERCISES

Answers to these exercises are not given in the text.

Give the numerator and the denominator of each fraction in Exercises 1–4.

1. $\frac{9}{17}$

2. $\frac{25}{3}$

3. $\frac{7}{1}$

4. $\frac{23}{23}$

What fractional part of each figure is shaded in Exercises 5–13?

5.

6.

7.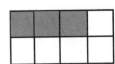

8.

9.

10.

11.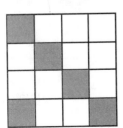

12.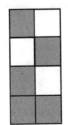

13.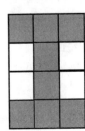

14. The square

represents one whole unit. What fraction of the unit is shaded below? Consider the whole figure. There is one answer, and it is an improper fraction.

15. The bar

represents one whole unit. What fraction of the unit is shaded below? Consider the whole figure. There is one answer, and it is an improper fraction.

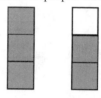

16. The circle

represents one whole unit. What fraction of the unit is shaded below?

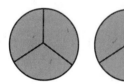

17. The bar

represents one whole unit. What fraction of the unit is shaded below?

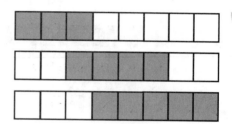

18. The numerator of the fraction $\frac{11}{7}$ stands for how many of the equal parts of a whole?

Solve each applied problem in Exercises 19–22.

19. **POLITICS**   In a local election Joe Richards got 231 of the 311 votes cast. What fractional part of the votes did Joe get?

20. **SPORTS**   A basketball player made 7 free throws in 11 attempts during the first half of a game. The number of free throws made is what fraction of his total attempts?

21. **CONSUMER**   Three pies are each cut into 6 pieces. Each of 11 people eats one piece. (a) What fractional part of one pie was eaten?   (b) What fractional part of one pie was not eaten?

22. **BANKING**   Maria Lopez had $500 in her checking account. She spent $100 for food, $125 for clothes, $50 for a night out, and put the rest in savings. What fractional part of the $500 went for (a) food? (b) clothes? (c) the night out? (d) savings?

In Exercises 23–26, express each fraction as a whole number.

23. $\dfrac{20}{4}$

24. $\dfrac{18}{1}$ = 18

25. $\dfrac{0}{101}$

26. $\dfrac{500}{500}$

CRITICAL THINKING

Let a and b represent natural numbers with $a > b$. Tell which of the fractions in Exercises 27–28 are proper and which are improper.

27. $\dfrac{a}{b}$

28. $\dfrac{2a}{a}$

29. **DEMOGRAPHY**   Suppose a fraction is formed by dividing the number of people in Montana by the number of people in California. Would this be a proper or an improper fraction?

30. Discuss the applications of *improper fractions.*

GROUP PROJECT

Collect examples of applications of fractions in newspapers and magazines. Discuss these applications in groups in order to understand how the fractions relate to the conclusions drawn by the published article. Write down any questions you have about the use of the fractions and try to answer them as you study the material in the following sections.

2.2 RENAMING FRACTIONS

STUDENT GUIDEPOSTS

1   DEFINING EQUIVALENT FRACTIONS
2   BUILDING AND REDUCING FRACTIONS
3   REDUCING TO LOWEST TERMS BY FACTORING INTO PRIMES
4   DIVIDING OUT COMMON, NONPRIME FACTORS

1 EQUIVALENT FRACTIONS

Every fraction has many names. This can be shown by the three bars in Figure 2.11. In each, exactly the same part of the bar is shaded. In **(a)**, the amount shaded is

$$\frac{1}{3} \quad \text{of the bar.}$$

In **(b)**,

$$\frac{2}{6} \quad \text{of the bar is shaded,}$$

and in **(c)**,

$$\frac{4}{12} \quad \text{of the bar is shaded.}$$

(a) $\frac{1}{3}$

(b) $\frac{1}{6}$ $\frac{1}{6}$

(c) $\frac{1}{12}$ $\frac{1}{12}$ $\frac{1}{12}$ $\frac{1}{12}$

FIGURE 2.11

Since the same part of the bar is shaded in all three cases,

$$\frac{1}{3}, \frac{2}{6}, \text{ and } \frac{4}{12}$$

are all names for the same fraction. Fractions that are names for the same number are **equivalent fractions.** Thus,

$$\frac{1}{3} = \frac{2}{6} = \frac{4}{12}.$$

Knowing that

$$\frac{2}{6} = \frac{4}{12}$$

leads us to a test for equivalent fractions. Multiply as indicated.

$$2 \cdot 12 = 24 \qquad \frac{2}{6} \diagdown \frac{4}{12} \qquad 6 \cdot 4 = 24$$

This gives the equality $2 \cdot 12 = 6 \cdot 4.$

These products are called **cross products.**

EQUIVALENT FRACTIONS

Two fractions are equivalent when the cross products are equal. This is,

$$\frac{a}{b} = \frac{c}{d} \text{ if } ad = bc.$$

We can use this to test for equivalence of any two fractions.

PRACTICE EXERCISE 1

Are the two fractions equivalent?

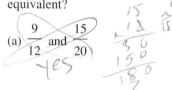

(a) $\dfrac{9}{12}$ and $\dfrac{15}{20}$

(b) $\dfrac{20}{50}$ and $\dfrac{16}{40}$

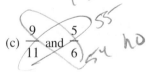

(c) $\dfrac{9}{11}$ and $\dfrac{5}{6}$

Answers: (a) yes (b) yes (c) no

TESTING FOR EQUIVALENCE   EXAMPLE 1

Are the two fractions equivalent?

(a) $\dfrac{3}{4}$ and $\dfrac{6}{8}$ $3 \cdot 8 = 24 \quad \dfrac{3}{4} \diagdown \dfrac{6}{8} \quad 4 \cdot 6 = 24$

Thus, $\dfrac{3}{4} = \dfrac{6}{8}.$

(b) $\dfrac{2}{9}$ and $\dfrac{6}{27}$ Since $2 \cdot 27 = 54$ and $9 \cdot 6 = 54,$

$$\frac{2}{9} = \frac{6}{27}.$$

(c) $\dfrac{5}{9}$ and $\dfrac{4}{7}$ Since $5 \cdot 7 = 35$ and $9 \cdot 4 = 36,$

$$\frac{5}{9} \neq \frac{4}{7}.$$

---

2 | BUILDING AND REDUCING FRACTIONS

You probably noticed that equivalent fractions are related in another way besides having equal cross products. For example, multiplying both the numerator and denominator of $\frac{1}{3}$ by 2 gives $\frac{2}{6}$.

$$\frac{1 \times 2}{3 \times 2} = \frac{2}{6}$$

Similarly, multiplying both the numerator and denominator of $\frac{1}{3}$ by 4 gives $\frac{4}{12}$.

$$\frac{1 \times 4}{3 \times 4} = \frac{4}{12}$$

These are examples of the Fundamental Principle of Fractions that is used to build and reduce fractions.

BUILDING FRACTIONS

If both the numerator and denominator of a fraction are *multiplied* by the same number (not 0) an equivalent fraction is formed. That is,

$$\frac{a}{b} = \frac{a \cdot c}{b \cdot c}.$$

EXAMPLE 2 BUILDING FRACTIONS

(a) Find a fraction with denominator 20 that is equivalent to $\frac{1}{4}$.

We are looking for a fraction of the form $\frac{a}{20}$ such that $\frac{1}{4} = \frac{a}{20}$.

To build an equivalent fraction, the numerator and denominator of $\frac{1}{4}$ must be multiplied by the *same* number. To get 20 for a denominator, that number a must be 5, since $4 \times 5 = 20$.

$$\frac{1}{4} = \frac{1 \times 5}{4 \times 5} = \frac{5}{20}$$

(b) Find a fraction with numerator 18 that is equivalent to $\frac{3}{2}$.

Find $\frac{18}{a}$ such that $\frac{3}{2} = \frac{18}{a}$.

What number multiplied by 3 gives 18? That number is 6, so $a = 2 \cdot 6 = 12$.

$$\frac{3}{2} = \frac{3 \times 6}{2 \times 6} = \frac{18}{12}$$

The reverse of building fractions is *reducing fractions*. Starting with the fraction $\frac{5}{20}$ and dividing both the numerator and the denominator by 5 gives

$$\frac{5 \div 5}{20 \div 5} = \frac{1}{4},$$

which is equivalent to $\frac{5}{20}$. This is an example of the following.

REDUCING FRACTIONS

If both the numerator and denominator of a fraction are *divided* by the same number (not 0) an equivalent fraction is formed. That is,

$$\frac{a}{b} = \frac{a \div c}{b \div c}.$$

EXAMPLE 3 REDUCING FRACTIONS

(a) Find a fraction with denominator 3 that is equal to $\frac{14}{21}$.

We are looking for a fraction of the form $\frac{a}{3}$ such that $\frac{14}{21} = \frac{a}{3}$.

To get an equivalent fraction, the numerator and denominator of $\frac{14}{21}$ must be divided by the *same* number. To get 3 for a denominator, that number must be 7, since $21 \div 7 = 3 \cdot$

$$\frac{14}{21} = \frac{14 \div 7}{21 \div 7} = \frac{2}{3}$$

Thus, $a = 2$.

(b) Find a fraction with numerator 2 that is equivalent to $\frac{22}{11}$.

Find $\frac{2}{a}$ such that $\frac{22}{11} = \frac{2}{a}$.

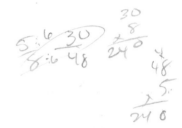
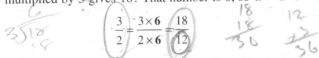

Divide numerator and denominator by 11, because $22 \div 11 = 2$.

$$\frac{22}{11} = \frac{22 \div \mathbf{11}}{11 \div \mathbf{11}} = \frac{2}{1}$$

Notice that this fraction is really the whole number 2, and $a = 1$.

EXPLORATION GUIDE

Over the next week take note of the use of fractions that are not reduced to lowest terms. Reduce each one and compare it to the original fraction. Can you decide why the one who originally used the fraction chose not to reduce it?

3 REDUCING TO LOWEST TERMS BY FACTORING INTO PRIMES

We have seen that every fraction has many names. For example, the fraction $\frac{1}{4}$ can be expressed as $\frac{1}{4}$, $\frac{2}{8}$, $\frac{3}{12}$, $\frac{4}{16}$, $\frac{5}{20}$, and so on.

In this list, every fraction to the right of $\frac{1}{4}$ has been *built up* from $\frac{1}{4}$ by multiplying numerator and denominator by some number. On the other hand, $\frac{1}{4}$ can be obtained by *reducing* each fraction to the right of it, by dividing numerator and denominator by some number.

Of all the possible names for the fraction $\frac{1}{4}$, 1 and 4 are the *smallest* numbers we can use in the name. In a sense, $\frac{1}{4}$ is the best name for the number since it cannot be reduced.

REDUCED TO LOWEST TERMS
When 1 is the only nonzero whole number divisor of both the numerator and denominator of a fraction, the fraction is **reduced to lowest terms.**

Notice that $\frac{2}{8}$ is not in lowest terms since 2 is a divisor of 2 and 8,

$\frac{3}{12}$ is not in lowest terms since 3 is a divisor of 3 and 12.

However, $\frac{1}{4}$ is in lowest terms since 1 is the only divisor of 1 and 4.

Reducing a fraction to lowest terms is simplified by using prime numbers. Recall from Section 1.9 that a whole number greater than 1 is *prime* if its only divisors are itself and 1. Also, recall that every whole number greater than 1 is either prime or can be expressed as a product of primes.

TO REDUCE A FRACTION TO LOWEST TERMS
1. Factor the numerator and denominator into primes.
2. Divide out all prime factors common to both the numerator and denominator.
3. Multiply remaining primes, first in the numerator and then in the denominator.

PRACTICE EXERCISE 4

Reduce $\frac{10}{25}$ to lowest terms.

Answer: $\frac{2}{5}$

REDUCING TO LOWEST TERMS   EXAMPLE 4

Reduce $\frac{4}{6}$ to lowest terms.

Factor the numerator and denominator into primes. $\frac{4}{6} = \frac{2 \cdot 2}{3 \cdot 2}$

Since 2 is a prime factor common to both the numerator and denominator, divide it out of both, giving an equivalent fraction.

$$\frac{(2 \cdot 2) \div \mathbf{2}}{(3 \cdot 2) \div \mathbf{2}} = \frac{2 \cdot (2 \div 2)}{3 \cdot (2 \div 2)}$$

$$= \frac{2 \cdot \mathbf{1}}{3 \cdot \mathbf{1}} = \frac{2}{3} \qquad \text{A number divided by itself equals 1}$$

A shorthand way of writing this division is by simply crossing out the common factors.

$$\frac{4}{6} = \frac{2 \cdot \overset{1}{\cancel{2}}}{3 \cdot \underset{1}{\cancel{2}}} = \frac{2 \cdot 1}{3 \cdot 1} = \frac{2}{3}$$

> **NOTE**   Notice that we inserted small "ones" in our work in Example 4. It is important to get in the habit of writing them so that you will not make mistakes when reducing fractions such as the following:
>
> $$\frac{3}{15} = \frac{\overset{1}{\cancel{3}}}{5 \cdot \underset{1}{\cancel{3}}} = \frac{1}{5}.$$
>
> Failure to write the 1s could lead you to the answer $\frac{0}{5}$ or 0, which is wrong.

The process of dividing out common factors by crossing them out, as shown in Example 4 and in the following examples, is sometimes called *canceling factors*. However, we will use the words *divide out*.

EXAMPLE 5   DIVIDING OUT COMMON PRIME FACTORS

Reduce to lowest terms by factoring into primes.

(a) $\dfrac{12}{42} = \dfrac{2 \cdot 2 \cdot 3}{2 \cdot 3 \cdot 7}$ Factor numerator and denominator into primes

$= \dfrac{2 \cdot 2 \cdot \overset{1}{\cancel{3}}}{\underset{1}{\cancel{2}} \cdot \underset{1}{\cancel{3}} \cdot 7}$ Divide out common prime factors 2 and 3

$= \dfrac{2}{7}$

(b) $\dfrac{5}{20} = \dfrac{5}{2 \cdot 2 \cdot 5}$ Factor numerator and denominator into primes

$= \dfrac{\overset{1}{\cancel{5}}}{2 \cdot 2 \cdot \underset{1}{\cancel{5}}}$ Divide out common prime factor 5

$= \dfrac{1}{4}$ Multiply remaining factors in the denominator

Remember to write the small 1s to avoid getting the wrong answer $\frac{0}{4}$ or 0.

(c) $\dfrac{210}{273} = \dfrac{2 \cdot \overset{1}{\cancel{3}} \cdot 5 \cdot \overset{1}{\cancel{7}}}{\underset{1}{\cancel{3}} \cdot \underset{1}{\cancel{7}} \cdot 13} = \dfrac{2 \cdot 5}{13} = \dfrac{10}{13}$

4   DIVIDING OUT COMMON, NONPRIME FACTORS

In Example 5 (a) we could have noticed that 6 was a factor of both the numerator and denominator and written $\dfrac{12}{42} = \dfrac{2 \cdot 6}{7 \cdot 6} = \dfrac{2 \cdot \overset{1}{\cancel{6}}}{7 \cdot \underset{1}{\cancel{6}}} = \dfrac{2}{7}.$

This technique does not require factoring into primes and can sometimes save a few steps.

PRACTICE EXERCISE 5

Reduce to lowest terms by factoring into primes.

(a) $\dfrac{98}{63}$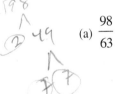

(b) $\dfrac{7}{35}$

(c) $\dfrac{330}{70}$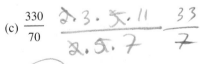

Answers: (a) $\frac{14}{9}$ (b) $\frac{1}{5}$ (c) $\frac{3}{7}$

Reduce to lowest terms.

(a) $\dfrac{5}{40}$

(b) $\dfrac{18}{63}$

(c) $\dfrac{20}{150}$

Answers:

(a) $\dfrac{1}{8}$ (b) $\dfrac{2}{7}$ (c) $\dfrac{2}{15}$

DIVIDING OUT COMMON, NONPRIME FACTORS — EXAMPLE 6

Reduce to lowest terms.

(a) $\dfrac{4}{20} = \dfrac{\cancel{4}}{5 \cdot \cancel{4}} = \dfrac{1}{5}$ (b) $\dfrac{16}{40} = \dfrac{2 \cdot \cancel{8}}{5 \cdot \cancel{8}} = \dfrac{2}{5}$ (c) $\dfrac{36}{120} = \dfrac{3 \cdot \cancel{12}}{10 \cdot \cancel{12}} = \dfrac{3}{10}$

> **CAUTION** When reducing fractions by dividing out common, nonprime factors, be sure to reduce the fraction to <u>lowest</u> <u>terms</u>. For example, in Example 6 (b), had we only divided out the common factor 4,
>
> $$\frac{16}{40} = \frac{4 \cdot \overset{1}{\cancel{4}}}{10 \cdot \underset{1}{\cancel{4}}} = \frac{4}{10}.$$
>
> we would not be finished since the fraction is not yet in lowest terms.

Before continuing, you should review the divisibility tests for 2, 3, 5, and 10 in Chapter 1. Reducing fractions can be simplified by using these tests.

SOLVING AN APPLICATION IN EDUCATION — EXAMPLE 7

On a math test, Marvin got 60 correct out of 80 problems. On his history test, he got 75 correct out of 100 problems. What fractional part of each test did he get correct? Compare Marvin's performance on the two tests.

On the math test, 60 correct out of 80 problems results in $\frac{60}{80}$ of the problems being correct. On the history test, he had $\frac{75}{100}$ correct. But

$$60 \cdot 100 = 6000 = 80 \cdot 75$$

Thus,

$$\frac{60}{80} = \frac{75}{100}$$

since the cross-products are equal. Also, note that each fraction reduces to $\frac{3}{4}$. Thus, Marvin performed the same on the two tests.

We now solve the application given in the chapter introduction.

Nina had 21 correct out of 30 on a math placement test and 70 out of 100 on an English test. What fractional part of each test did she get correct? Compare Nina's performance on the two placement tests.

Answer:

Math, $\frac{7}{10}$; English, $\frac{7}{10}$; she scored the same on both tests.

Use the data in Example 8 to determine what fraction of the first round *remained* when Terry McGovern knocked out his opponent.

Answer: 105/180 which reduces to 7/12 of the round remained.

FINDING FRACTIONS IN A SPORTS APPLICATION — EXAMPLE 8

There have been seven U.S. professional boxers who have knocked out their opponent in a world title match in less than 90 seconds of the first round. They are listed below with the year the fight took place and the number of seconds their match lasted.

Boxer	Year	Time
Al McCoy	1914	45 seconds
Bobby Czyz	1986	61 seconds
Michael Dokes	1982	63 seconds
Tony Canzoneri	1930	66 seconds
Marvin Hagler	1982	67 seconds
Terry McGovern	1899	75 seconds
Al Hostak	1939	81 seconds

Source: Guiness Book of World Records

The length of one round in a boxing match is 180 seconds (3 min). What fraction of the first round was required for Al McCoy to knock out his opponent?

Since the match lasted 45 seconds out of the usual 180 seconds, the fraction 45/180 represents the fraction of the first round that the match required. We can reduce the fraction as follows:

$$\frac{45}{180} = \frac{1 \cdot 45}{4 \cdot 45} = \frac{1}{4}$$

Thus, it took only $\frac{1}{4}$ of the first round for the fight to be over.

2.2 EXERCISES

Answers to these exercises are given on page 643.

The shaded portions of the bars in each of Exercises 1–2 illustrate which fractions are equivalent?

1. 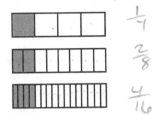 $\frac{1}{4}$

$\frac{2}{8}$

$\frac{4}{16}$

2. 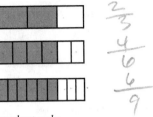 $\frac{2}{3}$

$\frac{4}{6}$

$\frac{6}{9}$

In Exercises 3–8, decide which fractions are equivalent by using the cross-product rule.

3. $\frac{9}{12}$ and $\frac{3}{4}$

4. $\frac{2}{5}$ and $\frac{3}{7}$

5. $\frac{6}{16}$ and $\frac{3}{8}$

6. $\frac{6}{8}$ and $\frac{3}{2}$

7. $\frac{12}{32}$ and $\frac{4}{11}$

8. $\frac{8}{9}$ and $\frac{96}{108}$

In Exercises 9–17, find the numerator of the new fraction having the given denominator.

9. $\frac{3}{4} = \frac{a}{12}$

10. $\frac{3}{2} = \frac{a}{6}$

11. $\frac{1}{2} = \frac{a}{22}$

12. $\frac{5}{8} = \frac{a}{16}$

13. $\frac{9}{18} = \frac{a}{6}$

14. $\frac{5}{20} = \frac{a}{4}$

15. $\frac{20}{18} = \frac{a}{9}$

16. $\frac{8}{12} = \frac{a}{3}$

17. $\frac{6}{18} = \frac{a}{3}$

In Exercises 18–23, find the denominator of the new fraction having the given numerator.

18. $\frac{2}{7} = \frac{4}{a}$

19. $\frac{1}{9} = \frac{3}{a}$

20. $\frac{3}{5} = \frac{9}{a}$

21. $\frac{12}{20} = \frac{3}{a}$

22. $\frac{9}{2} = \frac{27}{a}$

23. $\frac{36}{14} = \frac{18}{a}$

In Exercises 24–32, reduce each fraction to lowest terms.

24. $\frac{4}{10}$

25. $\frac{15}{10}$

26. $\frac{6}{18}$

27. $\frac{16}{8}$

28. $\frac{39}{52}$

29. $\frac{12}{30}$

30. $\frac{121}{22}$

31. $\frac{210}{105}$

32. $\frac{42}{18}$

Solve each applied problem in Exercises 33–34.

33. **ENVIRONMENT**   In an environmental study of Lake Blue 16 of the 216 samples taken showed some toxins. In a similar study on Lake Green 10 of 135 samples showed toxins. Compute the fractional part of each sample showing toxins and compare the two.

34. **BUSINESS**   During May, one scientific equipment dealer sold 21 microscopes from his inventory of 77 microscopes. A second dealer sold 18 microscopes from his inventory of 66 microscopes. Compute the fractional part of each dealer's stock sold and compare the two.

Use the graph to answer the questions in Exercises 35–37. Reduce each fraction requested.

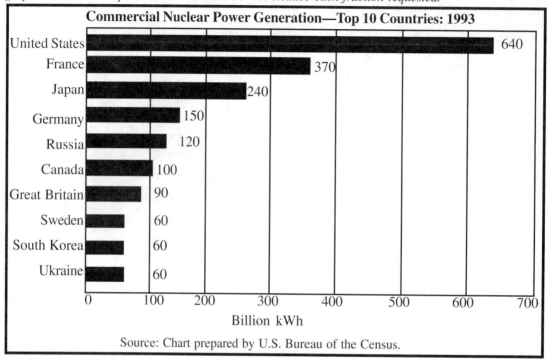

Commercial Nuclear Power Generation—Top 10 Countries: 1993

Source: Chart prepared by U.S. Bureau of the Census.

35. Find a fraction that compares the power generated by Germany to that of Russia by dividing the German production by the Russian production.

36. Find a fraction that compares the power generated by Great Britain to the total power generated by Sweden, South Korea, and the Ukraine.

37. Find a fraction that compares the power generated by the United States to the total power generated by all ten countries.

CRITICAL THINKING

Let a and b represent natural numbers. Reduce each fraction in Exercises 38–40 to lowest terms.

38. $\dfrac{3^3 4^2}{3^2 4}$

39. $\dfrac{27a^3}{81a^7}$

40. $\dfrac{5a^3 b^4}{10a^2 b^6}$

41. Give reasons why multiplying numerator and denominator of a fraction by the same whole number gives an equivalent fraction. By considering multiplying fractions in the next section you may be able to give a more complete discussion.

42. Burford knew that if he multiplied numerator and denominator of a fraction by the same number that he would get an equivalent fraction. Here is his work. $\dfrac{2}{3} = \dfrac{2 \cdot 0}{3 \cdot 0} = \dfrac{0}{0} = 1$

Burford knew that $2/3$ was not 1. Tell him what he did wrong.

REVIEW OR PREVIEW

What fractional part of each figure is shaded in Exercises 43–44?

43.   44.

Express each fraction as a whole number in Exercises 45–48.

45. $\dfrac{17}{17}$ 46. $\dfrac{0}{99}$ 47. $\dfrac{100}{5}$ 48. $\dfrac{84}{12}$

2.2 PARALLEL EXERCISES

Answers to these exercises are not given in the text.

The shaded portions of the bars in each of Exercises 1–2 illustrate which fractions are equivalent?

1. 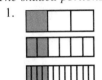   2.

In Exercises 3–8, decide which fractions are equivalent by using the cross-product rule.

3. $\dfrac{7}{8}$ and $\dfrac{21}{24}$ 4. $\dfrac{5}{12}$ and $\dfrac{6}{13}$ 65   5. $\dfrac{9}{6}$ and $\dfrac{18}{12}$

6. $\dfrac{13}{15}$ and $\dfrac{27}{30}$ 7. $\dfrac{11}{12}$ and $\dfrac{132}{144}$ 8. $\dfrac{4}{5}$ and $\dfrac{400}{500}$  2000 2000

In Exercises 9–17, find the numerator of the new fraction having the given denominator.

9. $\dfrac{3}{8} = \dfrac{a}{24}$ 10. $\dfrac{9}{7} = \dfrac{a}{35}$ 11. $\dfrac{1}{11} = \dfrac{a}{55}$

12. $\dfrac{a}{5} = \dfrac{8}{20}$ 13. $\dfrac{4}{12} = \dfrac{a}{3}$ 14. $\dfrac{21}{14} = \dfrac{a}{2}$

15. $\dfrac{25}{75} = \dfrac{a}{3}$ 16. $\dfrac{15}{12} = \dfrac{a}{4}$ 17. $\dfrac{100}{500} = \dfrac{a}{5}$

In Exercises 18–23, find the denominator of the new fraction having the given numerator.

18. $\dfrac{6}{a} = \dfrac{12}{10}$ 6×2 = 12   10÷2=5   19. $\dfrac{4}{a} = \dfrac{24}{18}$ 20. $\dfrac{28}{4} = \dfrac{7}{a}$

21. $\dfrac{25}{15} = \dfrac{5}{a}$ 22. $\dfrac{36}{24} = \dfrac{6}{a}$ 4   23. $\dfrac{100}{20} = \dfrac{5}{a}$

In Exercises 24–32, reduce each fraction to lowest terms.

24. $\dfrac{9}{18}$ ÷3 = $\dfrac{3}{6}$ ÷3 = $\dfrac{1}{3}$ 25. $\dfrac{24}{16}$ 26. $\dfrac{20}{4}$ 27. $\dfrac{36}{48}$ 28. $\dfrac{24}{60}$

29. $\dfrac{14}{126}$ 30. $\dfrac{55}{33}$ 31. $\dfrac{42}{6}$ 32. $\dfrac{96}{528}$

Solve each applied problem in Exercises 33–34.

33. **BUSINESS** In one shipment of tires 4 of the 200 were defective. The next shipment of 700 tires contained 14 that were defective. Compute the fraction of defective tires in each shipment and compare the two.

34. **POLITICS** In June a poll showed that 25 of 30 people surveyed favored the new freeway. The next month 55 of 66 people favored the freeway. Compute the fraction favoring the freeway in each survey and compare the two.

Use the bar graph from Exercises 35–37 on page 136 to answer the following. Reduce each fraction requested.

35. Find a fraction that compares the power generated by Germany to that of Canada by dividing the German production by the Canada production.

36. Find a fraction that compares the power generated by Great Britain to the total power generated by Germany and Russia.

37. Find the fraction that compares the power generated by Japan to the total power generated by all ten countries.

CRITICAL THINKING

Let a and b represent natural numbers. Reduce each fraction in Exercises 38–40 to lowest terms?

38. $\dfrac{5^4 a^2}{5^2 a}$

39. $\dfrac{6a^2 b^3}{6ab}$

40. $\dfrac{42a^4 b^2}{14ab^3}$

41. Discuss the need for renaming fractions.

42. Burford knew that he could simplify fractions by dividing out common factors. Here is his work.

$$\frac{4}{12} = \frac{4}{3 \cdot 4} = \frac{0}{3} = 0$$

Burford knew that $4/12$ was not equal to 0. Tell him what he did wrong.

GROUP PROJECT

Collect data similar to that used in Example 8 and in Exercises 35–37. Discuss the meaning of the data and try to relate different values by forming fractions for comparisons. Does reducing the fraction always help you better understand the relationship between data points?

2.3 MULTIPLYING FRACTIONS

STUDENT GUIDEPOSTS

1　MEANING OF MULTIPLICATION OF FRACTIONS
2　LEARNING THE RULE FOR MULTIPLYING FRACTIONS
3　LEARNING THE PROPERTIES OF MULTIPLICATION
4　WORKING WITH POWERS AND ROOTS OF FRACTIONS

1　MEANING OF MULTIPLICATION OF FRACTIONS

The simplest arithmetic operation on fractions is multiplication. Notice that the word *of* after a fraction means "times."

What is one half of 8?

Obviously, half of 8 is 4. Let us multiply $\frac{1}{2}$ times 8 as follows.

$$\frac{1}{2} \cdot 8 = \frac{1}{2} \cdot \frac{8}{1} \qquad \text{Write 8 as the faction } \frac{8}{1}$$

$$= \frac{1 \cdot 8}{2 \cdot 1} \qquad \begin{array}{l}\text{Multiply numerators}\\ \text{Multiply denominators}\end{array}$$

$$= \frac{8}{2} \qquad \text{Divide result}$$

$$= 4$$

The final answer is 4, which agrees with our intuitive notion of $\frac{1}{2}$ of 8.

Suppose we look at a second example and find the product of $\frac{1}{2}$ and $\frac{1}{3}$. The shaded part of the bar in Figure 2.12 corresponds to the fraction $\frac{1}{3}$. If we multiply $\frac{1}{2} \cdot \frac{1}{3}$, we recognize this as $\dfrac{1}{2}$ of $\dfrac{1}{3}$.

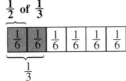

FIGURE 2.12   **FIGURE 2.13**

Just as we found $\frac{1}{2}$ of 8 (which we recognized as 4), suppose we find $\frac{1}{2}$ of $\frac{1}{3}$ by taking one half of the shaded part in Figure 2.12. Figure 2.13 shows that

$$\frac{1}{2} \text{ of } \frac{1}{3} \text{ is equal to } \frac{1}{6}.$$

Finding the product of $\frac{1}{2}$ and $\frac{1}{3}$ by multiplying numerators, multiplying denominators, and dividing the results gives the same answer.

$$\frac{1}{2} \cdot \frac{1}{3} = \frac{1 \cdot 1}{2 \cdot 3} = \frac{1}{6}$$

Thus, we can define **multiplication of fractions** as follows:

$$\frac{a}{b} \cdot \frac{c}{d} = \frac{a \cdot c}{b \cdot d}.$$

EXAMPLE 1   MULTIPLYING FRACTIONS

Find each product.

(a) $\dfrac{1}{3} \cdot \dfrac{1}{7} = \dfrac{1 \cdot 1}{3 \cdot 7} = \dfrac{1}{21}$ Multiply numerators, multiply denominators, and divide the products

(b) $\dfrac{2}{3} \cdot \dfrac{5}{9} = \dfrac{2 \cdot 5}{3 \cdot 9} = \dfrac{10}{27}$

2   RULE FOR MULTIPLYING FRACTIONS

In Example 1, we multiplied fractions by first multiplying the numerators, then multiplying the denominators, and then dividing the numerators' product by the denominators' product. For example, $\dfrac{3}{8} \cdot \dfrac{4}{5} = \dfrac{3 \cdot 4}{8 \cdot 5} = \dfrac{12}{40}$.

We know from Section 2.2 that to reduce $\frac{12}{40}$ to lowest terms, we need to factor both the numerator and the denominator into primes and divide out common prime factors.

$$\frac{12}{40} = \frac{\overset{1}{\cancel{2}} \cdot \overset{1}{\cancel{2}} \cdot 3}{\underset{1}{\cancel{2}} \cdot \underset{1}{\cancel{2}} \cdot 2 \cdot 5} = \frac{3}{10}$$

Multiplying and then reducing fractions can be time consuming. To reduce the number of steps, and thus have less chance of making an error, use the following rule.

To Multiply Two (or More) Fractions
1. Factor all numerators and denominators into primes.
2. Place all numerator factors over all denominator factors.
3. Divide out all prime factors common to both the numerator and denominator.
4. Multiply the remaining primes, first in the numerator, and then in the denominator.

EXPLORATION GUIDE

The definition of multiplication of fractions says that we multiply numerators and multiply denominators. Would you classify the rule given here as a shortcut, a trick, or something else? Write a short paragraph describing this rule and what it accomplishes.

If we return to the original example of $\frac{3}{8} \cdot \frac{4}{5}$ and use these rules, we get

$$\frac{3}{8} \cdot \frac{4}{5} = \frac{3}{2 \cdot 2 \cdot 2} \cdot \frac{2 \cdot 2}{5} = \frac{3 \cdot \cancel{2} \cdot \cancel{2}}{\cancel{2} \cdot \cancel{2} \cdot 2 \cdot 5} = \frac{3}{10}.$$

This gives us the same answer we obtained above, but has fewer steps. Notice that we could have divided out the common nonprime factor of 4 to shorten our work even further.

$$\frac{3}{8} \cdot \frac{4}{5} = \frac{3 \cdot \cancel{4}^{1}}{\cancel{8}_{2} \cdot 5} = \frac{3 \cdot 1}{2 \cdot 5} = \frac{3}{10}$$

PRACTICE EXERCISE 2

Find each product.

(a) $\dfrac{3}{10} \cdot \dfrac{5}{6}$

(b) $\dfrac{8}{13} \cdot 39$

(c) $\dfrac{7}{18} \cdot \dfrac{9}{2}$

Answers: (a) $\frac{1}{4}$ (b) 24 (c) $\frac{7}{4}$

MULTIPLYING FRACTIONS   EXAMPLE 2

Find each product.

(a) $\dfrac{2}{9} \cdot \dfrac{3}{4} = \dfrac{2}{3 \cdot 3} \cdot \dfrac{3}{2 \cdot 2}$ Factor into primes

$= \dfrac{\cancel{2} \cdot \cancel{3}}{3 \cdot \cancel{3} \cdot \cancel{2} \cdot 2}$ Put all numerator factors over all denominator factors and divide out common prime factors

$= \dfrac{1}{3 \cdot 2}$ Remember that the numerator is 1, not 0

$= \dfrac{1}{6}$

(b) $\dfrac{2}{7} \cdot 14 = \dfrac{2}{7} \cdot \dfrac{14}{1}$ Write 14 as the fraction $\frac{14}{1}$

$= \dfrac{2}{7} \cdot \dfrac{2 \cdot 7}{1}$ Factor

$= \dfrac{2 \cdot 2 \cdot \cancel{7}}{\cancel{7} \cdot 1}$ Indicate product and divide out 7

$= \dfrac{4}{1} = 4$

(c) $\dfrac{2}{15} \cdot \dfrac{3}{5} = \dfrac{2}{3 \cdot 5} \cdot \dfrac{3}{5} = \dfrac{2 \cdot \cancel{3}}{\cancel{3} \cdot 5 \cdot 5} = \dfrac{2}{25}$

By recognizing that 15 divided by 3 is 5, we can shorten our work as follows.

$$\frac{2}{\cancel{15}_{5}} \cdot \frac{\cancel{3}}{5} = \frac{2}{5 \cdot 5} = \frac{2}{25}$$

EXPLORATION GUIDE

In Section 2.2 we said that multiplying or dividing the numerator and denominator of a fraction by the same number gave an equivalent fraction. Can you use the fact that 1 is the multiplicative identity for fractions to tell why this works?

---

3   PROPERTIES OF MULTIPLICATION

Multiplication of fractions has the same properties as multiplication of whole numbers. The **commutative law of multiplication** states that changing the order of a product does not change the result. That is, if a and b are fractions,

$$a \cdot b = b \cdot a.$$

The **associative law of multiplication** states that regrouping products does not change the result. That is, if a, b, and c are fractions,

$$(a \cdot b) \cdot c = a \cdot (b \cdot c).$$

The number 1, written as $\frac{1}{1}$, is the **multiplicative identity**, since we can multiply any fraction by 1 and obtain that same fraction. If a is a fraction not 0,

$$1 \cdot a = a \cdot 1 = a.$$

The associative law allows us to multiply three fractions without using parentheses.

EXAMPLE 3 **MULTIPLYING THREE FRACTIONS**

Find the product of $\frac{4}{9}$, $\frac{3}{14}$, and $\frac{7}{6}$.

$$\frac{4}{9} \cdot \frac{3}{14} \cdot \frac{7}{6} = \frac{2 \cdot 2}{3 \cdot 3} \cdot \frac{3}{2 \cdot 7} \cdot \frac{7}{2 \cdot 3}$$ Factor all numerators and denominators into primes

$$= \frac{2 \cdot 2 \cdot 3 \cdot 7}{3 \cdot 3 \cdot 2 \cdot 7 \cdot 2 \cdot 3}$$ Indicate products and divide out common prime factors

$$= \frac{1}{3 \cdot 3}$$ Remember that the numerator is 1

$$= \frac{1}{9}$$

PRACTICE EXERCISE 3

Find the product of $\frac{7}{5}$, $\frac{10}{21}$, and $\frac{3}{8}$.

Answer: $\frac{1}{4}$

4 POWERS AND ROOTS OF FRACTIONS

In Section 1.9 we studied powers and roots of whole numbers. We can find powers and roots of fractions in a similar manner.

EXAMPLE 4 **FINDING POWERS OF FRACTIONS**

Find the value of each power.   ⌐→ **Two $\frac{2}{3}$ s**

(a) $\left(\frac{2}{3}\right)^2 = \frac{2}{3} \cdot \frac{2}{3} = \frac{2 \cdot 2}{3 \cdot 3} = \frac{4}{9}$

(b) $\left(\frac{5}{4}\right)^2 = \frac{5}{4} \cdot \frac{5}{4} = \frac{5 \cdot 5}{4 \cdot 4} = \frac{25}{16}$

PRACTICE EXERCISE 4

Find the value of each power.

(a) $\left(\frac{5}{7}\right)^2$ (b) $\left(\frac{8}{3}\right)^2$

Answers: (a) $\frac{25}{49}$ (b) $\frac{64}{9}$

EXAMPLE 5 **FINDING ROOTS OF FRACTIONS**

Find the value of each radical expression.

(a) $\sqrt{\frac{4}{9}}$ Since $\frac{2}{3} \cdot \frac{2}{3} = \frac{4}{9}$, $\sqrt{\frac{4}{9}} = \frac{2}{3}$. $\frac{2}{3}$ is a square root of $\frac{4}{9}$

(b) $\sqrt{\frac{121}{25}}$ Since $\frac{11}{5} \cdot \frac{11}{5} = \frac{121}{25}$, $\sqrt{\frac{121}{25}} = \frac{11}{5}$.

Many word problems involve finding products of fractions.

PRACTICE EXERCISE 5

Find the value of each radical expressions.

(a) $\sqrt{\frac{25}{16}}$ (b) $\sqrt{\frac{144}{49}}$

Answers: (a) $\frac{5}{4}$ (b) $\frac{12}{7}$

EXAMPLE 6 **FINDING AN AREA**

A farmer has a plot of land in the form of a rectangle $\frac{1}{3}$ mi wide and $\frac{7}{8}$ mi long. What is the area of the parcel of land?

First, make a sketch of the information as in Figure 2.14. Recall that the area of a rectangle is the length times the width.

PRACTICE EXERCISE 6

A picture is $\frac{3}{4}$ yd wide and $\frac{10}{7}$ yd long. What is the area of the picture?

$\frac{1}{3}$ mi $\frac{7}{8}$ mi

FIGURE 2.14

$$\text{Area} = \frac{7}{8} \cdot \frac{1}{3} = \frac{7}{2 \cdot 2 \cdot 2} \cdot \frac{1}{3}$$

$$= \frac{7 \cdot 1}{2 \cdot 2 \cdot 2 \cdot 3} = \frac{7}{24}$$

Thus, the area of the land is $\frac{7}{24}$ square miles. Figure 2.15 shows how this answer can be interpreted.

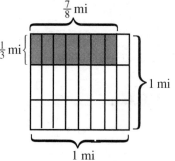

FIGURE 2.15

Notice that 1 square mile has been divided into 24 equal parts and that 7 of these parts, or $\frac{7}{24}$ of one square mile, corresponds to the area of the parcel of land.

Answer: $\frac{15}{14}$ sq yd

PRACTICE EXERCISE 7

If a large loaf of bread weighs 3 pounds, how much would $\frac{2}{3}$ of a loaf weigh?

READING A MAP   **EXAMPLE 7**

On a map, 1 inch represents 32 miles. How many miles does $\frac{3}{4}$ of an inch represent?

Find $\frac{3}{4}$ of 32 miles. Used in this way *of* means *multiply*.

$$\frac{3}{4} \text{ of } 32$$
$$\downarrow \downarrow \downarrow$$

$$\frac{3}{4} \cdot 32 = \frac{3}{4} \cdot \frac{32}{1} = \frac{3}{2 \cdot 2} \cdot \frac{2 \cdot 2 \cdot 2 \cdot 2 \cdot 2}{1}$$

$$= \frac{3 \cdot \cancel{2} \cdot \cancel{2} \cdot 2 \cdot 2 \cdot 2}{\cancel{2} \cdot \cancel{2} \cdot 1}$$

$$= \frac{3 \cdot 2 \cdot 2 \cdot 2}{1}$$

$$= \frac{24}{1} = 24$$

Answer: 2 pounds

Thus, $\frac{3}{4}$ of an inch represents 24 mi. If we notice that 4 divides into 32, we can shorten our work.

$$\frac{3}{4} \cdot \frac{32}{1} = \frac{3}{\cancel{4}} \cdot \frac{\overset{8}{\cancel{32}}}{1} = \frac{24}{1} = 24$$

2.3 EXERCISES

Answers to these exercises are given on page 643.

✎ *Answer* true *or* false *in Exercises 1–6. If the answer is false, explain why.*

1. The phrase "$\frac{3}{4}$ of a number" translates to $\frac{3}{4} \cdot$ (that number).

2. The product of two fractions can be found by multiplying all numerators and dividing the result by the product of all denominators.

3. When multiplying fractions, the final product should always be reduced to lowest terms.

4. The fact that $\left(\frac{2}{3}\cdot\frac{3}{4}\right)\cdot\frac{2}{5} = \frac{2}{3}\cdot\left(\frac{3}{4}\cdot\frac{2}{5}\right)$ illustrates the commutative law.

5. The fact that $1\cdot\frac{7}{8} = \frac{7}{8}$ illustrates the associative law.

6. The fact that $\frac{2}{3}\cdot\frac{8}{9} = \frac{8}{9}\cdot\frac{2}{3}$ illustrates the commutative law.

Find each product in Exercises 7–24.

7. $\frac{2}{9}\cdot\frac{1}{3}$

8. $\frac{4}{3}\cdot\frac{3}{10}$

9. $\frac{1}{4}\cdot\frac{8}{9}$

10. $\frac{6}{7}\cdot\frac{14}{3}$

11. $\frac{8}{9}\cdot\frac{3}{4}$

12. $\frac{3}{5}\cdot 40$

13. $7\cdot\frac{3}{21}$

14. $\frac{6}{5}\cdot\frac{1}{3}$

15. $\frac{6}{35}\cdot\frac{20}{12}$

16. $\frac{21}{6}\cdot\frac{4}{7}$

17. $\frac{37}{19}\cdot 0$

18. $\frac{7}{5}\cdot 10$

19. $\frac{7}{8}\cdot\frac{4}{35}$

20. $\frac{18}{84}\cdot\frac{36}{27}$

21. $\frac{35}{9}\cdot\frac{3}{28}$

22. $\frac{2}{3}\cdot\frac{10}{9}\cdot\frac{6}{5}$

23. $\frac{3}{8}\cdot\frac{24}{9}\cdot 7$

24. $\frac{160}{169}\cdot\frac{13}{8}\cdot\frac{26}{5}$

In Exercises 25–27, find the value of each power.

25. $\left(\frac{3}{4}\right)^2$

26. $\left(\frac{1}{9}\right)^2$

27. $\left(\frac{7}{3}\right)^2$

In Exercises 28–30, find the value of each radical.

28. $\sqrt{\dfrac{9}{16}}$

29. $\sqrt{\dfrac{1}{49}}$

30. $\sqrt{\dfrac{144}{25}}$

Solve each applied problem in Exercises 31–34.

31. **GEOMETRY** Claude owns a plot of land in the shape of a rectangle $\frac{4}{7}$ km wide by $\frac{7}{8}$ km long (**km** is the abbreviation for *kilometer*). What is the area of his plot?

32. **TRAVEL** On a map, 1 inch represents 27 miles. How many miles does $\frac{4}{3}$ inch represent?

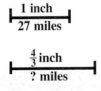

33. **WAGES** Max earned $225 for working one five-day week. How much would he earn working three days? [Hint: Three days is $\frac{3}{5}$ one five-day week.]

34. **FINANCE** Barbara Burnett has contracted to have a fence built at a cost of $2116. How much must she pay to get the job started if a down payment of one fourth is required?

 **CRITICAL THINKING**

Let a and b represent natural numbers. Find the products in Exercises 35–37.

35. $\dfrac{9}{a} \cdot \dfrac{a^2}{36}$

36. $\dfrac{7a^2}{6b^3} \cdot \dfrac{36ab}{35a^2}$

37. $\dfrac{2^2 a^4}{3^3 b^4} \cdot \dfrac{3a^2 b^3}{4ab}$

38. **RETAIL**   A grocer received a shipment of 1200 pounds of fruit, of which 1/3 were apples. Only 19/20 of the apples were still good. How many pounds of good apples did the grocer receive? Can you see that this problem can be done in one step or in two?

Burford was asked to explain a circle graph and its uses. He was given the graph below and told that the whole circle represented 240 hours. Since Burford does not have a clue, can you label each section with a fraction and tell how many hours are represented by the section?

39.

REVIEW OR PREVIEW

In Exercises 40–42, decide which fractions are equivalent by using cross products.

40. $\dfrac{4}{5}$ and $\dfrac{5}{6}$

41. $\dfrac{4}{16}$ and $\dfrac{3}{12}$

42. $\dfrac{9}{5}$ and $\dfrac{7}{4}$

In Exercises 43–45, reduce each fraction to lowest terms.

43. $\dfrac{12}{18}$

44. $\dfrac{65}{91}$

45. $\dfrac{273}{182}$

In Exercises 46–48, find the missing term in each fraction.

46. $\dfrac{16}{6} = \dfrac{a}{3}$

47. $\dfrac{30}{5} = \dfrac{12}{a}$

48. $\dfrac{9}{42} = \dfrac{a}{14}$

2.3 PARALLEL EXERCISES

Answers to these exercises are not given in the text.

Answer true or false in Exercises 1–6. If the answer is false, explain why.

1. To reduce the number of steps in multiplying fractions, divide out common factors before multiplying numerators and multiplying denominators.

2. When common factors are divided out before multiplying numerators and denominators, the resulting fraction will be reduced to lowest terms.

3. To square a fraction, square the numerator and square the denominator.

4. The fact that $\frac{1}{2} \cdot \frac{3}{7} = \frac{3}{7} \cdot \frac{1}{2}$ illustrates the associative law.

5. The fact that $\left(\frac{2}{9} \cdot \frac{5}{13}\right) \cdot \frac{4}{7} = \frac{2}{9} \cdot \left(\frac{5}{13} \cdot \frac{4}{7}\right)$ illustrates the commutative law.

6. Any fraction multiplied by 1 gives that fraction as the product.

Find each product in Exercises 7–24.

7. $\dfrac{7}{8} \cdot \dfrac{1}{2}$

8. $\dfrac{9}{4} \cdot \dfrac{4}{3}$

9. $\dfrac{6}{5} \cdot \dfrac{10}{3}$

10. $\dfrac{2}{7} \cdot \dfrac{21}{8}$

11. $\dfrac{3}{8} \cdot 40$

12. $9 \cdot \dfrac{17}{18}$

13. $\dfrac{20}{35} \cdot \dfrac{7}{4}$

14. $\dfrac{2}{3} \cdot \dfrac{5}{6}$

15. $\dfrac{62}{9} \cdot 0$

16. $\dfrac{7}{8} \cdot \dfrac{24}{42}$

17. $\dfrac{27}{26} \cdot \dfrac{13}{9}$

18. $10 \cdot \dfrac{9}{2}$

19. $\dfrac{35}{40} \cdot \dfrac{8}{7}$

20. $\dfrac{99}{13} \cdot \dfrac{39}{11}$

21. $\dfrac{32}{25} \cdot \dfrac{15}{16}$

22. $\dfrac{1}{3} \cdot \dfrac{20}{9} \cdot \dfrac{6}{5}$

23. $6 \cdot \dfrac{3}{7} \cdot \dfrac{28}{12}$

24. $\dfrac{169}{5} \cdot \dfrac{25}{13} \cdot \dfrac{1}{13}$

In Exercises 25–27, find the value of each power.

25. $\left(\dfrac{1}{7}\right)^2$

26. $\left(\dfrac{5}{8}\right)^2$

27. $\left(\dfrac{10}{3}\right)^2$

In Exercises 28–30, find the value of each radical.

28. $\sqrt{\dfrac{25}{9}}$

29. $\sqrt{\dfrac{1}{100}}$

30. $\sqrt{\dfrac{169}{121}}$

Solve each applied problem in Exercises 31–34.

31. **GEOMETRY**   A rectangular field is $\frac{3}{7}$ mi wide and $\frac{7}{9}$ mi long. What is the area of the field?

32. **TRAVEL**   On a map, 1 inch represents 12 miles. How many miles are represented by $\frac{5}{6}$ inches?

33. **FINANCE**   Tuition for one semester amounts to $2352. If Jack paid two thirds of this amount at early registration, how much is left to be paid?

34. **SALARY**   Greg Odjakjian has an annual salary of $55,420. How much will Greg save this year if he always saves one fifth of his salary?

CRITICAL THINKING

 *Let x and y represent natural numbers. Find the products in Exercises 35–37.*

35. $\dfrac{4}{x^2} \cdot \dfrac{x^3}{24}$

36. $\dfrac{3xy}{8x^2} \cdot \dfrac{16x^3}{27y^2}$

37. $\dfrac{4^2 x^2 y^2}{2^3 xy} \cdot \dfrac{3^3 x^2}{9^2 x^3}$

38. **CONSUMER**   Ruth Brown planned to fill her pool with 3600 gallons of water. She wanted to fill $1/3$ of the pool each day for three days. She had only done $3/4$ of the first day's filling when she had to stop. How much water was in the pool at that time? Can you see that this problem can be done in one step or in two?

Burford was asked to explain a circle graph and its uses. He was given the graph below and told that the whole circle represented 240 hours. Since Burford does not have a clue, can you label each section with a fraction and tell how many hours are represented by the section?

39.

GROUP PROJECT

Look for geometric formulas that involve multiplication by a fraction. For example,

$$\text{Area} = \frac{1}{2}bh$$

is the formula for the area of a triangle. Discuss the formulas that you find and see if you can use them.

2.4 DIVIDING FRACTIONS

STUDENT GUIDEPOSTS
1   FINDING THE RECIPROCAL OF A FRACTION
2   LEARNING THE METHOD OF DIVIDING FRACTIONS
3   WORKING WITH THE RELATED DIVISION EQUATION

1 RECIPROCAL OF A FRACTION

Division of fractions is closely related to multiplication. In fact, a division problem can be changed to an equivalent multiplication problem using a *reciprocal*.

RECIPROCAL OF A FRACTION
Two fractions are **reciprocals** if their product is 1.

Consider the fractions $\frac{3}{4}$ and $\frac{4}{3}$. $\qquad \frac{3}{4} \cdot \frac{4}{3} = \frac{\cancel{3} \cdot \cancel{4}}{\cancel{4} \cdot \cancel{3}} = \frac{1}{1} = 1$

Thus $\frac{3}{4}$ and $\frac{4}{3}$ are reciprocals of each other. Notice that $\frac{4}{3}$ is obtained when we interchange the numerator and denominator of $\frac{3}{4}$. This is true of all reciprocals and gives an easy way to find the reciprocal of a number.

FINDING RECIPROCALS
To find the reciprocal of a fraction, interchange the numerator and denominator. Thus the reciprocal of $\frac{a}{b}$ is $\frac{b}{a}$.

PRACTICE EXERCISE 1

Find the reciprocal of each number.

(a) $\dfrac{13}{11}$

(b) $\dfrac{1}{20}$

(c) 9

(d) 1

Answers:
(a) $\frac{11}{13}$ (b) 20 (c) $\frac{1}{9}$ (d) 1

FINDING RECIPROCALS   EXAMPLE 1

Find the reciprocal of each number.

(a) $\dfrac{3}{8}$ The reciprocal of $\frac{3}{8}$ is $\frac{8}{3}$.

(b) $\dfrac{1}{3}$ The reciprocal of $\frac{1}{3}$ is $\frac{3}{1}$ or 3.

(c) 5   Since 5 can be written as $\frac{5}{1}$, its reciprocal is $\frac{1}{5}$.

(d) 0   0 has no reciprocal since 0 is $\frac{0}{1}$ and $\frac{1}{0}$ is undefined.

2 | METHOD OF DIVIDING FRACTIONS

The fact that the product of reciprocals is 1 gives us a way to convert a division problem into a multiplication problem. For example, consider

$$\frac{2}{3} \div \frac{4}{9} \quad \text{or} \quad \frac{\dfrac{2}{3}}{\dfrac{4}{9}}.$$

Recall from Section 2.2 that when the numerator and denominator of a fraction are multiplied by the same nonzero whole number, an equivalent fraction is formed. The same holds true when both numerator and denominator are multiplied by the same nonzero fraction. Suppose we multiply numerator and denominator of

$$\frac{\dfrac{2}{3}}{\dfrac{4}{9}}$$

by $\frac{9}{4}$, the reciprocal of the denominator, $\frac{4}{9}$.

$$\frac{\dfrac{2}{3} \cdot \dfrac{9}{4}}{\dfrac{4}{9} \cdot \dfrac{9}{4}} = \frac{\dfrac{2}{3} \cdot \dfrac{9}{4}}{\dfrac{\cancel{4} \cdot \cancel{9}}{\cancel{9} \cdot \cancel{4}}} = \frac{\dfrac{2}{3} \cdot \dfrac{9}{4}}{1}$$

Just as $\dfrac{5}{1} = 5$, $\dfrac{10}{1} = 10$, and $\dfrac{127}{1} = 127$,

so, also, does

$$\frac{\dfrac{2}{3} \cdot \dfrac{9}{4}}{1} = \frac{2}{3} \cdot \frac{9}{4}.$$

We have just shown that the division problem

$$\frac{2}{3} \div \frac{4}{9}$$

can be converted to the multiplication problem

$$\frac{2}{3} \cdot \frac{9}{4}.$$

Thus, we can define **division of fractions** as follows:

$$\frac{a}{b} \div \frac{c}{d} = \frac{a}{b} \cdot \frac{d}{c}.$$

TO DIVIDE TWO FRACTIONS

1. Replace the divisor by its reciprocal and change the division sign to multiplication.
2. Proceed as in multiplication.

EXAMPLE 2 | DIVIDING FRACTIONS

Find each quotient.

(a) $\dfrac{7}{12} \div \dfrac{14}{9} = \dfrac{7}{12} \cdot \dfrac{9}{14}$ Replace divisor by its reciprocal and multiply

$$= \frac{7}{2 \cdot 2 \cdot 3} \cdot \frac{3 \cdot 3}{2 \cdot 7} \qquad \text{Factor}$$

PRACTICE EXERCISE 2

Find each quotient.

(a) $\dfrac{8}{15} \div \dfrac{2}{5}$

$$= \frac{\cancel{7} \cdot \cancel{3} \cdot 3}{2 \cdot 2 \cdot \cancel{3} \cdot 2 \cdot \cancel{7}} \quad \text{Divide out common factors}$$

$$= \frac{3}{2 \cdot 2 \cdot 2} = \frac{3}{8}$$

$$\frac{14}{9} \div 7$$

(b) $\dfrac{20}{3} \div \mathbf{5} = \dfrac{20}{3} \div \dfrac{\mathbf{5}}{\mathbf{1}}$ 5 can be written as $\frac{5}{1}$

$$= \frac{20}{3} \cdot \frac{\mathbf{1}}{\mathbf{5}} \quad \text{The reciprocal of } \tfrac{5}{1} \text{ is } \tfrac{1}{5}$$

$$= \frac{2 \cdot 2 \cdot 5}{5} \cdot \frac{1}{5}$$

Answers: (a) $\frac{4}{3}$ (b) $\frac{2}{9}$

$$= \frac{2 \cdot 2 \cdot \cancel{5} \cdot 1}{3 \cdot \cancel{5}} = \frac{2 \cdot 2 \cdot 1}{3} = \frac{4}{3}$$

Before considering applied problems, remember that $10 \div 2$ can be interpreted as the number of 2s in 10. There are five 2s in 10. Similarly, $\dfrac{2}{5} \div \dfrac{1}{10}$ means "How many $\frac{1}{10}$ ths are in $\frac{2}{5}$?" Consider Figure 2.16.

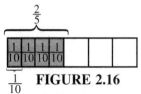

$$\frac{1}{10}$$ **FIGURE 2.16**

By counting we see that there are four $\frac{1}{10}$ ths in $\frac{2}{5}$. But notice that

$$\frac{2}{5} \div \frac{1}{10} = \frac{2}{5} \cdot \frac{10}{1} = \frac{2 \cdot 10}{5 \cdot 1}$$

$$= \frac{2 \cdot 2 \cdot \cancel{5}}{\cancel{5} \cdot 1} = 4.$$

Thus, using the division rule we find the number of $\frac{1}{10}$ ths in $\frac{2}{5}$ without relying on a figure.

PRACTICE EXERCISE 3

A butcher wants to cut a roast weighing 14 lb into steaks that each weigh $\frac{2}{3}$ lb. How many steaks will he get?

Answer: 21 steaks

APPLYING DIVISION   **EXAMPLE 3**

A piece of string 12 m long is to be cut into pieces each of length $\frac{3}{4}$ m. How many pieces can be cut?

Find the number of $\frac{3}{4}$ s in 12. That is, find $12 \div \frac{3}{4}$.

$$12 \div \frac{3}{4} = \frac{12}{1} \cdot \frac{4}{3} = \frac{3 \cdot 4}{1} \cdot \frac{4}{3} = \frac{\cancel{3} \cdot 4 \cdot 4}{1 \cdot \cancel{3}} = \frac{16}{1} = 16$$

Thus, 16 pieces of length $\frac{3}{4}$ m can be cut.

NOTE   Notice that 12 was not factored completely to primes in Example 3. Since the only factor (besides 1) in the denominator was 3, there was no need to factor 12 beyond $3 \cdot 4$. With practice, you can take shortcuts such as this.

3 | RELATED DIVISION EQUATION

EXPLORATION GUIDE

Describe what is happening when we determine the missing number in a multiplication or division equation. Make up different types of equations and see if you can find the missing number in each.

Many division problems are more easily solved by first considering a multiplication sentence and then changing it to the **related division equation.** For example, suppose we know that $\frac{1}{2}$ of a trip is 220 miles and want to know how long the whole trip is. If we know that

$$\frac{1}{2} \text{ of \textbf{the trip} is } 220.$$

and we let x represent the length of the whole trip, we can write

$$\frac{1}{2} \text{ of } x \text{ is } 220$$
$$\downarrow\downarrow \ \ \downarrow\downarrow \ \downarrow$$
$$\frac{1}{2} \cdot x = 220. \qquad \text{Multiplication equation}$$

We can find out what x is by writing the related division sentence.

$$x = \frac{220}{\frac{1}{2}} \qquad \text{Related division equation}$$

$$\frac{220}{\frac{1}{2}} = 220 \cdot \frac{2}{1} = \frac{220}{1} \cdot \frac{2}{1} = \frac{440}{1} = 440$$

Thus

$$\frac{1}{2} \cdot 440 = 220 \qquad \text{Multiplication equation}$$

and

$$\frac{220}{\frac{1}{2}} = 440 \qquad \text{Related division equation}$$

are two different forms of the same equation. We use this information in the next examples.

EXAMPLE 4 | USING THE RELATED DIVISION EQUATION

Find the missing number.

(a) $\frac{2}{3}$ of **a number** is 42.

Let x be the number.

$$\frac{2}{3} \text{ of } x \text{ is } 42$$
$$\downarrow\downarrow \ \ \downarrow \ \downarrow \ \downarrow$$
$$\frac{2}{3} \cdot x = 42 \qquad \text{Multiplication equation}$$

$$x = \frac{42}{\frac{2}{3}} \qquad \text{Related division equation}$$

$$= \frac{42}{1} \cdot \frac{3}{2}$$

$$= \frac{21 \cdot 2 \cdot 3}{1 \cdot 2} = 63$$

(b) $\frac{5}{9}$ of **the weight** is 20 lb.

$$\frac{5}{9} \text{ of } x \text{ is } 20$$
$$\downarrow \ \downarrow\downarrow \ \downarrow \ \downarrow$$
$$\frac{5}{9} \cdot x = 20 \qquad \text{Multiplication equation}$$

PRACTICE EXERCISE 4

Find the missing number.

(a) $\frac{9}{2}$ of a number is 30.

(b) $\frac{7}{8}$ of the length is 350 cm.

Answers: (a) $\frac{20}{3}$ (b) 400 cm

$$x = \frac{20}{\frac{5}{9}} \qquad \text{Related division equation}$$

$$= \frac{20}{1} \cdot \frac{9}{5}$$

$$= \frac{4 \cdot 5 \cdot 9}{1 \cdot 5} = 36 \text{ lb}$$

PRACTICE EXERCISE 5

After working 16 hours, Carla had completed $\frac{8}{11}$ of a job. How long will it take to do the total job?

$$\frac{8}{11} \text{ of the job is 16}$$
$$\downarrow \quad \downarrow \quad \downarrow \quad \downarrow \quad \downarrow$$
$$\frac{8}{11} \cdot a = 16$$

Answer: 22 hr

APPLYING DIVISION TO TRAVEL **EXAMPLE 5**

After driving 160 miles, the Carlsons had completed $\frac{5}{7}$ of their trip. What was the total length of their trip?

We know that $\frac{5}{7}$ *of* the trip *is* 160 miles. Remember *of* becomes *times* and *is* becomes *equals* in the multiplication sentence. Letting x be the total length of the trip, we have

$$\frac{5}{7} \text{ of } x \text{ is 160}$$
$$\downarrow \downarrow \downarrow \downarrow \quad \downarrow$$
$$\frac{5}{7} \cdot x = 160 \qquad \text{Multiplication equation}$$

$$x = \frac{160}{\frac{5}{7}} \qquad \text{Related division equation}$$

$$= \frac{160}{1} \cdot \frac{7}{5}$$

$$= \frac{5 \cdot 32 \cdot 7}{1 \cdot 5} = 224$$

Thus, the total length of the trip was 224 miles.

2.4 EXERCISES

Answers to these exercises are given on page 643.

In Exercises 1–5, find the reciprocal of each number.

1. $\frac{2}{3}$

2. $\frac{4}{5}$

3. $\frac{1}{7}$

4. 3

5. 0

In Exercises 6–17, find each quotient.

6. $\frac{1}{3} \div \frac{5}{6}$

7. $\frac{2}{3} \div \frac{1}{9}$

8. $\frac{2}{3} \div \frac{4}{9}$

9. $\frac{3}{7} \div \frac{9}{28}$

10. $7 \div \frac{14}{3}$

11. $\frac{5}{4} \div \frac{1}{2}$

12. $\frac{20}{9} \div \frac{10}{15}$

13. $\frac{8}{11} \div 4$

14. $\frac{13}{15} \div \frac{39}{5}$

15. $\frac{2}{7} \div \frac{2}{7}$

16. $\frac{4}{7} \div 44$

17. $\frac{20}{27} \div \frac{35}{36}$

Find the missing number x in Exercises 18–26.

18. $\frac{3}{8} \cdot x = 18$

19. $\frac{11}{2} \cdot x = 33$

20. $x \cdot \frac{7}{3} = 35$

21. $\frac{10}{7}$ of x is 20

22. $\frac{10}{9}$ of x is 25

23. $\frac{1}{8}$ of x is $\frac{2}{9}$

24. $\dfrac{2}{11}$ of x is 10

25. $\dfrac{8}{1}$ of x is 56

26. $\dfrac{10}{9}$ of x is $\dfrac{8}{3}$

Solve each applied problem in Exercises 27–30.

27. **CONSTRUCTION** A piece of rope 10 m long is to be cut into pieces each of length $\dfrac{2}{3}$ m. How many pieces can be cut?

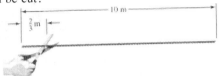

28. **CONSUMER** Beth needs $\dfrac{3}{8}$ of a yard of material to make a pillow. How many pillows can she make from 18 yards of material?

29. **SCIENCE** A lab technician has 6 liters of alcohol. If she needs samples that are three fifths of a liter, how many such samples can she prepare from the 6 liter supply?

30. **TRAVEL** After driving 280 miles, the Wilsons had completed $\dfrac{2}{3}$ of their trip. What was the total length of the trip?

CRITICAL THINKING

In Exercises 31–33, find each quotient.

31. $\dfrac{4a^4}{7} \div 44a^3$

32. $\dfrac{20x^2}{27y} \div \dfrac{35xy}{36}$

33. $\dfrac{8a^2b^3}{5a^4} \div \dfrac{2b}{25a^2}$

34. Burford says that the commutative and associative laws hold for division. Can you show him that this is not the case? Remember that for the laws to be true they must hold for every choice of numbers.

REVIEW OR PREVIEW

Find each product in Exercises 35–40.

35. $\dfrac{4}{11} \cdot \dfrac{121}{32}$

36. $13 \cdot \dfrac{7}{169}$

37. $\dfrac{2}{7} \cdot \dfrac{28}{3} \cdot \dfrac{9}{4}$

38. $\dfrac{5}{13} \cdot \dfrac{52}{55}$

39. $\dfrac{19}{144} \cdot 12$

40. $\dfrac{3}{4} \cdot \dfrac{42}{6} \cdot \dfrac{5}{14}$

Solve each applied problem in Exercises 41–44.

41. **CONSUMER** The Wilsons want to put down two fifteenths of the price of any house that they buy. How much would they have to have for a downpayment on a $120,000 house?

42. **INVESTMENT** Pam receives an inheritance of $8000. If she invests $\dfrac{3}{16}$ of this amount in bonds and $\dfrac{5}{8}$ of it in a mutual fund, how much does she invest in each category?

43. **EDUCATION** On a recent test in biology Jim Camp got four fifths of the points. If there were 60 total points on the test, how many points did Jim get?

44. **ENGINEERING** A container contains $\dfrac{2}{3}$ of a gallon of milk when full. How much milk is in the container when it is $\dfrac{1}{4}$ full?

2.4 PARALLEL EXERCISES

Answers to these exercises are not given in the text.

In Exercises 1–5, find the reciprocal of each number.

1. $\dfrac{4}{7}$

2. $\dfrac{11}{3}$

3. $\dfrac{1}{15}$

4. 6

5. $\dfrac{100}{99}$

In Exercises 6–17, find each quotient.

6. $\dfrac{1}{5} \div \dfrac{2}{15}$

7. $\dfrac{3}{4} \div \dfrac{1}{8}$

8. $\dfrac{2}{3} \div \dfrac{1}{6}$

9. $\dfrac{4}{9} \div \dfrac{1}{3}$

10. $9 \div \dfrac{18}{7}$

11. $\dfrac{7}{4} \div \dfrac{1}{2}$

12. $\dfrac{5}{7} \div \dfrac{15}{28}$

13. $\dfrac{8}{13} \div 4$

14. $\dfrac{13}{17} \div \dfrac{39}{34}$

15. $\dfrac{4}{3} \div \dfrac{4}{3}$

16. $\dfrac{6}{11} \div 36$

17. $\dfrac{20}{16} \div \dfrac{10}{8}$

Find the missing number x in Exercises 18–26

18. $\dfrac{2}{9} \cdot x = 12$

19. $\dfrac{13}{7} \cdot x = 39$

20. $x \cdot \dfrac{3}{20} = 27$

21. $\dfrac{5}{16}$ of x is 15

22. $\dfrac{8}{7}$ of x is 20

23. $\dfrac{1}{6}$ of x is $\dfrac{7}{13}$

24. $\dfrac{4}{15}$ of x is 30

25. $\dfrac{6}{1}$ of x is 24

26. $\dfrac{15}{7}$ of x is $\dfrac{5}{14}$

Solve each applied problem in Exercises 27–30.

27. **TRAVEL** After driving 365 miles, the Johnsons had completed $\frac{5}{6}$ of their trip. What was the total length of the trip?

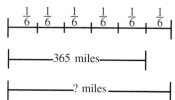

28. **ENGINEERING** A tank holds 220 gallons of fuel when it is $\frac{4}{5}$ full. What is the capacity of the tank?

29. **MINING** An earth mover can pick up three fourths of a ton of ore each time. How many times will it need to be operated to move 120 tons of ore?

30. **CONSTRUCTION** When Joey hammers a nail into a board, he sinks it $\frac{2}{9}$ of an inch with each blow. How many times will he have to hit a 4-inch nail to drive it completely into the board?

 **CRITICAL THINKING**

In Exercises 31–33, find each quatient.

31. $\dfrac{6x^3}{11} \div 36x$

32. $\dfrac{20a^3}{16b^2} \div \dfrac{10a}{8b}$

33. $\dfrac{5^3 a^2 b}{2^4 ab^2} \div \dfrac{25a^4 b^4}{8ab}$

34. Burford started with a number a and took its reciprocal 16 times. What number did he have? If he had taken the reciprocal 15 times, what number would he have had?

GROUP PROJECT

Find or design applications of multiplication and division of fractions. Discuss in a group which involve multiplication and which involve division. Can you write an application that uses both operations in one problem?

2.5 MULTIPLYING AND DIVIDING MIXED NUMBERS

STUDENT GUIDEPOSTS
1   DEFINING MIXED NUMBERS
2   USING A METHOD FOR MULTIPLYING AND DIVIDING MIXED NUMBERS
3   SOLVING APPLICATIONS OF MIXED NUMBERS

1 MIXED NUMBERS

Many of the answers to word problems are improper fractions that may look a bit strange. For example, $\frac{9}{2}$ miles is not as familiar to us as $4\frac{1}{2}$ miles. For this reason, improper fractions are often written as *mixed numbers*.

A **mixed number** is the sum of a whole number and a proper fraction. The improper fraction $\frac{7}{6}$ can be represented as in Figure 2.17.

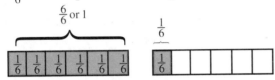

FIGURE 2.17

Since all 6 parts of the first bar and 1 additional part of the second are shaded,

$$\frac{7}{6} \text{ is } 1 + \frac{1}{6}. \qquad 1 \text{ bar} + \frac{1}{6} \text{ of another bar}$$

To write $1 + \frac{1}{6}$ as a mixed number, omit the plus sign and write

$$1\frac{1}{6}, \quad \text{read "one and one sixth."}$$

To change an improper fraction to a mixed number, think of the improper fraction as a division problem. For example, $\frac{7}{6}$ is $7 \div 6$.

Perform the division.   **Divisor** $\longrightarrow$ $6\overline{)7}$ $\begin{array}{l} 1 \longleftarrow \textbf{Quotient} \\ \longleftarrow \textbf{Dividend} \\ \underline{6} \\ 1 \longleftarrow \textbf{Remainder} \end{array}$

Recall that this division problem can be checked as follows:

$$7 = 6 \cdot 1 + 1 \qquad (\text{dividend}) = (\text{divisor}) \cdot (\text{quotient}) + (\text{remainder})$$

Dividing through by 6, $\dfrac{7}{6} = \dfrac{6 \cdot 1}{6} + \dfrac{1}{6} = 1 + \dfrac{1}{6} = 1\dfrac{1}{6}.$

This is a way to obtain a mixed number from an improper fraction.

TO CHANGE AN IMPROPER FRACTION TO A MIXED NUMBER
1.   Reduce the fraction to lowest terms (if necessary).
2.   Divide the numerator by the denominator to obtain the quotient and remainder.
3.   The mixed number is $$\text{quotient} + \frac{\text{remainder}}{\text{divisor}}.$$

PRACTICE EXERCISE 1

Change each improper fraction to a mixed number.

(a) $\dfrac{23}{7}$

(b) $\dfrac{114}{23}$

(c) $\dfrac{35}{15}$

Change each improper fraction to a mixed number.

(a) $\dfrac{15}{4}$

$$\text{Divisor} \longrightarrow 4\overline{)15} \xleftarrow{} \textbf{Dividend}$$
$$\begin{array}{r} 3 \leftarrow \textbf{Quotient} \\ \underline{12} \\ 3 \leftarrow \textbf{Remainder} \end{array}$$

Thus, the mixed number is $3\frac{3}{4}$, read "three and three fourths."

(b) $\dfrac{121}{35}$

$$\text{Divisor} \longrightarrow 35\overline{)121} \xleftarrow{} \textbf{Dividend}$$
$$\begin{array}{r} 3 \leftarrow \textbf{Quotient} \\ \underline{105} \\ 16 \leftarrow \textbf{Remainder} \end{array}$$

Thus, $\dfrac{121}{35} = 3\dfrac{16}{35}$.

(c) $\dfrac{27}{6}$

In this case, first reduce $\frac{27}{6}$ to lowest terms.

$$\frac{27}{6} = \frac{\cancel{3}\cdot 9}{\cancel{3}\cdot 2} = \frac{9}{2} \qquad 2\overline{)9} \begin{array}{r} 4 \\ \underline{8} \\ 1 \end{array}$$

Thus, $\dfrac{27}{6} = \dfrac{9}{2} = 4\dfrac{1}{2}$.

We now want to change a mixed number into an improper fraction. From Figure 2.18, we can see that the mixed number $3\frac{1}{2}$ is the same as the improper fraction $\frac{7}{2}$.

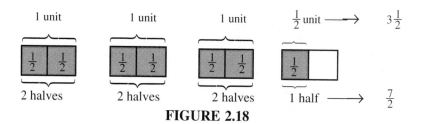

FIGURE 2.18

Each whole unit has 2 halves and there are 3 whole units plus 1 half unit.

$$2 \cdot 3 + 1 = 7.$$

Answers: (a) $3\frac{2}{7}$ (b) $4\frac{22}{23}$ (c) $2\frac{1}{3}$

Putting this result over the denominator, 2, gives the improper fraction $\frac{7}{2}$. The same result can be obtained by the following procedure.

$$3\,\frac{1}{2}\ \textbf{Over} = \frac{2\cdot 3 + 1}{2} = \frac{7}{2}$$

TO CHANGE A MIXED NUMBER TO AN IMPROPER FRACTION

1. Multiply the denominator by the whole number.
2. Add the result to the numerator of the fraction.
3. This sum, over the denominator, is the improper fraction.

EXAMPLE 2 — CHANGING MIXED NUMBERS TO IMPROPER FRACTIONS

Change each mixed number to an improper fraction.

(a) $3\frac{1}{4}$

$$3\frac{1}{4} \text{ Over} = \frac{4 \cdot 3 + 1}{4} = \frac{12 + 1}{4} = \frac{13}{4}$$

(b) $17\frac{2}{3}$

$$17\frac{2}{3} = \frac{3 \cdot 17 + 2}{3} = \frac{51 + 2}{3} = \frac{53}{3}$$

2 | METHOD FOR MULTIPLYING AND DIVIDING MIXED NUMBERS

Mixed numbers can be multiplied and divided just like proper and improper fractions. Change any mixed numbers to improper fractions and proceed as in Sections 2.3 and 2.4.

TO MULTIPLY MIXED NUMBERS

1. Change any mixed numbers to improper fractions.
2. Proceed as when multiplying or dividing fractions.

EXAMPLE 3 — MULTIPLYING MIXED NUMBERS

Multiply.

(a) $2\frac{1}{2} \cdot 3\frac{1}{4}$

First change to improper fractions.

$$2\frac{1}{2} = \frac{2 \cdot 2 + 1}{2} = \frac{5}{2} \text{ and } 3\frac{1}{4} = \frac{4 \cdot 3 + 1}{4} = \frac{13}{4}$$

$$2\frac{1}{2} \cdot 3\frac{1}{4} = \frac{5}{2} \cdot \frac{13}{4} = \frac{65}{8} = 8\frac{1}{8}$$ Change improper fraction to a mixed number

(b) $7\frac{3}{8} \cdot 4 = \frac{8 \cdot 7 + 3}{8} \cdot \frac{4}{1} = \frac{59}{8} \cdot \frac{4}{1} = \frac{59 \cdot \cancel{4}}{2 \cdot \cancel{4} \cdot 1}$

$$= \frac{59}{2} = 29\frac{1}{2}$$

PRACTICE EXERCISE 2

Change each mixed number to an improper fraction.

(a) $7\frac{2}{5}$

(b) $22\frac{1}{4}$

Answers: (a) $\frac{37}{5}$ (b) $\frac{89}{4}$

PRACTICE EXERCISE 3

Multiply.

(a) $1\frac{1}{5} \cdot 5\frac{2}{7}$

(b) $12 \cdot 10\frac{2}{9}$

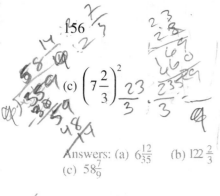

(c) $\left(7\frac{2}{3}\right)^2$ $\frac{23}{3} \cdot \frac{23}{3}$

Answers: (a) $6\frac{12}{35}$ (b) $122\frac{2}{3}$
(c) $58\frac{7}{9}$

EXPLORATION GUIDE

Indicate the product of two mixed numbers. Rewrite the numbers using the definition of a mixed number. Can you see why it does not work to multiply the whole numbers and fractions separately?

PRACTICE EXERCISE 4

Divide.

(a) $2\frac{4}{5} \div 1\frac{3}{4}$

(b) $10\frac{5}{8} \div 5$

(c) $\left(5\frac{1}{4}\right)^2$

Find $\left(5\frac{1}{4}\right)\left(5\frac{1}{4}\right)$.

$$5\frac{1}{4} = \frac{4 \cdot 5 + 1}{4} = \frac{21}{4}$$ Change to improper fraction

$$\left(5\frac{1}{4}\right)^2 = \left(\frac{21}{4}\right)^2 = \left(\frac{21}{4}\right)\left(\frac{21}{4}\right)$$

$$= \frac{21 \cdot 21}{4 \cdot 4} = \frac{441}{16} = 27\frac{9}{16}$$

CAUTION   It is tempting to try to multiply

$$2\frac{1}{2} \cdot 3\frac{1}{4}$$

by multiplying the whole numbers $(2 \cdot 3 = 6)$ and then multiplying the fractions $\left(\frac{1}{2} \cdot \frac{1}{4} = \frac{1}{8}\right)$. That would make the product $6\frac{1}{8}$. But from Example 1(a), this product is $8\frac{1}{8}$. Thus, the parts of mixed numbers *should not* be multiplied or divided separately.

DIVIDING MIXED NUMBERS   EXAMPLE 4

Divide.

(a) $4\frac{2}{3} \div 3\frac{1}{2}$

First change to improper fractions.

$$4\frac{2}{3} = \frac{3 \cdot 4 + 2}{3} = \frac{14}{3} \quad \text{and} \quad 3\frac{1}{2} = \frac{2 \cdot 3 + 1}{2} = \frac{7}{2}$$

$$4\frac{2}{3} \div 3\frac{1}{2} = \frac{14}{3} \div \frac{7}{2} = \frac{14}{3} \cdot \frac{2}{7}$$ Multiply by $\frac{2}{7}$, the reciprocal of $\frac{7}{2}$

$$= \frac{2 \cdot 7}{3} \cdot \frac{2}{7}$$

$$= \frac{2 \cdot 7 \cdot 2}{3 \cdot 7} = \frac{4}{3} = 1\frac{1}{3}$$

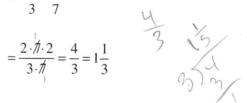

(b) $5\frac{3}{5} \div 2 = \frac{28}{5} \div 2$

$$= \frac{28}{5} \cdot \frac{1}{2} = \frac{2 \cdot 14 \cdot 1}{5 \cdot 2} = \frac{14}{5} = 2\frac{4}{5}$$

(c) $7 \div 8\frac{2}{5} = 7 \div \frac{42}{5} = 7 \cdot \frac{5}{42} = \frac{\cancel{7} \cdot 5}{\cancel{7} \cdot 6} = \frac{5}{6}$

(c) $4 \div 7\frac{1}{3}$

Answers: (a) $1\frac{3}{5}$ (b) $2\frac{1}{8}$ (c) $\frac{6}{11}$

3 | APPLICATIONS OF MIXED NUMBERS

Many applied problems can be expressed better with mixed numbers than with improper fractions. For example, we would normally say that Michael can hike $4\frac{1}{2}$ miles and not that he can hike $\frac{9}{2}$ miles.

EXAMPLE 5   SOLVING AN APPLICATION IN RECREATION

Michael can hike $4\frac{1}{2}$ miles in one hour. At the same rate, how far can he hike in 6 hours?

Since he can go $4\frac{1}{2}$ miles in one hour, he can go 6 times that distance in 6 hours.

$$6 \cdot 4\frac{1}{2} = 6 \cdot \frac{9}{2} \quad \text{Change to an improper fraction}$$

$$= \frac{6}{1} \cdot \frac{9}{2}$$

$$= \frac{\cancel{2} \cdot 3 \cdot 9}{\cancel{2}} = 27$$

Thus, Michael can go 27 miles in 6 hours.

EXAMPLE 6   SOLVING AN APPLICATION TO SEWING

A uniform requires $2\frac{5}{8}$ yards of material. How many uniforms can be made from $57\frac{3}{4}$ yards of material?

Since each uniform requires $2\frac{5}{8}$ yards, then $2\frac{5}{8}$ times the number of uniforms must be $57\frac{3}{4}$. We let x represent the number of uniforms.

$$2\frac{5}{8} \cdot x = 57\frac{3}{4}$$

$$x = 57\frac{3}{4} \div 2\frac{5}{8} \quad \text{Related division equation}$$

$$= \frac{231}{4} \div \frac{21}{8}$$

$$= \frac{231}{4} \cdot \frac{8}{21}$$

$$= \frac{11 \cdot \cancel{21} \cdot \cancel{4} \cdot 2}{\cancel{4} \cdot \cancel{21}} = 22$$

Thus, 22 uniforms can be made.

PRACTICE EXERCISE 5

One bag of fruit weighs $8\frac{3}{4}$ pounds. How much would 12 of these bags weigh?

Answer: 105 pounds

PRACTICE EXERCISE 6

How many $2\frac{2}{5}$ lb packages of fish can be obtained from 132 lb of fish?

Answer: 55 packages

2.5 EXERCISES

Answers to these exercises are given on page 644.

💡 *In Exercises 1–9, change each improper fraction to a mixed number.*

1. $\dfrac{7}{5}$

2. $\dfrac{17}{3}$

3. $\dfrac{23}{8}$

4. $\dfrac{45}{6}$

5. $\dfrac{71}{10}$

6. $\dfrac{19}{2}$

7. $\dfrac{135}{4}$

8. $\dfrac{257}{9}$

9. $\dfrac{142}{11}$

💡 *In Exercises 10–18, change each mixed number to an improper fraction.*

10. $3\dfrac{1}{3}$

11. $4\dfrac{3}{5}$

12. $7\dfrac{1}{8}$

13. $10\dfrac{3}{4}$

14. $9\dfrac{7}{11}$

15. $21\dfrac{2}{3}$

16. $5\dfrac{7}{8}$

17. $32\dfrac{7}{10}$

18. $66\dfrac{2}{3}$

Multiply the mixed numbers in Exercises 19–27. Give answers as proper fractions, whole numbers, or mixed numbers.

19. $3\dfrac{1}{5} \cdot 4\dfrac{2}{3}$

20. $5\dfrac{4}{7} \cdot 2\dfrac{2}{13}$

21. $12\dfrac{2}{9} \cdot 4\dfrac{1}{5}$

22. $6\dfrac{4}{5} \cdot 11$

23. $\left(3\dfrac{1}{2}\right)^2$

24. $\left(2\dfrac{2}{5}\right)^2$

25. $3 \cdot 1\dfrac{1}{2} \cdot 2\dfrac{1}{3}$

26. $2\dfrac{3}{5} \cdot 6\dfrac{1}{4} \cdot 12$

27. $11\dfrac{1}{2} \cdot 5\dfrac{1}{4} \cdot \dfrac{2}{7}$

Divide the mixed numbers in Exercises 28–36. Give answers as proper fractions, whole numbers, or mixed numbers.

28. $3\dfrac{1}{6} \div 2\dfrac{1}{2}$

29. $8\dfrac{5}{6} \div 4\dfrac{1}{9}$

30. $3 \div 7\dfrac{4}{5}$

31. $16\dfrac{1}{2} \div 8$

32. $\dfrac{7}{8} \div 5\dfrac{1}{4}$

33. $10\dfrac{1}{5} \div \dfrac{3}{10}$

34. $9\dfrac{2}{7} \div 1\dfrac{2}{3}$

35. $3\dfrac{1}{8} \div 30$

36. $80 \div 4\dfrac{2}{7}$

Solve each applied problem in Exercises 37–42.

37. **MANUFACTURING** A candy machine can produce $76\frac{3}{4}$ pounds of candy per hour. How many pounds can it produce in 24 hours?

38. **CONSUMER** The flow of water into the Monroe's swimming pool is $24\frac{2}{5}$ gallons per minute. How many gallons will go into the pool in $15\frac{1}{2}$ minutes?

39. **TRAVEL** A car traveled 420 miles on $12\frac{4}{5}$ gallons of gas. How many miles per gallon did it get?

40. **SEWING** A pompon girl's uniform requires $3\frac{1}{8}$ yards of material. How many uniforms can be made from 25 yards of material?

41. **SCIENCE** The weight of one cubic foot of water is $62\frac{1}{2}$ lb. How much does $3\frac{1}{3}$ cubic feet of water weigh?

42. **GEOMETRY** The area of a room is its length times its width. What is the area of a room that is $8\frac{3}{4}$ yards long and $6\frac{2}{5}$ yards wide?

CRITICAL THINKING

Let a and b be natural numbers and $a\frac{1}{2}$ and $b\frac{1}{3}$ be mixed numbers in Exercises 43–44.

43. Write $a\frac{1}{2}$ as an improper fraction.

44. What is 2 times $a\frac{1}{2}$?

45. Burford read the caution that warned him not to multiply whole numbers and fractions separately when multiplying mixed numbers, but he is still doing it that way. Can you use the distributive law to explain the difficulties with Burford's technique?

REVIEW OR PREVIEW

Find each quotient in Exercises 46–48.

46. $\frac{10}{21} \div \frac{20}{14}$

47. $\frac{5}{13} \div 10$

48. $38 \div \frac{19}{2}$

Solve each applied problem in Exercises 49–52.

49. **ENGINEERING** A tank holds 560 gallons of water when it is $\frac{5}{8}$ full. What is the capacity of the tank?

50. **CONSUMER** How many steaks each weighing $\frac{3}{8}$ pound can be cut from a 15-pound roast?

51. **ENGINEERING** A wire 20 inches long is to be cut into pieces each of length $\frac{5}{8}$ inch. How many pieces can be cut?

52. **RECREATION** After hiking 26 miles, the campers had completed $\frac{2}{3}$ of a hike. What was the total length of the hike?

2.5 PARALLEL EXERCISES

Answers to these exercises are not given in the text.

In Exercises 1–9, change each improper fraction to a mixed number.

1. $\frac{8}{5}$

2. $\frac{19}{3}$

3. $\frac{27}{8}$

4. $\frac{51}{6}$

5. $\frac{86}{10}$

6. $\frac{17}{2}$

7. $\dfrac{173}{4}$ 8. $\dfrac{269}{9}$ 9. $\dfrac{312}{11}$

💡 *In Exercises 10–18, change each mixed number to an improper fraction.*

10. $3\dfrac{3}{2}$ 11. $5\dfrac{2}{5}$ 12. $6\dfrac{3}{8}$

13. $12\dfrac{1}{4}$ 14. $11\dfrac{7}{11}$ 15. $26\dfrac{1}{3}$

16. $3\dfrac{7}{8}$ 17. $4\dfrac{7}{10}$ 18. $76\dfrac{2}{3}$

Multiply the mixed numbers in Exercises 19–27. Give answers as proper fractions, whole numbers, or mixed numbers.

19. $1\dfrac{3}{4}\cdot 2\dfrac{1}{7}$ 20. $6\dfrac{1}{8}\cdot 3\dfrac{3}{14}$ 21. $2\dfrac{2}{5}\cdot 8\dfrac{1}{3}$

22. $5\dfrac{2}{9}\cdot 12$ 23. $\left(2\dfrac{1}{3}\right)^2$ 24. $\left(6\dfrac{1}{2}\right)^2$

25. $4\cdot 2\dfrac{1}{3}\cdot 5\dfrac{1}{4}$ 26. $1\dfrac{1}{10}\cdot 5\dfrac{5}{7}\cdot 14$ 27. $\dfrac{2}{11}\cdot 7\dfrac{1}{3}\cdot 10\dfrac{1}{4}$

Divide the mixed numbers in Exercises 28–36. Give answers as proper fractions, whole numbers, or mixed numbers.

28. $5\dfrac{5}{6}\div 1\dfrac{1}{2}$ 29. $7\dfrac{4}{5}\div 3\dfrac{1}{4}$ 30. $5\div 7\dfrac{1}{4}$

31. $13\dfrac{1}{2}\div 5$ 32. $\dfrac{4}{7}\div 2\dfrac{2}{9}$ 33. $9\dfrac{3}{5}\div \dfrac{4}{15}$

34. $8\dfrac{1}{15}\div 7\dfrac{1}{5}$ 35. $6\dfrac{3}{4}\div 60$ 36. $20\div 5\dfrac{5}{6}$

Solve each applied problem in Exercises 37–42.

37. **RECREATION** Charles Hickman can walk at a rate of $4\dfrac{3}{10}$ miles per hour. How many miles can he hike in $3\dfrac{1}{2}$ hours?

38. **BUSINESS** Ed Young can type $15\dfrac{2}{3}$ pages in one hour. How many pages can he type in $7\dfrac{1}{2}$ hours?

39. **TRAVEL** A truck traveled 378 miles on $15\dfrac{2}{5}$ gallons of fuel. How many miles per gallon did it get?

40. **CONSTRUCTION** How many pieces of steel rod $3\dfrac{1}{3}$ feet long can be cut from a rod which is 110 feet long?

41. **CHEMISTRY** How many $5\dfrac{1}{2}$-gram samples can be obtained from 176 grams of a chemical?

42. **CONSUMER** There are 26 pieces of candy of the same size in a box. The total weight of the candy is $5\dfrac{1}{5}$ pounds. How much does each piece of candy weigh?

CRITICAL THINKING

💡 *Let a and b be natural numbers and $a\dfrac{1}{2}$ and $b\dfrac{1}{3}$ be mixed numbers in Exercises 43–44.*

43. Write $b\dfrac{1}{3}$ as an improper fraction.

44. What is 3 times $b\frac{1}{3}$?

💡 45. Burford said that the mixed number $8\frac{1}{4}$ was the same as 2. Can you explain to him what he is doing wrong?

GROUP PROJECT

Discuss applications of mixed numbers as measurements. Use specific examples to see how improper fractions are not as good as mixed numbers in giving us an understanding of distances, weights, and volumes.

2.6 MORE PROBLEM SOLVING WITH FRACTIONS

This section considers a variety of applications of fractions and mixed numbers. Having different types of problems in the same section will give practice at deciding which operation should be used.

EXAMPLE 1 **USING FRACTIONS IN CONSTRUCTION**

A rectangular room is $12\frac{1}{2}$ feet long and $10\frac{1}{5}$ feet wide. How many square feet of tile are needed to cover the floor of the room? If tile costs $1\frac{1}{5}$ dollars for one square foot, how much will it cost to tile the floor?

Since the area of the floor is the length of the room times its width, this problem requires multiplication. See Figure 2.19.

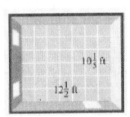

FIGURE 2.19

$$\text{Area} = \textbf{length} \cdot \textbf{width}$$

$$= 12\frac{1}{2} \cdot 10\frac{1}{5}$$

$$= \frac{25}{2} \cdot \frac{51}{5}$$

$$= \frac{\overset{5}{\cancel{25}}}{2} \cdot \frac{51}{\cancel{5}}$$

$$= \frac{255}{2} = 127\frac{1}{2}$$

Thus, $127\frac{1}{2}$ square feet of tile are required. The total cost is found by multiplying the number of square feet by the cost for each square foot.

$$127\frac{1}{2} \cdot 1\frac{1}{5} = \frac{255}{2} \cdot \frac{6}{5}$$

$$= \frac{51 \cdot \cancel{5} \cdot \cancel{2} \cdot 3}{\cancel{2} \cdot \cancel{5}}$$

$$= 153$$

The cost to tile the floor is 153 dollars.

PRACTICE EXERCISE 1

A rectangular room is $6\frac{2}{3}$ yards long and $4\frac{1}{4}$ yards wide. What is the area of the room? If carpet costs $16\frac{1}{2}$ dollars per square yard installed, how much will it cost to carpet the room?

Answer: $28\frac{1}{3}$ square yards, $467\frac{1}{2}$ dollars

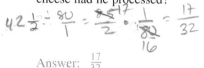

PRACTICE EXERCISE 2

After working for several hours, Andrew had processed $42\frac{1}{2}$ pounds of an 80-pound shipment of cheese. What fraction of the cheese had he processed?

$42\frac{1}{2} \div \frac{80}{1} = \frac{85}{2} \cdot \frac{1}{80} = \frac{17}{32}$

Answer: $\frac{17}{32}$

USING FRACTIONS IN THE HOUSEHOLD · EXAMPLE 2

Howard bought $27\frac{1}{3}$ pounds of nuts. If he put $18\frac{2}{3}$ pounds in the freezer, what fraction of the nuts did he freeze?

To find a fraction of the nuts, divide the number of pounds frozen by the total number of pounds of nuts.

$$18\frac{2}{3} \div 27\frac{1}{3} = \frac{56}{3} \div \frac{82}{3} \quad \text{Change to improper fractions}$$

$$= \frac{56}{3} \cdot \frac{3}{82}$$

$$= \frac{28 \cdot 2 \cdot 3}{3 \cdot 2 \cdot 41} = \frac{28}{41}$$

The fraction of the nuts which were frozen is $\frac{28}{41}$.

PRACTICE EXERCISE 3

When a fuel tank is $\frac{2}{5}$ full, it contains 320 gallons. How many gallons of fuel will the tank hold?

$\frac{2}{5}$ of x is 320

$\downarrow \ \downarrow \ \downarrow \ \downarrow \ \downarrow$

$\frac{2}{5} \cdot x = 320$

$x = 320 \div \frac{2}{5} =$

Answer: 800 gallons

MARKETING APPLICATION · EXAMPLE 3

Randee Wire owns a fruit market in northern California, and she sells grapes in $3\frac{1}{3}$-pound bags. On Wednesday Randee received an order of 120 pounds of grapes from the vineyard. How many bags can she prepare for sale from the shipment?

If we knew the number of bags we could multiply $3\frac{1}{3}$ times that number to obtain 120 pounds. We let x represent the number of bags.

$$3\frac{1}{3} \cdot x = 120$$

$$x = 120 \div 3\frac{1}{3} \quad \text{Related division equation}$$

$$= 120 \div \frac{10}{3}$$

$$= \frac{120}{1} \cdot \frac{3}{10}$$

$$= \frac{12 \cdot 10 \cdot 3}{1 \cdot 10} = 36$$

Thus, 36 bags can be prepared for sale.

PRACTICE EXERCISE 4

A flywheel turns at the rate of $102\frac{1}{2}$ revolutions per second. How many revolutions will it make in $5\frac{2}{5}$ seconds?

Answer: $553\frac{1}{5}$ revolutions

USING FRACTIONS IN RECREATION · EXAMPLE 4

A record revolves at a rate of $33\frac{1}{3}$ revolutions per minute. If it takes $15\frac{1}{2}$ minutes to play one song, how many revolutions does the record make during the song?

Look at a simpler case first: If the song lasted 2 minutes, the record would make $2 \cdot 33\frac{1}{3}$ revolutions. Since the song takes $15\frac{1}{2}$ minutes, the record makes $15\frac{1}{2} \cdot 33\frac{1}{3}$ revolutions.

$$15\frac{1}{2} \cdot 33\frac{1}{3} = \frac{2 \cdot 15 + 1}{2} \cdot \frac{3 \cdot 33 + 1}{3}$$

$$= \frac{31}{2} \cdot \frac{100}{3}$$

$$= \frac{31 \cdot 2 \cdot 50}{2 \cdot 3}$$

$$= \frac{1550}{3} = 516\frac{2}{3}$$

During the song, the record makes $516\frac{2}{3}$ revolutions.

Mixed numbers give a better idea of the size of a number than improper fractions.

For example, it is easier to understand

$$516\frac{2}{3} \text{ revolutions than } \frac{1550}{3} \text{ revolutions.}$$

> **CAUTION** It is easy to confuse the mixed number notation with multiplication. Often, when no symbol is used, multiplication is assumed. This is not true with mixed numbers.
>
> $$516\frac{2}{3} \text{ is } 516 + \frac{2}{3} \text{ NOT } 516 \cdot \frac{2}{3}$$
>
> To show this, $\quad 516 + \frac{2}{3} = 516\frac{2}{3} = \frac{1550}{3},$
>
> but, $\quad\quad 516 \cdot \frac{2}{3} = \frac{\overset{172}{\cancel{516}} \cdot 2}{\underset{1}{\cancel{3}}} = 172 \cdot 2 = 344.$

2.6 EXERCISES

Answers to these exercises are given on page 644.

Solve each applied problem in Exercises 1–14.

1. **ENGINEERING** A tank holds 240 gallons when it is $\frac{2}{3}$ full. How many gallons does it hold when full?

2. **ENGINEERING** A tank holds 240 gallons when it is full. How many gallons does it contain when it is $\frac{2}{3}$ full?

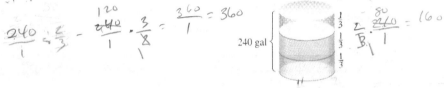

3. **POLITICS** An election committee has 3500 information sheets to distribute. If five sevenths of them are to go to Huntsville and the rest to Lufkin, how many go to Huntsville? How many go to Lufkin?

4. **CONSUMER** Walter ate $2\frac{1}{5}$ pounds of a $3\frac{1}{2}$ pound box of candy the first day. What fraction of the candy had he eaten?

5. **RECREATION** A steam locomotive travels at the rate of $14\frac{1}{2}$ miles per hour. How far can it travel in $3\frac{1}{5}$ hours?

6. **CONSUMER** Sam added $2\frac{1}{2}$ cups of flour to a cake recipe. He later found out that this was $2\frac{1}{2}$ times the amount that he should have added. How much should he have used?

7. **CONSUMER** A recipe calls for $1\frac{1}{4}$ cups of sugar. How much sugar should be used if the recipe is doubled? How much if $\frac{1}{3}$ of the recipe is to be used?

8. **PRODUCTION** Each print run on a commercial printer requires $3\frac{3}{10}$ gallons of ink. How many runs can be made before using up 99 gallons of ink?

9. **SPORTS** A domed stadium has rectangular floor dimensions of 120 yards by 70 yards. If $\frac{9}{10}$ of the floor area is to be covered with synthetic turf, how many square yards of turf must be laid? If the turf costs $15 a square yard installed, how much will the project cost?

10. **FINANCE** A family has an income of $18,000 a year. If $\frac{1}{5}$ the income is spent for food, $\frac{1}{4}$ for housing, $\frac{1}{10}$ for clothing, and $\frac{3}{8}$ for taxes, how much is spent for each?

11. **CHEMISTRY** A chemical reaction produces $10\frac{2}{5}$ grams per minute. How long will it take to make $34\frac{2}{3}$ grams?

12. **ENGINEERING** A tank holds 560 gallons of water when it is full. When a leak was discovered, $\frac{5}{8}$ of the water had drained out. How much water was left in the tank?

13. **RECREATION** A record makes 45 revolutions per minute. How long will it take to make $321\frac{1}{2}$ revolutions?

14. **RECREATION** A record makes $33\frac{1}{3}$ revolutions per minute. How many revolutions are made in $6\frac{3}{5}$ minutes?

CRITICAL THINKING

Let a, b, and c represent fractions. Write the equation described in each of Exercises 15–18.

15. If a is multiplied by $\frac{3}{4}$ the result is $\frac{1}{12}$.

16. If a is multiplied by b the result is c.

17. If a is divided by $\frac{5}{6}$ the result is $\frac{3}{25}$.

18. If a is divided by b the result is c.

19. Burford knows that if $2x = 3$ then $x = \frac{3}{2}$, but he doesn't have a clue what x is if $ax = b$. Can you tell him how to find x?

REVIEW OR PREVIEW

Perform the indicated operations in Exercises 20–25.

20. $2\frac{1}{9} \cdot 3\frac{3}{5}$

21. $5\frac{3}{7} \div 4\frac{2}{5}$

22. $\left(6\frac{2}{3}\right)^2$

23. $3 \cdot 5\frac{1}{7} \cdot 4\frac{2}{3}$

24. $9\frac{3}{5} \div 10$

25. $16 \div 7\frac{1}{3}$

2.6 PARALLEL EXERCISES

Answers to these exercises are not given in the text.
Solve each applied problem in Exercises 1–14.

1. **ENGINEERING** A container is $\frac{3}{10}$ full and has 15 quarts in it. How much will it hold when full?

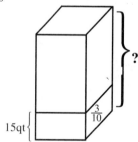

2. **ENGINEERING** A container holds 15 quarts when it is full. How many quarts does it contain when it is $\frac{3}{10}$ full?

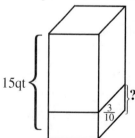

3. **EDUCATION** Of the total of 600 points in a course, one tenth comes from homework and the rest from tests. How many points are from homework? How many points are from tests?

4. **ENTERTAINMENT** There were $7\frac{1}{3}$ gallons of punch prepared for a party. If $6\frac{2}{5}$ gallons were drunk, what fraction of the punch was consumed?

5. **ENVIRONMENT** If the lake is rising at a rate of $2\frac{2}{3}$ feet per day how much higher will it be in $7\frac{1}{2}$ days?

6. **CHEMISTRY** A chemist added $5\frac{1}{4}$ liters of alcohol to a solution. She later discovered that this was $2\frac{1}{2}$ times as much as she should have added. How much should have been added?

7. **ENTERTAINMENT** To make a party punch, $2\frac{3}{4}$ quarts of ice cream are required. How much ice cream should be added if three times the punch recipe is to be made? How much if $\frac{1}{5}$ the recipe is to be made?

8. **PRODUCTION** Each machine part that is made requires $2\frac{7}{10}$ pounds of steel. How many parts can be made from 540 pounds of steel?

9. **CONSUMER** A large living room is 12 yards wide and 16 yards long. If $\frac{5}{8}$ of the floor area is to be carpeted, how many square yards are required? If carpet costs $24 per square yard installed, how much will the job cost?

10. **FINANCE** Gloria Moore has $2400 for college expenses. If she spends $\frac{1}{4}$ of the money for clothing, $\frac{1}{8}$ for books, $\frac{1}{6}$ for travel, and $\frac{2}{5}$ for tuition, how much is spent for each?

11. **TRAVEL** Kevin Carlson drove $137\frac{1}{2}$ miles in $2\frac{1}{5}$ hours. What was his rate per hour?

12. **ENGINEERING** A water truck holds 250 gallons when it is full. After $\frac{3}{5}$ of the tank is drained out, how much is left in the tank?

13. **RECREATION** A record makes $33\frac{1}{3}$ revolutions each minute. How long will it take to make $137\frac{1}{2}$ revolutions?

14. **ENGINEERING** A pulley on a machine is turning at a rate of $214\frac{1}{2}$ revolutions per minute. How many revolutions will it make in $10\frac{2}{3}$ minutes?

CRITICAL THINKING

Let a, b, and c represent fractions. Write the equation described in each of Exercises 15–18.

15. *a* times $\frac{2}{5}$ is equal to $\frac{1}{6}$.

16. *a* times *b* is equal to *c*.

17. *a* divided by $\frac{1}{3}$ is equal to $\frac{2}{7}$.

18. *a* divided by *b* is equal to *c*.

19. Burford knows that if $\frac{x}{2} = 3$ then $x = 6$, but he doesn't have a clue what *x* is if $\frac{x}{a} = b$. Can you tell him how to find *x*?

GROUP PROJECT

We have studied multiplication and division of fractions before addition and subtraction. Look briefly at Chapter 3 and discuss why we may have chosen this order of chapters. Is there a "natural" order? Could Chapter 3 have been done first?

CHAPTER 2 REVIEW

KEY WORDS

 2.1

- A **fraction** is the quotient of two whole numbers.
- The **numerator** is the top number in a fraction.
- The **denominator** is the bottom number in a fraction.
- A **proper fraction** is one whose numerator is less than its denominator.
- An **improper fraction** is one whose numerator is greater than or equal to its denominator.

 2.2

- A fraction is **reduced to lowest terms** when 1 is the only nonzero whole number rhat is a divisor of both the numerator and denominator.

 2.3

- The **commutative law of multiplication** states that changing the order of a product does not change the result.
- The **associative law of multiplication** states that regrouping products does not change the result.
- The **multiplicative identity** tells us we can multiply any number by 1 and always obtain that same number.

 2.4

- Two fractions are **reciprocals** if their product is 1.

2.5

- A **mixed number** is the sum of a whole number and a proper fraction.

KEY CONCEPTS

 2.1

1. Any fraction like $\frac{0}{9}$ is equal to 0.
2. Any fraction like $\frac{4}{4}$ is equal to 1.

2.2

1. Fractions are equal when their cross products are equal.
2. When the numerator and denominator of a fraction are multiplied or divided by the same whole number (except 0), an equal fraction is formed.
3. To reduce a fraction to lowest terms, factor the numerator and denominator into primes and divide out all common factors.

2.3

1. When multiplying fractions, divide out common factors of the numerator and denominator first before multiplying the remaining factors.
2. The word *of* translates to "times" when it follows a fraction in a word problem.
3. Fractions satisfy the commutative and associative laws of multiplication, and 1 is the multiplicative identity.

 2.4

1. The reciprocal of a fraction is found by interchanging the numerator and the denominator of the fraction.
2. To divide fractions, multiply the dividend by the reciprocal of the divisor.

3. Zero is the only number that does not have a reciprocal.
4. To solve some applied problems, we first write a multiplication sentence then change to the related division sentence.

2.5

1. A mixed number like $3\frac{1}{2}$ is $3 + \frac{1}{2}$ (not 3 times $\frac{1}{2}$).
2. Improper fractions can be changed to mixed numbers by dividing.
3. A mixed number such as $5\frac{2}{7}$ can be changed to an improper fraction as follows:
$$5\frac{2}{7} = \frac{7 \cdot 5 + 2}{7} = \frac{37}{7}$$
4. Change mixed numbers to improper fractions in order to multiply or divide.
5. You should not multiply whole number parts and fraction parts separately when multiplying mixed numbers.

2.6

When solving applied problems determine which of the following is required.
(a) Finding a fractional part
(b) Multiplying fractions
(c) Dividing fractions

CHAPTER 2 REVIEW EXERCISES

PART I

Answers to these exercises are given on page 644.

 2.1

1. What is the denominator of the fraction $\frac{2}{9}$?

2. Is the fraction $\frac{21}{2}$ a proper or an improper fraction?

3. Is $\frac{7}{7}$ a proper or an improper fraction?

4. The fraction $\frac{0}{10}$ is the same as what number?

What fractional part of each figure is shaded in Exercises 5–8?

5.   6.   7.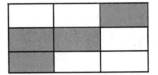

8. Let the figure be one whole unit. What fraction of the unit is shaded below?

9. **SPORTS** A ball player made 11 free throws in 14 attempts during a game. The number of shots made is what fraction of the shots attempted?

In Exercises 10–12, express each fraction as a whole number.

10. $\frac{9}{9}$ 11. $\frac{31}{0}$ 12. $\frac{0}{15}$

 2.2

Determine which fractions are equivalent in Exercises 13–14 by using the cross-product rule.

13. $\frac{8}{11}$ and $\frac{5}{7}$ 14. $\frac{3}{12}$ and $\frac{5}{20}$

In Exercises 15–17, find the missing term a of the fraction.

15. $\frac{5}{8} = \frac{a}{24}$ 16. $\frac{3}{9} = \frac{1}{a}$ 17. $\frac{4}{a} = \frac{32}{8}$

In Exercises 18–20, reduce each fraction to lowest terms.

18. $\frac{20}{30}$ 19. $\frac{180}{144}$ 20. $\frac{42}{28}$

 2.3

21. The word *of* translates to what operation when it follows a fraction in a problem?

22. The fact that $\frac{1}{3} \cdot \frac{7}{8} = \frac{7}{8} \cdot \frac{1}{3}$ illustrates which of the properties of multiplication?

Find each product in Exercises 23–25.

23. $\frac{2}{3} \cdot \frac{18}{7}$ 24. $5 \cdot \frac{3}{25}$ 25. $\frac{6}{5} \cdot \frac{4}{7} \cdot \frac{5}{12}$

Find the value of each power or root in Exercises 26–27.

26. $\left(\frac{7}{6}\right)^2$ 27. $\sqrt{\frac{121}{25}}$

28. **EDUCATION** An international club at the university has 135 members. If two fifteenths of the members are from Italy, how many of the members are not from Italy?

 2.4

29. What is the reciprocal of $\frac{13}{7}$?

30. What is the only number that does not have a reciprocal?

Find each quotient in Exercises 31–33.

31. $\frac{2}{9} \div \frac{4}{27}$ 32. $12 \div \frac{3}{4}$ 33. $\frac{7}{3} \div 21$

Find the missing number x in Exercises 34–35.

34. $\frac{5}{7} \cdot x = 25$ 35. $\frac{2}{9}$ of x is $\frac{4}{25}$

36. When a tank is $\frac{1}{6}$ full, it contains 130 gallons of water. What is the capacity of the tank?

 2.5

37. What do we call the sum of a whole number and a proper fraction?

38. What is the understood operation between 3 and $\frac{7}{8}$ in the mixed number $3\frac{7}{8}$?
In Exercises 39–41, change to a mixed number.

39. $\frac{127}{4}$ 40. $\frac{243}{11}$ 41. $\frac{97}{2}$

In Exercises 42-44, change to an improper fraction.

42. $3\frac{9}{13}$ 43. $21\frac{1}{5}$ 44. $16\frac{2}{3}$

Perform the indicated operations in Exercises 45–50.

45. $2\frac{3}{4} \cdot 5\frac{1}{8}$ 46. $7\frac{2}{3} \div 4\frac{3}{5}$ 47. $4\frac{2}{11} \cdot 8\frac{1}{4}$

48. $5 \cdot 7\frac{2}{3} \cdot 10\frac{1}{5}$ 49. $18 \div 12\frac{2}{5}$ 50. $22\frac{1}{2} \div 15$

Solve each applied problem in Exercises 51–58.

51. **PRODUCTION** A machine produces $77\frac{1}{2}$ cans of vegetable juice per minute. How many cans can be produced in $10\frac{4}{5}$ minutes?

52. **BUSINESS** An office printer will produce $92\frac{1}{2}$ pages per minute. How long will it take to print 3700 pages?

2.6

53. **TRAVEL** On a map 1 inch represents 35 miles. How many miles does $1\frac{3}{5}$ inch represent?

54. **CONSUMER** A rectangular room is $2\frac{1}{8}$ yards wide and $4\frac{1}{3}$ yards long. How much will it cost to carpet the room using carpet that sells for $13\frac{1}{2}$ dollars per sq yd?

55. **ENGINEERING** A container holds 186 gallons of fuel when it is $\frac{2}{3}$ full. What is the capacity of the container?

56. **ENGINEERING** A container holds 186 gallons of fuel when full. If $\frac{2}{3}$ of a full tank is drained off, how much fuel remains?

57. **RECREATION** A merry-go-round makes $8\frac{3}{4}$ revolutions per minute. How many revolutions will be made during a $3\frac{3}{5}$ minute ride?

58. **TRAVEL** An economy car traveled 480 miles on $13\frac{3}{4}$ gallons of gas. How many miles per gallon did it get?

PART II

💡 *Find the missing number x in Exercises 59–60.*

59. $\dfrac{3}{4} \cdot x = 12$

60. $\dfrac{1}{7}$ of x is $\dfrac{5}{21}$

Perform the indicated operations in Exercises 61–66.

61. $\left(\dfrac{2}{7}\right)^2$

62. $\sqrt{\dfrac{144}{4}}$

63. $\dfrac{3}{5} \cdot \dfrac{2}{9} \cdot \dfrac{5}{4}$

64. $\dfrac{16}{5} \div \dfrac{4}{25}$

65. $6\dfrac{2}{3} \cdot 8\dfrac{1}{2}$

66. $12\dfrac{3}{4} \div 4\dfrac{1}{2}$

💡 *In Exercises 67–68, find the missing term a for each fraction.*

67. $\dfrac{5}{12} = \dfrac{a}{36}$

68. $\dfrac{8}{a} = \dfrac{24}{15}$

Solve each applied problem in Exercises 69–70.

69. **TRAVEL** A Buick traveled 234 miles on $10\dfrac{2}{5}$ gallons of gas. How many miles per gallon did it get?

70. **TRAVEL** On a map 1 inch represents 50 miles. How many miles are represented by $5\dfrac{3}{4}$ inches?

In Exercises 71–72, express each fraction as a whole number.

71. $\dfrac{45}{45}$

72. $\dfrac{0}{21}$

Determine which fractions are equivalent by using the cross-product rule in Exercises 73–74.

73. $\dfrac{5}{30}$ and $\dfrac{2}{12}$

74. $\dfrac{11}{9}$ and $\dfrac{21}{18}$

Exercises 75–80 refer to the table below. Before determining the fraction requested, round the numbers from the table to the nearest hundred.

Wheat Exports and Imports of 10 Leading Countries: 1980 to 1992

[**In millions of dollars.** Countries listed are the ten leading exporters or importers in 1992]

LEADING EXPORTERS	EXPORTS			LEADING IMPORTERS	IMPORTS		
	1980	1990	1992		1980	1990	1992
WHEAT				WHEAT			
United States	**6,376**	**3,887**	**4,499**	Soviet Union (former)	2,891	2,490	3,420
Canada	3,302	2,863	3,871	China	2,582	2,157	1,663
France	2,110	3,296	3,302	Italy	773	1,217	1,651
Australia	2,425	1,971	1,161	Japan	1,236	1,019	1,177
Germany	198	504	883	Brazil	1,051	331	750
United Kingdom	260	760	776	Egypt	839	853	725
Argentina	816	871	716	India	108	(NA)	600
Turkey	52	4	341	Korea, South	367	419	544
Greece	27	156	262	Belgium-Luxembourg	360	384	535
Saudi Arabia	-	211	210	Indonesia	162	282	402

- Represents or rounds to zero. NA Not available.

Source: Food and Agriculture Organization of the United Nations, Rome, Italy, FAO AGRISTAT database.

75. Find the fraction that compares the wheat exported by the United States in 1992 to the exports in 1980 by dividing the 1992 exports by the 1980 exports.

76. Find the fraction that compares the exports of the United States to the exports of Australia in 1980.

77. Find the fraction that compares the exports of Germany in 1990 to the imports of Japan in 1990.

78. Find the fraction that compares the imports of India in 1992 to the exports of Germany in 1992.

79. Find the fraction that compares the imports of Indonesia in 1980 to the imports of Egypt in 1980.

80. Find the fraction that compares the imports of Japan in 1990 to the imports of South Korea in 1990.

CHAPTER 2 TEST

Answers to this test are given on page 644.

1. What kind of fraction has the numerator less than the denominator?

1. _____

2. Which law is illustrated by $\frac{2}{3} \cdot \left(\frac{3}{4} \cdot \frac{7}{8}\right) = \left(\frac{2}{3} \cdot \frac{3}{4}\right) \cdot \frac{7}{8}$?

2. _____

3. What fractional part of the figure is shaded?

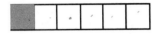

3. _____

4. Determine if $\frac{9}{2}$ and $\frac{36}{8}$ are equivalent fractions by using the cross-product rule.

4. _____

Find the missing term a.

5. $\frac{3}{5} = \frac{a}{35}$

5. _____

6. $\frac{9}{11} = \frac{27}{a}$

6. _____

7. Reduce $\frac{105}{45}$ to lowest terms.

7. _____

Perform the indicated operations.

8. $\frac{9}{5} \cdot \frac{20}{39}$

8. _____

9. $\frac{3}{8} \div \frac{21}{2}$

9. _____

10. $\frac{5}{8} \cdot \frac{12}{5} \cdot \frac{2}{11}$

10. _____

11. $\frac{9}{7} \div \frac{3}{35}$

11. _____

12. $\left(\frac{3}{8}\right)^2$

12. _____

13. $\sqrt{\frac{49}{144}}$

13. _____

14. Find the missing number x.

$\frac{4}{5}$ of x is 22

14. _____

CHAPTER 2 TEST

15. Change $\frac{48}{20}$ to a mixed number.

16. Change $7\frac{2}{11}$ to an improper fraction.

Perform the indicated operations and give the answer as a proper fraction, whole number, or mixed number.

17. $5\frac{1}{5} \cdot 4\frac{1}{4}$

18. $7\frac{1}{3} \div 9\frac{2}{9}$

19. $7 \cdot 4\frac{3}{8} \cdot 10\frac{2}{7}$

20. $6 \div 2\frac{4}{5}$

Solve.

21. A container holds 18 gallons when it is $\frac{8}{9}$ full. How many gallons does it contain when it is full?

22. If Lynn Butler travels at a rate of $57\frac{1}{2}$ miles per hour, how far can she go in $3\frac{3}{5}$ hours?

23. If the population of the United States in 1980 is divided by the population of the United States in 1990, would the fraction be proper or improper?

24. Use one example to show that the operation of division is not commutative.

25. Is $\frac{8}{0}$ a proper or an improper fraction?

15. _____

16. _____

17. _____

18. _____

19. _____

20. _____

21. _____

22. _____

23. _____

24. _____

25. _____

CUMULATIVE REVIEW CHAPTERS 1–2

💡 *Answers to these exercises are given on page 644.*

In Exercises 1–3, find the new fraction having the given denominator

1. $\dfrac{9}{10} = \dfrac{a}{50}$

2. $\dfrac{14}{21} = \dfrac{a}{3}$

3. $\dfrac{3}{16} = \dfrac{a}{128}$

Without finding the exact sum, determine if each sum in Exercises 4-6 seems correct or incorrect.

4.
```
   25
   37
   51
+  14
  227
```

5.
```
  328
   19
+476
  823
```

6.
```
  3291
   407
+ 6930
 10,628
```

💡 7. Write 41,075 in expanded notation.

💡 8. Write $10,000,000 + 16,000 + 200 + 5$ in standard notation.

In Exercises 9–11, reduce the fraction to lowest terms.

9. $\dfrac{28}{35}$

10. $\dfrac{60}{84}$

11. $\dfrac{144}{124}$

💡 12. Is 147 divisible by 3?

Solve each applied problem in Exercises 13–14.

13. **RECREATION** The gate receipts at a concert were $87,850. If tickets sold for $7 each, how many were in attendance?

14. **CONSUMER** Assuming equal quality, which is the better buy, a 43-oz box of soap for $1.29 (129¢) or a 78-oz box of soap for $1.56 (156¢)?

Find each product in Exercises 15–17.

15. $\dfrac{3}{4} \cdot \dfrac{24}{9}$

16. $\dfrac{112}{17} \cdot 0$

17. $\dfrac{130}{18} \cdot \dfrac{12}{15}$

Find each difference in Exercises 18–20. Check your work.

18.
```
  2000
-  743
```

19.
```
   307
 - 198
```

20.
```
  4632
- 3795
```

Divide the mixed numbers in Exercises 21–23.

21. $6\dfrac{1}{3} \div 2\dfrac{1}{9}$

22. $4\dfrac{3}{8} \div 15$

23. $13\dfrac{1}{2} \div 6\dfrac{3}{4}$

24. **TRAVEL** A car traveled 360 miles on $10\frac{2}{5}$ gallons of gasoline. How many miles per gallon did it get?

Translate each expression in Exercises 25–26.

25. *a* decreased by 17

26. *a* less than 30

Solve each equation in Exercises 27–28.

27. $a - 16 = 5$

28. $60a = 20$

CHAPTER *t·h·r·e·e*

ADDING AND SUBTRACTING FRACTIONS

It is generally conceded that the operations of addition and subtraction of whole numbers are somewhat simpler to learn than the operations of multiplication and division. With fractions, on the other hand, the reverse is true. In the previous chapter we learned to multiply and divide fractions, and now we turn our attention to the remaining operations of addition and subtraction. To perform these operations, we must first be able to rename fractions so that they have the same denominators. This is often accomplished using prime numbers, first studied in Chapter 1. Pierre Fermat (1601-1665), the famous French mathematician who worked extensively with number theory, contributed greatly to the knowledge of primes that we have today. Once we have learned to add and subtract fractions and mixed numbers, we will compare sizes of fractions and also be able to solve an assortment of applied problems such as the one given below. Its solution is presented in Example 5 in Section 3.5.

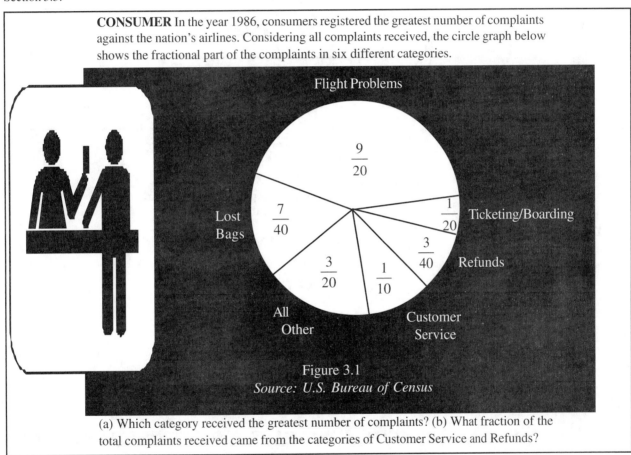

CONSUMER In the year 1986, consumers registered the greatest number of complaints against the nation's airlines. Considering all complaints received, the circle graph below shows the fractional part of the complaints in six different categories.

Figure 3.1
Source: U.S. Bureau of Census

(a) Which category received the greatest number of complaints? (b) What fraction of the total complaints received came from the categories of Customer Service and Refunds?

We begin the chapter by adding and subtracting like fractions. Next we consider the idea of the least common multiple of two or more numbers and use this concept to add and subtract unlike fractions and mixed numbers. We conclude with a discussion of the order of operations, the comparison of fractions, and additional applied problems involving fractions and mixed numbers.

3.1 ADDING AND SUBTRACTING LIKE FRACTIONS

STUDENT GUIDEPOSTS

1	DEFINING LIKE AND UNLIKE FRACTIONS
2	ADDING LIKE FRACTIONS
3	SUBTRACTING LIKE FRACTIONS
4	SOLVING COMBINATION PROBLEMS AND APPLICATIONS

1　　LIKE AND UNLIKE FRACTIONS

Fractions which have the same denominator are called **like fractions.** For example, the fractions

$$\frac{1}{6}, \ \frac{5}{6}, \ \frac{7}{6}, \ \frac{9}{6}, \ \frac{11}{6}$$

are like fractions. Fractions with different denominators are called **unlike fractions.** Thus,

$$\frac{2}{3}, \ \frac{1}{5}, \ \frac{3}{2}, \ \frac{1}{4}, \ \frac{7}{8}$$

are all unlike fractions.

2　　ADDING LIKE FRACTIONS

We begin the study of addition of fractions with like fractions. If we want to add

$$\frac{1}{8} + \frac{5}{8},$$

the sum becomes obvious when the problem is rewritten as

1 eighth + 5 eighths.

Just as

1 book + 5 books = 6 books,

That is,

1 eighth + 5 eighths = 6 eighths.

$$\frac{1}{8} + \frac{5}{8} = \frac{6}{8}.$$

We simply add numerators $(1 + 5)$ and place the result over the common denominator, 8. The sum, $\frac{6}{8}$, should then be reduced to lowest terms, $\frac{3}{4}$. The same is true in general.

If a, b, and c (c not 0) are numbers, we can define **addition of like fractions** as follows:

$$\frac{a}{c} + \frac{b}{c} = \frac{a+b}{c}.$$

EXPLORATION GUIDE

To help you understand how to add fractions we have said that it is just like adding books. Can you think of some other model that might help you personally remember that we add numerators and do not change the denominator when adding like fractions?

TO ADD LIKE FRACTIONS

1. Add their numerators.
2. Place this sum over the common denominator.
3. Reduce the fraction to lowest terms, if possible.

PRACTICE EXERCISE 1

Find each sum.

(a) $\dfrac{2}{5} + \dfrac{1}{5}$　　$\dfrac{3}{5}$

ADDING LIKE FRACTIONS

EXAMPLE 1

Find each sum.　　(a) $\dfrac{3}{4} + \dfrac{7}{4} = \dfrac{3+7}{4}$　　Place sum of numerators over denominator, 4

$$= \frac{10}{4}$$　　Add

$$= \frac{\cancel{2} \cdot 5}{\cancel{2} \cdot 2} = \frac{5}{2}$$　　Reduce to lowest terms

(b) $\dfrac{7}{30}+\dfrac{1}{30}+\dfrac{12}{30}=\dfrac{7+1+12}{30}$ Add numerators

$=\dfrac{20}{30}$

$=\dfrac{\cancel{10}\cdot 2}{\cancel{10}\cdot 3}=\dfrac{2}{3}$ Reduce

In (b), we took a shortcut and did not factor numerator and denominator to primes when reducing $\dfrac{20}{30}$, because we noticed that 10 was a common factor which could be divided out.

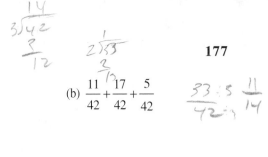

(b) $\dfrac{11}{42}+\dfrac{17}{42}+\dfrac{5}{42}$

Answers: (a) $\dfrac{3}{5}$ (b) $\dfrac{11}{14}$

3 | SUBTRACTING LIKE FRACTIONS

It is no more difficult to subtract like fractions than to add them. For example, to find

$$\frac{7}{8}-\frac{3}{8},$$

we think of

7 eighths − 3 eighths = 4 eighths

and subtract as we would if we were subtracting

7 books − 3 books = 4 books.

Thus,

$$\frac{7}{8}-\frac{3}{8}=\frac{4}{8}, \quad \text{which reduces to} \quad \frac{1}{2}.$$

If a, b, and c (c not 0) are numbers, we can define **subtraction of like fractions** as follows:

$$\frac{a}{c}-\frac{b}{c}=\frac{a-b}{c}.$$

TO SUBTRACT LIKE FRACTIONS

1. Subtract their numerators.
2. Place this difference over the common denominator.
3. Reduce the fraction to lowest terms, if possible.

EXAMPLE 2 | SUBTRACTING LIKE FRACTIONS

Find each difference.

(a) $\dfrac{5}{6}-\dfrac{1}{6}=\dfrac{5-1}{6}$ Place difference of numerators over common denominator, 6

$=\dfrac{4}{6}$ Subtract

$=\dfrac{\cancel{2}\cdot 2}{\cancel{2}\cdot 3}=\dfrac{2}{3}$ Reduce to lowest terms

(b) $\dfrac{7}{11}-\dfrac{7}{11}=\dfrac{7-7}{11}$ Subtract numerators and place difference over common denominator, 11

$=\dfrac{0}{11}=0$

PRACTICE EXERCISE 2

Find each difference.

(a) $\dfrac{7}{17}-\dfrac{2}{17}$

(b) $\dfrac{9}{15}-\dfrac{4}{15}$

Answers: (a) $\dfrac{5}{17}$ (b) $\dfrac{1}{3}$

CAUTION   Never add or subtract fractions by adding or subtracting denominators. For example,

$$\frac{2}{5}+\frac{1}{5} \quad \text{is not the same as} \quad \frac{2+1}{5+5}=\frac{3}{10},$$

since

$$\frac{2}{5}+\frac{1}{5}=\frac{3}{5}.$$

Also,

$$\frac{2}{5}-\frac{1}{5} \quad \text{is not the same as} \quad \frac{2-1}{5-5},$$

which is undefined.

4 COMBINATION PROBLEMS AND APPLICATIONS

We can find combinations of sums and differences of like fractions by adding or subtracting in order from left to right. An example will help to make this clear.

COMBINING ADDITION AND SUBTRACTION   EXAMPLE 3

Perform the indicated operations.

$$\frac{4}{13}+\frac{11}{13}-\frac{3}{13}=\frac{4+11-3}{13} \qquad \text{Combine numerators as indicated}$$

$$=\frac{15-3}{13} \qquad \text{Add first from left}$$

$$=\frac{12}{13} \qquad \text{Subtract}$$

ADDING IN AN ENTERTAINMENT PROBLEM   EXAMPLE 4

A recipe for a party drink calls for $\frac{3}{10}$ of a gallon of 7-Up, $\frac{7}{10}$ of a gallon of lemonade, and $\frac{1}{10}$ of a gallon of orange sherbet.

(a) How many gallons of drink can be made from the recipe?

Add: $\qquad \frac{3}{10}+\frac{7}{10}+\frac{1}{10}=\frac{3+7+1}{10}=\frac{11}{10}$

Thus, the recipe will make $\frac{11}{10}$ or $1\frac{1}{10}$ gallons of drink.

(b) If the recipe is doubled, how much of each ingredient is needed and how much drink will be made?

Multiply the amount of each ingredient by 2.

$$2\cdot\frac{3}{10}=\frac{2}{1}\cdot\frac{3}{10}=\frac{6}{10}=\frac{3}{5} \qquad \text{Amount of 7-Up}$$

$$2\cdot\frac{7}{10}=\frac{2}{1}\cdot\frac{7}{10}=\frac{14}{10}=\frac{7}{5} \qquad \text{Amount of lemonade}$$

$$2\cdot\frac{1}{10}=\frac{2}{1}\cdot\frac{1}{10}=\frac{2}{10}=\frac{1}{5} \qquad \text{Amount of orange sherbet}$$

Adding,

$$\frac{3}{5}+\frac{7}{5}+\frac{1}{5}=\frac{3+7+1}{5}=\frac{11}{5}$$

PRACTICE EXERCISE 3

Perform the indicated operations.

$$\frac{7}{23}+\frac{9}{23}-\frac{4}{23}$$

Answer: $\frac{12}{23}$

PRACTICE EXERCISE 4

A mixture of nuts calls for $\frac{1}{8}$ pound of almonds, $\frac{7}{8}$ pound of peanuts, and $\frac{5}{8}$ pound of walnuts.

(a) How many pounds are in the final mixture?

(b) If four times the recipe is to be made, how many pounds of each nut is required, and how many pounds are in the final mixture?

Answers: (a) $\frac{13}{8}$ pounds (b) $\frac{1}{2}$ pound of almonds, $\frac{7}{2}$ pounds of peanuts, $\frac{5}{2}$ pounds of walnuts, $\frac{13}{2}$ pounds of nuts

Thus, if the recipe is doubled, there will be $\frac{11}{5}$ or $2\frac{1}{5}$ gallons of drink which is reasonable since $2 \cdot \frac{11}{10} = \frac{2 \cdot 11}{2 \cdot 5} = \frac{11}{5}$.

| **EXAMPLE 5** | **SUBTRACTING IN A WORK PROBLEM** |

If it takes $\frac{11}{24}$ of a day to do a job and Mike has been working for $\frac{7}{24}$ of a day, how much longer will it take him to complete the job?

Subtract the time worked from the total time required to complete the job.

$$\frac{11}{24} - \frac{7}{24} = \frac{4}{24} = \frac{1}{6}$$

Thus, it will take Mike $\frac{1}{6}$ of a day to finish the job.

A contractor estimated that it would take about $\frac{24}{5}$ weeks to do a job.

$\frac{24}{5} - \frac{18}{5}$ $\frac{6}{5}$

After work has gone on for $\frac{18}{5}$ weeks, how many weeks are left to complete the job?

Answer: $\frac{6}{5}$ weeks

3.1 EXERCISES

Answers to these exercises are given on page 645.

Find each sum in Exercises 1–9.

1. $\frac{2}{7} + \frac{3}{7}$

2. $\frac{1}{4} + \frac{5}{4}$

3. $\frac{3}{12} + \frac{11}{12}$

4. $\frac{1}{6} + \frac{5}{6}$

5. $\frac{3}{2} + \frac{9}{2}$

6. $\frac{7}{16} + \frac{13}{16}$

7. $\frac{3}{8} + \frac{5}{8} + \frac{7}{8}$

8. $\frac{2}{35} + \frac{18}{35} + \frac{25}{35}$

9. $\frac{17}{24} + \frac{23}{24} + \frac{8}{24}$

Find each difference in Exercises 10–15.

10. $\frac{7}{6} - \frac{5}{6}$

11. $\frac{9}{11} - \frac{3}{11}$

12. $\frac{5}{9} - \frac{2}{9}$

13. $\frac{23}{25} - \frac{8}{25}$

14. $\frac{28}{35} - \frac{18}{35}$

15. $\frac{73}{81} - \frac{10}{81}$

In Exercises 16–21, perform the indicated operations.

16. $\frac{2}{13} + \frac{9}{13} - \frac{5}{13}$

17. $\frac{9}{25} - \frac{3}{25} + \frac{4}{25}$

18. $\frac{22}{12} - \frac{10}{12} - \frac{6}{12}$

19. $\frac{8}{3} + \frac{14}{3} - \frac{1}{3}$

20. $\frac{7}{10} - \frac{1}{10} + \frac{3}{10}$

21. $\frac{9}{5} - \frac{6}{5} - \frac{3}{5}$

Solve each applied problem in Exercises 22-25.

22. **RECREATION** Jim hiked from Skunk Creek to Hidden Valley, a distance of $\frac{11}{15}$ mi, and from there to Indian Cave, a distance of $\frac{8}{15}$ mi. How far did he hike?

23. **AGRICULTURE** A farmer planted $\frac{3}{20}$ of his field on Monday and $\frac{9}{20}$ on Tuesday. What fraction of the field did he have to do on Wednesday to finish planting?

24. **CONSTRUCTION** To get the exact color he wanted, Bjorn mixed $\frac{1}{12}$ of a gallon of white paint with $\frac{7}{12}$ of a gallon of yellow and $\frac{8}{12}$ of a gallon of red paint. How much paint did he get?

25. **CONSTRUCTION** If Bjorn in Exercise 24 decides to triple the amount used, how much of each color will he need, and how much paint will result?

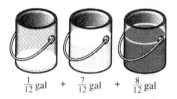

$\frac{1}{12}$ gal   + $\frac{7}{12}$ gal   + $\frac{8}{12}$ gal

CRITICAL THINKING

Let the variable a represent a natural number. Find the sum or difference in Exercises 26–27.

26. $\dfrac{16}{a} + \dfrac{11}{a}$

27. $\dfrac{16}{a} - \dfrac{11}{a}$

28. Burford added $\frac{1}{4}$ and $\frac{3}{4}$ as follows. $\dfrac{1}{4} + \dfrac{3}{4} = \dfrac{1+3}{4+4} = \dfrac{4}{8} = \dfrac{1}{2}$

What is wrong with his work?

REVIEW OR PREVIEW

Addition and subtraction of mixed numbers is discussed in Section 3.4. As a preview of this study, change each mixed number to an improper fraction and perform the indicated operation in Exercises 29–34. Give answers as mixed numbers when appropriate.

29. $3\dfrac{1}{5} + 1\dfrac{2}{5}$

30. $5\dfrac{1}{4} - 3\dfrac{3}{4}$

31. $7\dfrac{1}{3} - 3\dfrac{2}{3}$

32. $3\dfrac{2}{7} + 6\dfrac{5}{7}$

33. $1\dfrac{3}{10} + 5\dfrac{1}{10}$

34. $8\dfrac{1}{6} - 7\dfrac{5}{6}$

3.1 PARALLEL EXERCISES

Answers to these exercises are not given in the text.
Find each sum in Exercises 1–9.

1. $\dfrac{3}{5} + \dfrac{4}{5}$

2. $\dfrac{5}{8} + \dfrac{3}{8}$

3. $\dfrac{2}{15} + \dfrac{11}{15}$

4. $\dfrac{2}{9} + \dfrac{4}{9}$

5. $\dfrac{7}{3} + \dfrac{11}{3}$

6. $\dfrac{9}{20} + \dfrac{3}{20}$

7. $\dfrac{1}{4} + \dfrac{3}{4} + \dfrac{5}{4}$

8. $\dfrac{5}{48} + \dfrac{9}{48} + \dfrac{1}{48}$

9. $\dfrac{7}{60} + \dfrac{51}{60} + \dfrac{2}{60}$

Find each difference in Exercises 10–15.

10. $\dfrac{4}{9} - \dfrac{1}{9}$

11. $\dfrac{8}{13} - \dfrac{6}{13}$

12. $\dfrac{11}{15} - \dfrac{2}{15}$

13. $\dfrac{17}{12} - \dfrac{11}{12}$

14. $\dfrac{42}{55} - \dfrac{17}{55}$

15. $\dfrac{72}{105} - \dfrac{37}{105}$

In Exercises 16–21, perform the indicated operations.

16. $\dfrac{7}{17} + \dfrac{5}{17} - \dfrac{6}{17}$

17. $\dfrac{10}{30} - \dfrac{7}{30} + \dfrac{2}{30}$

18. $\dfrac{14}{6} - \dfrac{5}{6} - \dfrac{1}{6}$

19. $\dfrac{7}{15} + \dfrac{17}{15} - \dfrac{11}{15}$

20. $\dfrac{23}{28} - \dfrac{20}{28} + \dfrac{3}{28}$

21. $\dfrac{8}{12} - \dfrac{2}{12} - \dfrac{5}{12}$

Solve each applied problem in Exercises 22–25.

22. **ENGINEERING**   There was $\frac{5}{24}$ of a gallon of water in a container. How many gallons were in the container after $\frac{7}{24}$ gallon was added?

23. **AGRICULTURE** With deliveries the first week of the harvest season $\frac{4}{15}$ of a grain elevator was filled. If an additional $\frac{6}{15}$ of the elevator was filled the next week, what fraction was yet to be filled?

24. **CONSTRUCTION**   Nancy has $\frac{1}{9}$ gallon of white paint, $\frac{7}{9}$ gallon of blue paint, and $\frac{5}{9}$ gallon of green paint. How much paint would she have if she mixed them all together?

25. **CONSTRUCTION** If Nancy in Exercise 24 decided that she only wants $\frac{1}{4}$ of the amount of each color, how much of each would she mix and how much paint would result?

CRITICAL THINKING

Let the variable a represent a natural number. Find the sum or difference in Exercises 26–27.

 26. $\dfrac{10}{a} + \dfrac{21}{a}$

27. $\dfrac{15}{a} - \dfrac{7}{a}$

 28. Every time Burford subtracts fractions with a common denominator he gets a 0 in the denominator. Can you tell him how to prevent this?

GROUP PROJECT

The study of operations on fractions is complicated by the tendency to confuse the methods used in multiplication and division with those used in addition and subtraction. Begin discussions of the differences in these operations and continue as you go through the chapter.

3.2 FINDING LEAST COMMON MULTIPLES

STUDENT GUIDEPOSTS
1   USING THE LISTING METHOD FOR FINDING THE LCM
2   WORKING WITH THE PRIME FACTORIZATION METHOD FOR FINDING THE LCM
3   USING A SPECIAL ALGORITHM FOR FINDING THE LCM (OPTIONAL)
4   FINDING THE LCM OF DENOMINATORS

In order to add or subtract unlike fractions we must rename them as fractions with the same denominator. In this section we study ways of accomplishing this.

1 | LISTING METHOD FOR FINDING THE LCM

Recall from Section 1.5 that the multiples of a number are obtained by multiplying that number by each whole number. Consider the numbers 6 and 8. The nonzero multiples of 6 are   6, 12, 18, **24**, 30, 36, 42, **48**, 54, 60, 66, **72**,...,

and the nonzero multiples of 8 are   8, 16, **24**, 32, 40, **48**, 56, 64, **72**,....

Any number that is common to both lists of nonzero multiples is called a *common multiple*. The common multiples of 6 and 8 are   **24**, **48**, **72**,....

The smallest of the common multiples of two (or more) counting numbers is called the **least common multiple,** or **LCM,** of the numbers. Since 24 is the smallest number in the list of common multiples of 6 and 8, we say that 24 is the LCM of 6 and 8. This method of finding the LCM of two or more numbers is called the **listing method.** When using the listing method, it is a good idea to use a chart to organize your work as shown below.

Multiples of 6	6	12	18	**24**	30	36	42
Multiples of 8	8	16	**24**				

PRACTICE EXERCISE 1

Find the LCM of the given numbers.

(a) 14 and 18

(b) 5, 8, and 20

Answers: (a) 126 (b) 40

FINDING THE LCM USING THE LISTING METHOD							E X A M P L E 1

Find the LCM of the given numbers. (a) 12 and 30

Multiples of 12:	12,	24,	36,	48,	**60,**	72,	84
Multiples of 30:	30,	**60**					

We stop writing multiples of 30 once we find a multiple that is also in the first list. Since the smallest number common to both lists is 60, we say the LCM of 12 and 30 is 60.

(b) 6, 10, and 15

Multiples of 6:	6,	12,	18,	24,	**30,**	36,	42
Multiples of 10:	10,	20,	**30,**	40,	50,	60	
Multiples of 15:	15,	**30**					

Since 30 is in the first two lists, we can stop after 30 in the third list.
The LCM of 6, 10, and 15 is 30.

2 PRIME FACTORIZATION METHOD FOR FINDING THE LCM

Recall from Section 1.9 that every counting number greater than 1 is either prime or can be factored into primes. Any multiple (including the LCM) of two or more natural numbers must have as factors (divisors) all primes which are factors of each of the natural numbers. This leads to another efficient method for finding LCMs.

Suppose we factor both 6 and 8 into primes.

$$6 = 2 \cdot 3$$

$$8 = 2 \cdot 2 \cdot 2 = 2^3$$

The LCM of 6 and 8 must have $2 \cdot 3$ as a factor since the LCM is a multiple of 6. It must also have $2 \cdot 2 \cdot 2$ or 2^3 as a factor since it must be a multiple of 8. The smallest number which fits these restrictions is

$$2 \cdot 2 \cdot 2 \qquad\qquad 2 \cdot 3$$

Thus, the LCM is $2 \cdot 2 \cdot 2 \cdot 3 = 2^3 \cdot 3 = 24$. This illustrates a general method for finding LCMs.

TO FIND THE LCM USING PRIME FACTORS
1. Factor each number into primes and express it using exponents.
2. If there are no common prime factors, the LCM is the product of all the prime factors.
3. If there are common prime factors, the LCM is the product of the highest power of each prime factor.

EXPLORATION GUIDE

Which of the methods for finding the LCM do you find the best for you to use? Give advantages and disadvantages of each.

To use the rule above to find the LCM of 6 and 8, first factor each number into primes using exponents.

$$6 = 2 \cdot 3$$

$$8 = 2 \cdot 2 \cdot 2 = 2^3$$

Since these two numbers have a common prime factor of 2, we use the highest power of each prime factor. We highlight where each prime occurs the greatest number of times.

$$6 = 2 \cdot \mathbf{3} \qquad \text{One 2, one 3}$$

$$8 = \mathbf{2 \cdot 2 \cdot 2} = \mathbf{2^3} \qquad \text{Three 2s}$$

Now we can find the LCM by finding the product of 2^3 and 3.

$$\text{LCM} = 2 \cdot 2 \cdot 2 \cdot 3 = 2^3 \cdot 3 = 24$$

EXAMPLE 2   FINDING THE LCM USING PRIME FACTORS

Find the LCM of the numbers in Example 1 by using prime factors.

(a) 12 and 30

$$12 = 2 \cdot 2 \cdot 3 = 2^2 \cdot 3 = \qquad \text{Two 2s, one 3}$$
$$30 = 2 \cdot 3 \cdot 5 \qquad \text{One 2, one 3, one 5}$$

The LCM must be the product of two 2s, one 3, and one 5. Thus, the LCM of 12 and 30 is $2 \cdot 2 \cdot 3 \cdot 5 = 60$.

(b) 6, 10, and 15

$$6 = 2 \cdot 3 \qquad \text{One 2, one 3}$$
$$10 = 2 \cdot 5 \qquad \text{One 2, one 5}$$
$$15 = 3 \cdot 5 \qquad \text{One 3, one 5}$$

Thus, the LCM of 6, 10, and 15 is $2 \cdot 3 \cdot 5 = 30$.

Compare the results of Example 2 with those of Example 1.

EXAMPLE 3   FINDING THE LCM USING PRIME FACTORS

Find the LCM using prime factors.

(a) 7 and 28

$$7 = 7 \qquad \text{One 7}$$
$$28 = 2 \cdot 2 \cdot 7 = 2^2 \cdot 7 \qquad \text{Two 2s, one 7}$$

The $\text{LCM} = 2 \cdot 2 \cdot 7 = 2^2 \cdot 7 = 28$. Note that the LCM of 7 and 28 is one of the two numbers itself. This will happen when one number is a multiple of the other (28 is a multiple of 7).

(b) 6, 10, and 25

$$6 = 2 \cdot 3 \qquad \text{One 2, one 3}$$
$$10 = 2 \cdot 5 \qquad \text{One 2, one 5}$$
$$25 = 5 \cdot 5 = 5^2 \qquad \text{Two 5s}$$

The LCM is $2 \cdot 3 \cdot 5 \cdot 5 = 2 \cdot 3 \cdot 5^2 = 150$.

EXAMPLE 4   APPLYING THE LCM

A man wishes to apply ceramic tiles to a portion of a wall. He plans to use three types of tiles, one 5 inches long, another 6 inches long, and a third 14 inches long. What is the shortest length of wall space he can cover if the first row contains only 14-in tiles, the second row contains only 6-in tiles, and the third contains only 5-in tiles? See Figure 3.2 [Assume that the tiles are not cut and are laid with no space between them.]

FIGURE 3.2

The length of the first row is a multiple of 14 inches, the length of the second row is a multiple of 6 inches, and the length of the third row is a multiple of 5 inches. Thus, the shortest distance that can be covered by these three lengths of tile is the LCM of 5, 6, and 14.

$$5 = 5 \qquad \text{One 5}$$
$$6 = 2 \cdot 3 \qquad \text{One 2, one 3}$$
$$14 = 2 \cdot 7 \qquad \text{One 2, one 7}$$

PRACTICE EXERCISE 2

Find the LCM using prime factors.

(a) 14 and 18

(b) 5, 8, and 20

Answers: (a) 126 (b) 40

PRACTICE EXERCISE 3

Find the LCM using prime factors.

(a) 13 and 39

(b) 8, 12, and 30

Answers: (a) 39 (b) 120

PRACTICE EXERCISE 4

Three types of pipe are to be laid in the same ditch. One pipe is 3 feet long, another 4 feet long, and the third is 10 feet long. What is the shortest distance from the start to where the three will have a seam at the same point?

Answer: 60 feet

The LCM is $2 \cdot 3 \cdot 5 \cdot 7 = 210$. The shortest distance that can be covered is 210 inches by using 15 of the 14-in tiles $(210 \div 14 = 15)$ in the bottom row, 35 of the 6-in tiles $(210 \div 6 = 35)$ in the next row, and 42 of the 5-in tiles $(210 \div 5 = 42)$ in the third row.

3 SPECIAL ALGORITHM FOR FINDING THE LCM (OPTIONAL)

Although the prime factorization method is probably best for use in later mathematics courses, the following method works well for whole numbers. To explain the procedure we will find the LCM of 36 and 45 using this method.

The basic idea is to divide these numbers by the prime numbers to see which primes are factors of each. It is best to start with the lowest prime and work up. Remember the first few prime numbers are

$$2, 3, 5, 7, 11.$$

Try to divide 36 and 45 by 2.

2	36	45
	18	45

Two divides 36 but not 45. We put the quotient $18 = 36 \div 2$ below 36 and bring down 45 unchanged. Two will also divide 18.

2	36	45
2	18	45
9	45	

Since $18 \div 2 = 9$, we put 9 and 45 on the next line. Now 2 will not divide 9 or 45 so we try the next prime, 3.

2	36	45
2	18	45
3	9	45
	3	15

Since $9 \div 3 = 3$ and $45 \div 3 = 15$, the next line has a 3 and a 15. Divide by 3 again.

2	36	45
2	18	45
3	9	45
3	3	15
	1	5

We complete the process by dividing by 5.

2	36	45
2	18	45
3	9	45
3	3	15
5	1	5
	1	1

When the bottom row is all ones we stop the process and the LCM is the product of the prime factors in the left column since each divided one of the two numbers. Thus the LCM of 36 and 45 is

$$\text{LCM} = \mathbf{2 \cdot 2 \cdot 3 \cdot 3 \cdot 5} = 180.$$

In the next example we find the LCM of three numbers using this procedure.

FINDING THE LCM BY SPECIAL ALGORITHM   EXAMPLE 5

Find the LCM of 7, 9, and 12.

2	7	9	12	Divide by 2
2	7	9	6	Divide by 2 again
3	7	9	3	Divide by 3
3	7	3	1	Divide by 3 again
7	7	1	1	Divide by 7
	1	1	1	

PRACTICE EXERCISE 5

Find the LCM of 6, 11, and 14.

Answer: 462

Since the last row is all ones, the process stops and the

$$LCM = \mathbf{2 \cdot 2 \cdot 3 \cdot 3 \cdot 7} = 252.$$

4 LCM OF DENOMINATORS

We conclude this section by finding the LCM of the denominators of a pair of fractions and expressing each as an equivalent fraction having the LCM as denominator. This will prepare you for addition and subtraction of fractions in Section 3.3.

EXAMPLE 6 — FINDING THE LCM OF DENOMINATORS

Find the LCM of the denominators of $\frac{2}{15}$ and $\frac{3}{20}$ and express each as an equivalent fraction with the LCM as denominator.

We must find the LCM of 15 and 20.

$$15 = \mathbf{3 \cdot 5} \qquad \text{One 3, one 5}$$
$$20 = \mathbf{2 \cdot 2 \cdot 5} = \mathbf{2^2 \cdot 5} \qquad \text{Two 2s, one 5}$$

Thus the $LCM = \mathbf{2 \cdot 2 \cdot 3 \cdot 5} = 2^2 \cdot 3 \cdot 5 = 60$. To express $\frac{2}{15}$ with denominator 60, we must multiply numerator and denominator by 2^2, the missing factors which make the denominator equal $2^2 \cdot 3 \cdot 5$ or 60.

$$\frac{2}{15} = \frac{2 \cdot \mathbf{2^2}}{15 \cdot \mathbf{2^2}} = \frac{8}{60}$$

Now multiply numerator and denominator of $\frac{3}{20}$ by 3, the missing factor which makes the denominator equal $2^2 \cdot 3 \cdot 5$ or 60.

$$\frac{3}{20} = \frac{3 \cdot \mathbf{3}}{20 \cdot \mathbf{3}} = \frac{9}{60}$$

With the $LCM = 60$, then $\frac{2}{15} = \frac{8}{60}$ and $\frac{3}{20} = \frac{9}{60}$.

3.2 EXERCISES

Answers to these exercises are given on page 645.

Use the listing method to find the LCM in Exercises 1–6.

1. 24 and 18
2. 15 and 9
3. 20 and 30

4. 3 and 12
5. 10, 12, and 20
6. 8, 9, and 12

Use prime factors to find the LCM in Exercises 7–15.

7. 36 and 15
8. 30 and 28
9. 13 and 9

10. 2, 5, and 7
11. 121 and 22
12. 4, 6, and 9

13. 52 and 66
14. 18, 24, and 30
15. 22, 55, and 121

Use any method to find the LCM in Exercises 16–21.

16. 20 and 45
17. 18 and 28
18. 25 and 30

19. 10, 15, and 27
20. 12, 14, and 28
21. 9, 20, and 25

In Exercises 22–27, find the LCM of the denominators and express each fraction as an equivalent fraction with the LCM for a denominator.

22. $\frac{1}{8}$ and $\frac{7}{12}$

23. $\frac{2}{3}$ and $\frac{5}{6}$

24. $\frac{5}{28}$ and $\frac{11}{42}$

25. $\dfrac{18}{25}, \dfrac{1}{15}$, and $\dfrac{1}{3}$ 26. $\dfrac{3}{8}, \dfrac{2}{9}$, and $\dfrac{5}{12}$ 27. $\dfrac{3}{10}, \dfrac{7}{100}$, and $\dfrac{19}{1000}$

Solve each applied problem in Exercises 28–29.

28. **SPACE**   Mercury, Venus, and Earth revolve around the sun once every 3, 7, and 12 months, respectively. If the three planets are now in the same straight line, what is the smallest number of months that must pass before they line up again?

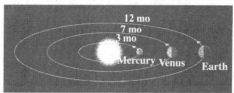

29. **CONSTRUCTION**   A blocklayer has three lengths of blocks: 8 inches, 9 inches, and 14 inches. He plans to lay a wall of each type of block so that the three walls are the same length. Neglecting the mortar seams, what is the shortest length of wall possible?

CRITICAL THINKING

30. If *m* is a factor of *n,* what is the LCM of *m* and *n?*
31. If *m* and *n* are different prime numbers, what is the LCM of *m* and *n?*
32. If *m* and *n* are different prime numbers, what is the LCM of *m* and *mn?*
33. Burford is having problems understanding the prime factorization method for finding the LCM. Write a summary of the method that you think he would understand.

REVIEW OR PREVIEW

In Exercises 34–39, perform the indicated operations.

34. $\dfrac{7}{12} + \dfrac{2}{12}$ 35. $\dfrac{13}{11} - \dfrac{6}{11}$ 36. $\dfrac{4}{7} + \dfrac{1}{7} + \dfrac{2}{7}$

37. $\dfrac{11}{6} - \dfrac{7}{6}$ 38. $\dfrac{18}{15} - \dfrac{13}{15} + \dfrac{1}{15}$ 39. $\dfrac{6}{3} - \dfrac{2}{3} - \dfrac{1}{3}$

40. **FINANCE**   The bond price went up $\dfrac{25}{32}$ and then went down $\dfrac{17}{32}$. Finally, the price went up $\dfrac{11}{32}$. (a) How far was the price from the starting point? (b) What was the total change in price?

3.2 PARALLEL EXERCISES

Answers to these exercises are not given in the text.
Use the listing method to find the LCM in Exercises 1–6.

1. 15 and 6   2. 30 and 40   3. 45 and 30
4. 5 and 16   5. 5, 8, and 12   6. 7, 21, and 18

Use prime factors to find the LCM in Exrcises 7–15.

7. 18 and 20   8. 30 and 21   9. 13 and 12
10. 3, 8, and 9   11. 169 and 26   12. 9, 15, and 22
13. 45 and 42   14. 20, 26, and 34   15. 49, 35, and 65

Use any method to find the LCM in Exercises 16–21.

16. 10 and 55   17. 15 and 42   18. 40 and 75
19. 9, 12, and 20   20. 8, 10, and 36   21. 12, 20, and 42

In Exercises 22–27, find the LCM of the denominators and express each fraction as an equivalent fraction with the LCM for a denominator.

22. $\dfrac{3}{10}$ and $\dfrac{4}{15}$

23. $\dfrac{5}{14}$ and $\dfrac{1}{4}$

24. $\dfrac{6}{55}$ and $\dfrac{5}{44}$

25. $\dfrac{2}{3}, \dfrac{5}{18},$ and $\dfrac{7}{30}$

26. $\dfrac{7}{27}, \dfrac{3}{4},$ and $\dfrac{1}{24}$

27. $\dfrac{7}{20}, \dfrac{9}{200}, \dfrac{11}{2000}$

Solve each applied problem in Exercises 28–29.

28. **SPACE**   Three satellites in the same plane revolve around the earth once every 6, 12, and 14 hours. If the three satellites are in the same straight line, what is the least number of hours that must pass before they line up again?

29. **CONSTRUCTION**   A bricklayer has three lengths of bricks: 4 inches, 5 inches, and 6 inches. He plans to lay a wall of each type of brick so that the three walls are the same length. Neglecting mortar seams, what is the shortest length of wall possible?

CRITICAL THINKING

30. If m and n are factors of k, what is the LCM of m, n, and k?
31. If m, n, and k are different prime numbers, what is the LCM of m, n, and k?
32. If m, n, and k are different prime numbers, what is the LCM of mn and k?
33. Burford is having problems understanding the special algorithm for finding the LCM. Write a summary of the method that you think he would understand.

GROUP PROJECT

Discuss how Section 1.9 was needed in the study of LCM and how this section and the previous section must be taken together to prepare for adding and subtracting unlike fractions in Section 3.3. Also, note that the material in this section relates to addition and subtraction of fractions and is not used in multiplying and dividing. With these examples in mind, discuss the difficulties that you have in deciding what material to use and what not to use when you are studying a particular topic.

3.3 ADDING AND SUBTRACTING UNLIKE FRACTIONS

STUDENT GUIDEPOSTS

1   FINDING THE LEAST COMMON DENOMINATOR (LCD)
2   USING A METHOD FOR ADDING AND SUBTRACTING UNLIKE FRACTIONS

1 LEAST COMMON DENOMINATOR (LCD)

In Section 3.2 we found the least common multiple (LCM) of the denominators of fractions. The LCM of the denominators of two or more fractions is called the **least common denominator (LCD)** of the fractions. The first step in adding or subtracting unlike fractions is to find the LCD and change unlike fractions to like fractions with the LCD as the denominator.

EXPLORATION GUIDE

Notice that multiplying numerator and denominator of $\frac{1}{3}$ by 4 is the same as multiplying $\frac{1}{3}$ by 1.

$$\frac{1}{3} \cdot 1 = \frac{1}{3} \cdot \frac{1}{1} = \frac{1}{3} \cdot \frac{4}{4} = \frac{1 \cdot 4}{3 \cdot 4} = \frac{4}{12}$$

Why does this prove that $\frac{1}{3}$ and $\frac{4}{12}$ are equivalent?

2 | METHOD FOR ADDING AND SUBTRACTING UNLIKE FRACTIONS

Suppose we use the problem

$$\frac{1}{3} + \frac{3}{4}$$

to illustrate the addition method. You can probably tell by inspection that the least common denominator (LCD) is 12. As we did at the end of Section 3.2, change each fraction to an equivalent fraction with the $LCD = 12$ as denominator.

$$\frac{1}{3} = \frac{1 \cdot \mathbf{4}}{3 \cdot \mathbf{4}} = \frac{4}{12}$$

Multiply numerator and denominator by 4, the missing factor which makes the denominator 12.

$$\frac{3}{4} = \frac{3 \cdot \mathbf{3}}{4 \cdot \mathbf{3}} = \frac{9}{12}$$

Multiply numerator and denominator by 3, the missing factor which makes the denominator 12.

Thus, $\dfrac{1}{3} + \dfrac{3}{4} = \dfrac{4}{12} + \dfrac{9}{12} = \dfrac{4+9}{12} = \dfrac{13}{12}, = 1\dfrac{1}{12}.$

TO ADD OR SUBTRACT UNLIKE FRACTIONS

1. Rewrite the sum or difference with each denominator written as a prime or factored into primes.
2. Find the LCD (the LCM of all denominators).
3. Multiply the numerator and denominator of each fraction by all factors present in the LCD but missing in the denominator of the particular fraction.
4. Add or subtract the resulting like fractions.

ADDING AND SUBTRACTING FRACTIONS | EXAMPLE 1

Perform the indicated operation.

PRACTICE EXERCISE 1

Perform the indicated operations.

(a) $\dfrac{2}{5} + \dfrac{1}{6}$

(a) $\dfrac{2}{3} + \dfrac{1}{4} = \dfrac{2}{3} + \dfrac{1}{2 \cdot 2}$

Rewrite denominators as primes; LCD is $2 \cdot 2 \cdot 3$

$\quad = \dfrac{\mathbf{2 \cdot 2} \cdot 2}{\mathbf{2 \cdot 2} \cdot 3} + \dfrac{1 \cdot \mathbf{3}}{2 \cdot 2 \cdot \mathbf{3}}$

Multiply by missing factors so denominators equal $2 \cdot 2 \cdot 3$

$\quad = \dfrac{8}{12} + \dfrac{3}{12}$

Simplify and add

$\quad = \dfrac{8+3}{12}$

$\quad = \dfrac{11}{12}$

(b) $\dfrac{1}{4} + \dfrac{3}{10}$

(b) $\dfrac{5}{9} + \dfrac{1}{6} = \dfrac{5}{3 \cdot 3} + \dfrac{1}{2 \cdot 3}$

Rewrite denominators as primes: LCD is $2 \cdot 3 \cdot 3$

$\quad = \dfrac{\mathbf{2} \cdot 5}{\mathbf{2} \cdot 3 \cdot 3} + \dfrac{1 \cdot \mathbf{3}}{2 \cdot 3 \cdot \mathbf{3}}$

Multiply by missing factors so denominators equal $2 \cdot 3 \cdot 3$

$\quad = \dfrac{10}{18} + \dfrac{3}{18}$

Simplify and add

$\quad = \dfrac{10+3}{18}$

$\quad = \dfrac{13}{18}$

With practice, we may be able to take some shortcuts. For example, if we know that 18 is the LCD of 9 and 6, we can skip the factoring step and add as follows.

$$\frac{5}{9} + \frac{1}{6} = \frac{5 \cdot \mathbf{2}}{9 \cdot \mathbf{2}} + \frac{1 \cdot \mathbf{3}}{6 \cdot \mathbf{3}}$$

Multiply by missing factors so denominators equal 18

$$= \frac{10}{18} + \frac{3}{18} = \frac{13}{18}$$

(c) $2 - \dfrac{3}{7} = \dfrac{2}{1} - \dfrac{3}{7}$　　　LCD = 7

$$= \frac{2 \cdot \mathbf{7}}{1 \cdot \mathbf{7}} - \frac{3}{7}$$　　Multiply by missing factor

$$= \frac{14 - 3}{7}$$　　Simplify and subtract

$$= \frac{11}{7}$$

(c) $7 - \dfrac{5}{11}$

Answers: (a) $\frac{17}{30}$ (b) $\frac{11}{20}$ (c) $\frac{72}{11}$

Sometimes fractions are added vertically. For example, $\frac{2}{3}$ and $\frac{1}{4}$ could be added as follows.

$$\frac{2}{3} = \frac{2}{3} = \frac{\mathbf{2} \cdot \mathbf{2} \cdot 2}{\mathbf{2} \cdot \mathbf{2} \cdot 3} = \frac{8}{12}$$

LCD $= 2 \cdot 2 \cdot 3 = 12$

$$+\frac{1}{4} = \frac{1}{2 \cdot 2} = \frac{1 \cdot \mathbf{3}}{2 \cdot 2 \cdot \mathbf{3}} = \frac{3}{12}$$

$$\frac{11}{12}$$　　　　$8 + 3 = 11$

Compare this with Example 1(a).

EXPLORATION GUIDE

Use the sum of $\frac{2}{3}$ and $\frac{1}{4}$ to show an example of the commutative law of addition of fractions. Show that

$$\frac{2}{3} + \frac{1}{4} = \frac{1}{4} + \frac{2}{3}.$$

EXAMPLE 2　　**ADDING AND SUBTRACTING FRACTIONS**

Perform the indicated operation.

(a) $\dfrac{7}{12} - \dfrac{2}{9} = \dfrac{7}{2 \cdot 2 \cdot 3} - \dfrac{2}{3 \cdot 3}$

Rewrite denominators
LCD $= 2 \cdot 2 \cdot 3 \cdot 3 = 36$

$$= \frac{7 \cdot \mathbf{3}}{2 \cdot 2 \cdot 3 \cdot \mathbf{3}} - \frac{\mathbf{2} \cdot \mathbf{2} \cdot 2}{\mathbf{2} \cdot \mathbf{2} \cdot 3 \cdot 3}$$

Multiply by missing factors so denominators equal $2 \cdot 2 \cdot 3 \cdot 3$

$$= \frac{21 - 8}{36}$$　　Simplify and subtract

$$= \frac{13}{36}$$

(b) $\dfrac{2}{3} - \dfrac{1}{6} = \dfrac{2}{3} - \dfrac{1}{2 \cdot 3}$

LCD $= 2 \cdot 3 = 6$

$$= \frac{\mathbf{2} \cdot 2}{\mathbf{2} \cdot 3} - \frac{1}{2 \cdot 3}$$

Multiply by missing factor

$$= \frac{4 - 1}{6}$$　　Simplify and subtract

$$= \frac{3}{6}$$

$$= \frac{1 \cdot \cancel{3}}{2 \cdot \cancel{3}}$$　　Reduce to lowest terms

PRACTICE EXERCISE 2

Perform the indicated operations.

(a) $\dfrac{11}{15} - \dfrac{3}{20}$

(b) $\dfrac{7}{9} - \dfrac{5}{18}$

(c) $\dfrac{4}{11} + 1$

$$= \dfrac{1}{2}$$

(c) $\dfrac{7}{9} + 3 = \dfrac{7}{3 \cdot 3} + \dfrac{3}{1}$ LCD $= 3 \cdot 3 = 9$

$$= \dfrac{7}{3 \cdot 3} + \dfrac{3 \cdot 3 \cdot 3}{1 \cdot 3 \cdot 3}$$ Multiply by missing factors

$$= \dfrac{7}{9} + \dfrac{27}{9}$$ Simplify and add

$$= \dfrac{7 + 27}{9}$$

$$= \dfrac{34}{9}$$

As with addition, fractions can also be subtracted vertically. For example, $\dfrac{7}{12} - \dfrac{2}{9}$ can be written as follows.

$$\dfrac{7}{12} = \dfrac{7}{2 \cdot 2 \cdot 3} = \dfrac{7 \cdot 3}{2 \cdot 2 \cdot 3 \cdot 3} = \dfrac{21}{36}$$ The LCD $= 2 \cdot 2 \cdot 3 \cdot 3 = 36$

$$-\dfrac{2}{9} = -\dfrac{2}{3 \cdot 3} = -\dfrac{2 \cdot 2 \cdot 2}{2 \cdot 2 \cdot 3 \cdot 3} = -\dfrac{8}{36}$$

$$\dfrac{13}{36}$$ $21 - 8 = 13$

Compare this with Example 2(a).

Sums and differences of more than two fractions can also be found.

PRACTICE EXERCISE 3

Perform the indicated operations.

(a) $\dfrac{1}{5} + \dfrac{3}{10} + \dfrac{5}{14}$

(b) $\dfrac{19}{20} - \dfrac{1}{4} - \dfrac{2}{3}$

USING OPERATIONS ON THREE FRACTIONS   **EXAMPLE 3**

Perform the indicated operations.

(a) $\dfrac{1}{3} + \dfrac{1}{4} + \dfrac{5}{6} = \dfrac{1}{3} + \dfrac{1}{2 \cdot 2} + \dfrac{5}{2 \cdot 3}$ Factor denominators: LCD $= 2 \cdot 2 \cdot 3 = 12$

$$= \dfrac{2 \cdot 2 \cdot 1}{2 \cdot 2 \cdot 3} + \dfrac{1 \cdot 3}{2 \cdot 2 \cdot 3} + \dfrac{2 \cdot 5}{2 \cdot 2 \cdot 3}$$ Supply missing factors

$$= \dfrac{4 + 3 + 10}{2 \cdot 2 \cdot 3} = \dfrac{17}{12}$$

(b) $\dfrac{13}{15} - \dfrac{1}{5} - \dfrac{1}{2} = \dfrac{13}{3 \cdot 5} - \dfrac{1}{5} - \dfrac{1}{2}$ LCD $= 2 \cdot 3 \cdot 5 = 30$

$$= \dfrac{2 \cdot 13}{2 \cdot 3 \cdot 5} - \dfrac{2 \cdot 3 \cdot 1}{2 \cdot 3 \cdot 5} - \dfrac{1 \cdot 3 \cdot 5}{2 \cdot 3 \cdot 5}$$

$$= \dfrac{26 - 6 - 15}{2 \cdot 3 \cdot 5}$$

$$= \dfrac{5}{2 \cdot 3 \cdot 5} = \dfrac{5}{2 \cdot 3 \cdot 5} = \dfrac{1}{6}$$ Reduce to lowest terms

NOTE In Example 3(b) we left the denominator in factored form, and this made it easier to reduce the answer to lowest terms.

EXAMPLE 4   **USING ADDITION IN A RECIPE**

In making three different kinds of pastries, Mr. Chandler used $\frac{3}{4}$ cup of flour for the first batch, $\frac{7}{8}$ cup for the second, and $\frac{5}{3}$ cups for the third. How much flour did he use?

Add the three fractions.

$$\frac{3}{4}+\frac{7}{8}+\frac{5}{3}=\frac{3}{2\cdot 2}+\frac{7}{2\cdot 2\cdot 2}+\frac{5}{3} \qquad LCD = 2\cdot 2\cdot 2\cdot 3=24$$

$$=\frac{3\cdot \mathbf{2}\cdot \mathbf{3}}{2\cdot 2\cdot \mathbf{2}\cdot \mathbf{3}}+\frac{7\cdot \mathbf{3}}{2\cdot 2\cdot 2\cdot \mathbf{3}}+\frac{\mathbf{2}\cdot \mathbf{2}\cdot \mathbf{2}\cdot 5}{\mathbf{2}\cdot \mathbf{2}\cdot \mathbf{2}\cdot 3}$$

$$=\frac{18+21+40}{24}=\frac{79}{24}=3\frac{7}{24}$$

Thus, Mr. Chandler used $3\frac{7}{24}$ cups of flour.

CAUTION   Never add or subtract fractions by adding or subtracting numerators and denominators. For example,

$$\frac{2}{5}+\frac{1}{4} \quad \text{IS NOT THE SAME AS} \quad \frac{2+1}{5+4}=\frac{3}{9}=\frac{1}{3},$$

since

$$\frac{2}{5}+\frac{1}{4}=\frac{2\cdot 4}{5\cdot 4}+\frac{1\cdot 5}{4\cdot 5}=\frac{8+5}{20}=\frac{13}{20}.$$

PRACTICE EXERCISE 4

Wilma ran $\frac{7}{8}$ mi, $\frac{3}{4}$ mi, and $\frac{9}{10}$ mi during one training session. How many miles did she run?

Answer: $\frac{101}{40}$ or $2\frac{21}{40}$ mi

EXPLORATION GUIDE

In Examples 3 and 4 we wrote the sum of three fractions without using parentheses. Use the sum in Example 4 as an example of the associative law of addition of fractions. Show that

$$\left(\frac{3}{4}+\frac{7}{8}\right)+\frac{5}{3}=\frac{3}{4}+\left(\frac{7}{8}+\frac{5}{3}\right).$$

3.3 EXERCISES

Answers to these exercises are given on page 645.

Add the fractions in Exercises 1–12.

1. $\frac{2}{3}+\frac{1}{2}$

2. $\frac{11}{12}+\frac{5}{6}$

3. $\frac{3}{10}+\frac{5}{12}$

4. $\frac{7}{10}+\frac{2}{3}$

5. $\frac{7}{12}+\frac{1}{18}$

6. $\frac{11}{21}+\frac{2}{35}$

7. $\frac{3}{28}+\frac{13}{70}$

8. $4+\frac{4}{5}$

9. $\frac{7}{8}+3$

10. $\frac{5}{12}$
$+\frac{3}{4}$

11. $\frac{1}{6}$
$+\frac{3}{5}$

12. $\frac{7}{15}$
$+\frac{4}{25}$

Subtract the fractions in Exercises 13–24.

13. $\frac{3}{8}-\frac{1}{4}$

14. $\frac{3}{4}-\frac{2}{3}$

15. $\frac{7}{11}-\frac{2}{7}$

16. $\frac{7}{15}-\frac{13}{35}$

17. $4-\frac{4}{5}$

18. $1-\frac{8}{9}$

19. $\frac{5}{24}-\frac{1}{8}$

20. $\frac{17}{12}-\frac{9}{16}$

21. $\dfrac{19}{15} - 1$

22. $\begin{array}{r} \dfrac{4}{7} \\ -\dfrac{1}{14} \\ \hline \end{array}$

23. $\begin{array}{r} \dfrac{8}{15} \\ -\dfrac{3}{20} \\ \hline \end{array}$

24. $\begin{array}{r} \dfrac{29}{12} \\ -\ 2 \\ \hline \end{array}$

Perform the indicated operations in Exercises 25–30.

25. $\dfrac{2}{3} + \dfrac{3}{4} + \dfrac{1}{6}$

26. $\dfrac{3}{5} + \dfrac{1}{3} + \dfrac{7}{10}$

27. $\dfrac{14}{15} - \dfrac{2}{5} - \dfrac{1}{3}$

28. $\dfrac{7}{20} - \dfrac{1}{4} + \dfrac{3}{8}$

29. $\dfrac{8}{15} + \dfrac{1}{12} - \dfrac{5}{20}$

30. $\dfrac{7}{3} - 2 + \dfrac{1}{7}$

Solve each applied problem in Exercises 31–32.

31. **CONSTRUCTION** To obtain the right shade of paint for her living room, Susan Wells mixed $\dfrac{7}{8}$ of a gallon of white paint with $\dfrac{2}{3}$ of a gallon of yellow and $\dfrac{3}{5}$ of a gallon of blue. How much paint did she have?

32. **CONSTRUCTION** Suppose Susan in Exercise 31 used 2 gallons of the paint that she mixed to paint her living room. How much paint did she have left?

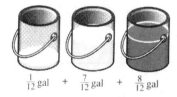

$\tfrac{1}{12}$ gal   + $\tfrac{7}{12}$ gal   + $\tfrac{8}{12}$ gal

 CRITICAL THINKING

Let the variables a and b represent natural numbers. Perform the indicated operations in Exercises 33–34.

33. $\dfrac{3}{a} + \dfrac{2}{b}$

34. $\dfrac{5}{ab} - \dfrac{2}{b}$

In Exercises 35, let a, b, and c represent fractions.

35. State the commutative law of addition for fractions using *a* and *b* as the fractions.

36. Burford still does not know the differences between multiplying fractions and adding them. Can you write a paragraph for him describing the differences in the two processes?

REVIEW OR PREVIEW

In Exercises 37–39, find the LCM.

37. 27 and 35

38. 10 and 45

39. 12, 14, and 21

Exercises 40–42 review material from Section 2.5. We review multiplication and division of mixed numbers to give a contrast with addition and subtraction of mixed numbers in the next section.

40. $3\dfrac{2}{3} \cdot 6\dfrac{1}{11}$

41. $5\dfrac{1}{2} \div 8\dfrac{3}{4}$

42. $10 \div 7\dfrac{6}{7}$

3.3 PARALLEL EXERCISES

Answers to these exercises are not given in the text.

Add the fractions in Exercises 1–12.

1. $\dfrac{1}{3} + \dfrac{1}{4}$

2. $\dfrac{5}{12} + \dfrac{1}{6}$

3. $\dfrac{1}{10} + \dfrac{7}{12}$

4. $\dfrac{2}{7} + \dfrac{3}{8}$

5. $\dfrac{9}{16} + \dfrac{5}{6}$

6. $\dfrac{9}{22} + \dfrac{4}{33}$

7. $\dfrac{21}{80} + \dfrac{11}{24}$

8. $\dfrac{3}{10} + 7$

9. $3 + \dfrac{9}{11}$

10. $\dfrac{7}{10}$
$+ \dfrac{2}{5}$

11. $\dfrac{5}{8}$
$+ \dfrac{5}{12}$

12. $\dfrac{8}{35}$
$+ \dfrac{11}{21}$

Subtract the fractions in Exercises 13–24.

13. $\dfrac{5}{8} - \dfrac{1}{3}$

14. $\dfrac{8}{11} - \dfrac{2}{7}$

15. $\dfrac{11}{15} - \dfrac{6}{35}$

16. $\dfrac{13}{14} - \dfrac{2}{21}$

17. $5 - \dfrac{3}{7}$

18. $7 - \dfrac{3}{8}$

19. $\dfrac{1}{7} - \dfrac{1}{13}$

20. $\dfrac{7}{24} - \dfrac{9}{40}$

21. $5 - \dfrac{34}{7}$

22. $\dfrac{7}{10}$
$- \dfrac{2}{5}$

23. $\dfrac{13}{22}$
$\dfrac{5}{33}$

24. $\quad 4$
$- \dfrac{17}{5}$

Perform the indicated operations in Exercises 25–30.

25. $\dfrac{1}{4} + \dfrac{1}{5} + \dfrac{3}{10}$

26. $\dfrac{3}{8} + \dfrac{1}{6} + \dfrac{5}{12}$

27. $\dfrac{20}{21} - \dfrac{2}{3} - \dfrac{2}{7}$

28. $\dfrac{13}{30} - \dfrac{2}{5} + \dfrac{7}{10}$

29. $\dfrac{7}{16} + \dfrac{9}{24} - \dfrac{7}{10}$

30. $\dfrac{11}{2} - 5 - \dfrac{3}{11}$

Solve each applied problem in Exercises 31–32.

31. **POLITICS**   There were three candidates from the Western Party in an election. One got $\frac{1}{5}$ of the votes, another $\frac{1}{12}$ of the votes, and the third $\frac{3}{8}$ of the votes. What total fraction of the votes did the Western Party receive?

32. **POLITICS**   Two candidates from the Northern Party received the remaining votes in the election in Exercise 31. What fraction of the votes did the Northern Party get?

 CRITICAL THINKING

Let the variables a and b represent natural numbers. Perform the indicated operations in Exerecises 33–34.

33. $\dfrac{5}{ab} + \dfrac{7}{a}$

34. $\dfrac{6}{a} - \dfrac{3}{b}$

In Exercises 35, let a, b, and c represent fractions.

35. State the associative law of addition for fractions using *a*, *b*, and *c* as the fractions.

36. Burford still does not know the differences between dividing fractions and subtracting them. Can you write a paragraph for him describing the differences in the two processes?

GROUP PROJECT

Many students find the addition and subtraction of fractions to be difficult to understand and carry out. Write down what seems to be hard for you and try to understand why it is. Discussing your list with others may improve the understanding and skills of the whole group.

3.4 ADDING AND SUBTRACTING MIXED NUMBERS

STUDENT GUIDEPOSTS
1   ADDING MIXED NUMBERS
2   SUBTRACTING MIXED NUMBERS
3   WORKING WITH APPLICATIONS OF MIXED NUMBERS

1   ADDING MIXED NUMBERS

In Chapter 2 we defined a mixed number as the sum of a whole number and a proper fraction. For example,

$$6\frac{3}{4} = 6 + \frac{3}{4}.$$

In Section 2.5 we changed mixed numbers to improper fractions before multiplying or dividing. This same procedure works for addition, but most problems are more easily done by adding the whole number parts and then adding the fraction parts.

PRACTICE EXERCISE 1

Add $7\frac{1}{10}$ and $3\frac{4}{15}$

Answer: $10\frac{11}{30}$

ADDING MIXED NUMBERS   EXAMPLE 1

Add $3\frac{5}{8}$ and $2\frac{1}{6}$.

$$3\frac{5}{8} = 3\frac{5}{2\cdot2\cdot2} = 3\frac{5\cdot3}{2\cdot2\cdot2\cdot3} = 3\frac{15}{24} \quad \text{LCD is 24}$$

$$+2\frac{1}{6} = 2\frac{1}{2\cdot3} \qquad = 2\frac{1\cdot2\cdot2}{2\cdot2\cdot2\cdot3} = 2\frac{4}{24}$$

$$\overline{\hphantom{xxxxxxxxxxxxxxxxxxxxxxxxxxxxxxxx}5\frac{19}{24}}$$

Add whole numbers   Add fractions

PRACTICE EXERCISE 2

Add $324\frac{2}{5}$ and $447\frac{3}{4}$

Answer: $772\frac{3}{20}$

ADDING THAT RESULTS IN AN IMPROPER FRACTION   EXAMPLE 2

Add $425\frac{3}{8}$ and $211\frac{2}{3}$.

$$425\frac{3}{8} = 425\frac{3}{2\cdot2\cdot2} = 425\frac{3\cdot3}{2\cdot2\cdot2\cdot3} = 425\frac{9}{24} \quad \text{LCD is 24}$$

$$+211\frac{2}{3} = +211\frac{2}{3} \qquad = +211\frac{2\cdot2\cdot2}{2\cdot2\cdot2\cdot3} = +211\frac{16}{24}$$

$$\overline{\hphantom{xxxxxxxxxxxxxxxxxxxxxxxxxxxxxxxx}636\frac{25}{24}}$$

Add whole numbers   Add fractions

Since $\frac{25}{24}$ is an improper fraction, change it to the mixed number $1\frac{1}{24}$ and rewrite the answer as follows.

$$636\frac{25}{24} = 636 + 1\frac{1}{24} \qquad \frac{25}{24} \text{ is } 1\frac{1}{24}$$

$$= 636 + 1 + \frac{1}{24} \qquad \text{Rewrite mixed number as a sum}$$

$$= 637 + \frac{1}{24} \qquad \text{Add whole numbers}$$

$$= 637\frac{1}{24} \qquad \text{Final answer}$$

Use the same method to add three or more mixed numbers.

EXAMPLE 3 **ADDING THREE MIXED NUMBERS**

Add $10\frac{1}{3}$, $5\frac{5}{6}$, and $3\frac{3}{4}$

$$10\frac{1}{3} = 10\frac{1\cdot4}{3\cdot4} = 10\frac{4}{12} \qquad \text{LCD is 12}$$

$$5\frac{5}{6} = 5\frac{5\cdot2}{6\cdot2} = 5\frac{10}{12}$$

$$+\ 3\frac{3}{4} = 3\frac{3\cdot3}{4\cdot3} = 3\frac{9}{12}$$

Add whole numbers $\rightarrow 18\frac{23}{12} \leftarrow$ Add fractions

Change $\frac{23}{12}$ to $1\frac{11}{12}$ and add to 18.

$$18 + 1\frac{11}{12} = 18 + 1 + \frac{11}{12}$$

$$= 19\frac{11}{12}$$

2 **SUBTRACTING MIXED NUMBERS**

As with addition, mixed numbers can be subtracted by subtracting the whole numbers and the fractions separately.

EXAMPLE 4 **SUBTRACTING MIXED NUMBERS**

Subtract: $48\frac{3}{4} - 27\frac{1}{3}$.

$$48\frac{3}{4} = 48\frac{3}{2\cdot2} = 48\frac{3\cdot3}{2\cdot2\cdot3} = 48\frac{9}{12}$$

$$-27\frac{1}{3} = -27\frac{1}{3} = -27\frac{2\cdot2\cdot1}{2\cdot2\cdot3} = -27\frac{4}{12}$$

Subtract whole numbers $\rightarrow 21\frac{5}{12} \leftarrow$ Subtract fractions

PRACTICE EXERCISE 3

Add $8\frac{1}{4}$, $3\frac{5}{12}$, and $1\frac{5}{6}$

Answer: $13\frac{1}{2}$

PRACTICE EXERCISE 4

Subtract: $121\frac{5}{8} - 102\frac{1}{5}$

Answer: $19\frac{17}{40}$

NOTE An extra step is sometimes needed for this kind of subtraction. Sometimes the fraction being subtracted from is smaller than the fraction being subtracted. When this occurs, borrow.

Subtract.

(a) $92\frac{1}{6}$

$\quad -54\frac{2}{3}$

Subtract.   (a) $57\frac{1}{4}$

$\qquad -33\frac{1}{2}$

When subtracting the fractions, we try

$$\frac{1}{4} - \frac{1}{2} = \frac{1}{4} - \frac{2}{4} = \frac{1-2}{4},$$

which we do not know how to do. Therefore, we must borrow 1 (in the form $\frac{4}{4}$) from 57 and add it to $\frac{1}{4}$ (making $\frac{5}{4}$) before we can subtract.

$56\frac{1}{4} + \frac{4}{4}$

$$57\frac{1}{4} = \not{5}7\frac{1}{4} = 56\frac{5}{4} = 56\frac{5}{4}$$

$$-33\frac{1}{2} = -33\frac{1}{2} = -33\frac{1}{2} = -33\frac{2}{4}$$

$$\qquad\qquad\qquad\qquad\qquad\qquad 23\frac{3}{4}$$

(b) $8\frac{9}{10}$

$\quad -6$

(b) $6\frac{3}{4} = 6\frac{3}{4}$

$\quad -2 = -2\frac{0}{4}$ $2 = 2 + 0 = 2 + \frac{0}{4}$

$\qquad\qquad 4\frac{3}{4}$ $\frac{3}{4} - \frac{0}{4} = \frac{3-0}{4} = \frac{3}{4}$

(c)   15

$\quad -10\frac{7}{8}$

(c) $6 = 5\frac{4}{4}$ Write $6\frac{0}{4}$ as $5\frac{4}{4}$ in order to subtract

$\quad -2\frac{3}{4} = -2\frac{3}{4}$ Compare this with (b) above

$\qquad\qquad 3\frac{1}{4}$

Answers: (a) $37\frac{1}{2}$ (b) $2\frac{9}{10}$ (c) $4\frac{1}{8}$

As was true with whole numbers, subtraction of mixed numbers can be checked by addition.

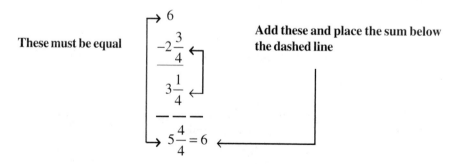

These must be equal

6

$-2\frac{3}{4}$

$3\frac{1}{4}$

- - -

$5\frac{4}{4} = 6$

Add these and place the sum below the dashed line

3 | APPLICATIONS OF MIXED NUMBERS

Many applications involve the addition or subtraction of mixed numbers.

EXAMPLE 6 — USING ADDITION IN A WEIGHT PROBLEM

Mike weighs $158\frac{1}{2}$ lb, Den weighs $138\frac{3}{4}$ lb, and Murph weighs $172\frac{1}{8}$ lb. Find the combined weight of these men.

We must add the three weights.

$$158\frac{1}{2} = 158\frac{4}{8} \qquad \text{LCD is 8}$$

$$138\frac{3}{4} = 138\frac{6}{8}$$

$$172\frac{1}{8} = 172\frac{1}{8}$$

$$468\frac{11}{8} = 468 + 1 + \frac{3}{8} = 469\frac{3}{8}$$

Thus, the combined weight of the men is $469\frac{3}{8}$ lb.

EXAMPLE 7 — USING SUBTRACTION IN SEWING

It took Barb $2\frac{3}{4}$ days to sew a set of draperies. Had she hired a professional seamstress, it would have taken $1\frac{1}{5}$ days. How much time could she have saved by using the professional?

The time she could have saved is the difference between the two times.

$$2\frac{3}{4} = 2\frac{3 \cdot 5}{4 \cdot 5} = 2\frac{15}{20} \qquad \text{LCD is 20}$$

$$-1\frac{1}{5} = -1\frac{1 \cdot 4}{5 \cdot 4} = -1\frac{4}{20}$$

$$1\frac{11}{20}$$

Thus, she could have saved $1\frac{11}{20}$ days.

PRACTICE EXERCISE 6

On a deep sea fishing trip Reva caught three fish weighing $122\frac{2}{5}$ lb, $97\frac{7}{10}$ lb, and $171\frac{4}{5}$ lb. What was the total weight of her fish?

Answer: $391\frac{9}{10}$ lb

PRACTICE EXERCISE 7

Randy had a job to do that required $6\frac{3}{8}$ days to finish. After he had worked for $4\frac{3}{4}$ days, how many days were left to complete the job?

Answer: $1\frac{5}{8}$

3.4 EXERCISES

Answers to these exercises are given on page 645.

Add the mixed numbers in Exercises 1–8.

1. $5\frac{3}{8}$
   $+2\frac{1}{2}$

2. $6\frac{1}{6}$
   $+5\frac{1}{5}$

3. $3\frac{2}{5}$
   $+4\frac{5}{6}$

4. $2\frac{2}{7}$
   $+4\frac{5}{21}$

5. $3\frac{3}{20}$
   $+2\frac{5}{24}$

6. $15\frac{7}{8}$
   $+\ 4$
   $19\frac{7}{8}$

7. $685\frac{2}{11}$
   $+296\frac{2}{3}$

8. $45\frac{5}{12}$
   $+88\frac{15}{16}$

Subtract the mixed numbers in Exercises 9–16.

9. $11\dfrac{4}{5}$
$-\ 5\dfrac{2}{3}$

10. $6\dfrac{3}{8}$
$-\ 5\dfrac{3}{4}$

11. $4\dfrac{8}{9}$
$-\ 3\dfrac{11}{15}$

12. $8\dfrac{1}{4}$
$-\ 3\dfrac{2}{3}$

13. $17\dfrac{6}{11}$
$-\ 8$

14. 15
$-\ 4\dfrac{9}{16}$

15. $485\dfrac{9}{10}$
$-316\dfrac{2}{5}$

16. $211\dfrac{3}{22}$
$-201\dfrac{7}{33}$

Add the mixed numbers in Exercises 17-20.

17. $10\dfrac{2}{3}$
$4\dfrac{1}{5}$
$+\ 7\dfrac{2}{15}$

18. $7\dfrac{1}{5}$
$3\dfrac{2}{3}$
$+1\dfrac{1}{15}$

19. $8\dfrac{3}{4}$
$2\dfrac{1}{12}$
$+4\dfrac{5}{6}$

20. $5\dfrac{8}{9}$
$2\dfrac{1}{3}$
$+1\dfrac{5}{12}$

Find the perimeter (distance around) each figure in Exercises 21–24.

21.

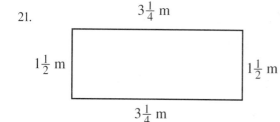

22.

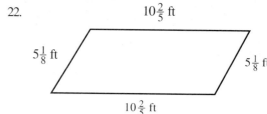

23.

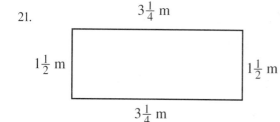

24.

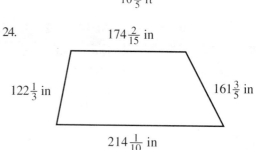

Solve each applied problem in Exercises 25–28.

25. **RECREATION**   Randee Wire took a three-day hike around a lake. The first day she hiked $5\frac{1}{3}$ miles, the second day $8\frac{3}{4}$ miles, and she returned to where she started on the third day by hiking $7\frac{7}{8}$ miles. How far did she hike in the three days?

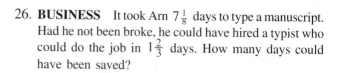

26. **BUSINESS**   It took Arn $7\frac{1}{8}$ days to type a manuscript. Had he not been broke, he could have hired a typist who could do the job in $1\frac{2}{3}$ days. How many days could have been saved?

27. **REAL ESTATE** Windy Horn owns $25\frac{1}{4}$ acres of land in Colorado, $160\frac{2}{3}$ acres in Utah, and $185\frac{1}{6}$ acres in Florida. What is the total number of acres that she owns?

28. **ENVIRONMENT** Before he improved his watering system, George Owen used $45\frac{3}{8}$ gallons of water to water the plants in his greenhouse. Using the new system only $29\frac{3}{4}$ gallons are required. How much water does George save each time he waters?

CRITICAL THINKING

In Exercises 29–34, let the variable a represent a fraction or mixed number. Find a by writing the related addition or subtraction equation.

29. $a + 1\frac{1}{2} = 2\frac{1}{2}$

30. $a - 1\frac{1}{3} = 2\frac{1}{6}$

31. $a + 17\frac{3}{8} = 25\frac{1}{2}$

32. $a - 10\frac{4}{5} = 6\frac{3}{10}$

33. $a + 100\frac{2}{3} = 216\frac{1}{6}$

34. $a - 45\frac{1}{7} = 38\frac{9}{14}$

35. When adding the fractions in mixed numbers we sometimes obtain an improper fraction. Can you explain how this problem is related to the carrying process used in addition of whole numbers?

REVIEW OR PREVIEW

Perform the indicated operations in Exercises 36–39.

36. $\frac{4}{5} + \frac{1}{15} + \frac{7}{30}$

37. $\frac{4}{7} + \frac{11}{14} - \frac{8}{21}$

38. $\frac{9}{5} - \frac{17}{15} - \frac{16}{25}$

39. $\frac{1}{10} + \frac{4}{35} - \frac{2}{21}$

Exercises 40–43 review material from Section 1.1 to help prepare you for the next section. Place the appropriate sign, < or >, between the whole numbers.

40. 16 ____ 4

41. 2 ____ 45

42. 0 ____ 6

43. 8 ____ 7

3.4 PARALLEL EXERCISES

Answers to these exercises are not given in the text.

Add the mixed numbers in Exercises 1–8.

1. $\begin{array}{r} 2\frac{3}{10} \\ + 3\frac{2}{5} \\ \hline \end{array}$

2. $\begin{array}{r} 7\frac{1}{8} \\ +9\frac{1}{6} \\ \hline \end{array}$

3. $\begin{array}{r} 8\frac{4}{15} \\ + 1\frac{4}{5} \\ \hline \end{array}$

4. $\begin{array}{r} 4\frac{7}{8} \\ +2\frac{7}{10} \\ \hline \end{array}$

5. $\begin{array}{r} 8\frac{5}{12} \\ +10\frac{7}{15} \\ \hline \end{array}$

6. $\begin{array}{r} 17 \\ + 1\frac{5}{8} \\ \hline \end{array}$

7. $\begin{array}{r} 106\frac{4}{5} \\ +317\frac{4}{15} \\ \hline \end{array}$

8. $\begin{array}{r} 21\frac{7}{10} \\ +19\frac{19}{20} \\ \hline \end{array}$

Subtract the mixed numbers in Exercises 9–16.

9. $\begin{array}{r} 15\frac{5}{7} \\ -12\frac{2}{3} \\ \hline \end{array}$

10. $\begin{array}{r} 7\frac{3}{10} \\ -4\frac{4}{5} \\ \hline \end{array}$

11. $\begin{array}{r} 3\frac{1}{6} \\ -1\frac{7}{18} \\ \hline \end{array}$

12. $\begin{array}{r} 8\frac{1}{8} \\ -4\frac{3}{5} \\ \hline \end{array}$

13. $12\dfrac{11}{15}$ 14. 11 15. $325\dfrac{4}{5}$ 16. $901\dfrac{1}{15}$

$-11\dfrac{5}{6}$ $-7\dfrac{3}{14}$ $-170\dfrac{1}{4}$ $-899\dfrac{20}{21}$

Add the mixed numbers in Exercises 17–20.

17. $1\dfrac{2}{11}$ 18. $4\dfrac{2}{3}$ 19. $4\dfrac{3}{4}$ 20. $9\dfrac{5}{6}$

$2\dfrac{3}{22}$ $6\dfrac{5}{6}$ $4\dfrac{3}{8}$ $7\dfrac{1}{4}$

$+4\dfrac{1}{2}$ $+7\dfrac{1}{12}$ $+4\dfrac{3}{16}$ $+1\dfrac{2}{3}$

Find the perimeter (distance around) each figure in Exercises 21–24.

21.   22.

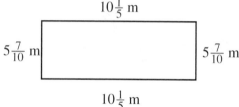

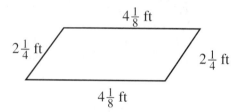

23.   24.

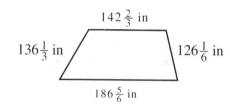

Solve each applied problem in Exercises 25–28.

25.   **AGRICULTURE**   George Smith planted $12\dfrac{3}{4}$ acres the first day, $15\dfrac{1}{8}$ acres the next day, and $21\dfrac{4}{5}$ acres the third day. How many acres did he plant in the three days?

26.   **EDUCATION**   Harry's paper for a history class has to be 16 pages long. How many more pages must he write if he has done $9\dfrac{2}{5}$ pages?

27.   **TRAVEL**   On a trip the Williamses filled their gas tank three times. They required $16\dfrac{2}{5}$ gallons, $21\dfrac{7}{10}$ gallons, and $19\dfrac{1}{5}$ gallons. How many gallons of gasoline did they buy on the trip?

28.   **ENVIRONMENT** If Melissa Martin drives her pickup to work, she uses $17\dfrac{3}{5}$ gallons of fuel per week. If she drives her car, she only uses $9\dfrac{7}{10}$ gallons in a week. How many gallons does she save by driving the car?

CRITICAL THINKING

In Exercises 29–34, let the variable a represent a fraction or mixed number. Find a by writing the related addition or subtraction equation.

29. $a + 2\dfrac{1}{5} = 3\dfrac{1}{5}$ 30. $a - 5\dfrac{1}{3} = 6\dfrac{1}{2}$ 31. $a + 31\dfrac{3}{7} = 64\dfrac{1}{21}$

32. $a - 22\dfrac{1}{6} = 16\dfrac{1}{12}$ 33. $a + 184\dfrac{5}{8} = 201\dfrac{1}{2}$ 34. $a - 72\dfrac{3}{5} = 86\dfrac{9}{10}$

35.   When subtracting the fractions in mixed numbers we sometimes must borrow from the whole number. Can you explain how this is related to the borrowing process used in the subtraction of whole numbers?

GROUP PROJECT

Let a and b be whole numbers and c and d be fractions. Then $a + c$ and $b + d$ are mixed numbers. Use these numbers, written this way, to see if your group can show why addition of whole numbers and fractions separately works but the same process does not work for multiplication.

3.5 ORDER OF OPERATIONS AND COMPARING FRACTIONS

STUDENT GUIDEPOSTS

1   USING THE RULE FOR THE ORDER OF OPERATIONS
2   COMPARING FRACTIONS

1 RULE FOR THE ORDER OF OPERATIONS

The order of operations on whole numbers that we studied in Section 1.9 applies to fractions as well and is reviewed below.

ORDER OF OPERATIONS

Operations should be performed in the following order.
1.   Operate within parentheses.
2.   Find all powers and roots in any order.
3.   Multiply and divide, in order, from left to right.
4.   Add and subtract, in order, from left to right.

EXAMPLE 1   USING ORDER OF OPERATIONS

Evaluate each expression. (Perform the indicated operations.)

(a) $\left(\dfrac{5}{6} - \dfrac{1}{6}\right) \cdot \dfrac{3}{4} = \dfrac{4}{6} \cdot \dfrac{3}{4}$ Operate inside parentheses first

$= \dfrac{2}{3} \cdot \dfrac{3}{4}$ Reduce fraction

$= \dfrac{2 \cdot 3}{3 \cdot 2 \cdot 2}$ Multiply

$= \dfrac{1}{2}$

(b) $\dfrac{5}{12} + \dfrac{3}{8} \div \dfrac{3}{4} = \dfrac{5}{12} + \dfrac{3}{8} \cdot \dfrac{4}{3}$ Divide first

$= \dfrac{5}{12} + \dfrac{3 \cdot 4}{2 \cdot 4 \cdot 3}$

$= \dfrac{5}{12} + \dfrac{1}{2} = \dfrac{5}{12} + \dfrac{6}{12}$ Then add; the LCD is 12

$= \dfrac{11}{12}$

PRACTICE EXERCISE 1

Evaluate each expression.

(a) $\dfrac{4}{15} \cdot \left(\dfrac{3}{8} + \dfrac{1}{8}\right)$

(b) $\dfrac{5}{9} \div \dfrac{5}{3} - \dfrac{1}{10}$

(c) $\dfrac{9}{20} \div \dfrac{3}{10} - \dfrac{4}{11} \cdot \dfrac{11}{20}$

(c) $\dfrac{5}{7} \cdot \dfrac{7}{2} - \dfrac{1}{11} \div \dfrac{3}{22} = \dfrac{5 \cdot 7}{7 \cdot 2} - \dfrac{1}{11} \cdot \dfrac{22}{3}$ Multiply and divide first

$= \dfrac{5 \cdot \cancel{7}}{\cancel{7} \cdot 2} - \dfrac{1 \cdot 2 \cdot \cancel{11}}{\cancel{11} \cdot 3}$

$= \dfrac{5}{2} - \dfrac{2}{3}$

$= \dfrac{15}{6} - \dfrac{4}{6}$ LCD is 6

Answers: (a) $\dfrac{2}{15}$ (b) $\dfrac{7}{30}$ (c) $1\dfrac{3}{10}$

$= \dfrac{11}{6} = 1\dfrac{5}{6}$ Subtract last

**PRACTICE
EXERCISE 2**

Evaluate each expression.

(a) $\left(\dfrac{2}{3}\right)^2 \div \left(\dfrac{4}{7} + \dfrac{5}{14}\right)$

USING ORDER OF OPERATIONS   **EXAMPLE 2**

Evaluate each expression.

(a) $\left(\dfrac{9}{11} - \dfrac{3}{11}\right) \cdot \left(\dfrac{1}{2}\right)^2 = \dfrac{6}{11} \cdot \left(\dfrac{1}{2}\right)^2$ Evaluate inside parentheses first

$= \dfrac{6}{11} \cdot \dfrac{1}{4}$ Find the square of $\dfrac{1}{2}$ next

$= \dfrac{\cancel{2} \cdot 3 \cdot 1}{11 \cdot \cancel{2} \cdot 2}$ Multiply

$= \dfrac{3}{22}$

(b) $\dfrac{3}{5} - \sqrt{\dfrac{16}{25}} \cdot \dfrac{1}{2}$

(b) $\sqrt{\dfrac{4}{9}} - \dfrac{1}{3} \cdot \dfrac{1}{2} = \dfrac{2}{3} - \dfrac{1}{3} \cdot \dfrac{1}{2}$ Find square root first

$= \dfrac{2}{3} - \dfrac{1}{6}$ Multiply

$= \dfrac{4}{6} - \dfrac{1}{6}$ Now subtract

$= \dfrac{3}{6} = \dfrac{1}{2}$ Reduce

(c) $\dfrac{4}{15} - \dfrac{3}{5} \cdot \dfrac{2}{15} + \left(\dfrac{1}{5}\right)^2$

(c) $\left(\dfrac{3}{4}\right)^2 + \dfrac{5}{3} \div \dfrac{4}{3} - \dfrac{2}{5} \cdot \dfrac{5}{4} = \dfrac{9}{16} + \dfrac{5}{3} \div \dfrac{4}{3} - \dfrac{2}{5} \cdot \dfrac{5}{4}$ Square first

$= \dfrac{9}{16} + \dfrac{5}{3} \cdot \dfrac{3}{4} - \dfrac{2 \cdot 5}{5 \cdot 4}$ Divide and multiply

$= \dfrac{9}{16} + \dfrac{5 \cdot \cancel{3}}{\cancel{3} \cdot 4} - \dfrac{\cancel{2} \cdot \cancel{5}}{\cancel{5} \cdot \cancel{2} \cdot 2}$

Answers: (a) $\dfrac{56}{117}$ (b) $\dfrac{1}{5}$ (c) $\dfrac{17}{75}$

$= \dfrac{9}{16} + \dfrac{5}{4} - \dfrac{1}{2}$

$$= \frac{9}{16} + \frac{20}{16} - \frac{8}{16}$$ 　Now add and subtract

$$= \frac{21}{16} = 1\frac{5}{16}$$

1 　COMPARING FRACTIONS

Recall that one whole number is greater than another if the first is to the right of the second on a number line. Deciding which of two fractions is larger is just as simple, when the denominators are the same. Consider the fractions

$$\frac{2}{3} \quad \text{and} \quad \frac{3}{5}.$$

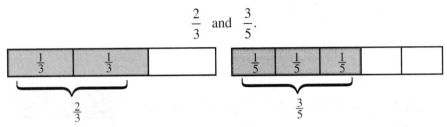

FIGURE 3.2

Compare the bars in Figure 3.2. It is not obvious which fraction is larger. Now find the LCD of these fractions.

$$\frac{2}{3} = \frac{2 \cdot 5}{3 \cdot 5} = \frac{10}{15} \quad \text{and} \quad \frac{3}{5} = \frac{3 \cdot 3}{3 \cdot 5} = \frac{9}{15}$$

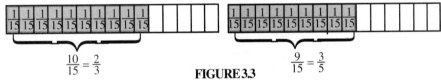

FIGURE 3.3

Comparing the bars in Figure 3.3 makes it clear that the shaded portion $\frac{10}{15}$ is larger than the shaded portion $\frac{9}{15}$. Thus

$$\frac{10}{15} > \frac{9}{15} \quad \text{and} \quad \frac{2}{3} > \frac{3}{5}.$$

But it is not necessary to compare fractional parts of bars since certainly

10 fifteenths is more than **9** fifteenths.

When two fractions have the same denominator, the larger fraction has the larger numerator.

TO TELL WHICH OF TWO FRACTIONS IS LARGER
1. Find a common denominator and convert each fraction to an equivalent fraction having that denominator.
2. The larger fraction has the larger numerator.

This rule allows us to compare fractions using what we know about the order of whole numbers.

EXAMPLE 3 　　COMPARING FRACTIONS

Which of the two fractions is larger?

(a) $\frac{5}{6}$ or $\frac{3}{4}$

$$\frac{5}{6} = \frac{5}{2 \cdot 3} = \frac{2 \cdot 5}{2 \cdot 2 \cdot 3} = \frac{10}{12}$$

The LCD of 4 and 6 is $2 \cdot 2 \cdot 3 = 12$

EXPLORATION GUIDE

In Section 2.2 we showed that two fractions were equivalent by showing that their cross products were equal. Can you think of a similar method for comparing fractions that are not equivalent?

PRACTICE EXERCISE 3

Which of the two fractions is larger?

(a) $\frac{7}{12}$ or $\frac{6}{11}$

(b) $\dfrac{1}{7}$ or $\dfrac{2}{17}$

$$\frac{3}{4} = \frac{3}{2 \cdot 2} = \frac{3 \cdot \mathbf{3}}{2 \cdot 2 \cdot \mathbf{3}} = \frac{9}{12}$$

Since $10 > 9$, $\dfrac{10}{12} > \dfrac{9}{12}$. Thus $\dfrac{5}{6} > \dfrac{3}{4}$.

(b) $\dfrac{3}{20}$ or $\dfrac{1}{5}$

$$\frac{3}{20} = \frac{3}{2 \cdot 2 \cdot 5} = \frac{3}{20}$$

$$\frac{1}{5} = \frac{\mathbf{2 \cdot 2} \cdot 1}{\mathbf{2 \cdot 2} \cdot 5} = \frac{4}{20}$$

The LCD of 5 and 20 is $2 \cdot 2 \cdot 5 = 20$

Since $4 > 3$, $\dfrac{4}{20} > \dfrac{3}{20}$. Thus $\dfrac{1}{5} > \dfrac{3}{20}$.

Answers: (a) $\dfrac{7}{12} > \dfrac{6}{11}$ (b) $\dfrac{1}{7} > \dfrac{2}{17}$

PRACTICE EXERCISE 4

In June, Chicago had two rainstorms, one which dropped $\frac{3}{8}$ inch and the other $1\frac{1}{4}$ inches of precipitation. During July, there were three storms with $\frac{1}{3}$, $\frac{4}{5}$, and $\frac{1}{8}$ inch of rain. During which of these months did Chicago have more precipitation? How much more?

APPLYING FRACTIONS TO RECREATION   **EXAMPLE 4**

A map of trails joining Blue Ridge Hill and the blackberry patch is shown in Figure 3.4. Is it farther from Blue Ridge Hill to the blackberry patch by way of Luna Pond or by way of White Rock Creek? How much farther?

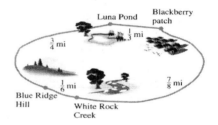

FIGURE 3.4

The distance from Blue Ridge Hill to the blackberry patch by way of Luna Pond can be found by adding $\frac{3}{4}$ and $\frac{1}{3}$.

$$\frac{3}{4} + \frac{1}{3} = \frac{3 \cdot \mathbf{3}}{4 \cdot \mathbf{3}} + \frac{1 \cdot \mathbf{4}}{3 \cdot \mathbf{4}} = \frac{9}{12} + \frac{4}{12} = \frac{13}{12}$$

The distance by way of White Rock Creek is found by adding $\frac{1}{6}$ and $\frac{7}{8}$.

$$\frac{1}{6} + \frac{7}{8} = \frac{1}{2 \cdot 3} + \frac{7}{2 \cdot 2 \cdot 2} = \frac{\mathbf{2 \cdot 2} \cdot 1}{\mathbf{2 \cdot 2} \cdot 2 \cdot 3} + \frac{7 \cdot \mathbf{3}}{2 \cdot 2 \cdot 2 \cdot \mathbf{3}}$$

$$= \frac{4 + 21}{24} = \frac{25}{24}$$

Write $\frac{13}{12}$ with the same denominator as $\frac{25}{24}$.

$$\frac{13}{12} = \frac{13 \cdot 2}{12 \cdot 2} = \frac{26}{24}$$

Since $26 > 25$, $\frac{26}{24} > \frac{25}{24}$. Thus, $\frac{13}{12} > \frac{25}{24}$ so it is farther by way of Luna Pond.

To find out how much farther it is, subtract $\frac{25}{24}$ from $\frac{13}{12}$. Using the fractions above,

$$\frac{13}{12} - \frac{25}{24} = \frac{26}{24} - \frac{25}{24} = \frac{1}{24}.$$

Answer: $\frac{11}{30}$ inch more in June

Thus, it is $\frac{1}{24}$ of a mile farther.

We now solve the applied problem given in the chapter introduction.

| EXAMPLE 5 | APPLYING FRACTIONS IN A CONSUMER PROBLEM |

In the year 1986, consumers registered the greatest number of complaints against the nation's airlines. Considering all complaints received, the circle graph below shows the fractional part of the complaints in six different categories.

Use the circle graph in Example 5 to answer the following questions.

Flight Problems

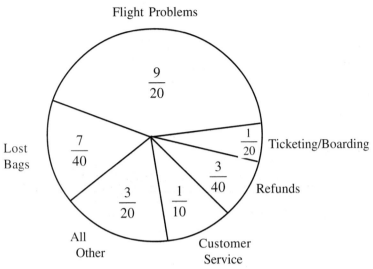

Source: U.S. Bureau of Census
FIGURE 3.5

(a) Which category received the greatest number of complaints?
We begin by finding the LCD of all denominators.

The LCD of 10, 20, and 40 is $2^3 \cdot 5 = 40$. We now convert each fraction to an equivalent fraction having 40 as the denominator.

Flight Problems: $\dfrac{9}{20} = \dfrac{2 \cdot 9}{2 \cdot 20} = \dfrac{18}{40}$ **Lost bags:** $\dfrac{7}{40}$

Customer Service: $\dfrac{1}{10} = \dfrac{4 \cdot 1}{4 \cdot 10} = \dfrac{4}{40}$ **Refunds:** $\dfrac{3}{40}$

Ticketing/Boarding: $\dfrac{1}{20} = \dfrac{2 \cdot 1}{2 \cdot 20} = \dfrac{2}{40}$ **All Other:** $\dfrac{3}{20} = \dfrac{2 \cdot 3}{2 \cdot 20} = \dfrac{6}{40}$

Since 18 is the largest numerator, $\frac{18}{40}$ is the largest fraction. Thus, Flight Problems received the greatest number of complaints. Note that the relative sizes of the parts of the graph reflect this conclusion.

(b) What fraction of the total complaints received came from the categories of Customer Service and Refunds?

To answer this, we must add the fractions corresponding to Customer Service, $\frac{1}{10}$, and Refunds, $\frac{3}{40}$. We can take advantage of the fact that we have already converted all fractions to equivalent fractions with denominator 40.

$$\frac{1}{10} + \frac{3}{40} = \frac{4}{40} + \frac{3}{40} = \frac{7}{40}$$

Thus, $\frac{7}{40}$ of the complaints came from these two categories.

(a) Which category received the fewest number of complaints?

(b) What fraction of the complaints came from the three categories: Lost Baggage, Ticketing/Boarding, and Refunds?

3.5 EXERCISES

Answers to these exercises are given on page 645.

Evaluate each expression in Exercises 1–12.

1. $\left(\dfrac{5}{9}+\dfrac{4}{9}\right)\cdot\dfrac{11}{15}$

2. $\dfrac{4}{5}\div\dfrac{2}{3}-\dfrac{2}{5}$

3. $\dfrac{4}{3}\cdot\left(\dfrac{7}{8}-\dfrac{1}{4}\right)$

4. $\dfrac{2}{3}\div\dfrac{1}{9}\cdot\dfrac{1}{4}$

5. $\dfrac{15}{16}-\dfrac{3}{4}\cdot\dfrac{1}{2}$

6. $\left(\dfrac{15}{16}-\dfrac{3}{4}\right)\cdot\dfrac{1}{2}$

7. $\sqrt{\dfrac{1}{4}}-\left(\dfrac{1}{4}\right)^2$

8. $\left(\dfrac{3}{5}\right)^2-\dfrac{1}{5}+\dfrac{6}{25}$

9. $\dfrac{2}{3}\cdot\dfrac{6}{11}-2\div\dfrac{11}{2}$

10. $\sqrt{\dfrac{1}{9}}+\dfrac{6}{7}\div\dfrac{3}{14}-3\cdot\dfrac{1}{9}$

11. $\left(\dfrac{4}{5}-\dfrac{1}{10}\right)^2\div\dfrac{7}{10}$

12. $\dfrac{5}{6}\div\dfrac{2}{3}-\dfrac{1}{4}\div\dfrac{1}{2}-\left(\dfrac{1}{2}\right)^2$

💡 *Which of the two fractions in Exercises 13–18 is larger?*

13. $\dfrac{4}{15}$ or $\dfrac{1}{4}$

14. $\dfrac{29}{21}$ or $\dfrac{25}{18}$

15. $\dfrac{4}{6}$ or $\dfrac{27}{42}$

16. $\dfrac{35}{11}$ or $\dfrac{41}{13}$

17. $\dfrac{17}{30}$ or $\dfrac{21}{40}$

18. $\dfrac{19}{8}$ or $\dfrac{81}{36}$

💡 *Answer* true *or* false *in Exercises 19–24.*

19. $\dfrac{1}{4}<\dfrac{1}{3}$

20. $\dfrac{3}{8}>\dfrac{4}{7}$

21. $\dfrac{25}{3}<\dfrac{35}{4}$

22. $3\dfrac{2}{5}>3\dfrac{5}{12}$

23. $\dfrac{1}{2}\div\dfrac{1}{4}>\dfrac{1}{3}\div\dfrac{1}{9}$

24. $\dfrac{1}{2}<\dfrac{1}{3}<\dfrac{1}{4}$

Solve each applied problem in Exercises 25–26.

25. **TEMPERATURE** Fahrenheit temperature can be found by multiplying Celsius temperature by $\dfrac{9}{5}$ and adding 32°. If Celsius temperature is 25°, what is the Fahrenheit temperature?

26. **WEATHER** In May there were two rains that dropped $\dfrac{3}{4}$ of an inch and $\dfrac{2}{3}$ of an inch. In June three rains were $\dfrac{4}{5}$ of an inch, $\dfrac{1}{4}$ of an inch, and $\dfrac{1}{5}$ of an inch. Which month had more rain and by how much?

In Exercises 27–30 compare merchant vessel production by determining the required fractions. Data given in the table are the number of vessels produced in the United States in the given year.

Type of Vessel	1970	1975	1980	1985	1988
Total Merchant	13	15	10	8	4
Cargo	6	3	6	4	3
Tankers	7	12	4	4	1

Source: U.S. Marine Administration

27. Divide the number of cargo ships by the total merchant ships for each year given. In what year was this fraction the largest?

28. Use the fractions determined in Exercise 27. In what year was the fraction the smallest?

29. Again use the fractions from Exercise 27. In what year was the fraction the nearest to one-half?

30. Determine the fraction of 1988 production to 1970 production for each of the total, cargo, and tanker. Which of these fractions is the largest?

CRITICAL THINKING

Evaluate each expression in Exercises 31–32.

31. $\left(\dfrac{1}{3} - \dfrac{1}{4}\right)^2 \div \dfrac{5}{12} + \sqrt{\dfrac{6}{25} - \dfrac{2}{25}} - \dfrac{3}{5} \cdot \dfrac{1}{6}$

32. $\left[\left(\dfrac{4}{7} - \dfrac{3}{14}\right) \div \dfrac{1}{21}\right] - \sqrt{\left(\dfrac{2}{7} + \dfrac{1}{7}\right)^2}$

Let a, b, and c represent fractions in Exercises 33–35.

33. If $a < b$ and $b < c$, can you give the relationship between a and c?

34. If $a < b$, write an inequality using > that relates a and b.

35. If $a < b$ is $a + c < b + c$?

36. Burford still has difficulties with the order of operations. Can you help him out by writing up the order in your own words?

REVIEW OR PREVIEW

In Exercises 37–44, perform the indicated operations.

37. $3\dfrac{2}{3}$
    $+2\dfrac{1}{6}$

38. $4\dfrac{2}{7}$
    $-3\dfrac{5}{14}$

39. $416\dfrac{1}{9}$
    $+201\dfrac{2}{3}$

40. $8\dfrac{3}{10}$
    $2\dfrac{4}{5}$
    $+5\dfrac{2}{5}$

41. $5\dfrac{3}{8}$
    $+7\dfrac{1}{4}$

42. $9\dfrac{2}{5}$
    $-8\dfrac{9}{10}$

43. $925\dfrac{3}{10}$
    $-416\dfrac{3}{8}$

44. $4\dfrac{1}{2}$
    $2\dfrac{3}{8}$
    $+9\dfrac{5}{24}$

3.5 PARALLEL EXERCISES

Answers to these exercises are not given in the text.

Evaluate each expression in Exercises 1–12.

1. $\left(\dfrac{9}{7} - \dfrac{3}{7}\right) \cdot \dfrac{7}{12}$

2. $\dfrac{2}{9} \cdot \dfrac{3}{4} - \dfrac{1}{6}$

3. $\left(\dfrac{8}{7} - \dfrac{9}{14}\right) \div \dfrac{3}{4}$

4. $\dfrac{3}{5} \cdot \dfrac{5}{6} \div \dfrac{1}{4}$

5. $\dfrac{9}{11} - \dfrac{2}{7} \div \dfrac{11}{7}$

6. $\left(\dfrac{9}{11} - \dfrac{2}{7}\right) \div \dfrac{11}{7}$

7. $\left(\dfrac{2}{3}\right)^2 - \sqrt{\dfrac{4}{81}}$

8. $\dfrac{5}{8} - \dfrac{1}{4} - \left(\dfrac{1}{2}\right)^2$

9. $\dfrac{15}{16} \div \dfrac{3}{8} - 4 \cdot \dfrac{1}{12}$

10. $\dfrac{14}{20} \cdot \dfrac{8}{7} - \sqrt{\dfrac{1}{25}} + \dfrac{1}{3} \div \dfrac{5}{3}$

11. $\dfrac{12}{21} \div \left(\dfrac{7}{3} - \dfrac{5}{3}\right)^2$

12. $\dfrac{6}{11} \div \dfrac{3}{22} - \left(\dfrac{1}{4}\right)^2 - \dfrac{5}{2} \div \dfrac{10}{3}$

Which of the two fractions in Exercises 13–18 is larger?

13. $\dfrac{2}{5}$ or $\dfrac{3}{7}$

14. $\dfrac{19}{18}$ or $\dfrac{37}{36}$

15. $\dfrac{22}{33}$ or $\dfrac{14}{22}$

16. $\dfrac{49}{10}$ or $\dfrac{64}{15}$ 17. $\dfrac{31}{50}$ or $\dfrac{13}{20}$ 18. $\dfrac{25}{6}$ or $\dfrac{109}{28}$

 Answer true or false in Exercises 19–24.

19. $\dfrac{2}{5} < \dfrac{4}{9}$ 20. $\dfrac{7}{11} > \dfrac{13}{20}$ 21. $\dfrac{71}{8} > \dfrac{53}{6}$

22. $5\dfrac{9}{13} < 5\dfrac{17}{26}$ 23. $\dfrac{3}{28} \cdot \dfrac{41}{9} < \dfrac{2}{3} \div 5$ 24. $\dfrac{1}{2} > \dfrac{1}{3} > \dfrac{1}{4}$

Solve each applied problem in Exercises 25–26.

25. **TEMPERATURE** Celsius temperature can be found by subtracting 32° from Fahrenheit temperature and then multiplying by $\dfrac{5}{9}$. If Fahrenheit temperature is 95°, what is the Celsius temperature?

26. **BUSINESS** On Monday the Sweet Shop received three shipments of candy that weighed $22\dfrac{1}{2}$ pounds, $31\dfrac{1}{5}$ pounds, and $16\dfrac{3}{10}$ pounds. On Tuesday there were shipments of $42\dfrac{5}{8}$ pounds and $28\dfrac{3}{4}$ pounds. On which day did the shop receive more candy and by how much?

Use the data given in the table above Exercises 27–30 to answer the following questions.

27. Divide the number of tankers by the number of cargo ships for each year given.
    In what year was this fraction the largest?

28. Use the fractions determined in Exercise 27. In what year was the fraction the smallest?

29. Again use the fractions from Exercise 27. In what year was the fraction the nearest to one?

30. Determine the fraction of 1988 production to 1970 production for each of the total, cargo, and tanker.
    Which of these fractions is the smallest?

CRITICAL THINKING

 Evaluate each expression in Exercises 31–32.

31. $\left(\dfrac{2}{5} + \dfrac{1}{10}\right)^2 \cdot \dfrac{50}{3} - \sqrt{\dfrac{3}{4} + \dfrac{3}{2}} \div \dfrac{3}{4} - \dfrac{1}{2} \cdot \dfrac{5}{2}$ 32. $\sqrt{\dfrac{4}{9} - \dfrac{1}{3}} \div \dfrac{4}{27} - \left(\dfrac{1}{2} + \dfrac{3}{8}\right)^2 \div \dfrac{7}{16} \cdot \dfrac{1}{2}$

 Let a, b, and c represent fractions in Exercises 33–35.

33. If $a > b$ and $b > c$, can you give the relationship between a and c?

34. If $a > b$, write an inequality using $<$ that relates a and b.

35. If $a > b$ is $ac > bc$?

36. Burford thinks that he can get away with not following the rule for order of operation. Write up an explanation showing him several examples where changing the order gives different answers.

GROUP PROJECT

In Example 5 and Exercises 27–30 we compared data from business and industry by using fractions. Look for examples of this type of comparison in newspapers and magazines or form your own fractions from data you obtain. Discuss your examples with the idea of understanding better how to compare data. In Chapter 6 we will compare by using fractions with 100 as denominator in our discussion of percent.

3.6 MORE PROBLEM SOLVING WITH FRACTIONS

This section is designed to give practice with a variety of applications. Read each problem carefully to determine which operations are required and in what order.

EXAMPLE 1 — APPLYING LCM TO CONSTRUCTION

Vince is building a cabin in the mountains. To minimize transportation costs he wants to buy boards from which he can cut pieces that are either all 10 inches in length, all 12 inches, or all 16 inches. What is the shortest board that he can buy and have no waste?

To prevent waste the board must be a length which is a multiple of each of the numbers 10, 12, and 16. The shortest such board will be of length the least common multiple (LCM).

$$10 = 2 \cdot 5 \qquad \text{Factor 10}$$

$$12 = 2 \cdot 2 \cdot 3 = 2^2 \cdot 3 \qquad \text{Factor 12}$$

$$16 = 2 \cdot 2 \cdot 2 \cdot 2 = 2^4 \qquad \text{Factor 16}$$

The LCM is $2 \cdot 2 \cdot 2 \cdot 2 \cdot 3 \cdot 5 = 2^4 \cdot 3 \cdot 5 = 240$. Thus the shortest board that will work is 240 inches or 20 ft long.

EXAMPLE 2 — APPLYING FRACTIONS TO AGRICULTURE

The Midwestern Grain Association has a silo that it wishes to fill over a three-day period. During the first day, deliveries received filled $\frac{3}{8}$ of the silo. The next day an additional $\frac{1}{3}$ of the silo was filled.

(a) How much of the silo was filled after two days?

The fraction in the silo is the sum of the two days' deliveries.

$$\frac{3}{8} + \frac{1}{3} = \frac{3 \cdot 3}{8 \cdot 3} + \frac{1 \cdot 8}{3 \cdot 8} \qquad \text{LCD} = 8 \cdot 3 \text{ since 8 and 3 have no common factors}$$

$$= \frac{9}{24} + \frac{8}{24}$$

$$= \frac{9 + 8}{24} = \frac{17}{24}$$

Thus, $\frac{17}{24}$ of the silo was filled.

(b) What fraction of the silo must be filled during the third day to complete the job?

First note that the fraction for a full silo is 1 and then subtract $\frac{17}{24}$ from 1.

$$1 - \frac{17}{24} = \frac{24}{24} - \frac{17}{24} \qquad \text{LCD} = 24$$

$$= \frac{24 - 17}{24} = \frac{7}{24}$$

Thus, $\frac{7}{24}$ of the silo must be filled the third day.

PRACTICE EXERCISE 1

An artist makes three kinds of geometric decorations out of wire. He uses 8 inches of wire for one kind, 14 inches of wire for another, and 21 inches for the third. What is the shortest length of wire from which he can cut pieces all of which are either 8 inches, 14 inches, or 21 inches, with no waste?

Answer: 168 inches, the LCM of 8, 14, and 21

PRACTICE EXERCISE 2

A family business is owned by a father and his two children. The son owns $\frac{5}{14}$ of the business and the daughter owns $\frac{2}{7}$ of it.

(a) How much do the children own?

(b) How much does the father own?

Answers: (a) $\frac{9}{14}$ (b) $\frac{5}{14}$

On Thursday, Dennis ran $3\frac{2}{3}$ miles, on Friday he ran $4\frac{1}{2}$ miles, and on Saturday, $\frac{3}{4}$ mile. What is the total distance that he ran on the three days?

Answer: $8\frac{11}{12}$ mi

Use the table in Example 4.

(a) Form the fraction that compares the production of Saudi Arabia to total production in 1991. Estimate as in Example 4(a).

(b) Form the fraction that relates the production of Venezuela the year it produced the most to the production of Indonesia that year.

Answers: (a) $\frac{2}{15}$ (b) $\frac{8}{5}$

APPLYING FRACTIONS TO WORK   **EXAMPLE 3**

Carrie worked $6\frac{1}{2}$ hours on Monday, $5\frac{2}{3}$ hours on Tuesday, and $2\frac{1}{4}$ hours on Wednesday. How many hours did she work during the three days?

To find her total hours, add the three mixed numbers.

$$6\frac{1}{2} = 6\frac{6}{12} \qquad \text{LCD} = 12$$

$$5\frac{2}{3} = 5\frac{8}{12}$$

$$+2\frac{1}{4} = 2\frac{3}{12}$$

$$13\frac{17}{12} = 13 + 1 + \frac{5}{12} = 14\frac{5}{12}$$

Carrie worked $14\frac{5}{12}$ hours.

COMPARING OIL PRODUCTION   **EXAMPLE 4**

The following table gives world oil production between 1980 and 1993.

World Crude Oil Production: 1980 to 1993
[In thousands of barrels]

COUNTRY	1980	1985	1988	1989	1990	1991	1992	1993
Total[1]	59,599	53,981	58,662	59,773	60,471	60,105	60,255	60,070
Algeria	1,106	1,037	1,040	1,095	1,175	1,230	1,217	1,190
Kuwait	1,656	1,023	1,492	1,783	1,175	190	1,029	1,872
Libya	1,787	1,059	1,175	1,150	1,375	1,483	1,483	1,377
Saudi Arabia	9,900	3,388	5,086	5,064	6,410	8,115	8,438	8,198
United Arab Emirates	1,709	1,193	1,565	1,860	2,117	2,386	2,325	2,241
Indonesia	1,577	1,325	1,342	1,409	1,462	1,592	1,566	1,507
Iran	1,662	2,250	2,240	2,810	3,088	3,312	3,429	3,650
Nigeria	2,055	1,495	1,450	1,716	1,810	1,892	1,982	2,050
Venezuela	2,168	1,677	1,903	1,907	2,137	2,375	2,334	2,377
Canada	1,435	1,471	1,616	1,560	1,553	1,548	1,598	1,678
Mexico	1,936	2,745	2,512	2,520	2,553	2,680	2,668	2,671
United Kingdom	1,622	2,530	2,232	1,802	1,820	1,797	1,825	1,909
United States	8,597	8,971	8,140	7,613	7,355	7,417	7,171	6,847
China	2,114	2,505	2,730	2,757	2,774	2,835	2,838	2,911
U.S.S.R. (former)	11,706	11,585	11,978	11,625	10,880	9,887	8,388	7,297

[1]Includes countries not shown separately.
Source: U.S. Energy Information Administration, *Monthly Energy Review*.

(a) Form the fraction that compares United States production to total world production in 1980 by dividing the U.S. production by the world production. Simplify the fraction for better understanding.

In 1980 the U.S. production was 8597 (in thousands of barrels) and the total production was 59,599. If we divide these numbers, the fraction is hard to interpret. Thus, we first round 8597 to 8600 and 59,599 to 59,600. The fraction desired is

$$\frac{8600}{59,600} = \frac{86}{596} = \frac{43}{298}.$$

This would be interpreted as: For every 43 barrels produced in the U.S. there were 298 produced worldwide. Estimating further

$$\frac{43}{298} \approx \frac{40}{300} = \frac{4}{30} = \frac{2}{15}.$$

It is easier to understand that for every 2 barrels produced in the U.S. there were approximately 15 barrels produced worldwide.

(b) Form the fraction that relates the U.S. production the year it produced the most to the production of the United Arab Emirates that year.

The U.S. production in 1985 was the largest at 8971 which rounds to 9000. The United Arab Emirates production in 1985 was 1193 which rounds to 1200. The fraction is

$$\frac{9000}{1200} = \frac{90}{12} = \frac{45}{6} = \frac{15}{2}.$$

This fraction is simple enough without further estimate. Thus, for every 15 barrels produced in the U.S. there were 2 barrels produced in the United Arab Emerates in

3.6 EXERCISES

Answers to these exercises are given on page 645.

Solve each applied problem in Exercises 1–12.

1. **SALES** The Super Sales Company has three salespersons. Harry has $\frac{1}{3}$ of the sales accounts and Betty has $\frac{2}{5}$ of the accounts. If Walter has the rest of the accounts, what fraction does he have?

3. **AGRICULTURE** A grain dealer received shipments of $7\frac{3}{8}$ tons, $9\frac{1}{6}$ tons, and $5\frac{1}{4}$ tons of wheat. How much wheat did she receive in the three shipments?

5. **ELECTRONICS** For a wiring job, an electronic technician needs lengths of 9 cm, 12 cm, and 15 cm. What is the shortest piece of wire from which he can cut pieces of the same length with no waste?

7. **RECREATION** Kelly Bell entered a race that involved running for $7\frac{1}{2}$ miles and then riding a bike for $15\frac{3}{5}$ miles. How far does she have to go before she has covered one half the total distance of the race?

9. **LABOR** Lon worked $7\frac{3}{8}$ days, $6\frac{2}{5}$ days, $5\frac{4}{5}$ days, $8\frac{1}{4}$ days, and $7\frac{1}{2}$ days to complete a project. What was his total number of days worked?

11. **RECREATION** On Friday Carlos walked $1\frac{1}{5}$ mi and ran $\frac{5}{8}$ mi. On Saturday, he walked $\frac{3}{4}$ mi and ran $1\frac{1}{6}$ mi. On which day did he travel a greater distance? How much greater?

2. **RECREATION** It is $8\frac{2}{3}$ miles around a lake. If Bill Bass has hiked $5\frac{7}{10}$ miles on the trail around the lake, how far does he have to go?

4. **AGRICULTURE** If the dealer in Exercise 3 needed a total of 30 tons of wheat, how much more must be received?

6. **WEATHER** In June, Pittsburgh had two rainstorms, one which dropped $\frac{5}{16}$ inch and the other $2\frac{1}{2}$ inches of precipitation. During August, there were three storms with $\frac{1}{4}$, $\frac{7}{8}$, and $1\frac{5}{12}$ inches of rain. During which month did Pittsburgh have more precipitation? How much more?

8. **GEOMETRY** Three sides of a four-sided pen are $120\frac{1}{4}$ ft, $135\frac{2}{3}$ ft, and $160\frac{1}{5}$ ft. If the perimeter of the pen is $515\frac{4}{15}$ ft, what is the length of the fourth side?

10. **LABOR** What was Lon paid for working the days in Exercise 9 if he received $40 per day?

12. **INVESTMENT** The stock of the Mina Corporation opened at $\$121\frac{3}{8}$. It increased $\$1\frac{3}{4}$ during the first hour of trading, but fell $\$3\frac{1}{8}$ before noon. It then increased $\$2\frac{7}{8}$ before closing time. What was the closing value of the stock?

In Exercises 13–16 use the table in Example 4 to compare productions by dividing the first number indicated by the second. Round numbers from the table to the nearest hundred. Follow Example 4(a) if further estimate is desired to make the fraction more understandable.

13. Compare the 1992 production of the U.S.S.R. to total world production that year.

14. Compare the 1980 production of Nigeria to the production of Saudi Arabia that year.

15. Compare the U.S. production in 1985 to the U.S. production in 1988.

16. Compare the largest production of Canada in the years given to its smallest production.

CRITICAL THINKING

Let a represent a natural number in Exercises 17-18.

17. If one shipment was $2\frac{1}{2}a$ units and a second shipment was $4\frac{2}{3}a$ units, what was the total of the two shipments?

18. Lonna Mills has $10\frac{3}{4}a$ units and Maria Lopez has $7\frac{2}{5}a$ units. How many more units does Lonna have?

19. Burford cannot seem to use the correct operation when working with applied problems. Write out a list of words and phrases for him that might be used when the appropriate operation is addition.

REVIEW OR PREVIEW

Evaluate each expression in Exercises 20–22.

20. $\left(\dfrac{7}{9} - \dfrac{1}{3}\right) \div \dfrac{1}{3} \cdot \dfrac{1}{4}$

21. $\sqrt{\dfrac{25}{16} - \left(\dfrac{3}{4}\right)^2}$

22. $\dfrac{2}{5} \div \dfrac{3}{10} - \dfrac{4}{9} \cdot \dfrac{3}{2}$

💡 *Answer true or false in Exercises 23–25.*

23. $\dfrac{3}{8} < \dfrac{8}{24}$

24. $\dfrac{22}{7} < \dfrac{10}{3}$

25. $\dfrac{4}{5} \cdot \dfrac{1}{2} > \dfrac{5}{6} \div \dfrac{10}{3}$

3.6 PARALLEL EXERCISES

Answers to these exercises are not given in the text.

Solve each applied problem in Exercises 1–12.

1. **BUSINESS** Because of low inventory an order of machine parts had to be shipped over a several day period. If $\frac{3}{4}$ of the order was received on Monday and $\frac{1}{5}$ was received on Friday, how much of the order was yet to be received?

2. **EDUCATION** If there are $16\frac{1}{3}$ points on Part A of a test and $18\frac{1}{5}$ points on Part B of the test, how many more points are on Part B?

3. **CONSTRUCTION** A contractor for a construction job ordered three loads of gravel. One weighed $2\frac{1}{4}$ tons, one $5\frac{5}{6}$ tons, and the other $4\frac{5}{8}$ tons. What total weight of gravel did he receive?

4. **CONSTRUCTION** If the contractor in Exercise 3 really needed 20 tons of gravel, how much more must he order?

5. **CONSTRUCTION** To construct a brick wall, three lengths of bricks are used, 6 inches, 14 inches, and 16 inches. What is the shortest length of wall that can be constructed if only one length of brick is used in any one row?

6. **RECREATION** During the first week of the spring thaw, two measurements of lake level were made. On the first, the lake level had increased $2\frac{3}{4}$ ft from the previous measurement. On the second, the level had increased another $3\frac{5}{12}$ ft. Three measurements the second week showed increases of $1\frac{5}{6}$ ft, $2\frac{2}{3}$ ft, and $2\frac{1}{4}$ ft. During which week did the level increase more? How much more?

7. **RECREATION** Joan McKee started at a point on the trail marked $32\frac{1}{4}$ miles. If she wants to get to the point marked $57\frac{1}{3}$ in two days, how far will she need to hike the first day to cover one half the total distance?

8. **ENTERTAINMENT** Jo must have $216\frac{1}{2}$ points to win a contest. If for three projects she has received $25\frac{1}{4}$ points, $17\frac{1}{6}$ points, and $42\frac{3}{8}$ points, how many more points does she need to win?

9. **LABOR** Fran worked for $32\frac{3}{4}$ hours, $28\frac{5}{6}$ hours, $42\frac{1}{6}$ hours, and $19\frac{3}{4}$ hours over a four-week period. What was her total number of hours worked?

10. **LABOR** Fran in Exercise 9 is paid $10 per hour. How much should she be paid for the four weeks' work?

11. **BUSINESS** On Wednesday a grocery distributor received two shipments of grapes, $395\frac{3}{8}$ lb and $215\frac{3}{4}$ lb. On Thursday two more shipments of $198\frac{1}{2}$ lb and $416\frac{1}{8}$ lb were received. On which day did he receive more grapes? How many pounds more?

12. **INVESTMENT** The opening quote for stock of the Nina Corporation was $\$62\frac{1}{8}$. During the morning it dropped $\$4\frac{3}{4}$ but increased again $\$6\frac{5}{8}$ before noon. It then dropped $\$1\frac{1}{8}$ before closing time. What was the closing value of the stock?

Use the table from Example 4 to compare productions by dividing the first number indicated by the second. Round numbers from the table to the nearest hundred. Follow Example 4(a) if further estimate is desired to make the fraction more understandable.

13. Compare the 1989 production of the Mexico to total world production that year.

14. Compare the 1992 production of Kuwait to the production of Libya that year.

15. Compare the United Kingdom production in 1992 to the United Kingdom production in 1988.

16. Compare the smallest production of Kuwait in the years given to its largest production.

CRITICAL THINKING

Let a represent a natural a number in Exercises 17–18.

17. On Monday $102\frac{2}{5}a$ units were produced at the plant and on Tuesday $116\frac{9}{10}a$ units were produced. What was the total production for the two days?

18. A shipment of $22\frac{3}{8}a$ units was received at the downtown warehouse while a shipment of $29\frac{1}{4}a$ units was coming into the Bennett Street warehouse. How much more did the Bennett Street warehouse receive?

19. Burford cannot seem to use the correct operation when working with applied problems. Write out a list of words and phrases for him that might be used when the appropriate operation is subtraction.

GROUP PROJECT

In Example 4 and Exercises 13–16 we used rounding and estimation to give fractions that we could more easily understand in the comparisons that we were making. Discuss the use of estimation in the presentation of all kinds of data. What is the meaning of the word precision? Study and discuss the relationship between precision and estimation.

CHAPTER 3 REVIEW

KEY WORDS

 3.1
- **Like fractions** have the same denominator.
- **Unlike fractions** have different denominators.

 3.2
- A whole number that is in the lists of non-zero multiples of two or more numbers is called a **common multiple.**

- The **least common multiple (LCM)** of two or more counting numbers is the smallest of all common multiples of the numbers.

 3.3
- The **least common denominator (LCD)** is the least common multiple of the denominators of fractions in an addition or subtraction problem.

KEY CONCEPTS

 3.1
1. Like fractions are added or subtracted by adding or subtracting the numerators and placing the result over the common denominator.
2. *Never* add or subtract fractions by adding or subtracting denominators.

 3.2
Three methods of finding LCMs are the listing method, finding prime factors, and the special optional algorithm.

 3.3
Fractions to be added or subtracted must be changed to equivalent fractions with the same LCD. You should *not* find the LCD when multiplying or dividing fractions.

 3.4
The method used for adding or subtracting mixed numbers is to add or subtract the whole number parts and the proper fraction parts separately. Do *not* try to multiply or divide mixed fractions using this method.

 3.5
1. Operations should be performed in the following order.
   a. Operate within parentheses.
   b. Evaluate powers and roots.
   c. Multiply and divide from left to right.
   d. Add and subtract from left to right.
2. To tell which of two fractions is larger, change them to equivalent fractions with the same LCD and compare numerators.

CHAPTER 3 REVIEW EXERCISES

PART I

Answers to these exercises are given on page 646.

3.1

Perform the indicated operations in Exercises 1–6.

1. $\dfrac{3}{22}+\dfrac{9}{22}$

2. $\dfrac{17}{18}-\dfrac{1}{18}$

3. $\dfrac{4}{25}+\dfrac{1}{25}$

4. $\dfrac{8}{35}-\dfrac{3}{35}$

5. $\dfrac{7}{10}+\dfrac{11}{10}-\dfrac{3}{10}$

6. $\dfrac{9}{17}-\dfrac{3}{17}-\dfrac{6}{17}$

3.2

Find the LCM of the numbers in Exercises 7–12.

7. 40 and 8

8. 12 and 30

9. 15 and 35

10. 9 and 30

11. 120 and 14

12. 12, 14, and 18

3.3

In Exercises 13–18, perform the indicated operations.

13. $\dfrac{5}{12}+\dfrac{3}{18}$

14. $3+\dfrac{7}{9}$

15. $\dfrac{4}{7}-\dfrac{1}{6}$

16. $3 - \dfrac{4}{3}$

17. $\dfrac{12}{15} + \dfrac{2}{3} - \dfrac{1}{5}$

18. $\dfrac{5}{3} - 1 + \dfrac{2}{7}$

3.4

In Exercises 19–24, perform the indicated operations.

19. $\begin{array}{r} 2\dfrac{1}{8} \\ +7\dfrac{3}{4} \\ \hline \end{array}$

20. $\begin{array}{r} 5\dfrac{2}{7} \\ -3\dfrac{2}{3} \\ \hline \end{array}$

21. $\begin{array}{r} 6\dfrac{2}{5} \\ +8\dfrac{7}{8} \\ \hline \end{array}$

22. $\begin{array}{r} 9\dfrac{3}{7} \\ -4\dfrac{5}{6} \\ \hline \end{array}$

23. $\begin{array}{r} 215\dfrac{1}{4} \\ +375\dfrac{2}{11} \\ \hline \end{array}$

24. $\begin{array}{r} 627\dfrac{1}{2} \\ -421\dfrac{5}{8} \\ \hline \end{array}$

3.5

💡 *Evaluate each expression in Exercises 25–30.*

25. $\left(\dfrac{2}{5} - \dfrac{1}{15} \right) \div \dfrac{5}{3}$

26. $\sqrt{\dfrac{4}{9} + \left(\dfrac{1}{3} \right)^2}$

27. $\dfrac{1}{8} \cdot \dfrac{2}{3} - \dfrac{1}{12}$

28. $\dfrac{1}{2} \cdot \left(\dfrac{7}{9} + \dfrac{1}{3} \right) \div \dfrac{5}{6}$

29. $\left(\dfrac{3}{8} - \dfrac{1}{4} \right)^2 \cdot \dfrac{8}{9}$

30. $\dfrac{1}{6} \div \dfrac{5}{9} - \left(\dfrac{1}{5} \right)^2$

💡 *Which of the two fractions in Exercises 31–33 is larger?*

31. $\dfrac{4}{17}$ or $\dfrac{1}{4}$

32. $\dfrac{8}{11}$ or $\dfrac{5}{7}$

33. $\dfrac{38}{9}$ or $\dfrac{47}{11}$

💡 *Answer* true *or* false *in Exercises 34–36.*

34. $\dfrac{7}{12} < \dfrac{10}{18}$

35. $\dfrac{25}{3} > \dfrac{41}{5}$

36. $7\dfrac{19}{21} < 7\dfrac{49}{51}$

3.6

Solve each applied problem in Exercises 37–40.

37. **CONSTRUCTION**   A contractor needs steel rods which measure 2 feet, 6 feet, and 9 feet. He will cut only one length from each rod. What is the shortest rod that he can order and be able to cut each length with no waste?

38. **WEATHER**   The rainfall for January was $3\frac{1}{3}$ inches, for February was $2\frac{3}{4}$ inches, for March was $8\frac{7}{8}$ inches, and for April was $7\frac{2}{3}$ inches. What was the total rainfall for the first one third of the year?

PART II

39. **CONSTRUCTION**   It takes $3\frac{11}{15}$ weeks to complete a building project, and the contractor has been working for $2\frac{2}{5}$ weeks. How much longer will it be before the job is finished?

40. **RECREATION**   Robert ran $7\frac{3}{4}$ miles and $6\frac{2}{3}$ miles during one week. The next week he ran $5\frac{1}{2}$ miles, $3\frac{1}{3}$ miles, and $5\frac{1}{4}$ miles. During which week did he run farther? How much farther?

Find the LCM of the numbers in Exercises 41–43.

41. 16 and 22

42. 35 and 45

43. 6, 14, and 24

💡 *In Exercises 44–46, place the appropriate sign, < or >, between the two fractions.*

44. $\dfrac{5}{6}$ ___ $\dfrac{9}{11}$

45. $\dfrac{16}{7}$ ___ $\dfrac{23}{9}$

46. $\dfrac{41}{37}$ ___ $\dfrac{62}{55}$

In Exercises 47–52, perform the indicated operations.

47. $3\dfrac{1}{2}$

    $+7\dfrac{2}{3}$

48. $16\dfrac{1}{9}$

    $-12\dfrac{17}{18}$

49. $6\dfrac{2}{5}$

    $9\dfrac{1}{10}$

    $+12\dfrac{14}{15}$

50. $\left(\dfrac{2}{3}-\dfrac{1}{9}\right)\div\dfrac{11}{18}$

51. $\dfrac{6}{11}+\dfrac{13}{22}-\dfrac{5}{33}$

52. $\sqrt{\dfrac{25}{64}}-\left(\dfrac{1}{4}\right)^2$

According to the Bureau of Labor and Statistics, the average American household spends about $88 per day on living expenses. The bar graph below shows the breakdown of the daily amount spent on the indicated categories. Use the graph to answer exercises 53–56.

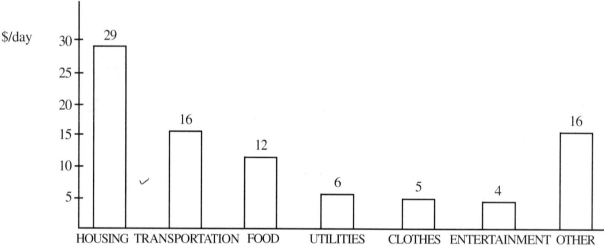

Source: Consumer Expenditure Survey, Bureau of Labor and Statistics

53. What fraction of the total daily expenses is spent on transportation?

54. What fraction of the total daily expenses is spent on food?

55. What is the difference between the fraction of the total daily expenses spent on housing and the fraction spent on utilities?

56. What is the quotient of the fraction spent on transportation and the fraction spent on entertainment?

CHAPTER 3 TEST

Answers to this test are given on page 646.
Find the LCM of the given numbers.

1. 14 and 15

2. 8, 12, and 20

Perform the indicated operations.

3. $\dfrac{5}{21} + \dfrac{2}{21}$

4. $\dfrac{14}{15} - \dfrac{4}{15}$

5. $\dfrac{7}{12} + \dfrac{3}{8}$

6. $\dfrac{9}{20} - \dfrac{1}{6}$

7. $\dfrac{12}{7} - \dfrac{13}{14} + \dfrac{1}{2}$

8. $\dfrac{7}{8} - \dfrac{5}{12} - \dfrac{1}{6}$

9. $\begin{array}{r} 2\dfrac{5}{9} \\[2mm] +7\dfrac{1}{3} \\ \hline \end{array}$

10. $\begin{array}{r} 42\dfrac{7}{15} \\[2mm] -33\dfrac{3}{5} \\ \hline \end{array}$

11. $\begin{array}{r} 3\dfrac{3}{4} \\[2mm] 8\dfrac{1}{3} \\[2mm] +5\dfrac{7}{12} \\ \hline \end{array}$

1.＿＿＿＿＿＿＿＿＿＿＿＿

2.＿＿＿＿＿＿＿＿＿＿＿＿

3.＿＿＿＿＿＿＿＿＿＿＿＿

4.＿＿＿＿＿＿＿＿＿＿＿＿

5.＿＿＿＿＿＿＿＿＿＿＿＿

6.＿＿＿＿＿＿＿＿＿＿＿＿

7.＿＿＿＿＿＿＿＿＿＿＿＿

8.＿＿＿＿＿＿＿＿＿＿＿＿

9.＿＿＿＿＿＿＿＿＿＿＿＿

10.＿＿＿＿＿＿＿＿＿＿＿＿

11.＿＿＿＿＿＿＿＿＿＿＿＿

12. $4\dfrac{3}{8}$

$2\dfrac{3}{4}$

$+1\dfrac{1}{2}$

12._____

Evaluate each expression.

13. $\sqrt{\dfrac{4}{9}} - \dfrac{2}{3} \cdot \dfrac{15}{20} + 4 \div \dfrac{1}{2}$

13._____

14. $\left(\dfrac{8}{9} - \dfrac{2}{3}\right)^2 \div \dfrac{4}{9} - \dfrac{1}{2} \cdot \dfrac{1}{5}$

14._____

Answer true *or* false.

15. $\dfrac{17}{20} < \dfrac{27}{30}$

15._____

16. $5\dfrac{12}{13} > 5\dfrac{43}{40}$

16._____

Solve.

17. During one day a market received $25\dfrac{2}{5}$ pounds of oranges, $36\dfrac{1}{4}$ pounds of apples, and $18\dfrac{5}{8}$ pounds of peaches. What was the total weight of fruit received that day?

17._____

18. A repair job is estimated to require $6\dfrac{5}{6}$ hours to complete. If Hank has been working for $2\dfrac{11}{12}$ hours, how much longer will he have to work to finish the job?

18._____

19. If fractions were added by adding numerators and adding denominators, what would be the sum of $\dfrac{1}{2}$ and $\dfrac{1}{2}$?

19._____

20. Write the number 0 as a fraction.

20._____

21. Are $4 \cdot \dfrac{1}{2}$ and $4\dfrac{1}{2}$ the same? Explain.

21._____

_____

22. Insert parentheses in $\dfrac{1}{2} - \dfrac{1}{2} \cdot \dfrac{1}{4} + \dfrac{1}{3}$ to make the answer $\dfrac{1}{3}$.

22._____

CUMULATIVE REVIEW: CHAPTERS 1–3

Answers to these exercises are on page 646.

Perform the indicated operations in Exercises 1–12.

1. $\dfrac{3}{4} + \dfrac{5}{4}$

2. $\dfrac{7}{21} \cdot \dfrac{3}{5}$

3. $\dfrac{7}{8} - \dfrac{1}{2}$

4. $\begin{array}{r} 625 \\ +781 \\ \hline \end{array}$

5. $\begin{array}{r} 2030 \\ -1621 \\ \hline \end{array}$

6. $\begin{array}{r} 6110 \\ 217 \\ +5123 \\ \hline \end{array}$

7. $16\dfrac{1}{3} \div 6\dfrac{1}{8}$

8. $5\dfrac{1}{2} \cdot \dfrac{4}{33}$

9. $6\dfrac{1}{2} - 2\dfrac{1}{3}$

10. $3^2 - 2 \cdot 4 + \sqrt{9}$

11. $\dfrac{1}{2} \div \dfrac{1}{3} - \sqrt{\dfrac{4}{9}}$

12. $\left(\dfrac{3}{4}\right)^2 - \left(\dfrac{1}{2}\right)^2 \div 2$

Solve each applied problem in Exercises 13–14.

13. **CHEMISTRY**   Dr. Johnson, a chemist, pours 384 milliliters of acid into 4 flasks in such a way that each flask has the same amount. How much acid is in each flask?

14. **CONSUMER**   Assuming equal quality, which is a better buy, a 5-lb bag of dog food for $2.00 (200¢), or an 8-lb bag of dog food for $3.04 (304¢)?

Check each subtraction in Exercises 15–16.

15. $\begin{array}{r} 4002 \\ -\ 938 \\ \hline 3064 \end{array}$

16. $\begin{array}{r} 2090 \\ -1357 \\ \hline 1743 \end{array}$

♀17.   Find all the divisors of 80.

♀18.   Find the prime factorization of 4875.

♀   *Answer* true *or* false *in Exercises 19–24.*

19. $17 > 9$

20. $\dfrac{3}{4} < \dfrac{4}{3}$

21. $\dfrac{5}{18} > \dfrac{4}{9}$

22. $2\dfrac{3}{8} < 2\dfrac{2}{5}$

23. $\dfrac{1}{2} \cdot \dfrac{3}{4} > \dfrac{1}{3} \div \dfrac{2}{3}$

24. $\dfrac{7}{9} - \dfrac{1}{3} < \dfrac{2}{9} + \dfrac{1}{3}$

25.   A tank holds 480 gallons when it is $\dfrac{3}{4}$ full. How many gallons does it hold when full?

CHAPTER *f•o•u•r*

DECIMALS

An alternative notation for representing fractions and mixed numbers, a notation that has become even more important in recent years with the advent of the calculator, involves the use of decimals. In about 1600, Simon Stevin (1548-1620) was one of the first to use decimal notation. However, his treatment was so confusing that it was many years before the notation was simplified for practical purposes. Surprisingly, Stevin did not use a decimal point, and historians are not certain who actually invented it, but it was introduced sometime in the seventeenth century. In fact, many European countries even today use a comma instead of a decimal point. Operations with numbers in decimal notation provide useful tools for solving many types of problems, especially with the aid of a calculator. One such application is given below and solved in Example 9 in Section 4.7.

RECREATION When very large numbers are used in graphs and tables, the notation is often simplified by using decimals. For example, consider the table below which gives the number of recreational vehicles sold in five different years. Notice that instead of using the number 226,500 for the total number of motorhomes sold in 1990, the number given is 226.5 and it represents thousands of units.

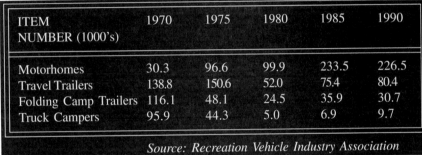

ITEM NUMBER (1000's)	1970	1975	1980	1985	1990
Motorhomes	30.3	96.6	99.9	233.5	226.5
Travel Trailers	138.8	150.6	52.0	75.4	80.4
Folding Camp Trailers	116.1	48.1	24.5	35.9	30.7
Truck Campers	95.9	44.3	5.0	6.9	9.7

Source: Recreation Vehicle Industry Association

(a) During which of these five years was the total number of recreation vehicles sold the greatest, and how many vehicles were sold in that year? (b) In 1990, how many more motorhomes were sold than all other recreation vehicles combined? (c) If the retail value of all folding camping trailers sold in 1990 was $134,000,000, what was the approximate price per unit sold during that year?

We begin this chapter with a development of decimal notation, conversion between decimals and fractions, and rounding decimals for use in estimation. Next we add, subtract, multiply, and divide decimals with emphasis on realistic applications. The order of operations and a method of comparing decimals follows, and we conclude with a brief discussion of the use of a calculator for various operations with decimals.

4.1 DECIMAL NOTATION

STUDENT GUIDEPOSTS
1 DEFINING DECIMAL FRACTIONS AND DECIMALS
2 WRITING DECIMALS IN EXPANDED NOTATION
3 USING DECIMALS FOR AMOUNTS OF MONEY

1 DEFINING DECIMAL FRACTIONS AND DECIMALS

As we saw in Chapter 2, a fraction has many names. For example,

$$\frac{1}{2}, \ \frac{2}{4}, \ \frac{3}{6}, \ \frac{4}{8}, \ \frac{5}{10}, \ \frac{25}{50}, \ \frac{50}{100}$$

are all names for the fraction *one half.* A fraction which has a denominator equal to a power of 10 (10, 100, 1000, 10,000, and so forth) is called a **decimal fraction.** The following are decimal fractions.

$\frac{5}{10}$ is read "**five tenths.**"

$\frac{3}{100}$ is read "**three hundredths.**"

$\frac{47}{1000}$ is read "**forty-seven thousandths.**"

$\frac{121}{10,000}$ is read "**one hundred twenty-one ten thousandths.**"

Decimal fractions are usually referred to simply as **decimals.** Each decimal has two forms, a *fractional form,*

$$\frac{5}{10}, \ \frac{3}{100}, \ \frac{47}{1000}, \ \frac{121}{10,000}$$

and a *decimal form* or *decimal notation,*

0.5, 0.03, 0.047, and 0.0121.

Recall that the number system is a place-value system. The decimal form of a number is part of this system, as shown in the following revised place-value chart first seen in Chapter 1. Notice that the value of any position is one tenth the value of the position to its immediate left.

Thousands	Hundreds	Tens	Ones	Tenths	Hundredths	Thousandths	Ten thousandths	Hundred thousandths	Millionths
1000	100	10	1	$\frac{1}{10}$	$\frac{1}{100}$	$\frac{1}{1000}$	$\frac{1}{10,000}$	$\frac{1}{100,000}$	$\frac{1}{1,000,000}$

When a number is written in decimal form, a period, called a **decimal point,** separates the ones digit from the tenths digit. It serves as a reference point: positions to the left of the decimal point end in *s* while those to the right end in *ths.* Consider the number 352.1783 shown on the next page.

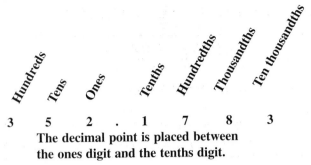

| 3 | 5 | 2 | . | 1 | 7 | 8 | 3 |

The decimal point is placed between the ones digit and the tenths digit.

This number is read: **three hundred fifty-two** *and* **one thousand seven hundred eighty-three ten thousandths.**

The three points to remember about word names for decimals are given below.

TO READ A DECIMAL

1. The part of the number to the left of the decimal point is read just like a whole number.
2. The decimal point is read "and."
3. The part of the number to the right of the decimal point is read like a whole number but is followed by the name of the place filled by the farthest right digit.

EXAMPLE 1   WRITING WORD NAMES FOR DECIMALS

Give the word name for each decimal.
(a) .5 or 0.**5** is read "five tenths."

Tenths place

Both .5 and 0.5 are correct ways to write five tenths. The second form is preferred since it calls attention to the decimal point.

(b) 3.5 is read "three and five tenths."
(c) 0.0**3** is read "three hundredths."

    ↑

Hundredths place

(d) 4.03 is read "four and three hundredths."
(e) 0.00**8** is read "eight thousandths."

  ↑

Thousandths place

(f) 21.008 is read "twenty-one and eight thousandths."
(g) 4.107 is read "four and one hundred seven thousandths."

If there are no digits (or possibly only zeros) to the right of the decimal point, the decimal is actually a whole number. In such cases, the decimal point is usually omitted. For example,

47, 47., and 47.0

are all names for the whole number forty-seven.

Write each number in decimal notation.
(a) **Three and nine tenths** is written 3.9.

$$\downarrow \qquad \downarrow \qquad \downarrow$$
$$3 \qquad \cdot \qquad 9$$

(b) **Thirteen and three hundredths** is written 13.03.

$$\downarrow \qquad \downarrow \qquad \downarrow$$
$$13 \qquad \cdot \qquad 03$$

(c) Five thousand four and twenty-seven thousandths is written 5004.027.
(d) Forty-two thousandths is written 0.042.

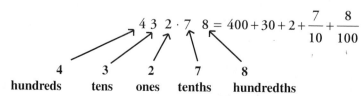

NOTE   A less formal method for reading decimals is commonly used. For example,

3.42	is often read "three *point* four two,"
10.001	is often read "one zero *point* zero zero one,"
6254.398	is often read "six two five four *point* three nine eight."

We simply read each digit in order from left to right and say "point" when we reach the decimal point.

When whole numbers were first studied, we discussed expanded notation. For example,

$$2375 \text{ is } 2000 + 300 + 70 + 5$$

in expanded notation. This notation can be extended to all decimals, as shown below for the decimal 23.456.

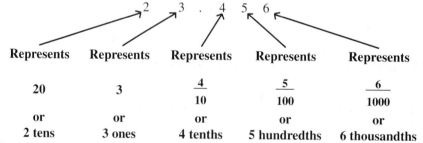

Represents	Represents	Represents	Represents	Represents
20	3	$\dfrac{4}{10}$	$\dfrac{5}{100}$	$\dfrac{6}{1000}$
or	or	or	or	or
2 tens	3 ones	4 tenths	5 hundredths	6 thousandths

Thus, we can write 23.456 in expanded notation as

$$20 + 3 + \frac{4}{10} + \frac{5}{100} + \frac{6}{1000}.$$

Write each decimal in expanded notation.
(a) 432.78

$$4\,3\,2 \cdot 7\,8 = 400 + 30 + 2 + \frac{7}{10} + \frac{8}{100}$$

hundreds   tens   ones   tenths   hundredths

PRACTICE EXERCISE 2

Write each number in decimal notation.

(a) Six and four tenths

(b) Thirty-five and two hundredths

(c) Eight thousand forty-five and six hundred eight thousandths

(d) Ninety-three ten thousandths

Answers: (a) 6.4 (b) 35.02 (c) 8045.608 (d) 0.0093

PRACTICE EXERCISE 3

Write each decimal in expanded notation.
(a) 258.65

$$200 + 50 + 8 + \frac{6}{10} + \frac{5}{100}$$

(b) $25.6794 = 20 + 5 + \dfrac{6}{10} + \dfrac{7}{100} + \dfrac{9}{1000} + \dfrac{4}{10,000}$

(c) $403.002 = 400 + 3 + \dfrac{2}{1000}$

(d) $3050.7020 = 3000 + 50 + \dfrac{7}{10} + \dfrac{2}{1000}$

The final zero to the right does not affect the value of the decimal and could be omitted.

3 | USING DECIMALS FOR AMOUNTS OF MONEY

Perhaps the most common use of decimal notation is for amounts of money. For example, we could read

$25.76 as **twenty-five *and* seventy-six hundredths dollars.**

However, since one hundredth of a dollar is one *cent* (1¢) we usually say

twenty-five dollars *and* seventy-six cents.

Notice that the word *and* is still identified with the decimal point. We must put the decimal point in the right place. For instance,

$25   ·and $0.25

do not represent the same amount: $25 or $25.00 is twenty-five dollars while $0.25 is twenty-five hundredths of a dollar or twenty-five cents (25¢).

EXAMPLE 4 | WRITING WORD NAMES FOR MONEY

Write a word name for each amount of money.

(a) $4.76   Four and seventy-six hundredths dollars *or* four dollars and seventy-six cents

(b) $1327.03 ·   One thousand three hundred twenty-seven and three hundredths dollars *or* one thousand three hundred twenty-seven dollars and three cents

(c) $41.00   Forty-one and zero hundredths dollars *or* forty-one dollars and no cents *or simply* forty-one dollars

EXAMPLE 5 | WRITING DECIMALS FOR AMOUNTS OF MONEY

Write a decimal for each amount of money.

(a) Three hundred twenty-seven and twelve hundredths dollars is written $327.12.

(b) Two dollars and thirty-seven cents is written $2.37.

(c) Seventy-six and no hundredths dollars is written $76.00.

Writing checks requires writing word names for decimals. It has become customary to write fractions for the cents portion of an amount of money. For example, $3.48 is written

$$\text{three and } \frac{48}{100} \text{ dollars}$$

instead of

three and forty-eight hundredths dollars.

This is done on the sample check in Figure 4.1.

FIGURE 4.1

(b) 43.2963

(c) 605.007

(d) 1060.05030

Answers: (a) $200 + 50 + 8$
$+ \dfrac{6}{10} + \dfrac{5}{100}$
(b) $40 + 3 + \dfrac{2}{10}$
$+ \dfrac{9}{100} + \dfrac{6}{1000} + \dfrac{3}{10,000}$
(c) $600 + 5 + \dfrac{7}{1000}$
(d) $1000 + 60 + \dfrac{5}{100} + \dfrac{3}{10,000}$

PRACTICE EXERCISE 4

Write a word name for each amount of money.

(a) $3.98
(b) $2650.07
(c) $75.00

Answers: (a) Three and ninety-eight hundredths dollars *or* three dollars and ninety-eight cents   (b) Two thousand six hundred fifty and seven hundredths dollars *or* two thousand six hundred fifty dollars and seven cents
(c) Seventy-five and zero hundredths dollars *or* seventy-five dollars and no cents *or simply* seventy-five dollars

PRACTICE EXERCISE 5

Write a decimal for each amount of money

(a) Six hundred fifty-four and twenty-three hundredths dollars
(b) Ten dollars and ninety-five cents
(c) Eighty-four and no hundredths dollars

Answers: (a) $654.23
(b) $10.95 (c) $84.00

4.1 EXERCISES

Answers to these exercises are given on page 646.

1. What are fractions called that have a denominator equal to a power of 10?
2. What do we call the period used in decimal notation?

Give the formal word name for each decimal in Exercises 3–8.

3. 0.7   4. 2.05   5. 43.29

6. 127.562   .   7. 302.008   8. 0.0009

Write each number in decimal notation in Exercises 9–14.

9. four hundredths
10. two hundred twenty-eight and nine tenths
11. twenty-three and seven hundred forty-eight thousandths
12. eight hundred one and one hundred eight thousandths
13. three and one ten thousandth
14. four hundred ninety-seven and six thousand forty-three ten thousandths

In Exercises 15–18, write each decimal in expanded notation.

15. 41.8   16. 30.07

17. 2050.703   18. 40.1005

In Exercises 19–22, write a word name for the dollar amount using dollars and cents.

19. $1.47   *one dollar and forty seven cents*   20. $18.09
21. $162.00   22. $10.40

In Exercises 23–25, write a word name as it would appear on a check.

23. $427.68   24. $20.00   25. $3.02

CRITICAL THINKING

26. One of the most famous numbers in mathematics is π, the number obtained by dividing the circumference of any circle by its diameter. As a decimal, π is often approximated using 3.1416. Give the formal word name for this approximation of π.

27. Write a word name for $32,529.75 as it would appear on a check.

28. *Burford was asked to make a sign for a bake sale at his school. A copy of the sign is below.* Did Burford really mean to say that a piece of pie was selling for less than a penny? Explain to Burford how the sign should be corrected.

SCHOOL BAKE SALE

Cup of Coffee: .50¢

Piece of Pie: .75¢

REVIEW AND PREVIEW

The following exercises will help you prepare for the next section. In Exercises 29–31, write each improper fraction as a mixed number.

29. $\dfrac{9}{4}$

30. $\dfrac{42}{11}$

31. $\dfrac{103}{100}$

In Exercises 32–34, write each mixed number as an improper fraction.

32. $2\dfrac{1}{5}$

33. $5\dfrac{7}{10}$

34. $7\dfrac{23}{100}$

4.1 PARALLEL EXERCISES

Answers to these exercises are not given in the text.

1. Decimal fractions have denominators that are powers of what number?

2. The decimal point in decimal notation separates which two digits?

Give the formal word name for each decimal in Exercises 3–8.

3. 0.9

4. 3.06

5. 52.39 *fifty two and thirty nine hundredths*

6. 147.053

7. 602.007

8. 0.0005

Write each number in decimal notation in Exercises 9–14.

9. seven hundredths

10. three hundred thirty-five and eight tenths

11. forty-two and eight hundred sixty-five thousandths

12. seven and two ten thousandths

13. five hundred one and one hundred five thousandths

14. three hundred six and one thousand forty-two ten thousandths

In Exercises 15–18, write each decimal in expanded notation.

15. 32.5

16. 60.03

17. 51.006

18. 80.2006

In Exercises 19–22, write a word name for the dollar amount using dollars and cents.

19. $1.58

20. $47.09

21. $20.06

22. $535.00

In Exercises 23–25, write a word name as it would appear on a check.

23. $6.05

24. $70.00

25. $395.49

CRITICAL THINKING

26. The speed of light is approximately 273,213.6 feet per second. Give the formal word name for this number.

27. Write a word name for $10,428.64 as it would appear on a check.

28. *Burford was asked to make a sign for a bake sale at his school. A copy of the sign is given to the right.* Certainly a cup of coffee sold for more than half a cent! If Burford would have written a 0 in front of the decimal point, do you think this might have helped him to avoid the error that he made? Explain.

> **SCHOOL BAKE SALE**
>
> Cup of Coffee: .50¢
>
> Piece of Pie: .75¢

GROUP PROJECT

Although our number system is based on the number ten, therefore called a decimal system, there is really nothing magical about that number. Numbers can be written in many ways using many different base numbers. For example, consider writing numbers using base four. The symbols that are used are 0, 1, 2, and 3. The number four would then be written as 10 since this corresponds to 1 four plus 0 ones. The number 100 would represent 1 sixteen plus 0 fours plus 0 ones, or simply sixteen. The number 1.2 would represent 1 one plus 2 fourths, which we would recognize as the number 1.5 in decimal notation. Try to write several other numbers using four as a base, then experiment with using other base numbers. Could the number one be used for a base? Explain.

4.2 CONVERSIONS BETWEEN FRACTIONS AND DECIMALS

STUDENT GUIDEPOSTS
1   CHANGING DECIMALS TO FRACTIONS
2   CHANGING FRACTIONS TO DECIMALS
3   SUMMARIZING EQUIVALENT FRACTIONS AND DECIMALS

1   CHANGING DECIMALS TO FRACTIONS

Recall from Section 4.1 that any decimal fraction has two forms, a decimal form and a fractional form. We now consider how to change from one form to the other.

Converting decimals to fractions is simply a matter of thinking of the decimal in words and writing the fraction, as in the following table.

Decimal	Word Name	Fraction
0.7	seven tenths	$\dfrac{7}{10}$
0.23	twenty-three hundredths	$\dfrac{23}{100}$
0.423	four hundred twenty-three thousandths	$\dfrac{423}{1000}$
3.1	three and one tenth	$3\dfrac{1}{10}$

The resulting fraction (which may be part of a mixed number) should be reduced to lowest terms.

TO CHANGE A DECIMAL TO A FRACTION (FIRST METHOD)

1. Say the word name for the decimal.
2. Write the word name as a fraction or a mixed number.
3. Reduce the fraction to lowest terms.

EXAMPLE 1   **CHANGING DECIMALS TO FRACTIONS (FIRST METHOD)**

Change each decimal to a fraction or mixed number.

(a) 0.6 is read "six tenths." Thus,

$$0.6 = \frac{6}{10} = \frac{2 \cdot 3}{2 \cdot 5} = \frac{3}{5}.$$ Reduce $\frac{6}{10}$ to lowest terms

(b) 0.35 is read "thirty-five hundredths."

$$0.35 = \frac{35}{100} = \frac{5 \cdot 7}{5 \cdot 20} = \frac{7}{20}$$ Reduce to lowest terms

(c) 0.348 is read "three hundred forty-eight thousandths."

$$0.348 = \frac{348}{1000} = \frac{4 \cdot 87}{4 \cdot 250} = \frac{87}{250}$$

(d) 4.8 is read "four and eight tenths."

$$4.8 = 4 + \frac{8}{10} = 4\frac{8}{10} = 4\frac{2 \cdot 4}{2 \cdot 5} = 4\frac{4}{5}$$

Another method of conversion allows us to write any decimal as a proper or improper fraction. Consider 0.38, for example. Since *two* digits follow the decimal point, put *two* zeros after 1 to form the denominator of the fraction. When the decimal point is removed, the resulting number is the numerator of the desired fraction. Sometimes the fraction must be reduced.

$$0.38 = \frac{38}{100} = \frac{2 \cdot 19}{2 \cdot 50} = \frac{19}{50}$$ Reduced

    ↑   ↑

Two digits after the decimal point   **Two zeros after 1**

TO CHANGE A DECIMAL TO A FRACTION (SECOND METHOD)

1. Count the digits following the decimal point; put that number of zeros after 1 in the denominator of the fraction.
2. Remove the decimal point; put the resulting whole number in the numerator of the fraction.
3. Reduce the fraction to lowest terms.

PRACTICE EXERCISE 1

Change each decimal to a fraction or mixed number.

(a) 0.2

(b) 0.65

(c) 0.804

(d) 53.625

Answers: (a) $\frac{1}{5}$ (b) $\frac{13}{30}$

(c) $\frac{201}{250}$ (d) $53\frac{5}{8}$

Change each decimal to a
fraction or mixed number
using the second method of
conversion.

(a) 0.2

CHANGING DECIMALS TO FRACTIONS (SECOND METHOD)

EXAMPLE 2

Change each decimal to a fraction or mixed number using the second method of conversion.

(a) 0.6

$$\frac{6}{10} \longleftarrow$$ Remove the decimal point and put 6 in the numerator

$\longleftarrow$ Since one digit follows the decimal point in 0.6, 1 followed by one zero, or 10, is the denominator

$$= \frac{\not{2} \cdot 3}{\not{2} \cdot 5} = \frac{3}{5}$$ Reduce to lowest terms

(b) 0.65

(b) 0.35

$$\frac{35}{100} \longleftarrow$$ Remove decimal point

$\longleftarrow$ 1 followed by two zeros (0.35 two digits)

$$= \frac{\not{5} \cdot 7}{\not{5} \cdot 20} = \frac{7}{20}$$ Reduce to lowest terms

(c) 0.804

(c) 0.348

$$\frac{348}{1000} \longleftarrow$$ Remove decimal point

$\longleftarrow$ 1 followed by three zeros (0.348 three digits)

$$= \frac{\not{4} \cdot 87}{\not{4} \cdot 250} = \frac{87}{250}$$ Reduce

(d) 53.625

(d) 4.8

$$\frac{48}{10} \longleftarrow$$ Remove decimal point

$\longleftarrow$ 1 followed by one zero

$$= \frac{\not{2} \cdot 24}{\not{2} \cdot 5}$$ Reduce

$$= \frac{24}{5} \text{ or } 4\frac{4}{5}$$

Answers: (a) $\frac{1}{5}$ (b) $\frac{13}{20}$
(c) $\frac{201}{250}$ (d) $53\frac{5}{8}$

2 | CHANGING FRACTIONS TO DECIMALS

Next we change fractions to decimals. Remember that one meaning for a fraction is division. For example,

$$\frac{2}{3} \text{ means } 2 \div 3 \text{ or } 3\overline{)2} .$$

In Chapter 1 we learned how to divide one whole number (dividend) by a smaller whole number (divisor). The same method can be used when the divisor is greater than the dividend, as in the fractions $\frac{2}{3}$ or $\frac{1}{4}$. The result is a decimal. Place a decimal point to the right of the dividend and attach zeros as necessary. Place a decimal point in the quotient directly above the decimal point in the dividend. Divide as if there were no decimals present. The following example illustrates.

To change $\frac{1}{4}$ to a decimal, divide 1 by 4.

$\overset{\cdot}{}$ ⟵ ③ **Place decimal point in quotient above decimal point in dividend**

$4\overline{)1.0}$ ⟵ ② **Attach one zero**

① **Place decimal point after 1**

Ignore the decimal points and divide 10 by 4. Then, attach a second 0 to the dividend, bring it down, and divide 4 into 20.

$$\begin{array}{r} .25 \\ 4\overline{)1.00} \\ \underline{8} \\ 20 \\ \underline{20} \\ 0 \end{array} \qquad \mathbf{20 \div 4 = 5}$$

Stop when the remainder is 0. The quotient is the desired decimal.

$$\frac{1}{4} = 0.25$$

We can check that the method is correct by reversing the steps and changing 0.25 to a fraction.

$$0.25 \text{ is } \frac{25}{100}, \text{ which reduces to } \frac{1 \cdot \cancel{25}}{4 \cdot \cancel{25}} = \frac{1}{4}.$$

Suppose we change $\frac{2}{3}$ to a decimal.

$\overset{\cdot}{}$ ⟵ ① **Place decimal point in quotient**

$3\overline{)2.0}$ ⟵ ② **Attach one zero after decimal point**

We divide 20 by 3, then attach another zero, bring it down, and again divide 20 by 3.

$$\begin{array}{r} .66 \\ 3\overline{)2.00} \\ \underline{18}\downarrow \\ 20 \\ \underline{18} \\ 2 \end{array}$$

EXPLORATION GUIDE

When we change $\frac{2}{3}$ to a decimal we get the repeating decimal $0.\overline{6}$. There are techniques that we have not discussed for changing the other way, that is, changing a repeating decimal to a fraction. Think of letting

$$n = 0.666 \cdots$$

and then we have

$$10n = 6.666 \cdots.$$

Now by subtracting n from $10n$ can you show that $n = \frac{2}{3}$?

If we attach another zero and bring it down, we would again divide 20 by 3. By now, it is clear that this pattern will continue. Therefore, $\frac{2}{3}$ can be represented by

0.666...

The three dots show that the pattern of sixes continues. We often omit the dots and place a bar over the repeating digit (or digits) to shorten the notation.

$$0.\overline{6} \text{ means } 0.666...$$

The two examples above illustrate the following important property of fractions.

TERMINATING AND REPEATING DECIMALS

Every fraction can be written as a decimal.
1. If the division process ends with a remainder of zero, the decimal is a **terminating decimal.**
2. If the division process does not end, there is a digit or block of digits which repeats, and the decimal is a **repeating decimal.**

Thus, 0.25 is a terminating decimal and $0.\overline{6}$ or 0.666... is a repeating decimal.

TO CHANGE A FRACTION TO A DECIMAL

1. Use the numerator as the dividend and the denominator as the divisor in a division problem.
2. Place decimal points after the numerator (dividend) and in the same position in the quotient.
3. Attach one zero at a time to the numerator (now the dividend) and divide as whole numbers.
4. Stop when a remainder of 0 is obtained or when a repeating pattern is found.

PRACTICE EXERCISE 3

Change each fraction to a decimal.

(a) $\frac{1}{5}$

(b) $\frac{7}{8}$

CHANGING FRACTIONS TO DECIMALS   EXAMPLE 3

Change each fraction to a decimal.

(a) $\frac{1}{2}$ Put in decimal points and attach a zero, then divide 10 by 2.

$$\begin{array}{r} .5 \\ 2\overline{)1.0} \\ \underline{1\,0} \\ 0 \end{array}$$

Since the remainder is 0, division stops. Thus, $\frac{1}{2}$ is the terminating decimal 0.5 (remember that $0.5 = \frac{5}{10} = \frac{1 \cdot 5}{2 \cdot 5} = \frac{1}{2}$).

(b) $\frac{3}{8}$

$$\begin{array}{r} .375 \\ 8\overline{)3.000} \\ \underline{24}\downarrow \\ 60 \\ \underline{56}\downarrow \\ 40 \\ \underline{40} \\ 0 \end{array}$$

Thus, $\frac{3}{8}$ is the terminating decimal 0.375 (remember that $0.375 = \frac{375}{1000} = \frac{3 \cdot 125}{8 \cdot 125} = \frac{3}{8}$).

(c) $\frac{1}{3}$

$$\begin{array}{r} .33 \\ 3\overline{)1.000} \\ 9\downarrow \\ \hline 10 \\ 9\downarrow \\ \hline 10 \end{array}$$

(c) $\frac{2}{9}$

Obviously, the pattern of threes will continue. Thus, $\frac{1}{3}$ is the repeating decimal

$0.\overline{3}$ or $0.333\ldots$.

(d) $\frac{7}{33}$

$$\begin{array}{r} .2121 \\ 33\overline{)7.0000} \\ 6\,6\downarrow \\ \hline 40 \\ 33\downarrow \\ \hline 70 \\ 66\downarrow \\ \hline 40 \\ 33 \\ \hline 7 \end{array}$$

(d) $\frac{12}{33}$

Again, we see a pattern: the block of two digits, 21, will continue to repeat. Thus, $\frac{7}{33} = 0.2121\cdots = 0.\overline{21}$. Notice that the bar is placed over the *two* repeating digits, 2 and 1.

Answers: (a) 0.2 (b) 0.875 (c) 0.2 (d) 0.36

Improper fractions can be changed to decimals using the same procedure.

E X A M P L E 4	CHANGING IMPROPER FRACTIONS TO DECIMALS

Change each fraction to a decimal.

(a) $\frac{7}{4}$

$$4\overline{)7.0}$$

Place decimal points
Attach a zero

Change each fraction to a decimal.

(a) $\frac{11}{4}$

This time we divide 7 by 4 and place 1 in the quotient above 7 before the decimal point.

$$\begin{array}{r} 1.75 \\ 4\overline{)7.00} \\ 4\downarrow \\ \hline 30 \\ 28\downarrow \\ \hline 20 \\ 20 \\ \hline 0 \end{array}$$

Place decimal points and attach a zero

Attach and bring down another zero

Thus, $\frac{7}{4}$ is equal to 1.75.

(b) $\dfrac{11}{3}$

(b) $\dfrac{14}{3}$

$$\begin{array}{r} 4.66 \\ 3\overline{)14.00} \\ \underline{12} \\ 20 \\ \underline{18} \\ \overline{20} \\ \underline{18} \\ 2 \end{array}$$

The pattern of sixes will repeat. Thus, $\dfrac{14}{3} = 4.666\cdots = 4.\overline{6}$.

Answers: (a) 2.75 (b) $3.\overline{6}$

3 | SUMMARIZING EQUIVALENT FRACTIONS AND DECIMALS

Certain basic conversions occur often enough that we should make special note of them. If you learn the following conversions now, the exercises for this section will be easier for you to complete.

$$\frac{1}{8} = 0.125 \qquad\qquad \frac{1}{9} = 0.\overline{1} \qquad\qquad \frac{1}{10} = 0.1$$

$$\frac{1}{4} = \frac{2}{8} = 0.25 \qquad\qquad \frac{2}{9} = 0.\overline{2} \qquad\qquad \frac{1}{5} = \frac{2}{10} = 0.2$$

$$\frac{3}{8} = 0.375 \qquad\qquad \frac{1}{3} = \frac{3}{9} = 0.\overline{3} \qquad\qquad \frac{3}{10} = 0.3$$

$$\frac{1}{2} = \frac{4}{8} = 0.5 \qquad\qquad \frac{4}{9} = 0.\overline{4} \qquad\qquad \frac{2}{5} = \frac{4}{10} = 0.4$$

$$\frac{5}{8} = 0.625 \qquad\qquad \frac{5}{9} = 0.\overline{5} \qquad\qquad \frac{1}{2} = \frac{5}{10} = 0.5$$

$$\frac{3}{4} = \frac{6}{8} = 0.75 \qquad\qquad \frac{2}{3} = \frac{6}{9} = 0.\overline{6} \qquad\qquad \frac{3}{5} = \frac{6}{10} = 0.6$$

$$\frac{7}{8} = 0.875 \qquad\qquad \frac{7}{9} = 0.\overline{7} \qquad\qquad \frac{7}{10} = 0.7$$

$$\frac{8}{9} = 0.\overline{8} \qquad\qquad \frac{4}{5} = \frac{8}{10} = 0.8$$

$$\frac{9}{10} = 0.9$$

4.2 EXERCISES

Answers to these exercises are given on page 646.

In Exercises 1–8, change each decimal to a fraction (or mixed number).

1. 1.4 $1\dfrac{4 \div 2}{10 \div 2} = 1\dfrac{2}{5}$

2. 3.25 $3\dfrac{25}{100} = 3\dfrac{1}{4}$

3. 21.9 $21\dfrac{9}{10}$

4. 4.05 $4\dfrac{5}{100}$

5. 3.002 $3\dfrac{2}{1000} \div 2 \; \dfrac{1}{500}$

6. 0.015 $\dfrac{15 \div 5}{1000 \div 5} = \dfrac{3}{200}$ $\begin{array}{r}200\\5\overline{)1000}\\ \underline{10}\\ 00\end{array}$

7. 0.1302 $\dfrac{1302}{10,000}$

8. 493.72 $493\dfrac{72}{100}$

In Exercises 9–14, change each decimal to a fraction or mixed number using the second method as shown in Example 2.

9. 0.3

10. 0.55

11. 2.7

12. 0.305

13. 1.29

14. 2.005

In Exercises 15–22, change each fraction to a decimal.

15. $\dfrac{3}{4}$

16. $\dfrac{5}{6}$

17. $\dfrac{4}{9}$

18. $\dfrac{7}{11}$

19. $\dfrac{1}{16}$

20. $\dfrac{7}{3}$

21. $\dfrac{11}{4}$

22. $\dfrac{19}{16}$

Write each decimal in Exercises 23–37, as a fraction. Most of these are in the table in the text.

23. $0.\overline{3}$

24. 0.375

25. 0.125

26. 1.5

27. $0.\overline{6}$

28. 0.875

29. 0.2

30. 0.625

31. $0.\overline{1}$

32. 0.25

33. 0.1

34. 1.25

35. 0.5

36. 0.75

37. $1.\overline{3}$

CRITICAL THINKING

38. Change 236.525 to a mixed number.

39. Change 1000.001 to a mixed number and give its formal word name.

40. Change $\dfrac{1}{7}$ to a decimal.

41. Change $\dfrac{7}{13}$ to a decimal.

In Exercises 42–44, convert each repeating decimal to a fraction. For a decimal with one repeating digit multiply the decimal by 10 and subtract n from 10n. If the decimal has two repeating digits, multiply by 100 as in the following example, which converts $n = 0.292929\cdots$ to a fraction.

$$100n = 29.292929\cdots$$
$$-n = -0.292929\cdots$$
$$99n = 29$$
$$n = \dfrac{29}{99}$$

42. 0.3333⋯

43. 0.171717⋯

44. 0.123123123⋯

REVIEW AND PREVIEW

45. Give the formal word name for 401.003.

46. Write twenty-three and one hundred seven thousandths in decimal notation.

47. Write a word name for $34.85 (a) as it would appear on a check; (b) using dollars and cents.

Exercises 48–50 review material from Section 1.3 and will help you prepare for the next section. Round each number to the nearest (a) ten, (b) hundred, and (c) thousand.

48. 1365

49. 12,501

50. 7494

4.2 PARALLEL EXERCISES

Answers to these exercises are not given in the text.

In Exercises 1–8, change each decimal to a fraction (or mixed number).

1. 2.4   2. 5.75   3. 22.8   4. 7.03

5. 4.002   6. 0.035   7. 0.3212   8. 525.25

In Exercises 9–14, change each decimal to a fraction or mixed number using the second method as shown in Example 2.

9. 0.4   10. 0.85   11. 2.8

12. 0.205   13. 1.39   14. 3.007

In Exercises 15–22, change each fraction to a decimal.

15. $\dfrac{1}{4}$ 16. $\dfrac{3}{20}$ 17. $\dfrac{7}{9}$ 18. $\dfrac{3}{11}$

19. $\dfrac{3}{16}$ 20. $\dfrac{19}{5}$ 21. $\dfrac{13}{4}$ 22. $\dfrac{10}{3}$

Write each fraction in Exercises 23–37, as a decimal. Most of these are in the table in the text.

23. $\dfrac{2}{3}$ 24. $\dfrac{1}{10}$ 25. $\dfrac{3}{2}$ 26. $\dfrac{1}{5}$ 27. $\dfrac{7}{8}$

28. $\dfrac{5}{8}$ 29. $\dfrac{1}{2}$ 30. $\dfrac{4}{3}$ 31. $\dfrac{3}{4}$ 32. $\dfrac{3}{8}$

33. $\dfrac{1}{8}$ 34. $\dfrac{1}{3}$ 35. $\dfrac{1}{4}$ 36. $\dfrac{1}{9}$ 37. $\dfrac{5}{4}$

   ## CRITICAL THINKING

38. Change 421.425 to a mixed number and reduce.

39. Change 2000.002 to a mixed number and give its formal word name.

40. Change $\dfrac{2}{7}$ to a decimal.

41. Change $\dfrac{3}{13}$ to a decimal.

In Exercises 42–44, convert each repeating decimal to a fraction. For a decimal with one repeating digit multiply the decimal by 10 and subtract n from 10n. If the decimal has two repeating digits, multiply by 100 as the example from Exercise 42–44.

42. 0.444...   43. 0.373737...   44. 0.417417417...

GROUP PROJECT

Repeating decimals present many interesting problems, some of which are a bit troubling. Consider the statement

$$1 = 0.99999...$$

Does this bother you in any way? Use the technique shown in the exercises to verify that the statement is indeed true. Can you show that $0.5 = 0.49999...$? Investigate other numbers like this. Also, find the decimal form of the numbers $\dfrac{1}{7}$, $\dfrac{2}{7}$, $\dfrac{3}{7}$, $\dfrac{4}{7}$, $\dfrac{5}{7}$, and $\dfrac{6}{7}$. Do you see anything interesting about these numbers. Write a report on your findings and present it to the class.

4.3 ROUNDING DECIMALS AND ESTIMATION

STUDENT GUIDEPOSTS
1 FINDING THE NUMBER OF DECIMAL PLACES
2 ROUNDING DECIMALS
3 ESTIMATING DECIMAL COMPUTATIONS

 FINDING THE NUMBER OF DECIMAL PLACES

In Section 1.3 we learned how to round whole numbers to the nearest ten, hundred, thousand, and so forth. We now see how to round decimals to the nearest one, tenth, hundredth, and so forth, using the notion of *decimal places.*

NUMBER OF DECIMAL PLACES

If a number is written in decimal notation, the number of digits to the right of the decimal point is called the number of **decimal places** in the number.

E X A M P L E 1   FINDING THE NUMBER OF DECIMAL PLACES

Give the number of decimal places in each number.
(a) 3.**15** has *two* decimal places.
     ↑
   ***Two* digits to the right of the decimal point**
(b) 40.**397** has *three* decimal places.
      ↑
   ***Three* digits**
(c) 12 or 12. has zero or no decimal places.
(d) 0.600 has three decimal places.
(e) 2.6060 has four decimal places.

> CAUTION COMPARE THE THREE DECIMALS 0.6, 0.60, AND 0.600, HAVING ONE, TWO, AND THREE DECIMAL PLACES, RESPECTIVELY. ALTHOUGH THESE NUMBERS HAVE THE SAME VALUE, BY USING ZEROS TO THE RIGHT OF THE DIGIT 6, WE ARE EMPHASIZING A GREATER DEGREE OF PRECISION OR ACCURACY. IF THE NUMBERS WERE USED FOR MEASUREMENTS, 0.600 WOULD INDICATE ACCURACY TO THE NEAREST THOUSANDTH, 0.60 TO THE NEAREST HUNDREDTH, AND 0.6 TO THE NEAREST TENTH.

 ROUNDING DECIMALS

The following table summarizes the relationship between the number of decimal places and the position corresponding to this number and is helpful when rounding decimals.

Decimal Places	Last Position on the Right	Example
0	ones	5 or 5.
1	tenths	5.7
2	hundredths	5.76
3	thousandths	5.764
4	ten thousandths	5.7648

EXPLORATION GUIDE
Suppose you measured a metal part and found it to be 3.1474 inches long. However, after a drop in temperature, you measured again and got 3.1467 inches. Since you have no control over the temperature, can you see that rounding the reported length to 3.147 inches would be appropriate? Can you think of other situations where rounding decimal numbers would be the thing to do?

TO ROUND A DECIMAL TO A PARTICULAR NUMBER OF PLACES

1. Locate the position (ones, tenths, hundredths, etc.) corresponding to this number of places.
2. If the first digit to the right of this position is less than 5, drop it and all digits to the right of it. Do not change the digit in the place to which you are rounding.
3. If the first digit to the right of this position is greater than or equal to 5, increase the digit in the desired place by one and drop all digits to the right of it.

Other methods of rounding can be used. However, the method given here is perhaps the most useful and certainly the simplest. Notice that rounding decimals is much like rounding whole numbers.

ROUNDING TO ONE DECIMAL PLACE   EXAMPLE 2

Round 35.24 to one decimal place (to the nearest tenth).

We are rounding to the tenths position.

35. 2̲4
      ↑
Round to this position

Since **4**, the first digit to the right of **2**, is less than 5, we drop 4 and do not change 2. Thus, rounded to one decimal place, 35.24 becomes 35.2.

We often round to obtain approximate values for numbers. For example, 35.24 is approximately equal to 35.2. The symbols $\approx$ and $\doteq$ stand for "is approximately equal to." Thus, from Example 2, $35.24 \approx 35.2$ or $35.24 \doteq 35.2$.

ROUNDING TO TWO DECIMAL PLACES   EXAMPLE 3

Round 2.3482 to two decimal places (to the nearest hundredth).

Round to the hundredths position.

┌── **First digit to the right of rounding position**
↓
2.3**4**82
   ↑
Round to this position

Since the first digit to the right of the hundredths position is 8, which is greater than 5, increase 4 to 5 and drop 8 and 2. Thus,

$2.3482 \approx 2.35$, rounded to two decimal places.

ROUNDING TO THE NEAREST TENTH   EXAMPLE 4

Round 53.85 to the nearest tenth (to one decimal place).

┌── **First digit is 5, so increase 8 to 9 and drop 5**
↓
53.8**5**
    ↑
Round to this position

Thus, $53.85 \approx 53.9$, rounded to the nearest tenth.

Increases in a particular digit may need to be carried over to the next digit. This is shown in the next example.

ROUNDING ACROSS A DIGIT   EXAMPLE 5

Round 1.3895 to three decimal places (to the nearest thousandth).

┌── **Drop 5 and increase 9 by 1**
↓
1.38**9**5
     ↑
Round to here

When **9** is increased by 1, the result is 10, so replace 9 by 0 and increase 8 to 9. Thus,

$1.3895 \approx 1.390$ ·

Do not give 1.39 for the answer; 1.39 has only two decimal places. The final zero in 1.390 must be present.

PRACTICE EXERCISE 2

Round 68.32 to one decimal place (to the nearest tenth).

Answer: 68.3

PRACTICE EXERCISE 3

Round 6.5473 to two decimal places (to the nearest hundredth).

Answer: 6.55

PRACTICE EXERCISE 4

Round 3.125 to the nearest hundredth (to two decimal places).

Answer: 3.13

PRACTICE EXERCISE 5

Round 41.4975 to two decimal places (to the nearest hundredth).

Answer: 41.50

CAUTION WHEN ROUNDING, DO NOT ROUND OFF ONE DIGIT AT A TIME FROM THE RIGHT. FOR EXAMPLE, TO ROUND 2.6149 TO THE NEAREST HUNDREDTH, DO NOT ROUND TO THE NEAREST THOUSANDTH,

2.615

AND THEN TO THE NEAREST HUNDREDTH,

2.62.

THIS IS INCORRECT, SINCE USING OUR METHOD,

2.6149 ≈ 2.61. ROUNDED TO THE NEAREST HUNDREDTH

EXAMPLE 6   ROUNDING TO THE NEAREST ONE

Round 21.654 to the nearest one (0 decimal places).

Since 6 is greater than 5, increase 1 to

21.654   2 and drop 6, 5, and 4

Round to here

Thus, $21.654 \approx 22$, rounded to the nearest one (or whole number).

Decimals that do not terminate, but have repeating blocks of digits such as

$$0.333\cdots \quad \text{or} \quad 0.\overline{3} \quad \text{and} \quad 0.212121\cdots \quad \text{or} \quad 0.\overline{21},$$

can also be rounded. The procedure is identical to that for terminating decimals.

EXAMPLE 7   ROUNDING REPEATING DECIMALS

(a) Round $0.\overline{3}$ to the nearest tenth.

$3 < 5$, so drop remaining digits

$$0.\overline{3} = 0.\textbf{3}33\cdots$$

Round to here

Thus, $0.\overline{3} \approx 0.3$.

(b) Round $0.\overline{6}$ to the nearest thousandth.

$6 > 5$, so increase thousandths digit from 6 to 7 and drop remaining digits

$$0.\overline{6} = 0.\textbf{666}6\cdots$$

Round to here

Thus, $0.\overline{6} \approx 0.667$.

(c) Round $0.\overline{28}$ to the nearest tenth.

$8 > 5$ so increase tenths digit from 2 to 3 and drop remaining digits

$$0.\overline{28} = 0.\textbf{2}82828\cdots$$

Round to here

Thus, $0.\overline{28} \approx 0.3$.

PRACTICE EXERCISE 6

Round 16.539 to the nearest one (0 decimal places).

Answer: 17

PRACTICE EXERCISE 7

(a) Round $0.\overline{2}$ to the nearest tenth.

(b) Round $0.\overline{8}$ to the nearest hundredth.

(c) Round $0.\overline{51}$ to the nearest hundredth.

(d) Round $0.\overline{51}$ to the nearest thousandth.

(d) Round $0.\overline{28}$ to the nearest hundredth.

$$0.\overline{28} = 0.28\underset{\uparrow}{28}28\cdots \qquad \text{2 < 5 so drop remaining digits}$$

Round to here

Thus, $0.\overline{28} \approx 0.28$.

Calculations involving amounts of money must often be rounded to the nearest dollar (one) or to the nearest cent (hundredths). For example, suppose we obtain

$$\$57.432$$

as an answer. Since our smallest unit of money is the cent, or one hundredth of a dollar, we usually round such figures to the nearest cent and write

$$\$57.43 \quad \text{instead of} \quad \$57.432.$$

At times (when completing an income tax form, for example), we may round an amount of money to the nearest dollar. For example, to the nearest dollar,

$$\$57.43 \approx \$57.00 \text{ or } \$57,$$

and

$$\$112.50 \approx \$113.00 \quad \text{or} \quad \$113.$$

3 | ESTIMATING DECIMAL COMPUTATIONS

In the sections that follow we will consider sums, differences, products, and quotients of decimals. Often in real-life practical situations, an estimated result might be all that is needed. For example, if we were deciding whether to buy 50 pounds of ground beef at $1.97 per pound, we might want to know the approximate cost. Since $1.97 is about $2.00, the cost is approximately

$$50 \times \$2 = \$100.$$

Similarly, if we have borrowed $8897.50 and plan to pay it back in 30 equal monthly payments, the approximate monthly payment is

$$\$9000 \div 30 = \$300.$$

In the first situation, we rounded $1.97 to the nearest dollar, and in the second, we rounded to the nearest thousand dollars. Such estimates are useful in daily activities and can often be made mentally.

The Randolphs borrowed $8095.50 and plan to pay it back in 30 equal monthly payments. Estimate their monthly payment.

ESTIMATING IN A CONSUMER PROBLEM   EXAMPLE 8

The Thoresons plan to carpet their living room using carpeting that costs $14.95 a sq yd. If the room is rectangular with length 8.1 yd and width 5.8 yd, what would be the approximate cost of the job?

The approximate area of the room is

$$8 \times 6 = 48 \text{ sq yd} \qquad \text{Rounding 8.1 and 5.8 to the nearest one}$$

Since each square yard of carpeting costs approximately $15 (rounding to the nearest one), the total cost is about

$$15 \times 48 = \$720.$$

Answer: $270 (using 8100 ÷ 30)

NOTE In any applied problem involving decimals, try to estimate the solution by rounding to the nearest whole numbers and use this estimation to help you decide whether the answer you obtain seems reasonable and accurate.

4.3 EXERCISES

Answers to these exercises are given on page 647.

💡 *In Exercises 1–8, give the number of decimal places in each number.*

1. 32.1   2. 4.23   3. 6.453   4. 42.3965
5. 13   6. 42.80   7. 4.280   8. 0.4280

In Exercises 9–14, round each number to one decimal place (to the nearest tenth).

9. 3.21   3.2   10. 4.67   4.7   11. 3.256
12. 5.4249   13. 32.75   14. 151.951

In Exercises 15–20, round each number to two decimal places (to the nearest hundredth).

15. 7.321   16. 3.487   17. 4.3209
18. 5.4249   19. 34.0085   20. 34.0995

In Exercises 21–26, round each number to three decimal places (to the nearest thousandth).

21. 3.4579   22. 7.2571   23. 3.4906
24. 5.4249   25. 45.0085   26. 9.0307

In Exercises 27–32, round each number to the nearest one.

27. 24.1   28. 63.5129   29. 5.4249
30. 9.003   31. 19.84   32. 39.099

In Exercises 33–38, round each repeating decimal to the nearest (a) tenth, (b) hundredth, and (c) thousandth.

33. $0.\overline{4}$ 34. $0.3\overline{5}$ 35. $0.1\overline{23}$

36. $0.\overline{7}$ 37. $0.9\overline{3}$ 38. $0.4\overline{55}$

In Exercises 39–42, round each amount of money to the nearest cent.

39. $4.237   4.24   40. $6.235   6.24   41. $7.231   7.23   42. $8.105   8.11

In Exercises 43–46, round each amount of money to the nearest dollar.

43. $37.29   37.00   44. $13.49   13.00   45. $28.50   29.00   46. $16.99   17

Solve each applied problem in Exercises 47–48.

47. **BUSINESS** The Computer Place ordered 395 computer parts for $2.05 each. Find the approximate amount of the bill.

48. **CONSUMER** What is the approximate cost of 95 pounds of beans selling for $0.41 per pound?

CRITICAL THINKING

💡 49. Change $\frac{2}{7}$ to a decimal and round the result to the nearest (a) tenth, (b) hundredth, and (c) thousandth.

💡 50. **CONSUMER** What is the approximate value of 21 computers in a school lab if each sold for $2995.50?

💡 51. **FINANCE** The Babbitts will receive $6150.95 in moving expenses to be paid over the next year. If they are paid weekly, approximately how much of this amount can they expect to receive in each paycheck?

💡 52. **EDUCATION** Professor Gene Robbins has 297 books in his library. He estimates that the average value of each book is $19.50. What is the approximate value of the books in Professor Robbins' library?

💡*The Troutmans plan to put carpeting on their living room floor. The room is rectangular in shape as shown below, and they plan to lay the carpet over padding that costs $4.75 a square yard. Assume that installation charges are included in the price of the carpet and that there is no waste.*

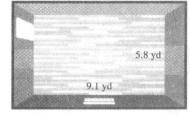

5.8 yd

9.1 yd

53. Approximately how much will the project cost if the Troutmans select carpet that sells for $24.95 a square yard?

The bar graph below depicts the average speed of winds (mph) in various U.S. cities during 1994:

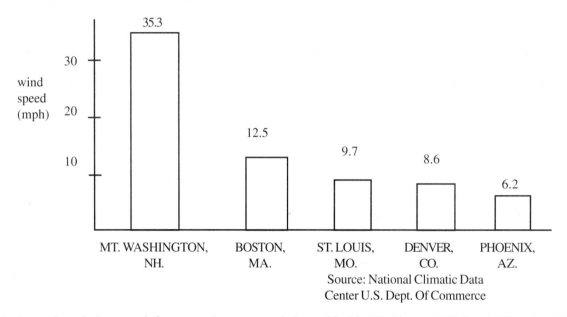

Source: National Climatic Data
Center U.S. Dept. Of Commerce

54. Approximately how much faster was the average wind speed in Mt. Washington, NH than in Phoenix, AZ?

REVIEW AND PREVIEW

55. Change 7.08 to a mixed number.

56. Change 2.016 to a mixed number.

57. Change $\frac{8}{9}$ to a decimal.

58. Change $\frac{5}{33}$ to a decimal.

4.3 PARALLEL EXERCISES

Answers to these exercises are not given in the text.

In Exercises 1–8, give the number of decimal places in each number.

1. 63.1
2. 7.45
3. 8.425
4. 51.405
5. 15
6. 71.90
7. 7.190
8. 0.7190

In Exercises 9–14, round each number to one decimal place (to the nearest tenth).

9. 4.31
10. 5.87
11. 6.357
12. 2.6249
13. 41.06
14. 0.964

In Exercises 15–20, round each number to two decimal places (to the nearest hundredth).

15. 9.432
16. 6.278
17. 12.4208
18. 13.5091
19. 3.0995
20. 0.0355

In Exercises 21–26, round each number to three decimal places (to the nearest thousandth).

21. 4.3569
22. 2.3581
23. 6.3585
24. 76.0095
25. 8.0606
26. 7.4008

In Exercises 27–32, round each number to the nearest one.

27. 26.1

28. 32.507

29. 7.499

30. 6.005

31. 29.78

32. 8.0099

In Exercises 33–38, round each repeating decimal to the nearest (a) tenth, (b) hundredth, and (c) thousandth.

33. $0.\overline{9}$

34. $0.1\overline{7}$

35. $0.\overline{234}$

36. $0.\overline{1}$

37. $0.8\overline{4}$

38. $0.6\overline{55}$

In Exercises 39–42, round each amount of money to the nearest cent.

39. $7.382

40. $4.535

41. $9.448

42. $10.205

In Exercises 43–46, round each amount of money to the nearest dollar.

43. $62.38

44. $41.48

45. $74.50

46. $32.98

Solve each applied problem in Exercises 47–48.

47. **BUSINESS** To test a new car it was driven over a course 692.7 miles per day for 215 days. Approximately how many miles were put on the car during the test?

48. **CONSUMER** A clock radio sells for $39.95. If Bill has $243.65 in his checking account, approximately how many radios could he buy?

 CRITICAL THINKING

49. Change $\frac{4}{7}$ to a decimal and round the result to the nearest (a) tenth, (b) hundredth, and (c) thousandth.

50. **CONSUMER** What is the approximate cost of 305 books each selling for $9.95?

51. **FINANCE** In Lynn Butler's contract there is a provision that will give her $7925.50 in expense money over the next four years. What is the approximate amount that she will have per month?

52. **CONSTRUCTION** A paneling job requires 592 sheets of wood paneling at a cost of $20.75 per sheet. What is the approximate cost of the paneling?

The Troutmans plan to put carpeting on their living room floor. The room is rectangular in shape , and they plan to lay the carpet over padding that costs $4.75 a square yard. Assume that installation charges are included in the price of the carpet and that there is no waste. Refer to the figure above Exercise 53.

53. Approximately how much will the project cost if the Troutmans select carpet that sells for $15.49 a square yard?

Refer to the bar graph given above Exercise 54 on page 242 to answer the following.

54. Approximately how much faster was the average wind speed in Boston, MA than in Denver, CO?

GROUP PROJECT

Many of the numbers that appear in newspaper and magazine articles are actually approximate values. Collect a number of such articles and bring them to class for discussion. Determine why a particular number is an approximation and discuss some of the advantages and disadvantages of using estimated or approximated values in decimal calculations.

4.4 ADDING AND SUBTRACTING DECIMALS

STUDENT GUIDEPOSTS

1	ADDING TWO OR MORE DECIMALS
2	SOLVING APPLICATIONS INVOLVING ADDING DECIMALS
3	SUBTRACTING TWO DECIMALS
4	SOLVING APPLICATIONS INVOLVING SUBTRACTING DECIMALS

1 ADDING TWO OR MORE DECIMALS

When we studied the basic operations on fractions, we began with multiplication and division and then went on to the more difficult operations of addition and subtraction. For numbers in decimal notation, addition and subtraction are easier. For example, suppose we want to find the following sum.

$$\begin{array}{r} 2.35 \\ +1.21 \end{array}$$

We might convert each decimal to fractional form and then add the fractions. But if we add the columns in the original problem and move the decimal point straight down, we obtain the same sum much more easily.

$$\begin{array}{r} 2.35 \\ \underline{1.21} \\ 3.56 \end{array}$$

This illustrates a general method.

TO ADD TWO OR MORE DECIMALS

1. Arrange the numbers in columns so that the decimal points line up.
2. Add in columns from right to left as if adding whole numbers. (Additional zeros may be placed to the right of the decimal points if needed.)
3. Place the decimal point in the sum in line with the other decimal points.

PRACTICE EXERCISE 1

Find each sum.

(a) $154.5 + 60.7$

(b)
$3.8 + 68 + 40.07 + 653.009$

Answers: (a) 215.2
(b) 764.879

ADDING DECIMALS   EXAMPLE 1

Find each sum.

(a) $21.3 + 4.8$

$$\begin{array}{r} 1 \\ 21.3 \\ +\ 4.8 \\ \hline 26.1 \end{array}$$

① **Arrange the numbers in columns so that the decimal points line up**

② **Carry 1 after adding 8 and 3 just as in addition of whole numbers**

③ **Place the decimal point in line with others**

(b) $37 + 2.5 + 10.03 + 425.008$

$$\begin{array}{r} 37. \\ 2.5 \\ 10.03 \\ +425.008 \\ \hline 474.538 \end{array} \quad \text{or} \quad \begin{array}{r} 37.000 \\ 2.500 \\ 10.030 \\ +425.008 \\ \hline 474.538 \end{array}$$

Writing 0s to the right of the decimal points may help you keep the decimal points lined up vertically

2 SOLVING APPLICATIONS ADDING DECIMALS

You can see that adding decimals is much like adding whole numbers. Following are several examples of word problems that involve adding decimals. Make certain that your answers are reasonable.

EXAMPLE 2 ADDING DECIMALS IN A MILEAGE PROBLEM

Before leaving on a trip, Mike's odometer read 43,271.9. If he drove 827.6 miles on the trip, what did it read when he returned?

The return reading must be the beginning reading plus the number of miles traveled.

$$43271.9$$
$$+\quad 827.6$$
$$\overline{44099.5}$$

Thus, when he returned, his odometer read 44,099.5.

EXAMPLE 3 ADDING DECIMALS ON A TELEPHONE BILL

A good example of adding decimals can be found in a long-distance telephone bill. A typical bill is shown in Figure 4.2.

602 555-0801 FEB. 25, 1998						
ITEMIZED CALLS					**Mountain Bell**	
NO.	DATE	TIME	TO PLACE	TO AREA-NO.	MIN	AMOUNT
1	115	747P	MONTGOMERY, AL	205 999-4801	2	$1.46
2	123	1035A	NEWARK, NJ	503 888-3213	3	2.56
3	2 1	346P	LOS ANGELES, CA	301 777-4243	1	0.87
4	219	832A	BROOKLYN, NY	212 423-2131	5	3.27
			TOTAL OF ITEMIZED CALLS EXCLUDING TAX			$8.16

FIGURE 4.2

The total due on long-distance calls is $8.16, the sum of the decimals in the last column.

EXAMPLE 4 ADDING DECIMALS IN A DISTANCE PROBLEM

Consider the map in Figure 4.3. Starting in West Yorkville, Margot hiked the complete circular trail past Devon Falls, Mount Blanc, Sanditon, Brunswick, East Yorkville, and back to West Yorkville. How long was her hike?

Add the distances on the map.

$$
\begin{array}{r}
5.6 \\
3.2 \\
4.7 \\
1.2 \\
3.8 \\
+\ 7.2 \\
\hline
25.7
\end{array}
$$

Thus, Margot hiked a distance of 25.7 miles.

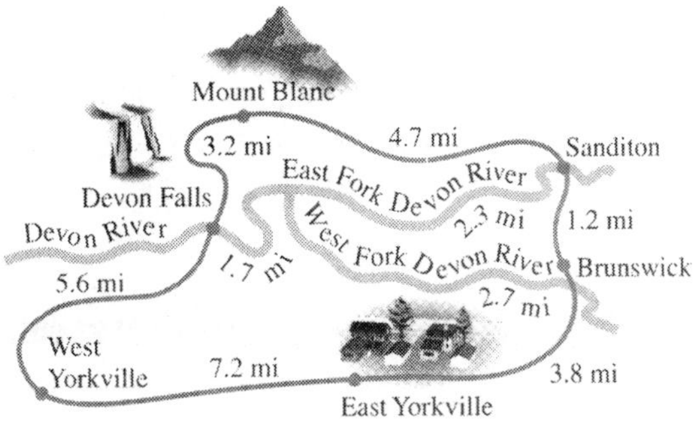

FIGURE 4.3

EXAMPLE 5 ADDING DECIMALS ON A DEPOSIT SLIP

A typical bank checking account deposit slip is shown in Figure 4.4. The total deposit is found by adding all amounts in the right-hand column. Notice that a vertical line separates the dollars column from the cents column. It is used instead of a decimal point because it has been found that people are more likely to arrange the numbers correctly using this method.

PRACTICE EXERCISE 2

On a two-day trip, Steve drove 489.3 miles the first day and 501.8 miles the second. How far did he drive on the trip?

Answer: 991.1 miles

PRACTICE EXERCISE 3

Part of a monthly telephone bill is given below. Find the total bill for long-distance calls.

Southern Telephone	
MIN	AMOUNT
4	$2.63
7	8.48
12	11.73
TOTAL	

Answer: $22.84

PRACTICE EXERCISE 4

Use the map in Figure 4.3. Henry decided to hike along the river from Sanditon to Devon Falls and then on to West Yorkville where his wife would meet him with their car. How long was his hike?

Answer: 9.6 mi

PRACTICE EXERCISE 5

Part of a bank checking account deposit slip is shown below. Find the total deposit.

DEPOSIT		
	Dollars	Cents
CASH	3025	51
CHECKS	431	68
	15	06
	283	93
	4	58
TOTAL		

Answer: $3760.76

First Federal Bank Date *August 2* 19*98* New Orleans, LA Account No. **894-667-0523** Sarah Williams 120 Charles Pl. New Orleans, LA 70124	DEPOSIT	
	Dollars	Cents
CASH	13	27
CHECKS (List	127	40
Separately)	312	80
	4	95
TOTAL DEPOSIT	458	42

FIGURE 4.4

3 | SUBTRACTING TWO DECIMALS

Subtraction of decimals is similar to addition. For example, suppose we want to find the following difference.

$$\begin{array}{r} 2.35 \\ -1.21 \\ \hline \end{array}$$

By subtracting in columns, we obtain the difference.

$$\begin{array}{r} 2.35 \\ -1.21 \\ \hline 1.14 \end{array}$$

The decimal point is moved straight down just as in an addition problem.

TO SUBTRACT TWO DECIMALS

1. Arrange the numbers in columns so that the decimal points line up.
2. Subtract in columns from right to left as if subtracting whole numbers. (Additional zeros may be placed to the right of the decimal points if needed.)
3. Place the decimal point in the difference in line with the other decimal points.

PRACTICE EXERCISE 6

Find each difference.

(a) $75.8 - 23.6$

(b) $433.41 - 84.3$

SUBTRACTING DECIMALS | EXAMPLE 6

Find each difference.

(a) $43.7 - 12.5$

Arrange the numbers in columns so that the decimal points line up, then subtract.

$$\begin{array}{r} 43.7 \\ -12.5 \\ \hline 31.2 \end{array}$$
$$\uparrow$$

Place decimal point in line with others

(b) $121.4 - 48.23$

$$\begin{array}{r} \overset{111}{121.40} \leftarrow \textbf{Supply extra zero} \\ -\ \ 48.23 \\ \hline 73.17 \end{array}$$

$$7 = 10 - 3$$
$$1 = 3 - 2$$
$$3 = 11 - 8$$
$$7 = 11 - 4$$

Notice that we had to borrow 1 ten from the 2 tens (or 20) in order to subtract 8.

(c) $48.52 - 19.67$

(c) $94.31 - 36.58$

$$
\begin{array}{r}
\overset{17\ 14}{} \\
\overset{37\ \ 412}{} \\
48\ .\ \cancel{5}2 \\
-19\ .\ 67 \\
\hline
28\ .\ 85
\end{array}
$$

$5 = 12 - 7$ **(borrow 1 tenth from .5)**

$8 = 14 - 6$ **(borrow 1 from 8)**

$8 = 17 - 9$ **(borrow 1 ten from 40)**

$2 = 3 - 1$

Answers: (a) 52.2 (b) 349.11 (c) 57.73

Borrowing is done as if we were subtracting whole numbers. Of course, with practice, the small numbers and the "crossing out" can be eliminated. The problem would then look like

$$
\begin{array}{r}
48.52 \\
-19.67 \\
\hline
28.85
\end{array}
$$

NOTE Computationally, the only real difference between adding and subtracting decimals and adding and subtracting whole numbers is placing the decimal point. This is easy to do once the numbers have been written with the decimal points lined up.

4 SOLVING APPLICATIONS SUBTRACTING DECIMALS

Many word problems involve subtracting decimals. As before, use common sense and estimation to be sure that your answers are reasonable.

EXAMPLE 7 SUBTRACTING DECIMALS IN A DISTANCE PROBLEM

It is 13.6 miles from Wetumpka to Slapout and 32.1 miles from Wetumpka to Pine Level. How much farther is it from Wetumpka to Pine Level than to Slapout? See Figure 4.5.

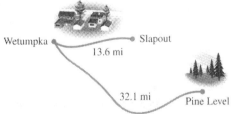

PRACTICE EXERCISE 7

Donna noticed that the odometer on her car read 35,126.8 miles when she filled her gas tank in Oklahoma City. She then drove to Houston where her odometer reading was 35,576.1. How far is it from Oklahoma City to Houston?

Wetumpka · · · · · Slapout
13.6 mi

32.1 mi · · · Pine Level

FIGURE 4.5

Subtract 13.6 from 32.1.

$$
\begin{array}{r}
32.1 \\
-13.6 \\
\hline
18.5
\end{array}
$$

It is 18.5 miles farther to Pine Level.

Answer: 449.3 miles

EXAMPLE 8 SUBTRACTING DECIMALS IN A TAX PROBLEM

Mr. Wong had a total income of $27,085.50 last year. He had deductions of $427.56, $2037.15, $402.03, and $1327.48. If taxable income is total income minus deductions, what was Mr. Wong's taxable income?

Dr. Weston bought a shirt for $22.95 and a pair of pants for $34.98. Tax on the two purchases was $1.15 and $1.75, respectively. He paid for the items with a $100 bill and received a $20 bill, a $10 bill, a $5 bill, four $1 bills, one dime, one nickel, and two pennies in change. Was the change correct?

Answer: Yes; the change should be $39.17.

On April 1, Cindi Franks had $958.12 in her checking account. During the month, she made two deposits, one of $327.50 and a second of $693.73. She wrote three checks in the amounts $483.16, $103.09, and $723.49. What was her balance at the end of the month?

Answer: $669.61

First find the total of all deductions.

$$\begin{array}{r} \$\ 427.56 \\ 2037.15 \\ 402.03 \\ +\ 1327.48 \\ \hline \$4194.22 \end{array}$$

Next subtract this total from his total income.

$$\begin{array}{r} \$27085.50 \\ -\ \ \ \ 4194.22 \\ \hline \$22891.28 \end{array}$$

Thus, Mr. Wong had a taxable income of $22,891.28.

Example 8 illustrates that more than one operation is often used when solving a word problem. This is also shown in the next example.

OPERATIONS IN A CHECKING ACCOUNT   EXAMPLE 9

To keep track of the balance in a checking account, most people use a check register similar to the one in Figure 4.6.

The "Balance Forward" of $608.27 is copied from the preceding page in the register. The first entry is a check written for $85.23. This amount is entered in the "Amount of Check" column and also in the working column under $608.27. The balance in the account, $523.04, is found by subtracting. Next, a deposit of $728.30 is entered in both the "Amount of Deposit" column and in the working column. Adding gives the new balance of $1251.34. The next check for $435.75 is entered as before, and the amount subtracted in the working column yields a new balance of $815.59. Thus, keeping a check register involves repeated additions and subtractions of decimals.

Check No.	Data	Checks Issued to or Deposit Description	Amount of Check		Amount of Deposit				Balance Forward	
									608	27
301	6/22	Marvin's Market	85	23			Check or deposit		85	23
							Balance		523	04
	6/25	Paycheck Deposited			728	30	Check or deposit		728	30
							Balance		1251	34
302	7/1	Home Mortgage for July	435	75			Check or deposit		435	75
							Balance		815	59

FIGURE 4.6

4.4 EXERCISES

Answers to these exercises are given on page 647.

Find each sum in Exercises 1–9.

1. $41.2 + 33.9$

2. $4.37 + 2.09$

3. $22.3 + 2.23 + 223$

4. $0.003 + 2.107 + 135.1$

5. $6.035 + 10.09 + 100.9$

6. $4.3 + 5.01 + 0.005 + 41.376$

7. $$\begin{array}{r} 6.05 \\ 21.3 \\ +\ 4.712 \\ \hline \end{array}$$

8. $$\begin{array}{r} 32.079 \\ 1.428 \\ 403.6 \\ +\ 10.05 \\ \hline \end{array}$$

9. $$\begin{array}{r} 105.30 \\ 6.4193 \\ 10.03 \\ +\ 4217.508 \\ \hline \end{array}$$

Arrange the numbers in Exercises 10–11 in columns and find their sum.

10. $132.57, $41.03, $1.79, $10.00

11. $4237.88, $1.23, $14.40, $103.05, $15.00

Parts of monthly telephone bills are shown in Exercises 12–13. Find the total bills for the long-distance calls.

12.

Pacific Telephone

MIN	AMOUNT
3	$1.57
5	6.23
1	0.37
TOTAL	

13.

New England Telephone

MIN	AMOUNT
10	$13.25
2	4.40
5	7.23
1	0.87
TOTAL	

Exercises 14–15 refer to the following map.

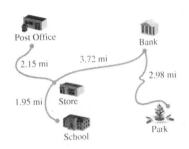

14. **TRAVEL** How far is it by road from the post office to the park?

15. **TRAVEL** How far is it by road from the park to the school?

Parts of bank checking account deposit slips are shown in Exercises 16–17. Find the total deposits.

16.

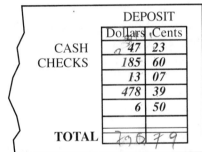

	DEPOSIT	
	Dollars	Cents
CASH	47	23
CHECKS	185	60
	13	07
	478	39
	6	50
TOTAL		

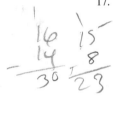

17.

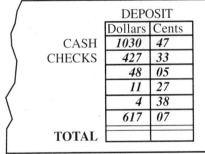

	DEPOSIT	
	Dollars	Cents
CASH	1030	47
CHECKS	427	33
	48	05
	11	27
	4	38
	617	07
TOTAL		

18. Find the perimeter of the figure. (Perimeter is the distance around.)

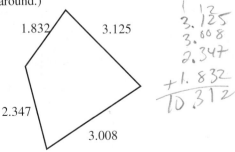

1.832   3.125

2.347

3.008

19. Find the sum of the following numbers: two thousand one hundred thirty-six and forty-one hundredths; five hundred three and two hundred seven thousandths; nine thousand one and one thousand nine ten thousandths. Give the answer in decimal notation and in words.

Find each difference in Exercises 20–28.

20. 41.3 − 22.5

21. 6.03 − 4.2

22. 42.0 − 7.5

23. 101.3 − 1.013

24. 4.00 − 3.75

25. 12.056 − 3.009

26. 67.284
    −13.498

27.   28.4
    − 3.45

28.   7
    −1.009

Solve each applied problem in Exercises 29–38.

29. **TAX**   The Marshall family had a total income of $31,255.75 last year. If they had deductions of $1237.40, $725.36, $2347.01, and $444.83, how much taxable income did they have?

30. **SCIENCE**   There were 32.94 grams of salt for use in an experiment. If 5.22 grams were used during the first hour, 9.71 grams during the next hour, and 15.84 grams during the third hour, how much of the salt was left?

31. **BANKING**   Complete the missing items in the following check register.

Check No.	Date	Checks Issued to or Deposit Description	Amount of Check	Amount of Deposit		Balance Forward 325 40
420	3/2	Harry's Hair Hut	25 50		Check or deposit	
					Balance	
421	3/3	Credit Union March Car Payment	165 35		Check or deposit	
					Balance	
	3/4	Gift from Uncle Claude		225 00	Check or deposit	
					Balance	

(a)

(b)

(c)

(d)

(e)

(f)

32. **MEDICINE**   For a medicine to be effective the reading on the lab test must be at least 6.25. If the patient's reading is 5.79, how much is this below where it should be?

33. **FINANCE**   Mark Spangler took $3478.39 out of savings to invest in bonds. If fees of $23.95, $31.75, and $6.74 were deducted, how much did he have left for the actual investment?

34. **CONSUMER**   Lucy bought a record for $8.65 and paid with a $10 bill. She received one dime, one quarter, and one $1 bill in change. Was this the correct change?

35. Subtract three hundred twenty-seven and eight hundredths from two thousand seven and seven hundred three thousandths. Give the difference in decimal notation and in words.

36. **MEDICINE**   When Jerri was sick in the hospital, she received four antibiotic injections of 2.65 milligrams, 2.75 milligrams, 3.5 milligrams, and 4.0 milligrams.

(a) What was the total of the four injections?

(b) If all injections were drawn from the same bottle that contained 30.5 milligrams of the antibiotic, how much remained in the bottle?

37. **GEOMETRY**   In the figure below, find the length of *x* and *y*.

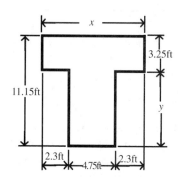

38. **METEOROLOGY**   The table below shows the amount of rainfall for three months during the summer. If the normal rainfall for this three-month period is 9.6 inches, was the rainfall above or below average and by how much?

Month	Rainfall (in inches)
June	2.1
July	4.3
August	3.7

CRITICAL THINKING

39. **AVERAGES**   The average of three numbers is their sum divided by 3. If the three starting defensive linemen for Denver weigh 267.8 lb, 279.7 lb, and 286.5 lb, what is the average weight of the starting line?

Consider the figure given below. Both rectangles in the figure are squares, that is, all four sides are equal.

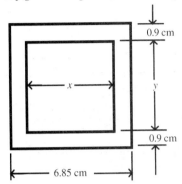

40. What is the length of y?

41. Discuss the similarities and differences between decimal and whole number addition.
42. Burford was told to subtract 4.35 from 6.21. His work is shown below. Explain to Burford where he made his error. What is the correct answer?

$$4.35 - 6.21 = 2.14$$

Exercises 43–45 refer to the life expectance information provided by the U.N. Center for Health Statistics as published in the January 30, 1995 edition of Time Magazine.

43. On the average, how much longer will a citizen of Canada live than a U.S. citizen?

44. On the average, how much longer will a citizen of Canada live than a citizen of Cambodia?

45. On the average, how much longer will a U.S. citizen live than a citizen of Brazil?

In Chapter 1 we solved a number of equations by changing from the related addition equation to the related subtraction equation, and conversely. Use this technique to solve the equations involving decimals given in Exercises 46–48.

46. $x - 2.1 = 3.4$ 47. $4.2 = y + 1.7$

48. $2.5 + x = 8.9$

49. Suppose we are told that on the average, a person from some country listed in the table for Exercises 43–45 lives 7.1 years longer than a person who lives in Mexico. In what country does this person live?

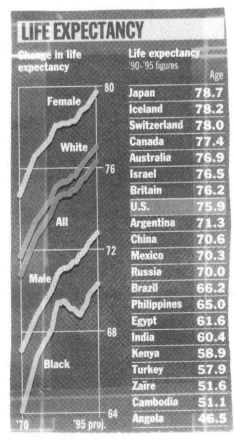

REVIEW AND PREVIEW

In Exercises 50–53, give the number of decimal places in each number.

50. 42.37   51. 103.301   52. 21.0506   53. 1139

54. Round 3.1594 to the nearest (a) tenth, (b) hundredth, (c) thousandth.

💡 **CONSUMER**   *Use the following newspaper advertisements to answer Exercises 55–58.*

55. Estimate the cost of one TV and one stereo. Then find the exact cost.

56. About how much more is the price of the TV than the price of the stereo? What is the exact difference in price?

57. About how many stereos could be purchased for $600?

58. Estimate the total cost of purchasing 5 television sets.

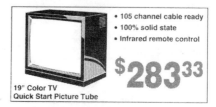

4.4 PARALLEL EXERCISES

Answers to these exercises are not given in the text.

Find each sum in Exercises 1–9.

1. $6.21 + 70.3$

2. $2.59 + 1.07$

3. $46.3 + 4.63 + 0.463$

4. $4.032 + 40.32 + 403.2$

5. $1.017 + 40.08 + 200.6$

6. $2.5 + 6.02 + 0.009 + 23.765$

7.   9.01
    37.005
    + 2.3

8.   65.028
       1.351
     609.5
     + 20.07

9.   121.73
       2.407
      52.1
    +1035.113

Arrange the numbers in Exercises 10–11 in columns and find their sum.

10. $20.00, $55.95, $1.32, $163.55

11. $135.62, $827.03, $2.06, $11,427.21, $25.33

Parts of monthly telephone bills are shown in Exercises 12–13. Find the total bills for the long-distance calls.

12.

Southern Bell

MIN	AMOUNT
5	$11.39
2	4.06
1	0.89

TOTAL

13.

New York Bell

MIN	AMOUNT
6	$14.28
3	5.74
1	0.79

TOTAL

Exercises 14–15 refer to the following map.

14. **RECREATION**   How far is it from the trail head to Long's Peak by way of Bow Lake?

15. **RECREATION**   How far is it from Long's Peak back to the trail head by the shortest route?

Parts of bank checking account deposit slips are shown in Exercises 16–17. Find the total deposits.

16.

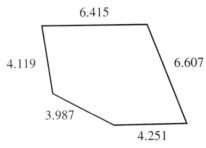

	DEPOSIT	
	Dollars	Cents
CASH	62	09
CHECKS	477	51
	1035	20
	6	05
TOTAL		

17.

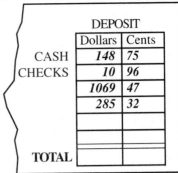

	DEPOSIT	
	Dollars	Cents
CASH	148	75
CHECKS	10	96
	1069	47
	285	32
TOTAL		

18. Find the perimeter of the figure.

6.415

4.119   6.607

3.987

4.251

19. Find the sum of the following numbers: three thousand and twenty-one hundredths; four hundred two and six thousandths; fifty-six and two hundred forty-nine ten thousandths. Give the answer in decimal notation and in words.

Find each difference in Exercises 20–28.

20. $42.1 - 31.5$

21. $7.05 - 6.2$

22. $51.0 - 6.3$

23. $202.5 - 2.025$

24. $3.00 - 1.25$

25. $15.055 - 2.009$

26. $\begin{array}{r} 97.317 \\ -18.529 \\ \hline \end{array}$

27. $\begin{array}{r} 38.6 \\ -\ 9.75 \\ \hline \end{array}$

28. $\begin{array}{r} 8 \\ -1.003 \\ \hline \end{array}$

Solve each applied problem in Exercises 29–38.

29. **TAX** The Lopez family had a total income of $42,621.35 last year. If they had deductions of $2427.51, $425.30, $612.12, and $1230.07, how much taxable income did they have?

30. **MINING** An ore processing plant has a supply of 6357.4 tons of ore on hand. If 985.4 tons were processed on Monday, 1269.5 tons on Tuesday, and 1091.3 tons on Wednesday, how much of the supply was left?

31. **BANKING** Complete the misiing items in the check register shown below.

Check No.	Date	Checks Issued to or Deposit Description	Amount or check		Amount of Deposit				Balance Forward	
									614	30
315	10/2	*Graydon's Grocery Store*	32	47			Check or deposit			
							Balance			
	10/2	*Deposit Week's Wages*			176	19	Check or deposit			
							Balance			
316	10/5	*County Farm Insurance*	110	59			Check or deposit			
							Balance			

32. **MEDICINE** In order for a medicine to be effective, the patient must take at least 22.50 grams per day. If Burford took doses of 7.25 grams, 6.05 grams, and 8.95 grams, did he have eaough for the day?

33. **FINANCE** Before Melissa Lerner withdrew the $4194.38 in her savings account, the bank added $23.57 interest and subtracted fees of $9.65 and $5.83. What was the amount that Melissa could withdraw?

34. **CONSUMER** Jack bought a stereo for $289.75, and paid with three $100 bills and three quarters. He received one $10 bill, one $1 bill, and one quarter in change. Was this the correct change?

35. Subtract two hundred fifty-seven and three thousandths from four thousand six and one tenth. Give the difference in decimal notation and in words.

36. **SPORTS**   The times recorded for the members of the ASU 400-meter relay team were 10.5 sec, 10.8 sec, 11.2 sec, and 10.3 sec.
(a) What was the combined time for the event?
(b) The team's best time prior to this race was 42.9 sec. Did the team better its time; and if so, by how much?

37. **GEOMETRY**   In the figure below find the length of *x* and *y*.

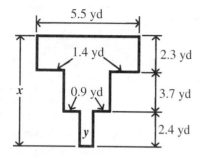

38. **CONSUMER**   The table below shows the number of gallons of gasoline used by a delivery truck during a four-month period. During the same period last year a total of 642.3 gallons were used. How many gallons more or less were used this year than last?

Month	Number of Gallons
January	132.5
February	147.8
March	201.3
April	187.6

CRITICAL THINKING

39. **AVERAGES**   The average of three numbers is their sum divided by 3. Marvin owns three cats weighing 9.1 lb, 3.3 lb, and 11.6 lb. What is the average weight of his cats?

Refer to the figure given above Exercise 40 to answer the following.

40. What is the length of *x*?

41. Identify several instances of addition and subtraction of decimals found in newspaper or magazine articles and write a description of how they are used.

42. Burford was told to subtract 4.35 from 6.21. His work is shown below. Explain to Burford where he made his error. What is the correct answer?

$$6.21 - 4.35 = 2.86$$

Refer to the life expectancy information given above Exercise 43 to answer the following.
43. On the average, how much longer will a citizen of Japan live than a U.S. citizen?
44. On the average, how much longer will a citizen of Japan live than a citizen of Angola?
45. On the average, how much longer will a U.S. citizen live than a Chinese citizen?
In Chapter 1, we solved a number of equations by changing from the related addition equation to the related subtraction equation, and conversely. Use this technique to solve the equations involving decimals given in Exercises 46–48.

46. $x - 4.5 = 1.4$ 47. $3.8 = y + 2.7$ 48. $3.7 + x = 7.2$

49. Suppose we are told that on the average, a person from some country listed in the table for Exercises 43-45 lives 16.6 years longer than a person who lives in Egypt. In what country does this person live?

GROUP PROJECT

There are several ways to round decimal numbers. One way that differs from our method is to *truncate*. Using truncation, we simply drop all digits to the right of the position to which we are rounding. For example, to round 42.56978 to the hundredths position, we would obtain 42.56. Some calculators will round in this way. Clearly the result here is different from what we would obtain (namely 42.57) using the method we have chosen. Consider whether you think the differences would be significant enough to cause any problems. For example, what if the rounded number were to be used in an application? Could there be different answers to the resulting problem? Construct several examples where the differences might be notable and report your observations to the rest of the class.

4.5 MULTIPLYING DECIMALS

STUDENT GUIDEPOSTS
1   LEARNING ABOUT BASIC MULTIPLICATION
2   MULTIPLYING DECIMALS BY A POWER OF 10
3   CONVERTING DOLLARS TO CENTS
4   MULTIPLYING DECIMALS BY 0.1, 0.01, AND 0.001
5   CONVERTING CENTS TO DOLLARS
6   SOLVING APPLICATIONS INVOLVING MULTIPLYING DECIMALS

1   LEARNING ABOUT BASIC MULTIPLICATION

Multiplying decimals is very much like multiplying whole numbers once we decide what to do with the decimal points. Suppose we multiply

$$0.7 \times 0.21$$

as fractions. We know

$$0.7 = \frac{7}{10} \qquad \text{and} \qquad 0.21 = \frac{21}{100}.$$

Then

$$0.7 \times 0.21 = \frac{7}{10} \times \frac{21}{100}$$

$$= \frac{7 \times 21}{10 \times 100} = \frac{147}{1000}$$

$$= 0.147.$$

Now write the problem vertically. Ignoring the decimal points, multiply as if multiplying whole numbers.

$$\begin{array}{r} 0.21 \\ \times\, 0.7 \\ \hline 147 \end{array} \quad \text{Decimal point not yet placed}$$

Placing the decimal point in the product depends on the number of decimal places in the numbers multiplied. The factor 0.21 has two decimal places and 0.7 has one, so the product has three decimal places, the sum of the decimal places in the factors.

$$\begin{array}{r} 0.21 \\ \times 0.7 \\ \hline 0.147 \end{array} \quad \begin{array}{l} 1 \text{ decimal place} \\ 2 \text{ decimal places} \\ 3 \text{ decimal places } (2+1=3) \end{array}$$

This agrees with $\dfrac{7}{10} \cdot \dfrac{21}{100} = \dfrac{147}{1000} = 0.147$ as shown above and leads to the following rule.

TO MULTIPLY TWO DECIMALS
1.   Ignore the decimal points and multiply as if the numbers were whole numbers.
2.   Find the sum of the decimal places in the two factors.
3.   Place the decimal point so that the product has the same number of decimal places as the sum in Step **2**. If the whole number product obtained in Step **1** has zeros on the end, they must be counted when placing the decimal point.

EXPLORATION GUIDE

To justify the rule for multiplying decimals we multiplied 0.7 and 0.21 two different ways. In order to get a better feel for why the multiplication rule works, select several different pairs of fractions, multiply them as regular fractions, multiply them as decimals, and compare the results to check the rule that we have stated.

PRACTICE
EXERCISE 1

MULTIPLYING DECIMALS

EXAMPLE 1

Find each product.

Find each product.

(a) 0.4×2.8

(a) 0.6×1.7

```
   2.8
 ×0.4
 1.1 2
```

$$\begin{array}{rl} 1.7 & \text{1 decimal place} \\ \times 0.6 & \text{1 decimal place} \\ \hline 1.02 & \text{2 decimal places in product } (1+1=2) \end{array}$$

Place decimal point here

(b) 0.3×0.3

(b) 0.2×0.3

0.09

$$\begin{array}{rl} 0.3 & \text{1 decimal place} \\ \times 0.2 & \text{1 decimal place} \\ \hline 0.06 & \text{2 decimal places } (1+1=2) \end{array}$$

Place decimal point here after inserting
a **0** to the left of the 6.

Notice that the product is 0.06 and *not* 0.6 or 0.60.

(c) 0.6×2.45

(c) 0.4×1.35

```
  2 3
  2.45
  0.6
1.4 7 0
```

$$\begin{array}{rl} 1.35 & \text{2 decimal places} \\ \times 0.4 & \text{1 decimal place} \\ \hline 0.540 & \text{3 decimal places in product } (2+1=3) \end{array}$$

Count the zero for placing decimal point
Place decimal point here

(d) 1.2×4.007

(d) 1.3×6.002

```
    4.007
     1.2
   8 0 1 4
  40 0 7 0
  4.8 0 8 4
```

$$\begin{array}{rl} 6.002 & \text{3 decimal places} \\ \times 1.3 & \text{1 decimal place} \\ \hline 18006 & \\ 6002 & \\ \hline 7.8026 & \text{4 decimal places in product } (3+1=4) \end{array}$$

Place decimal point here

(e) 10.05×23

(e) 42×11.03

$$\begin{array}{rl} 11.03 & \text{2 decimal places} \\ \times 42 & \text{0 decimal places} \\ \hline 2206 & \\ 4412 & \\ \hline 463.26 & \text{2 decimal places in product } (2+0=2) \end{array}$$

Answers: (a) 1.12   (b) 0.09
(c) 1.470 or 1.47   (d) 4.8084
(e) 231.15

NOTE   Incorrect placing of the decimal point in the answer to a problem is a common error. Estimating can give a quick check. For example, suppose we had to multiply

$$3.2 \times 21.037 .$$

```
  21.037
  × 3.2
  42074
  63101
  67.3084
```

We could round 3.2 to 3 and 21.037 to 21. Since $3 \times 21 = 63$, we would expect the product to be somewhere near 63.

Decimal point *must* be placed here according to the estimated product.

EXAMPLE 2	PLACING THE DECIMAL POINT BY ESTIMATION

Find 2.07×495.3 and place the decimal point by estimating the product.

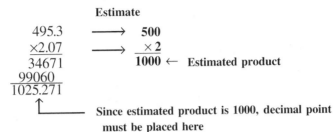

Estimate

$$
\begin{array}{r}
495.3 \\
\times 2.07 \\
\hline
34671 \\
99060 \\
\hline
1025.271
\end{array}
\quad \longrightarrow \quad
\begin{array}{r}
500 \\
\times 2 \\
\hline
1000 \leftarrow \text{ Estimated product}
\end{array}
$$

Since estimated product is 1000, decimal point must be placed here

Notice that counting decimal places would give the same placement. The shaded work should be done mentally.

PRACTICE
EXERCISE 2

Find 29.1×195.07 and place the decimal point by estimating the product.

Answer: 5676.537 [using $30 \times 200 = 6000$, the decimal point must be placed as shown]

2 MULTIPLYING DECIMALS BY A POWER OF 10

Multiplying decimals by a power of 10 (10, 100, 1000, 10,000, and so forth), can be simplified by merely moving the decimal point. For example, consider the two products below.

$$
\begin{array}{r}
12.428 \\
\times 10 \\
\hline
124.280
\end{array}
\qquad
\begin{array}{r}
12.428 \\
\times 1000 \\
\hline
12,428.000
\end{array}
$$

Place decimal point here ——↑   —— Place decimal point here

When we multiplied 12.428 by 10, the product 124.28 could be obtained by moving the decimal point one place to the right in 12.428. Similarly, the product of 12.428 and 1000 could be obtained by moving the decimal point three places to the right. In general, we have the following rule.

TO MULTIPLY A DECIMAL BY A POWER OF 10

Move the decimal point to the *right* the same number of decimal places as the number of zeros in the power of 10.

EXAMPLE 3	MULTIPLYING BY POWERS OF 10

Find each product.

(a) 2.135×10

Since there is one zero in 10, move the decimal point in 2.135 one place to the right.

$$2.135 \times 10 = 21.35$$

1 zero   **Right 1 place**

(b) 2.135×1000

Move the decimal point 3 places to the right.

$$2.135 \times 1000 = 2135.$$

3 zeros   **Right 3 places**

(c) $2.135 \times 100,000$

Move the decimal point 5 places to the right.

$$2.135 \times 100,000 = 213500. = 213,500$$

5 zeros   **Right 5 places**

Notice that we needed to attach two zeros when moving the decimal point.

PRACTICE
EXERCISE 3

Find each product.

(a) 10×48.215

48.215

(b) 100×48.215

4821.5

(c) $10,000 \times 48.215$

482,150

Answers: (a) 482.15
(b) 4821.5
(c) 482,150

3 | CONVERTING DOLLARS TO CENTS

A familiar application of multiplying by 100 involves converting dollars to cents. For example,

$1.98 converted to cents is 198¢.

Multiplying 1.98 by 100 gives 198.

TO CONVERT DOLLARS TO CENTS

Discard the $ sign, move the decimal point two places to the right (multiply by 100), and attach a ¢ sign to the right of the result.

CONVERTING DOLLARS TO CENTS | EXAMPLE 4

Convert from dollars to cents.

(a) $45.35   Discard the $ sign, move the decimal point two places to the right, and attach the ¢ symbol. The result is 4535¢.

(b) $0.25 = 25¢

---

4 | MULTIPLYING DECIMALS BY 0.1, 0.01, AND 0.001

When a decimal is multiplied by 0.1, 0.01, or 0.001, the product can also be found by moving the decimal point, this time to the left.

TO MULTIPLY A DECIMAL BY 0.1, 0.01, OR 0.001

Move the decimal point to the *left* the same number of decimal places as decimal places in 0.1, 0.01, or 0.001.

MULTIPLYING BY 0.1, 0.01, AND 0.001 | EXAMPLE 5

Find the product.

(a) 0.1×2.135

Since 0.1 has 1 decimal place, the decimal point in 2.135 is moved 1 place to the left.

$$0.1 \times 2.135 = 0.2135$$

1 decimal place   Left 1 place

2.135	3 decimal places
0.1	1 decimal place
0.2135	$3 + 1 = 4$ decimal places

The product to the right shows the accuracy of this method.

(b) 0.01×2.135

Move the decimal point 2 places to the left.

$$0.01 \times 2.135 = 0.02135$$

2 decimal places   Left 2 places

Notice that an extra zero was attached.

(c) 0.001×2.135

Move the decimal point 3 places to the left.

$$0.001 \times 2.135 = 0.002135$$

3 decimal places   Left 3 places

This time two zeros were supplied.

5 | CONVERTING CENTS TO DOLLARS

Multiplying by 0.01 converts from cents to dollars. For example,

198¢ converted to dollars is $1.98.

Multiplying 198 by 0.01 gives 1.98.

TO CONVERT CENTS TO DOLLARS

Discard the ¢ sign, move the decimal point two places to the left (multiply by 0.01), and attach a $ sign at the left of the result.

EXAMPLE 6 CONVERTING CENTS TO DOLLARS

Convert from cents to dollars.

(a) 7955¢ Discard the ¢ sign, move the decimal point two places to the left, and attach a $ sign. The result is $79.55.

(b) 8¢ = $0.08

Notice that the extra zeros are supplied in the result.

6 | SOLVING APPLICATIONS INVOLVING MULTIPLYING DECIMALS

Many applied problems are solved by multiplying decimals.

EXAMPLE 7 MULTIPLYING DECIMALS IN A CONSUMER PROBLEM

Bob bought 8 books at a cost of $2.95 each. How much did he spend?
   Multiply $2.95 by 8.

$$
\begin{array}{ll}
\$2.95 & 2\text{ decimal places} \\
\underline{\times 8} & 0\text{ decimal places} \\
\$23.60 & 2\text{ decimal places } (2+0=2)
\end{array}
$$

Thus, Bob spent $23.60 for the books. Since 8 books at $3 each would cost $24 [24 = 8 × 3], our work appears correct.

EXAMPLE 8 CALCULATING WEEKLY EARNINGS

Jeff Plank earns $7.23 an hour working part time in the university bookstore. His hourly time card for one week is shown below. How much was Jeff paid that week?

   To find out how much he was paid, we need to know the total number of hours that he worked.

Day	Hours Worked
Mon	5.7
Tues	3.25
Wed	4.9
Thur	6.5
Fri	7.8

$$
\begin{array}{r}
5.7 \\
3.25 \\
4.9 \\
6.5 \\
+\ 7.8 \\
\hline
28.15
\end{array}
$$

Since he worked 28.15 hours at $7.23 per hour, multiply.

$$
\begin{array}{r}
28.15 \\
\times\ 7.23 \\
\hline
8445 \\
5630 \\
19705 \\
\hline
203.5245
\end{array}
$$

Rounded to the nearest cent, Jeff earned $203.52. Since 30 hours at $7 an hour would result in $210, our work appears to be correct.

PRACTICE EXERCISE 9

Rounded to the nearest cent, what is the cost in dollars and cents of 22.5 gallons of gasoline at 131.9¢ per gallon?

Answer: $29.68

MULTIPLYING DECIMALS IN A PHYSICS PROBLEM

EXAMPLE 9

The air pressure at sea level is 14.7 pounds per square inch of surface area. The surface area of the body of a man is approximately 2225 square inches. To the nearest pound, what is the total air pressure on his body at sea level?

Multiply the pressure per square inch by the total number of square inches of surface area.

$$
\begin{array}{r}
2225 \\
\times 14.7 \\
\hline
15575 \\
8900 \\
2225 \\
\hline
32707.5
\end{array}
$$

$0 + 1 = 1$ decimal place

Thus, the total pressure on the man's body (to the nearest pound) is 32,708 pounds, a result that may surprise you.

4.5 EXERCISES

Answers to these exercises are given on page 647.

In Exercises 1–8, find the products. Check placement of the decimal point by estimating the product.

1. $\begin{array}{r}14.03 \\ \times 0.5 \\ \hline\end{array}$
2. $\begin{array}{r}6.58 \\ \times 1.2 \\ \hline\end{array}$
3. $\begin{array}{r}12.05 \\ \times 2.3 \\ \hline\end{array}$
4. $\begin{array}{r}3.004 \\ \times 1.7 \\ \hline\end{array}$

5. $\begin{array}{r}5.107 \\ \times 8.4 \\ \hline\end{array}$
6. $\begin{array}{r}4.0108 \\ \times 2.6 \\ \hline\end{array}$
7. $\begin{array}{r}12.411 \\ \times 5.4 \\ \hline\end{array}$
8. $\begin{array}{r}12.28 \\ \times 13 \\ \hline\end{array}$

💡 Without making actual computations in Exercises 9–12, use an estimate to decide which of the given answers is correct.

9. 4.1×39.047 (a) 1.60093   (b) 16.0093   (c) 160.093   (d) 1600.93

10. 2.15×403.7 (a) 8.67955   (b) 86.7955   (c) 867.955   (d) 8679.55

11. 32.3×48.1 (a) 1553.63   (b) 15,536.3   (c) 155,363.0   (d) 1,553,630.0

12. 203.475×9.407 (a) 191.409   (b) 1914.09   (c) 19,140.9   (d) 191,409

Find the products in Exercises 13–18.

13. 15.237×10 *152,370*
14. 15.237×100 *1523,760*
15. $15.237 \times 10,000$ *15.237 4*

16. 15.237×0.1 *15237*
17. 15.237×0.01 *.15237*
18. 15.237×0.001 *.01523*

In Exercises 19–21, convert from dollars to cents.

19. $5.45
20. $21.98
21. $0.79

In Exercises 22–24, convert from cents to dollars.

22. 250¢
23. 7936¢
24. 4¢

152.370

Solve each applied problem in Exercises 25–38.

25. **BUSINESS** Cynthia Wolfe needs 16 art boards for a commercial art project. If each board costs $1.47, how much will these supplies cost?

26. **WAGES** Carlos is paid $8.19 per hour. His time card for one week is shown in the figure. How much was he paid that week?

Day	Hours Worked
Mon	6.3
Tues	4.7
Wed	8.2
Thur	6.9
Fri	7.4

27. **TRAVEL** The EPA-estimated miles per gallon for a midsized car is 21.8 mpg. The capacity of its gas tank is 19.4 gallons. To the nearest mile, what is the driving range of the car?

28. **PHYSICS** The air pressure at sea level is 14.7 pounds per square inch of surface area. The surface area of a student's body is approximately 2085 square inches. To the nearest pound, what is the total air pressure on his body at sea level?

29. **SALES** John Cross can give out as much as $500 worth of textbooks during the month. If he has sent out 7 books worth $27.25 each and 9 books worth $31.75 each, how much does he have left in the book account?

30. **GEOMETRY** A garden is 15.93 meters long and 11.24 meters wide. To the nearest hundredth of a square meter, what is the area of the rectangular garden?

31. **CONSUMER** If a special floor covering costs $4.25 per square foot, how much will it cost to cover a floor that is 15.3 feet long and 12.9 feet wide?

32. **SALARY** Steve Garza's contract specifies that he be paid $14.38 per hour for a 40-hour work week. For all hours over 40, he must be paid time and a half (1.5 times the normal hourly rate). Last week Mr. Garza worked 51 hours. How much was he paid?

33. **CONSUMER** It costs $17.50 a day plus $0.18 per mile to rent a car at Cheapo Car Rentals. How much would it cost to rent the car for two days if it is driven a total of 240 miles?

34. **SALARY** Dave worked 41 hours one week and was paid $7.87 an hour. What was his approximate pay for the week? His exact pay?

35. **CONSUMER** Herman wishes to buy four new tires for his car. He is interested in the tires shown in the advertisement to the right. What would be the approximate cost of the tires? The exact cost?

All Season Radials with White Walls

EVERYDAY LOW PRICES

$38⁷⁵

CRITICAL THINKING

36. **CONSTRUCTION** It costs $0.25 per square foot to put sod down for a new lawn at a construction site. How much will it cost to sod a rectangular area that is 30.3 yards long and 12.6 yards wide? [Hint: You must convert yards to feet by multiplying the number of yards by 3.]

37. **TAX** The Hoffmans must pay $8.35 in property tax for every $1000 of assessed value on their home. How much property tax do they pay if the assessed value of their home is $102,000?

38. Discuss the similarities and differences between multiplying by powers of 10 and multiplying by 0.1, 0.01, and 0.001.

39. Burford was asked to multiply 241.567 by 100. He said "That's easy, all I do is move the decimal point 2 places to obtain 2.41567." What is Burford doing wrong? What is the correct answer?

💡 *In Chapter 2 we solved a number of equations by changing from the related division equation to the related multiplication equation, and conversely. Use this technique to solve the equations involving decimals given in Exercises 40–42.*

40. $\dfrac{x}{4} = 1.3$ 41. $\dfrac{y}{2.2} = 9$ 42. $\dfrac{z}{4.2} = 2.9$

REVIEW AND PREVIEW

43. **RECREATION** Mr. and Ms. Bonnett-McDonald stayed at the Frontier Hotel in Las Vegas on a 3-day/2-night package. Their room cost $139.95, and they charged $37.28 in food and beverage to their room account. If Ms. Bonnett-McDonald paid the bill with two $100 bills, how much change did she receive?

44. **GEOMETRY** Find the perimeter of the garden sketched in the figure below.

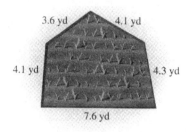

45. **TRAVEL** On a five-day trip, a family traveled 2450.3 miles. On the first day they traveled 233.2 mi, on the second 537.3 mi, on the third 641.4 mi, and on the fourth 596.3 mi.

(a) How far did they travel on the fifth day?

(b) What is the answer to (a) rounded to the nearest mile?

(c) What is the answer to (a) if all distances are rounded to the nearest mile before any calculation?

(d) Compare the answers to (b) and (c).

💡**CONSUMER** *Use the following newspaper advertisements to answer Exercises 46–49.*

46. Estimate the cost of one video recorder and one microwave oven. Then find the exact cost.

47. About how much more is the recorder than the oven? What is the exact difference in price?

48. About how many video recorders could be purchased for $3000?

49. Estimate the total cost of purchasing 6 microwave ovens.

4.5 PARALLEL EXERCISES

Answers to these exercises are not given in the text.

In Exercises 1–8, find the products. Check placement of the decimal point by estimating the product.

1. 21.02
   ×0.7

2. 2.59
   ×1.5

3. 14.06
   ×5.4

4. 2.001
   ×1.2

5. 3.109
   ×5.6

6. 3.0109
   ×4.3

7. 13.611
   ×3.2

8. 14.56
   ×18

   11648
   14560
   262.18

💡 *Without making actual computations in Exercises 9–12, use an estimate to decide which of the given answers is correct.*

9. 6.2×51.075 (a) 3.16665   (b) 31.6665   (c) 316.665   (d) 3166.65

10. 4.25×291.8 (a) 1.24015   (b) 12.4015   (c) 124.015   (d) 1240.15

11. 41.5×62.3 (a) 2585.45   (b) 258.545   (c) 25.8545   (d) 2.58545

12. 195.625×3.508 (a) 68.62525   (b) 686.2525   (c) 6862.525   (d) 68625.25

Find the products in Exercises 13–18.

13. 341.59×10 14. 341.59×1000 15. 341.59×100

16. 341.59×0.1 17. 341.59×0.001 18. 341.59×0.01

In Exercises 19–21, convert from dollars to cents.

19. $8.23   20. $45.15   21. $0.67

In Exercises 22–24, convert from cents to dollars.

22. 705¢   23. 2009¢   24. 12¢

Solve each applied problem in Exercises 25–38.

25. **BUSINESS** The Supply House ordered 25 boxes of pencils that cost $7.83 per box. How much will they be billed for the order?

26. **SALARY** Peter is paid $11.53 per hour. His hourly time card for one week is shown below. How much was he paid that week (to the nearest cent)?

Day	Hours Worked
Mon	7.2
Tues	6.5
Wed	8.1
Thur	6.9
Fri	5.4

27. **TRAVEL** What is the driving range (to the nearest mile) of a car with EPA-estimated miles per gallon of 26.2 and a gas tank with capacity of 14.5 gallons?

28. **PHYSICS** The air pressure at sea level is 14.7 pounds per square inch of surface area. If the surface area of a young child is 1125 square inches, to the nearest pound, what is the total air pressure on his body at sea level?

29. **SALES** Sandra Broom bought 32.3 pounds of nails at $0.65 per pound and 124.9 pounds of staples at $0.52 per pound. If Sandra had a $900 account at the supply house where she made these purchases, how much was left in the account?

30. **GEOMETRY** A rectangular table top is 5.95 ft long and 4.67 ft wide. Find the area of the table top to the nearest hundredth of a square foot.

31. **CONSTRUCTION** A wall is 9.5 ft high and 16.25 ft long. How much will it cost to insulate the wall if insulating material sells for $0.45 per square foot?

32. **SALARY** Ms. Morgan is paid $12.35 per hour for a 40-hour work week. For all hours over 40 she is paid time and a half as overtime. If she worked 53 hours one week, how much was she paid?

33. **CONSUMER** It costs $18.25 a day plus $0.22 per mile to rent a car at Local Car Rentals. How much would it cost to rent the car for three days if it is driven 395 miles?

34. **PRODUCTION** It costs $12.05 per hour to operate a particular machine. What is the approximate cost of running the machine for 48 hours? The exact cost?

35. **CONSUMER** Mr. and Mrs. Washington decide to purchase a vacuum cleaner, advertised below, for each of their five children. What would be the approximate cost of the cleaners? The exact cost?

Upright Vacuum Cleaner with 12" Beater Bar Brush

$59⁸⁸

 CRITICAL THINKING

36. **CONSUMER** Jesse Valdivia plans to carpet his family room with carpeting that costs $2.15 a square foot. If the room is rectangular in shape, 7.2 yards long and 4.9 yards wide, what would be the cost of the job? [Hint: You must convert yards to feet by multiplying the number of yards by 3.]

37. **TAX** Kelly and Ralph must pay $9.25 in property tax for every $1000 of assessed value on their home. How much property tax do they pay if the assessed value of their home is $121,000?

38. In the metric system of measurement (which we will study in detail in Chapter 5), conversions between units are made by multiplying by a power of 10 or by 0.1, 0.01, or 0.001. Discuss why making conversion in this system is merely a matter of moving a decimal.

39. Burford was asked to multiply 241.567 by 0.01. He said "That's easy, all I do is move the decimal point 2 places to obtain 24,156.7." What is Burford doing wrong? What is the correct answer.

In Chapter 2 we solved a number of equations by changing from the related division equation to the related multiplication equation, and conversely. Use this technique to solve the equations involving decimals given in Exercises 40–42.

40. $\dfrac{x}{3} = 2.4$

41. $\dfrac{y}{3.1} = 7$

42. $\dfrac{z}{5.8} = 1.7$

GROUP PROJECT

Sometimes advertisements in newspapers or magazines can be confusing if not downright misleading. For example, consider the ads given in Exercise 35 above. Notice that the decimal point is not written. Could this cause any confusion? Also, why do you suppose that prices are always given as $59.88 instead of $60.00, or as $38.75 instead of $39.00? Gather some interesting advertisements from newspapers and discuss different ways that these ads can mislead or confuse the consumer.

4.6 DIVIDING DECIMALS

STUDENT GUIDEPOSTS
1   DIVIDING A DECIMAL BY A WHOLE NUMBER
2   DIVIDING A DECIMAL BY A DECIMAL
3   FINDING QUOTIENTS ROUNDED TO A GIVEN DECIMAL PLACE
4   DIVIDING DECIMALS BY A POWER OF 10
5   DIVIDING DECIMALS BY 0.1, 0.01, AND 0.001
6   FINDING QUOTIENTS WITH A REPEATING BLOCK OF DIGITS
7   FINDING QUOTIENTS OF TWO WHOLE NUMBERS
8   SOLVING APPLICATIONS INVOLVING DIVIDING DECIMALS

1 DIVIDING A DECIMAL BY A WHOLE NUMBER

Dividing decimals is much like dividing whole numbers, except for placing the decimal point. Converting fractions to decimals as was done in Section 4.2 is a special case of this division process.

Suppose we divide

$$2.7 \div 3$$

using fractions. We know

$$2.7 = 2\frac{7}{10} = \frac{27}{10}.$$

Then

$$2.7 \div 3 = \frac{27}{10} \div \frac{3}{1} = \frac{27}{10} \times \frac{1}{3} = \frac{9 \cdot \cancel{3} \cdot 1}{10 \cdot \cancel{3}} = \frac{9}{10} = 0.9.$$

Thus, 2.7 divided by 3 must be 0.9. Now, suppose we write the quotient as follows.

$$3\overline{)2.7}$$

Ignoring the decimal point and dividing as we divided whole numbers gives the following result.

$$
\begin{array}{r}
9 \quad \textbf{Decimal point not yet placed} \\
3\overline{)2.7} \\
\underline{2\ 7} \\
0
\end{array}
$$

Moving the decimal point in the dividend (2.7) straight up results in the desired quotient, 0.9.

$$
\begin{array}{r}
.9 \\
3\overline{)2.7} \\
\underline{2\ 7} \\
0
\end{array}
$$

This illustrates a general procedure.

TO DIVIDE A DECIMAL BY A WHOLE NUMBER
1.   Place a decimal point directly above the decimal point in the dividend.
2.   Divide as if both numbers were whole numbers.

PRACTICE EXERCISE 1

Find the quotients.

(a) $1.08 \div 4$

(b) $15.04 \div 32$

Answers: (a) 0.27 (b) 0.47

Find the quotients.

(a) $1.12 \div 7$

Place a decimal point in the quotient directly above the decimal point in the dividend, then divide as if the dividend were a whole number.

$$
\begin{array}{r}
.16 \\
7\overline{)1.12} \\
\underline{7} \\
42 \\
\underline{42} \\
0
\end{array}
$$

The quotient is 0.16.

(b) $11.34 \div 21$

$$
\begin{array}{r}
.54 \\
21\overline{)11.34} \\
\underline{105} \\
84 \\
\underline{84} \\
0
\end{array}
$$

Place decimal point
Divide as if whoe numbers

The quotient is 0.54.

2   **DIVIDING A DECIMAL BY A DECIMAL**

Division problems with decimals for both the dividend and the divisor can be changed into problems with whole number divisors. For example, suppose we write the division problem

$$0.35\overline{)1.498}$$

as a fraction.

$$\frac{1.498}{0.35}$$

Multiplying numerator and denominator by 100,

$$\frac{1.498 \times \mathbf{100}}{0.35 \times \mathbf{100}} = \frac{149.8}{35},$$

would give a fraction which has a whole number in the denominator. That is, to divide 1.498 by 0.35 we could just as well divide 149.8 by 35. To do this, a zero must be supplied to the right of 8 as shown.

$$
\begin{array}{r}
4.28 \\
35\overline{)149.80} \\
\underline{140} \\
9\,8 \\
\underline{7\,0} \\
2\,80 \\
\underline{2\,80} \\
0
\end{array}
$$

Attach a zero to continue the process

TO DIVIDE A DECIMAL BY A DECIMAL
1. Move the decimal point to the right in the divisor (multiply by a power of 10) to obtain a whole number.
2. Move the decimal point in the dividend the same number of places to the right (multiply by the same power of 10). Extra zeros may need to be attached.
3. Divide by the whole number divisor as before.

For example, suppose we consider $1.498 \div 0.35$ again.

$$0.35\overset{\frown}{\smile}\,)\overline{1.49\overset{\frown}{\smile}8}$$

① **Move the decimal point two places to the right to obtain the whole number 35**

② **Move this decimal point two places to the right also**

EXAMPLE 2   **DIVIDING DECIMALS**

Find the quotients.

(a) $4.465 \div 1.9$

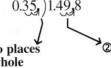

① **Move decimal point one place to the right in both divisor and dividend**

$$\begin{array}{r} 2.35 \\ 19\overline{)44.65} \\ \underline{38} \\ 6\,6 \\ \underline{5\,7} \\ 95 \\ \underline{95} \\ 0 \end{array}$$

② **Place decimal point directly above and divide by the whole number 19**

(b) $2.7168 \div 0.48$

$$\begin{array}{r} 5.66 \\ 0.48.\overline{)2.71.68} \\ \underline{2\,40} \\ 31\,6 \\ \underline{28\,8} \\ 2\,88 \\ \underline{2\,88} \\ 0 \end{array}$$

(c) $42 \div 1.4$ The whole number 42 can be thought of as the decimal 42. or 42.0.

$$\begin{array}{r} 30. \\ 1.4.\overline{)42.0.} \\ \underline{42} \\ 0\,0 \end{array}$$

3 | FINDING QUOTIENTS ROUNDED TO A GIVEN DECIMAL PLACE

In Example 2, each quotient was a terminating decimal which had very few decimal places. When this is not the case, we often round answers to a given number of decimal places.

<table>
<tr>
<td>

PRACTICE EXERCISE 3

(a) Find $2.107 \div 3.1$ rounded to the nearest tenth.

</td>
<td>

FINDING QUOTIENTS TO A GIVEN DECIMAL PLACE

EXAMPLE 3

</td>
</tr>
</table>

(a) Find $3.257 \div 2.7$, rounded to the nearest tenth.

$$
\begin{array}{r}
1.20 \\
2.7_{\curvearrowright}\overline{)3.2_{\curvearrowright}57} \\
2\,7 \\
\overline{5\,5} \\
5\,4 \\
\overline{17}
\end{array}
$$

We could continue dividing, but since the first digit to the right of the tenths position is 0, the quotient is approximately 1.2, rounded to the nearest tenth. That is,

$$3.257 \div 2.7 \approx 1.2.$$

(b) Find $3.205 \div 0.22$ rounded to the nearest hundredth.

(b) Find $2.551 \div 0.16$, rounded to the nearest hundredth.

$$
\begin{array}{r}
15.943 \\
0.16_{\curvearrowright}\overline{)2.55_{\curvearrowright}100} \\
1\,6 \\
\overline{95} \\
80 \\
\overline{15\,1} \\
14\,4 \\
\overline{70} \\
64 \\
\overline{60} \\
48 \\
\overline{12}
\end{array}
$$

Answers: (a) 0.7 (b) 14.57

Since the first digit to the right of the hundredths position is 3, the quotient is approximately 15.94, rounded to the nearest hundredth. That is,

$$2.551 \div 0.16 \approx 15.94.$$

> **NOTE** In Section 4.5 we placed decimals and checked decimal products by estimating the answer. Use the same technique when dividing decimals.

EXAMPLE 4 **ESTIMATING TO LOCATE DECIMAL PLACE**

Find $156.3 \div 12$ and place the decimal point by estimating the answer.

Since the quotient is about $150 \div 10$, the result should be about 15.

$$\begin{array}{r} 13.025 \\ 12\overline{)156.300} \\ \underline{12} \\ 36 \\ \underline{36} \\ 30 \\ \underline{24} \\ 60 \\ \underline{60} \\ 0 \end{array}$$

Decimal point *must* be placed here according to estimated quotient

4 DIVIDING DECIMALS BY A POWER OF 10

The quotient in Example 4 was approximated by dividing 150 by 10. Dividing a decimal by 10 is the same as multiplying the decimal by 0.1 since

$$150 \div \mathbf{10} = 150 \times \frac{\mathbf{1}}{\mathbf{10}} = 150 \times \mathbf{0.1}.$$

As a result, from Section 4.5, dividing by 10 (multiplying by 0.1) is simply a matter of moving the decimal point one place to the left. Similar rules apply when dividing by any power of 10 such as 10, 100, 1000, or 10,000.

TO DIVIDE A DECIMAL BY A POWER OF 10

Move the decimal point to the *left* the same number of decimal places as the number of zeros in the power of 10.

EXAMPLE 5 **DIVIDING DECIMALS BY A POWER OF 10**

Find each quotient.

(a) $43.21 \div 100$

Since there are 2 zeros in 100, move the decimal point in 43.21 two places to the left.

$$43.21 \div \mathbf{100} = 0.4321$$

2 zeros   Left 2 places

(b) $43.21 \div 1000$

Move the decimal point 3 places to the left.

$$43.21 \div \mathbf{1000} = 0.04321$$

3 zeros   Left 3 places

Notice that an extra zero was needed when moving the decimal point.

(c) $43.21 \div 100,000$

Move the decimal point 5 places to the left.

$$43.21 \div 100,000 = 0.0004321$$

5 DIVIDING DECIMALS BY 0.1, 0.01, AND 0.001

Suppose we divide 1.235 by 0.1. Dividing by 0.1 is the same as multiplying by 10.

$$1.235 \div \mathbf{0.1} = 1.235 \div \frac{\mathbf{1}}{\mathbf{10}} = 1.235 \times \frac{\mathbf{10}}{\mathbf{1}} = 1.235 \times \mathbf{10}$$

As a result, from Section 4.5, dividing by 0.1 (multiplying by 10) is the same as moving the decimal point one place to the right. Similar rules apply when dividing by 0.01 or 0.001. This is summarized in the following rule.

TO DIVIDE A DECIMAL BY 0.1, 0.01, OR 0.001
Move the decimal point to the *right* the same number of decimal places as decimal places in 0.1, 0.01, or 0.001.

DIVIDING DECIMALS BY 0.1, 0.01, OR 0.001   EXAMPLE 6

PRACTICE EXERCISE 6
Find each quotient.
(a) $439.7 \div 0.1$

(b) $439.7 \div 0.01$

Answers: (a) 4397 (b) 43,970

Find each quotient.

(a) $54.32 \div 0.1$
Since 0.1 has one decimal place, move the decimal point in 54.32 one place to the right.

$$54.32 \div 0.1 = 543.2$$
Right 1 place

(b) $54.32 \div 0.001$
Move the decimal point three places to the right since 0.001 has three decimal places.
$$54.32 \div 0.001 = 54320.$$
Right 3 places

Notice that a zero must be attached to obtain the quotient 54,320.

NOTE   The difference between multiplying a decimal by a power of 10 and dividing by a power of 10 is simply reversing the direction we move the decimal point. This is easy to remember since multiplication and division are opposite processes. The same remarks apply to multiplying and dividing by 0.1, 0.01, or 0.001.

6 | QUOTIENTS WITH A REPEATING BLOCK OF DIGITS

Some division problems result in quotients that have a repeating block of digits, as mentioned in Section 4.2. When this repetition is discovered, stop the process and place a bar over the repeating digits.

A QUOTIENT WITH A REPEATING BLOCK OF DIGITS   EXAMPLE 7

PRACTICE EXERCISE 7
Find $1.74 \div 0.33$.

Answer: $5.\overline{27}$

Find $2.19 \div 0.99$.

```
           2.2121
    0.99.)2.19.0000
           1 98
            21 0
            19 8
             1 20
               99
              210
              198
              120
               99
               21
```

We can see that the digits 21 will continue to repeat after the decimal point. Thus,

$$2.19 \div 0.99 = 2.\overline{21}.$$

7 FINDING QUOTIENTS OF TWO WHOLE NUMBERS

When one whole number is divided by another, the quotient is sometimes given as a decimal rounded to a particular degree of accuracy.

EXAMPLE 8 DIVIDING WHOLE NUMBERS

Find $431 \div 29$, rounded to the nearest hundredth.

```
        14.862
   29)431.000      Add three zeros
      29
     ───
      141
      116
      ───
       25 0
       23 2
      ─────
        1 80
        1 74
        ────
          60
          58
          ──
           2
```

Since the first digit to the right of the hundredths position is 2, the quotient is approximately 14.86, rounded to the nearest hundredth.

8 SOLVING APPLICATIONS INVOLVING DIVIDING DECIMALS

Many applied problems are solved by dividing one decimal by another. As always, estimate the answer and ask yourself if the actual answer seems reasonable.

EXAMPLE 9 CALCULATING MONTHLY PAYMENTS

How many months will it take to pay off a loan of $894.18 if the monthly payments are $42.58?

Divide the total to be paid ($894.18) by the amount paid each month ($42.58).

```
            21.
   42.58.)894.18.
          851 6
          ─────
           42 58
           42 58
           ─────
               0
```

Thus, it will take 21 months to pay off the loan. Since $900 \div 40 = 22.5$ this answer seems reasonable.

PRACTICE EXERCISE 10

Burford earned a C in a 4-credit English course, a D in a 3-credit biology course, a B in a 2-credit physical education course, and an F in a 4-credit history course. Calculate Burford's GPA (rounded to the nearest hundredth) on a 4-point scale.

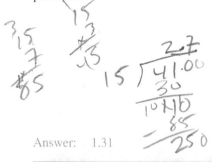

Answer: 1.31

EXAMPLE 10   FINDING A GRADE POINT AVERAGE

Finding the grade point average (GPA) of a student is an important application of decimals. Calculate a GPA using a 4-point scale, that is, a perfect GPA (every grade an A) is 4.00. Each letter grade is assigned a value: $A = 4$, $B = 3$, $C = 2$, $D = 1$, and $F = 0$. The first step is to find the course value, that is, the product of the credits and the grade value, as shown in the following table.

Course	Credits	Grade	Value	Course Value
Math	4	B	3	$4 \cdot 3 = 12$
English	3	A	4	$3 \cdot 4 = 12$
Music	2	A	4	$2 \cdot 4 = 8$
History	3	C	2	$3 \cdot 2 = 6$
Physics	3	D	1	$3 \cdot 1 = 3$
Totals	15			41

$$\text{GPA} = \frac{\text{sum of course values}}{\text{total credits}} = \frac{41}{15} = 2.733$$

The student's GPA, rounded to the nearest hundredth, is 2.73.

4.6 EXERCISES

Answers to these exercises are given on page 648.

In Exercises 1–12, find the quotients.

1. $6\overline{)5.4}$ 2. $8\overline{)18.4}$ 3. $12\overline{)43.2}$ 4. $25\overline{)171.5}$

5. $1.4\overline{)1.12}$ 6. $1.4\overline{)0.112}$ 7. $0.27\overline{)0.378}$ 8. $0.31\overline{)2.232}$

9. $4.2\overline{)8.988}$ 10. $0.015\overline{)0.0945}$ 11. $1.6\overline{)56}$ 12. $25\overline{)69.0}$

In Exercises 13–15, find the quotient, rounded to the nearest tenth.

13. $1.9\overline{)2.36}$ 14. $48\overline{)315}$ 15. $1.02\overline{)3.185}$

In Exercises 16–18, find the quotient, rounded to the nearest hundredth.

16. $1.9\overline{)2.36}$ 17. $48\overline{)315}$ 18. $1.02\overline{)3.185}$

💡*Without making actual calculations in Exercises 19–22, use an estimate to decide which of the given answers is correct.*

19. $243.41 \div 19$ (a) 1.28111   (b) 12.8111   (c) 128.111   (d) 1281.11

20. $625.03 \div 25.1$ (a) 24.9016   (b) 2.49016   (c) 2490.16   (d) 24,901.6

21. $357.103 \div 62.8$ (a) 0.56864   (b) 5.6864   (c) 56.864   (d) 568.64

22. $403.229 \div 6.417$ (a) 0.062838   (b) 0.62838   (c) 6.2838   (d) 62.838

In Exercises 23–31, find the quotients.

23. $32.71 \div 10$ 24. $41.38 \div 100$ 25. $5.329 \div 10,000$

26. $621.43 \div 100,000$ 27. $8.319 \div 1000$ 28. $0.0327 \div 0.1$

29. $426.5 \div 0.001$ 30. $0.627 \div 0.1$ 31. $4.398 \div 0.01$

In Exercises 32–34, find the quotient. (Each quotient is a repeating decimal.)

32. $1.8\overline{)21.2}$

33. $1.05\overline{)2.135}$

34. $0.36\overline{)2.58}$

Solve each applied problem in Exercises 35–40.

35. **MONTHLY PAYMENTS** The Warrens just received notice that they still owe $3039.68 on a loan. How many more months must they pay if the monthly payment is $217.12?

36. **CONSTRUCTION** The Rappaports used 260 stepping stones to build a patio. If the total cost of the stones was $107.15, how much did each stone cost (to the nearest tenth of a cent)?

37. **TAX** The assessed value of a parcel of property can be found by dividing the amount of tax by the tax rate. Margaret's property was taxed at a rate of 0.147, and she paid a property tax of $382.40. Find the assessed value of her property.

38. **FINANCE** There were 125 people who agreed to pay equal shares to rebuild a house that was destroyed by fire. How much must each person pay if the total construction cost was $52,256.25?

39. **EDUCATION** The following table shows Sam's grades during one semester. Complete the table and calculate his GPA, correct to the nearest hundredth.

Course	Credits	Grade	Value	Course Value
History	3	D	1	
English	3	A	4	
Algebra	5	B	3	
Chemistry	3	F	0	
Art	2	C	2	

40. **CONSUMER** Which is the better buy, 9 apples for $1.62 or 13 apples for $2.21?

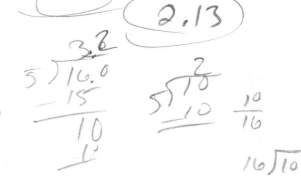

CRITICAL THINKING

41. **RECREATION** On his two-week summer vacation, Sam Passamonte drove 715.6 miles the first week and 527.3 miles the second week. He purchased gas three times during the vacation, the last time when he arrived home. If he left home with a full tank and bought 17.2 gallons, 21.3 gallons, and 19.7 gallons, to the nearest tenth, how many miles did he get to the gallon?

42. Discuss how estimation can be used to place the decimal point in a division problem.

43. Discuss how changing a divisor to a whole number can simplify the division process with decimals.

44. Burford was asked to divide 241.567 by 100. He said "That's easy, all I do is move the decimal point 2 places to obtain 24,156.7." What is Burford doing wrong? What is the correct answer?

In Chapter 2 we solved a number of equations by changing from the related division equation to the related multiplication equation, and conversely. Use this technique to solve the equations involving decimals given in Exercises 45–47.

45. $4x = 24.8$

46. $1.2y = 7.2$

47. $0.31z = 2.232$

REVIEW AND PREVIEW

Find the products in Exercises 48–53.

48. $\begin{array}{r} 3.02 \\ \times 0.5 \\ \hline \end{array}$

49. $\begin{array}{r} 7.38 \\ \times 1.2 \\ \hline \end{array}$

50. $\begin{array}{r} 7.011 \\ \times 2.01 \\ \hline \end{array}$

51. 691.35×100

52. 691.35×0.1

53. 691.35×0.01

54. Convert $12.45 to cents.

55. Convert 17¢ to dollars.

Solve each applied problem in Exercises 56–61.

56. **BUSINESS** Frank Capek had $250 available to purchase office supplies. If he bought 6 boxes of paper for $23.25 a box and paid taxes of $8.37, how much is left in his office supply fund?

57. **CONSUMER** It costs $98.00 a week plus 16.5¢ ($0.165) per mile to rent a car at Horn's Rentals. How much would it cost to rent the car for one week if it is driven a total of 683 miles?

58. **SALARY** A blocklayer earns $13.78 per hour for a 40-hour work week and time and a half for each hour of overtime. If Pete worked 52 hours during the week laying blocks, how much was he paid?

59. **WAGES** Suppose all we knew was that Pete earned the total amount in the answer to Exercise 58 by working 52 hours. What would we say was his hourly rate?

60. **GEOMETRY** Find the area of the region below by dividing the region into two rectangles.

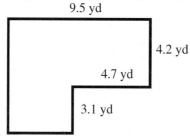

61. **RECREATION** The Bennings spent three nights at the Desert Oasis Hotel in Palm Springs. The price of the room was $105.50 per night, and they charged $62.39 in food and beverages to their room. If the bill was paid with four $100 bills, how much change was received?

💡 *The following exercises will help you prepare for the next section. In Exercises 62–64, place the correct symbol (< or >) between each pair of numbers.*

62. 0 7

63. $\dfrac{3}{2}$ $\dfrac{5}{4}$

64. 6 $\dfrac{25}{4}$

💡 *Perform the indicated operations in Exercises 65–67.*

65. $2 + 8 \div 4 - 1$

66. $\left(\dfrac{1}{2} + \dfrac{1}{4}\right) \cdot 2 - 1$

67. $\sqrt{9} \div 4 + \dfrac{1}{4}$

4.6 PARALLEL EXERCISES

Answers to these exercises are not given in the text.

In Exercises 1–12, find the quotients.

1. $9\overline{)23.4}$

2. $5\overline{)0.45}$

3. $14\overline{)37.8}$

4. $35\overline{)89.6}$

5. $1.7\overline{)7.31}$

6. $1.7\overline{)0.731}$

7. $0.41\overline{)0.8487}$

8. $0.52\overline{)3.536}$

9. $5.1\overline{)116.79}$

10. $0.022\overline{)0.1056}$

11. $1.3\overline{)74.1}$

12. $32\overline{)86}$

In Exercises 13–15, find the quotient, rounded to the nearest tenth.

13. $1.8\overline{)2.47}$

14. $41\overline{)365}$

15. $1.05\overline{)4.172}$

In Exercises 16–18, find the quotient, rounded to the nearest hundredth.

16. $1.8\overline{)2.47}$

17. $41\overline{)365}$

18. $1.05\overline{)4.172}$

💡 *Without making actual calculations in Exercises 19–22, use an estimate to decide which of the given answers is correct.*

19. $321.7 \div 21$	(a) 1.53190	(b) 15.3190	(c) 153.190	(d) 1531.90
20. $489.02 \div 92.2$	(a) 530.390	(b) 53.0390	(c) 5.30390	(d) 0.0530390
21. $449.207 \div 49.3$	(a) 0.091117	(b) 0.91117	(c) 9.1117	(d) 91.117
22. $702.116 \div 9.328$	(a) 0.0752697	(b) 0.752697	(c) 7.52697	(d) 75.2697

In Exercises 23–31, find the quotients.

23. $64.85 \div 100$

24. $31.65 \div 10$

25. $1.357 \div 1000$

26. $435.07 \div 10{,}000$

27. $921.05 \div 100{,}000$

28. $0.0569 \div 0.1$

29. $327.5 \div 0.001$

30. $0.0659 \div 0.01$

31. $2.678 \div 0.001$

In Exercises 32–34, find the quotient. (Each quotient is a repeating decimal.)

32. $4.5\overline{)1.45}$

33. $33\overline{)189}$

34. $2.16\overline{)11.16}$

Solve each applied problem in Exercises 35–40.

35. **MONTHLY PAYMENTS** After paying $495.37 per month for 86 months, the Newtons still owe $16,842.58. How many more months will be required to pay this amount?

36. **CONSTRUCTION** The Giffords used 320 tiles to build a patio. If the total cost of the tiles was $45.75, how much did each tile cost (to the nearest tenth of a cent)?

37. **TAX** The assessed value of a lot can be found by dividing the amount of tax by the tax rate. If Denise's lot was taxed at a rate of 0.151, and she paid a property tax of $468.10, find the assessed value of her property.

38. **RECREATION** There are 16 people who agree to pay equal shares to charter a ship for a vacation cruise. How much will each have to pay if the total bill comes to $52,029.44?

39. **EDUCATION** The following table shows Wes's grades during the fall term. Complete the table and calculate his GPA, correct to the nearest hundredth.

Course	Credits	Grade	Value	Course Value
English	3	B	3	
Chemistry	4	C	2	
French	3	A	4	
Geometry	3	B	3	
History	2	F	0	

40. **CONSUMER** Which is the better buy, a 32-ounce bottle of ketchup for $1.60 or a 48-ounce bottle for $2.88?

CRITICAL THINKING

41. **HYDROLOGY** A water tank is filled with water. The tank, when empty, weighs 187.6 pounds and, when full, weighs 839.4 pounds. If one cubic foot of water weighs 62.5 pounds, how many cubic feet of water does the tank hold? Give the answer rounded to the nearest tenth of a cubic foot.

42. Discuss the various possible cases that occur when dividing a decimal by a decimal.

43. Describe the conditions under which a quotient will be a repeating decimal.

44. Burford was asked to divide 241.567 by 0.01. He said "That's easy, all I do is move the decimal point 2 places to obtain 2.41567." What is Burford doing wrong? What is the correct answer?

In Chapter 2 we solved a number of equations by changing from the related division equation to the related multiplication equation, and conversely. Use this technique to solve the equations involving decimals given in Exercises 45–47.

45. $3x = 25.5$

46. $1.2y = 8.4$

47. $0.52z = 3.536$

GROUP PROJECT

We are introduced to numerical information on a daily basis. Some of the information is unimportant, but some can be quite valuable. The ability for us to determine which data might be important and which might not takes some practice. Estimating, or in fact even guessing to some extent, can be quite helpful. For example, suppose you go to a hardware store to buy some screws to repair a small portion of a wooden deck. You have determined ahead of time that each board will require 4 screws, and there are 16 boards for a total of 64 screws. When you locate the deck screws in the store, you discover that they are sold 15 to a package. If you divide 64 by 15 to obtain 4.2666..., you realize that the answer you obtain is not the number of packages of screws needed since a package cannot be broken. Instead, you would probably solve the problem by saying 4 packages of 15 screws each would be 60 screws, and since 64 are needed, you must buy 5 packages. In this case, rounding to obtain an approximate number means rounding up to the next whole number. Thus, we have yet another way to round decimals. Discuss other examples where estimating by rounding in this manner would be required to solve an application problem, and present your findings to the class.

4.7 ORDER OF OPERATIONS AND COMPARING DECIMALS

STUDENT GUIDEPOSTS
1 OPERATING WITH BOTH FRACTIONS AND DECIMALS
2 USING ORDER OF OPERATIONS FOR DECIMALS
3 ARRANGING DECIMALS IN ORDER OF SIZE
4 COMPARING UNIT PRICES

1 | OPERATING WITH BOTH FRACTIONS AND DECIMALS

In Chapters 2 and 3 we considered operations on fractions, and in this chapter we considered the same operations on decimals. At times, fractions and decimals may occur in the same problem.

PRACTICE EXERCISE 1

Find the quotient.

$$4.9 \div \frac{7}{8}$$

MULTIPLYING A FRACTION AND A DECIMAL   EXAMPLE 1

Find the product. $\frac{3}{4} \times 4.28$

We could change $\frac{3}{4}$ to decimal form, 0.75, and then multiply.

$$\begin{array}{r} 4.28 \\ \times 0.75 \\ \hline 2140 \\ 2996 \\ \hline 3.2100 \end{array}$$

Or, we could change 4.28 to fractional form,

$$4.28 = 4\frac{28}{100} = \frac{100 \cdot 4 + 28}{100} = \frac{428}{100},$$

and then multiply.

$$\frac{3}{4} \times \frac{428}{100} = \frac{3}{4} \times \frac{4 \cdot 107}{100} = \frac{3 \cdot 4 \cdot 107}{4 \cdot 100} = \frac{321}{100} = 3\frac{21}{100}$$

In general, problems which involve both decimals and fractions may be solved either by changing all numbers to decimals or by changing all numbers to fractions. When fractions are changed to decimals we must often make approximations.

Answer: $5\frac{3}{5}$ or 5.6

PRACTICE EXERCISE 2

Find the difference.

$$2.25 - \frac{2}{3}$$

ADDING A FRACTION AND A DECIMAL   EXAMPLE 2

Find the sum. $\frac{1}{3} + 5.75$

Since $\frac{1}{3} = 0.\overline{3} = 0.333\ldots$, we can only *approximate* the sum using decimals. As a result, it might be better to change 5.75 to fractional form.

$$5.75 = 5\frac{75}{100} = 5\frac{3}{4} = \frac{4 \cdot 5 + 3}{4} = \frac{23}{4}$$

Thus,

$$\frac{1}{3} + 5.75 = \frac{1}{3} + \frac{23}{4} = \frac{1}{3} + \frac{23}{2 \cdot 2} \qquad \text{LCD} = 2 \cdot 2 \cdot 3 = 12$$

$$= \frac{2 \cdot 2 \cdot 1}{2 \cdot 2 \cdot 3} + \frac{23 \cdot 3}{2 \cdot 2 \cdot 3} \qquad \text{Supply missing numbers}$$

$$= \frac{2 \cdot 2 + 23 \cdot 3}{2 \cdot 2 \cdot 3} \qquad \text{Add numerators over LCD}$$

$$= \frac{4 + 69}{12}$$

$$= \frac{73}{12}$$

$$= 6\frac{1}{12}.$$

If we had used the decimal 0.33 to approximate $\frac{1}{3}$, we would have found the sum as follows.

$$\frac{1}{3} + 5.75 \approx 0.33 + 5.75 = 6.08$$

Check: Does $6\frac{1}{12} = 6.08$?

Since $\frac{1}{12} = 0.08\overline{3}$ (dividing 1 by 12), $6\frac{1}{12} = 6.08\overline{3}$. Thus, using 0.33 to approximate $\frac{1}{3}$ makes $\frac{1}{3} + 5.75 \approx 6.08$ correct to the nearest hundredth. In some problems, this approximation may be accurate enough, and we can avoid adding fractions.

EXAMPLE 3	APPLYING FRACTIONS AND DECIMALS TO SEWING

A certain fabric costs $4.29 per yard. How much will $3\frac{1}{8}$ yards cost?

Multiply $3\frac{1}{8} \times 4.29$. Since $\frac{1}{8} = 0.125$ has a terminating decimal form, find the product using decimals.

$$
\begin{array}{r}
3.125 \\
\times 4.29 \\
\hline
28125 \\
6250 \\
12500 \\
\hline
13.40625
\end{array}
\qquad 3\frac{1}{8} = 3.125
$$

Rounding to the nearest cent, the fabric will cost $13.41.

2 USING ORDER OF OPERATIONS FOR DECIMALS

The order of operations was first considered in Section 1.9 relative to whole numbers and again in Section 3.5 when fractions were involved. The same order applies to decimals and to decimals mixed with fractions. For easy reference and review, the basic rules are repeated here.

ORDER OF OPERATIONS

Operations should be performed in the following order.

1. Operate within parentheses.
2. Evaluate all powers and roots in any order.
3. Multiply and divide, in order, from left to right.
4. Add and subtract, in order, from left to right.

PRACTICE EXERCISE 4

Perform the indicated operations.

(a) $4.32 \div 1.6 + 6.7$

(b) $15.45 - (2.3)(4.1)$

(c) $4.3 \cdot (6.7 - 5.1)$

(d) $8.76 - (2.4)^2 \div 0.8$

Answers: (a) 9.4 (b) 6.02 (c) 6.88 (d) 1.56

USING THE ORDER OF OPERATIONS ON DECIMALS — EXAMPLE 4

Perform the indicated operations.

(a) $\mathbf{2.5} + \mathbf{3.7} - 1.9 = \mathbf{6.2} - 1.9$ — Add first

$= 4.3$ — Then subtract

(b) $\mathbf{(1.8)(3.4)} - 2.24 = \mathbf{6.12} - 2.24$ — Multiply first

$= 3.88$ — Then subtract

(c) $6.75 \div \mathbf{(1.5 + 3.5)} = 6.75 \div \mathbf{5}$ — Add inside parentheses first

$= 1.35$ — Then divide

(d) $\mathbf{(1.2)^2} + 2.8 \div 1.4 = \mathbf{1.44} + 2.8 \div 1.4$ — Square first

$= 1.44 + \mathbf{2}$ — Divide next

$= 3.44$ — Then add

PRACTICE EXERCISE 5

Perform the indicated operations.

(a) $\left(\frac{2}{3}\right)\left(\frac{3}{5}\right) \div 0.8$

(b) $4.8 \div \left(\frac{1}{4}\right)^2 + 6.9$

(c) $\left(\frac{7}{8}\right)(0.12) - 0.005$

Answers: (a) 0.5 (b) 83.7 (c) 0.1

USING ORDER OF OPERATIONS ON FRACTIONS AND DECIMALS — EXAMPLE 5

Perform the indicated operations.

(a) $\frac{1}{2} + \mathbf{(3.5)(2.4)} = \frac{1}{2} + \mathbf{8.4}$ — Multiply first

$= 0.5 + 8.4$ — Change $\frac{1}{2}$ to a decimal

$= 8.9$ — Then add

(b) $\mathbf{\left(\frac{1}{4}\right)^2} + \mathbf{(1.5)^2} - 2.3 = \mathbf{\frac{1}{16}} + \mathbf{2.25} - 2.3$ — Square first

$= 0.0625 + 2.25 - 2.3$ — Change $\frac{1}{16}$ to a decimal

$= 2.3125 - 2.3$ — Add first

$= 0.0125$ — Then subtract

(c) $3.2 \div \frac{1}{4} - 6\frac{4}{5} = 3.2 \times \mathbf{4} - 6.8$ — Multiply by the reciprocal of $\frac{1}{4}$, 4

$= 12.8 - 6.8$ — Multiply first

$= 6$ — Then subtract

3 | ARRANGING DECIMALS IN ORDER OF SIZE

The next topic involves comparing decimals. For example, we might want to arrange

$$0.3, \quad 0.31, \quad 0.301$$

in order of size from left to right, the smallest first. To make such comparisons, first write each number with the same number of decimal places attaching zeros as needed.

$$0.3\mathbf{00}, \quad 0.31\mathbf{0}, \quad 0.301$$

Since the largest number of decimal places in the given numbers is three (in 0.301), we have written each number with three decimal places. We ignore the decimal points and compare sizes as if comparing whole numbers. Left to right, smallest first, the arrangement is

$$300, \quad 301, \quad 310.$$

Thus, the original decimals arranged by size are

$$0.3, \quad 0.301, \quad 0.31.$$

EXAMPLE 6	ARRANGING DECIMALS IN ORDER OF SIZE

Arrange the following decimals in order of size, with the smallest on the left.

$$0.05, \quad 3.5, \quad 3.05, \quad 3.4, \quad 0.5$$

First write all numbers with two decimal places.

$$0.05, \quad 3.50, \quad 3.05, \quad 3.40, \quad 0.50$$

Ignoring decimals, arrange

$$5, \quad 350, \quad 305, \quad 340, \quad 50.$$

The two-place decimals, arranged by size, are

$$0.05, \quad 0.50, \quad 3.05, \quad 3.40, \quad 3.50,$$

so the original decimals are arranged by size as follows.

$$0.05, \quad 0.5, \quad 3.05, \quad 3.4, \quad 3.5$$

Decimals can be compared with fractions by changing the fractions to decimals.

EXAMPLE 7	ARRANGING FRACTIONS AND DECIMALS

Arrange the following numbers in order of size with the smallest on the left.

$$0.26, \quad 2.6, \quad \frac{1}{4}, \quad \frac{2}{5}, 0.39$$

First change the fractions to decimals. Since $\frac{1}{4} = 0.25$ and $\frac{2}{5} = 0.4$ the list becomes:

$$0.26, \quad 2.6, \quad 0.25, \quad 0.4, \quad 0.39.$$

Next write all the numbers with two decimal places.

$$0.26, \quad 2.60, \quad 0.25, \quad 0.40, \quad 0.39.$$

Ignoring the decimals, we must arrange

$$26, \quad 260, \quad 25, \quad 40, \quad 39.$$

The two-place decimals arranged by size are

$$0.25, \quad 0.26, \quad 0.39, \quad 0.40, \quad 2.60,$$

so the original numbers are arranged by size as follows:

$$\frac{1}{4}, 0.26, 0.39, \frac{2}{5}, 2.6.$$

4 | COMPARING UNIT PRICES

Comparing sizes of decimals is important in unit-pricing problems. The **unit price** of an item is

$$\text{unit price} = \frac{\text{total price}}{\text{number of units}}.$$

For example, if a 16-ounce (abbreviated **oz**) can of juice sells for 89¢,

$$\text{unit price} = \frac{\text{total price}}{\text{number of units}} = \frac{89¢}{16 \text{ oz}} \approx 5.56¢ \text{ per oz.}$$

Also, if a box of 300 facial tissues sells for 58¢, the unit price is

$$\frac{\text{total price}}{\text{number of units}} = \frac{58¢}{300} \approx 0.19¢ \text{ per tissue.}$$

The wise shopper compares unit prices of various brands of an item.

**PRACTICE
EXERCISE 8**

A 360-sheet roll of paper towels sells for 69¢ while a 440-sheet roll sells for 79¢. Assuming equal quality, which is the better buy?

Answer: The 440-sheet roll at approximately 0.18¢ per sheet is a better buy than the 360-sheet roll at 0.19¢ per sheet.

**PRACTICE
EXERCISE 9**

Use the table given in Example 9 to answer the following questions.

COMPARING UNIT PRICES   **EXAMPLE 8**

The following table contains information about four brands of detergent. Comparing unit prices, we see that Brand Z is the best buy (assuming that the quality of all products is the same).

Brand	Ounces	Total Price	Unit Price
W	18	$0.87	0.87 ÷ 18 ≈ $0.048
X	20	$0.93	0.93 ÷ 20 ≈ $0.047
Y	16	$0.78	0.78 ÷ 16 ≈ $0.049
Z	25	$1.16	1.16 ÷ 25 ≈ $0.046

We now solve the applied problem presented in the introduction to the chapter.

COMPARING DECIMALS IN A RECREATION APPLICATION   **EXAMPLE 9**

When very large numbers are used in graphs and tables, the notation is often simplified by using decimals. For example, consider the table below which gives the number of recreational vehicles sold in five different years. Notice that instead of using the number 226,500 for the total number of motorhomes sold in 1990, the number given is 226.5 and it represents thousands of units.

ITEM NUMBER (1000's)	1970	1975	1980	1985	1990
Motorhomes	30.3	96.6	99.9	233.5	226.5
Travel Trailers	138.8	150.6	52.0	75.4	80.4
Folding Camp Trailers	116.1	48.1	24.5	35.9	30.7
Truck Campers	95.9	44.3	5.0	6.9	9.7

Source: Recreation Vehicle Industry Association

(a) During which of these five years was the total number of recreation vehicles sold the greatest, and how many vehicles were sold in this year?
We must add the total number of vehicles sold in each of the five years.

1970: $30.3 + 138.8 + 116.1 + 95.9 = 381.1$ (Which represents 381,100 vehicles.)

1975: $96.6 + 150.6 + 48.1 + 44.3 = 339.6$ (Which represents 339,600 vehicles.)

1980: $99.9 + 52.0 + 24.5 + 5.0 = 181.4$ (Which represents 181,400 vehicles.)

1985: $233.5 + 75.4 + 35.9 + 6.9 = 351.7$ (Which represents 351,700 vehicles.)

1990: $226.5 + 80.4 + 30.7 + 9.7 = 347.3$ (Which represents 347,300 vehicles.)

Thus, the greatest number of recreational vehicles was sold in 1970.

(a) How many motorhomes were sold in total during these five years?

(b) In 1990, how many more motorhomes were sold than all other recreation vehicles combined?
We first find the total number of vehicles other than motorhomes that were sold in 1990.

(b) In 1985, how many more motorhomes were sold than all other recreation vehicles combined?

$$80.4 + 30.7 + 9.7 = 120.8 \quad \text{(Which represents 120,800 vehicles.)}$$

Since the number of motorhomes sold was 226.5 (representing 226,500), we can find the number more by subtracting.

$$226.5 - 120.8 = 105.7 \quad \text{(Which represents 105,700 vehicles.)}$$

Thus, there were 105,700 more motorhomes sold than all other types of recreational vehicles together.

(c) If the retail value of all folding camp trailers sold in 1990 was $134,000,000, what was the approximate price per unit sold during that year?

To find the approximate price of each folding camp trailer sold in 1990, we must divide the retail value of all folding camp trailers sold, $134,000,000, by the number of folding camp trailers sold, 30,700.

$$134,000,000 \div 30,700 \approx \$4365$$

Thus, the approximate price of each folding camp trailer sold in 1990 was about $4365.

(c) If the retail value of all truck campers sold in 1985 was $46,000,000, what was the approximate price per unit sold during that year?

ANSWERS: (a) 686.8 (representing 686,800 motorhomes) (b) 115.3 (representing 115,300 more) (c) Approximately $6667

4.7 EXERCISES

Answers to these exercises are given on page 648.

In Exercises 1–6, perform the indicated operations by changing all decimals to fractions.

1. $\dfrac{1}{4} + 2.6$

2. $3.25 - \dfrac{3}{8}$

3. $5\dfrac{1}{7} + 7.4$

4. $\dfrac{2}{3} \times 1.75$

5. $4.1 \div \dfrac{5}{6}$

6. $2\dfrac{2}{3} \times 3.25$

In Exercises 7–12, perform the indicated operations by first changing all fractions to decimals, correct to two decimal places. Give answers to the nearest hundredth.

7. $\dfrac{1}{4} + 2.6$

8. $3.25 - \dfrac{3}{8}$

9. $5\dfrac{1}{7} + 7.4$

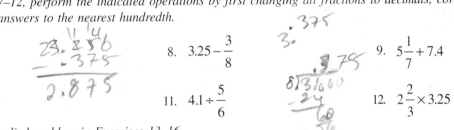

10. $\dfrac{2}{3} \times 1.75$

11. $4.1 \div \dfrac{5}{6}$

12. $2\dfrac{2}{3} \times 3.25$

Solve each applied problem in Exercises 13–16.

13. **TRAVEL** Diane Gray drove for $3\dfrac{1}{2}$ hours at a rate of 62.5 miles per hour. How far did she drive?

14. **SALARY** Kerry earns $5.85 per hour working as a dance instructor. She substituted for Janine one week and received $2\dfrac{1}{2}$ times her usual hourly rate. What was her pay per hour that week?

15. **SCIENCE** How many $1\dfrac{3}{4}$ gram samples of sulfur can be prepared from a total of 173.25 grams of sulfur?

16. **RECREATION** Two hikers gave the number of miles that they hiked on Saturday as 7.25 miles and $6\dfrac{7}{8}$ miles. How much farther did the one hike than the other?

Perform the indicated operations in Exercises 17–24 using decimals.

17. $3.7 - 2.1 + 8.8$

18. $(4.3)(6.5) + 7.29$

19. $9.45 \div [(1.4)(2.5)]$

20. $(6.2)^2 - 6.6 \div 1.1$

21. $\dfrac{1}{4} + (3.5)(6.4)$

22. $(2.5)^2 + \left(\dfrac{1}{3}\right)^2 - 1.9$

23. $7.2 \div \dfrac{1}{2} - 2\dfrac{1}{3}$

24. $(3.7)^2 \div \left(\dfrac{1}{4}\right)^2 + \dfrac{1}{8}$

In Exercises 25–28, arrange the given numbers in order of size with the smallest on the left.

25. 0.085, 0.85, 8.5, 8.05   26.   0.047, 0.048, 0.08, 0.04

27. 0.51, $\frac{1}{2}$, $\frac{7}{16}$, 0.15, 5.1   28. $\frac{2}{3}$, 0.65, 6.05, $\frac{7}{10}$, 6.5

Solve each applied problem in Exercises 29–30.

29. **CONSUMER**   What is the unit price (price per pound) if $4\frac{3}{4}$ pounds of white meat of chicken costs $18.43?

30. **CONSUMER**   If $16\frac{1}{4}$ ounces of drink sell for 87¢, what is the price per ounce (the unit price) to the nearest tenth of a cent?

In Exercises 31–32, complete the unit price column in each table and decide which item is the best buy.

31.

Brand	Ounces	Total Price	Unit Price
A	12	$1.27	
B	8	$0.83	
C	16	$1.61	

32.

Brand	Number of Tissues	Total Price	Unit Price
Western	200	47¢	
Eastern	250	56¢	
Southern	400	93¢	

 Use the table given in Example 9 to solve Exercises 33–34.

33. How many more travel trailers were sold in 1975 than in 1980?

34. If the retail value of all truck campers sold in 1990 was $86,000,000, what was the approximate price per unit sold that year?

CRITICAL THINKING

35. **TRAVEL**   On a recent trip, George used $28\frac{1}{2}$ gallons of gas which was purchased at 122.9¢ per gallon. How much did George spend for gas on the trip?

36. After studying this section, Burford concluded that he would never buy an item before comparing unit prices and then he would *always* select the item with the lowest unit price. Is Burford a wise shopper?   Explain.

37. Discuss the advantages of using decimal notation over regular fractional notation.

38. Describe in detail the process for arranging decimals in order of size. Can you think of a way to determine the order without changing the decimal to a whole number?

In our previous work, we have solved simple equations by changing from the related addition equation to the related subtraction equation, and conversely. Also we have solved equations by changing from the related multiplication equation to the related division equation, and conversely. Solve the equations in Exercises 39–42 using these techniques.

39. $x + \frac{1}{2} = 3.4$ 40. $y - 2.5 = \frac{3}{4}$

41. $\frac{x}{3.3} = \frac{7}{10}$ 42. $4.5w = \frac{3}{2}$

REVIEW OR PREVIEW

Solve each applied problem in Exercises 43–46.

43. **EDUCATION**   The table below shows Wilma's grades during one quarter. Complete the table and calculate her GPA.

Course	Credits	Grade	Value	Course	Value
Geology	4	A	4		
Calculus	4	B	3		
Western Art	3	D	1		
Sociology	3	A	4		
Psychology	3	C	2		

44. **GEOMETRY**   Find the perimeter of the roped-off lot sketched in the figure.

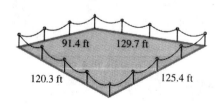

45. **GAS MILEAGE** At the start of a trip, Gordy noticed that his odometer reading was 32,043.6. At the end of the trip it was 35,581.0. If he used 165.3 gallons of gas, how many miles per gallon did he get, to the nearest tenth?

46. **CONSUMER** It costs $17.85 a day plus 15¢ per mile for every mile driven over 100 to rent a car. How much will it cost to rent the car for three days if it is driven a total of 437 miles?

4.7 PARALLEL EXERCISES

Answers to these exercises are not given in the text.

In Exercises 1–6, perform the indicated operations by changing all decimals to fractions.

1. $\frac{3}{4} + 4.2$

2. $2.25 - \frac{7}{8}$

3. $6.2 + 3\frac{4}{5}$

4. $\frac{1}{3} \times 6.25$

5. $8.4 \div \frac{1}{6}$

6. $2.75 \times 4\frac{1}{3}$

In Exercises 7–12, perform the indicated operations by first changing all fractions to decimals, correct to two decimal places. Give answers to the nearest hundredth.

7. $\frac{3}{4} + 4.2$

8. $2.25 - \frac{7}{8}$

9. $6.2 + 3\frac{4}{5}$

10. $\frac{1}{3} \times 6.25$

11. $8.4 \div \frac{1}{6}$

12. $2.75 \times 4\frac{1}{3}$

Solve each applied problem in Exercises 13–16.

13. **SEWING** The pattern for a dress calls for $3\frac{5}{8}$ yards of material. If the best material for the job costs $6.80 per yard, how much will the material for the dress cost?

14. **INVESTMENT** Kathy Shipp has $295.50 in a passbook savings account and $3\frac{1}{4}$ times that much in a money market fund. How much does she have in the money market fund?

15. **CONSUMER** Lillie Chalmers bought a $\frac{3}{4}$-acre lot for $18,381.50. What was the price per acre?

16. **TRAVEL** One tank holds 21.6 gallons of fuel and another holds $12\frac{1}{8}$ gallons. What is the combined fuel capacity of the two tanks?

Perform the indicated operations in Exercises 17–24 using decimals.

17. $5.9 + 6.2 - 8.7$

18. $12.8 + (3.9)(4.2)$

19. $3.85 \div [(1.4)(2.5)]$

20. $(4.9)^2 - 8.4 \div 1.2$

21. $\frac{1}{8} + (2.1)^2$

22. $(4.1)^2 + \left(\frac{1}{4}\right)^2 - 2.7$

23. $6.8 \div \frac{1}{4} + 3\frac{1}{5}$

24. $(1.6)^2 \div \left(\frac{1}{2}\right)^2 - \frac{3}{8}$

In Exercises 25–28, arrange the given numbers in order of size with the smallest on the left.

25. $0.074, 7.04, 0.74, 70.4$

26. $0.95, 0.095, 0.59, 5.9$

27. $\frac{1}{4}, 0.23, \frac{1}{5}, 2.25, 0.02$

28. $0.32, 3.2, \frac{3}{10}, \frac{1}{3}, 3.02$

Solve each applied problem in Exercises 29–30.

29. **TRAVEL** How many miles per gallon does a car get if it can go 695.5 miles on $21\frac{2}{5}$ gallons of gasoline?

30. **CONSUMER** A roll of aluminum foil costing 39¢ contains 25.5 square feet of foil. To the nearest tenth of a cent, what is the price per square foot?

In Exercises 31–32 complete the unit price column in each table and decide which item is the best buy.

31.

Brand	Grams	Total Price	Unit Price
X	40	84¢	
Y	35	77¢	
Z	30	57¢	

32.

Brand of Corn	Ounces	Total Price	Unit Price
High Quality	19	$0.85	
Top Crop	$14\frac{1}{2}$	$0.76	
Generic	12.9	$0.69	

Use the table given in Example 9 to solve Exercises 33–34.

33. How many more motorhomes were sold in 1990 than in 1970?

34. If the retail value of all travel trailers sold in 1990 was $1,220,000,000 what was the approximate price per unit sold that year?

CRITICAL THINKING

35. **SALARY** Conchita earns $12.35 per hour for a 40-hour work week and $1\frac{1}{2}$ times this amount per each hour of overtime. How much was Conchita paid last week if she worked a total of 54 hours?

36. After studying this section, Burford concluded that unit pricing is just a lot of extra work. For example, if he wants an item such as a loaf of bread, he will just go to the store and buy the loaf that is the cheapest. Is Burford a wise shopper? Why is it important to consider the **unit** in unit pricing?

37. Discuss the disadvantages of using decimal notation over regular fractional notation.

38. What are some of the problems with getting your money's worth that are eliminated if unit pricing is used? Think of ways that advertising and packaging of products can be deceiving.

In our previous work we have solved simple equations by changing from the related addition equation to the related subtraction equation, and conversely. Also we have solved equations by changing from the related multiplication equation to the related division equation, and conversely. Solve the equations in Exercises 39–42 using these techniques.

39. $x + \frac{1}{4} = 2.45$

40. $y - 6.5 = \frac{1}{4}$

41. $\frac{z}{4.4} = \frac{3}{10}$

42. $2.4w = \frac{8}{5}$

GROUP PROJECT

Four brands of soap were selected in a grocery store (the names have been changed to protect the innocent!) and the total price and number of units tabulated below. Complete the table to determine the unit price for each. Which is the best buy if we assume that they are all of equal quality? Even if all items are of equal quality, is the one with the lowest unit price necessarily the best choice for every individual? Explain.

Brand	Ounces	Total Price	Unit Price
Klean	5	36¢	**7.2¢**
Skrub	6	39¢	**6.5¢**
Shine	4.5	35¢	**7.8¢**
Zust	$3\frac{7}{8}$	29¢	**7.5¢**

Select a number of common items that would be purchased in a grocery store and calculate the unit price for each. Report your results to the rest of the class.

4.8 THE CALCULATOR

STUDENT GUIDEPOSTS
1   USING A BASIC FOUR-OPERATION CALCULATOR
2   USING A SCIENTIFIC OR GRAPHING CALCULATOR

You may have wondered why calculators have not been discussed until now. The reason is simple. The basic skills of arithmetic must be well understood. While the calculator can help perform complex arithmetic calculations, it does *not* tell what calculations to perform.

Although simple computations can easily be done by hand, lengthy computations, especially those involving decimals, are greatly simplified by using a calculator.

Since there are many calculators on the market, and since they all have different features, it is difficult to give a thorough discussion of how to use any particular one of them. The best advice is to study the instruction manual that comes with your model.

Although differences exist, most calculators consist of three major parts:

> 1. A **display** on which numbers are shown.
> 2. A **keyboard** with buttons called **keys,** which include **number keys** (the ten digits and a decimal point), and **operation keys**
>
>   (+, −, ×, ÷, and =).
> 3. A **register** in which numbers are stored (not displayed) and used in computations.

Number keys place numbers in the display, and operation keys transfer numbers to the register or calculate results using numbers already in the register. Also, there is a **clear key** which "clears" the calculator of number or operation entries. The clear key removes all numbers used in previous calculations and places the number 0 in the display so that a new calculation can begin.

We begin with a very basic introduction to entering numbers and performing operations on a four-operation calculator (one that will add, subtract, multiply, and divide numbers). If you are experienced in doing this and already own a scientific or graphing calculator, you might wish to skip to the second objective of the chapter which introduces the use of these types of calculator. For this course, however, all that is really necessary would be a basic calculator that performs the four arithmetic operations.

1 USING A BASIC FOUR-OPERATION CALCULATOR

A basic four-operation calculator is shown in Figure 4.7.

The decimal point key is ⊙ , and © is the clear key. The number

$$421.3672$$

is shown in the display and is entered into the calculator by pressing the following keys in order from left to right.

④ ② ① · ③ ⑥ ⑦ ②

Making calculations is merely a matter of pressing the right keys in the right order. For example, to find the sum

$$3 + 8$$

the keys to press, and the order in which they are pressed, are shown below.

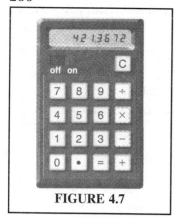

FIGURE 4.7

③
First
This places the number 3 in the display.

⊕
Second
This transfers 3 to the register where it is ready to be added to the next number.

⑧
Third
This places 8 in the display.

⊜
Fourth
This adds the number in the display (8) to the number in the register (3) and places the result (11) in the display.

To find the difference

$$15 - 6,$$

press the following keys in order.

① ⑤ ⊖ ⑥ ⊜

The display will show the difference, which is 9.

To find the product

$$12.3 \times 1.05,$$

press the following keys in the order shown.

① ② · ③ ⊗ ① · ⓪ ⑤ ⊜

The display will show the product, which is 12.915.

Lengthy division problems are greatly simplified by using a calculator. For example, to find

$$4.23738 \div 4.13,$$

press, in order,

④ · ② ③ ⑦ ③ ⑧ ÷ ④ · ① ③ ⊜ .

The quotient, 1.026, is shown in the display.

> **NOTE** It is easy to make a mistake using a calculator by pressing the wrong key or by pressing a key too lightly. As a result, it is always a good idea to estimate the answer to a problem to see if the answer you obtained with your calculator is reasonable. For example, in the division problem above, since 4.23738 is about 4 and 4.13 is also about 4, their quotient should be approximately 4 ÷ 4 which is 1. Since we obtained 1.026 for the quotient, we would assume that we made no errors.

A calculator can find sums of more than two addends. For example, to find

$$1.3 + 2.06 + 4.32 + 11.5$$

press, in order,

① · ③ ⊕ ② · ⓪ ⑥ ⊕ ④ · ③ ② ⊕ ① ① · ⑤ ⊜ .

The sum, 19.18, will appear in the display. Is this reasonable?

Most basic calculators are limited by the number of digits that can be displayed, usually eight.

EXAMPLE 1 — BASIC OPERATIONS ON A CALCULATOR

Perform the following calculations using your calculator.

(a) $5.3 + 7.6$

The sequence of keys to press is shown below.

⑤ ⨀ ③ ⊕ ⑦ ⨀ ⑥ ⊜

The sum, 12.9, will appear in the display.

(b) $8.5 - 1.9$

⑧ ⨀ ⑤ ⊖ ① ⨀ ⑨ ⊜

The difference, 6.6, will appear in the display when the above keys are pressed.

(c) 12.9×18.1

① ② ⨀ ⑨ ⊗ ① ⑧ ⨀ ① ⊜

The product is 233.49.

(d) $3.948 \div 3.76$

③ ⨀ ⑨ ④ ⑧ ⊘ ③ ⨀ ⑦ ⑥ ⊜

The quotient is 1.05.

(e) $10.7 - 2.4 + 8.5$

① ⓪ ⨀ ⑦ ⊖ ② ⨀ ④ ⊕ ⑧ ⨀ ⑤ ⊜

The answer is 16.8.

(f) $\dfrac{3}{4} + 2.6$

③ ⊘ ④ ⊕ ② ⨀ ⑥ ⊜

When the first four keys have been pressed, the display will show 0.75, which is $\frac{3}{4}$ as a decimal. Continuing gives the sum 3.35.

PRACTICE EXERCISE 1

Perform the following calculations using your calculator.

(a) $2.1 + 3.5$

(b) $6.7 - 5.9$

(c) 14.5×8.6

(d) $69.1932 \div 5.29$

(e) $2.5 + 3.6 - 1.8$

(f) $\dfrac{1}{4} + 3.7$

Answers: (a) 5.6 (b) 0.8
(c) 124.7 (d) 13.08 (e) 4.3
(f) 3.95

2 — USING A SCIENTIFIC OR GRAPHING CALCULATOR

With the basic introduction to the use of a calculator now complete, we turn attention to calculators that are much more powerful and have many more functions, scientific and graphing calculators. There are many brands of scientific calculators available. However, models that use Algebraic Logic (like the TI-30 from *Texas Instruments*) might be more desirable at this level since the order of keystroke entries more closely follows the order of operations in arithmetic. The newer graphing calculators (like the TI-82 or TI-83 from *Texas Instruments*) perform the same functions as a scientific calculator, but have the added graphing capabilities. Again, such calculators are not really necessary for our work in this text, but since many students already own one, we will include a brief summary of some of the important operations.

Many operations on a graphing calculator are the same as those on a scientific calculator. However, expressions entered on a graphing calculator remain in the display along with the value of the expression, (wheras scientific calculators display only the value of an entered expression).

Numbers are entered on a scientific and graphing calculator in exactly the same way they are entered using a basic four-operation calculator. As a result, we will now assume that you are familiar with this and simplify our presentation. For each problem we consider, we present two sequences of calculator entry steps: one for scientific calculators, identified by SC, and a second for graphing calculators, identified by GC. In fact, the steps we give are for a TI-30 and a TI-82. Remember that calculators can differ from one brand to another, so the best advice we can offer is the following:

> **Refer to the *Owner's Manual* that came with your calculator if you need further assistance.**

We begin with a quick summary of the four basic operations. The steps used to add two numbers are illustrated by finding the following sum:

$$23,245.67 + 32.895$$

SC: 23245.67 ⊞ 32.895 ⊟ --> 23278.565

GC: 23245.67 ⊞ 32.895 ENTER --> 23245.67+32.895
                                                          23278.565

The final appearance of the display in each case appears to the right of the arrow. Several observations might be made. Notice that when entering numbers, the comma is not entered. Also, the scientific calculator (SC) uses an ⊟ key while the graphing calculator (GC) uses an ENTER key.

The steps used to subtract two numbers are illustrated by finding the following difference: $1246.1 - 98.75$

SC: 1246.1 ⊟ 98.75 ⊟ --> 1147.35

GC: 1246.1 ⊟ 98.75 ENTER --> 1246.1-98.75
                                                    1147.35

One observation is important. On the GC, be sure to use the subtraction key ⊟ on the right column of keys. The key denoted (−) on the bottom row has another function and does not mean subtract. We will discuss, (−) later.

The steps used to multiply two numbers are illustrated by finding the following product: 2.348×57.36

SC: 2.348 ⊠ 57.36 ⊟ --> 134.68128

GC: 2.348 ⊠ 57.36 ENTER --> 2.348*57.36
                                                    134.68128

Notice that the symbol used for multiplication on both the SC and GC is the ⊠ instead of the multiplication dot. This is because the multiplication dot · could be confused with the decimal point key. Also, in the display of the GC, the × is replaced by *.

Finally, the steps used to find a quotient are illustrated by finding:

$$153.25 \div 25.6$$

SC: 153.25 ⊡ 25.6 ⊟ --> 5.9863281

GC: 153.25 ⊡ 25.6 ENTER --> 153.25/25.6
                                                    5.986328125

Notice that the GC uses a "slanted" division bar / instead of ÷ in the display, and that the GC gave the answer to more decimal places than did the SC. This is because the SC can only display 8 digits, and it has rounded the answer shown on the GC to seven decimal places.

We now turn our attention to some of the more sophisticated features available on scientific and graphing calculators that are not found on the basic four-operation calculator. These features are related to the topics that we studied in Section 1.9. The first involves squaring a number. Of course we can always square a number by multiplying it times itself, however there is an easier way using the x^2 key.

PRACTICE EXERCISE 2

Square each number.

(a) 21

(b) 18.09

Answers: (a) 441
(b) 327.2481

SQUARING A NUMBER ON A CALCULATOR

EXAMPLE 2

Square each number.

(a) 12

The steps to use are:

SC: 12 x^2 --> 144

GC: 12 x^2 ENTER --> 12^2
                                            144

Notice how using the squaring key cuts the number of steps that would be necessary if we were to multiply 12 by itself.

(b) 31.75

SC: 31.75 $\boxed{x^2}$ --> $\boxed{1008.0625}$

GC: 31.75 $\boxed{x^2}$ $\boxed{\text{ENTER}}$ --> 31.75^2
1008.0625

NOTE   Since a calculator has a limited display, when a number with many decimal places is squared, the calculator will give only a rounded approximation of the result. For example, if you square 10.62358, we know that the answer should have 10 decimal places. However, the SC calculator gives the rounded answer 112.86045 (correct to five decimal places) and the GC gives 112.860452, one additional decimal place.

The next special function key we consider is the square root key, $\boxed{\sqrt{}}$, used for finding the square root of a number. For many numbers, a calculator will give only an approximation of the square root.

EXAMPLE 3   FINDING SQUARE ROOTS ON A CALCULATOR

Find the square root of each number.
(a) 16

We already know that $\sqrt{16} = 4$, but we use the calculator to verify this result.

SC: 16 $\boxed{\sqrt{}}$ --> $\boxed{\qquad 4}$

GC: $\boxed{\text{2nd}}$ $\boxed{x^2}$ 16 $\boxed{\text{ENTER}}$ --> $\sqrt{16}$
4

Notice that the $\boxed{\sqrt{}}$ key on the GC is reached by using the second function key $\boxed{\text{2nd}}$ and the $\boxed{x^2}$ key. Also, on some SC calculators, the square root key will appear as $\boxed{\sqrt{x}}$.

(b) 13.25

SC: 13.25 $\boxed{\sqrt{}}$ --> $\boxed{3.6400549}$

GC: $\boxed{\text{2nd}}$ $\boxed{x^2}$ 13.25 $\boxed{\text{ENTER}}$ --> $\sqrt{13.25}$
3.640054945

Notice the difference again in the number of decimal places given. In a practical situation, however, we might use 3.6 or 3.64 as a reasonable approximation for

$\sqrt{13.25}$.

CAUTION   IN EXAMPLE 3(b), WE FOUND $\sqrt{13.25}$ TO BE 3.6400549. THIS MEANS THAT $(3.6400549)^2$ SHOULD BE 13.25. SUPPOSE WE USE 3.64 AS AN APPROXIMATION OF $\sqrt{13.25}$. SQUARING 3.64 WE OBTAIN 13.2496, WHICH IS A CLOSE APPROXIMATION TO 13.25. REMEMBER THAT WHEN USING A CALCULATOR, APPROXIMATE VALUES ARE OFTEN OBTAINED SO DON'T BE CONCERNED IF YOUR ANSWERS DIFFER SLIGHTLY FROM THOSE OBTAINED BY SOMEONE ELSE OR FROM THOSE GIVEN IN THE TEXT.

PRACTICE EXERCISE 3

Find the square root of each number.
(a) 81

(b) 28.76

Answer: (a) 9   (b) 5.3628351

The third special key y^x on the SC and $\wedge$ on the GC is the exponential key which is used to find powers of numbers other than squares (for which we usually use x^2). When using the y^x key, the base y is always entered first followed by the exponent x. The following example will make this clear.

<table>
<tr><td>**PRACTICE
EXERCISE 4**</td></tr>
</table>

PRACTICE EXERCISE 4

Find each power.

(a) 5^3

(b) $(4.36)^7$

FINDING POWERS ON A CALCULATOR

EXAMPLE 4

Find each power.

(a) 2^4

We know that $2^4 = 2 \cdot 2 \cdot 2 \cdot 2 = 16$, but now use the calculator to verify this.

SC: 2 $\boxed{y^x}$ 4 $\boxed{=}$ --> $\boxed{16}$

GC: 2 $\boxed{\wedge}$ 4 $\boxed{\text{ENTER}}$ --> 2^4
                                                              16

(b) $(1.09)^{10}$

SC: 1.09 $\boxed{y^x}$ 10 $\boxed{=}$ --> $\boxed{2.3673637}$

GC: 1.09 $\boxed{\wedge}$ 10 $\boxed{\text{ENTER}}$ --> 1.09^10
                                                                    2.367363675

We should note that both versions of calculators are programmed to follow the rules we have set for order of operations, including parentheses. For example, if we evaluate $2 + 3 \times 5$, we know that we must multiply first to obtain $2 + 15$, then add to obtain 17. Both versions follow this same rule.

SC: 2 $\boxed{+}$ 3 $\boxed{\times}$ 5 $\boxed{=}$ --> $\boxed{17}$

GC: 2 $\boxed{+}$ 3 $\boxed{\times}$ 5 $\boxed{\text{ENTER}}$ --> 2 + 3 * 5
                                                                            17

Also, both versions have left and right parentheses keys. The use of these keys as well as more on the order of operations is given in the next example.

Answer: (a) 125
(b) 29,950.593

PRACTICE EXERCISE 5

Calculate each number.

(a) $20 \div (7 + 3)$

(b) $4.3 \times (7.1 + 2.8) - 3.6$

Answers: (a) 2   (b) 38.97

USING PARENTHESES KEYS

EXAMPLE 5

Calculate each number.

(a) $6 \times (8 + 3)$

Notice that if the parentheses are removed, we would have to multiply 6 times 8 first, then add 3. This is clearly not what is requested, so the parentheses keys must be used.

SC: 6 $\boxed{\times}$ $\boxed{(}$ 8 $\boxed{+}$ 3 $\boxed{)}$ $\boxed{=}$ --> $\boxed{66}$

GC: 6 $\boxed{\times}$ $\boxed{(}$ 8 $\boxed{+}$ 3 $\boxed{)}$ $\boxed{\text{ENTER}}$ --> 6 * (8 + 3)
                                                                                            66

Verify directly that 66 is the correct answer.

(b) $12.8 \div (6.1 - 2.3) + 5.5$

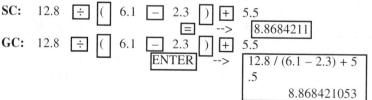

SC: 12.8 $\boxed{\div}$ $\boxed{(}$ 6.1 $\boxed{-}$ 2.3 $\boxed{)}$ $\boxed{+}$ 5.5
                                      $\boxed{=}$ --> $\boxed{8.8684211}$

GC: 12.8 $\boxed{\div}$ $\boxed{(}$ 6.1 $\boxed{-}$ 2.3 $\boxed{)}$ $\boxed{+}$ 5.5
                                      $\boxed{\text{ENTER}}$ --> 12.8 / (6.1 - 2.3) + 5
                                                                .5
                                                                        8.868421053

Notice that the expression "wraps" to the second line in the GC version, and also the GC gives more decimal places in the answer.

Suppose that we attempt to square 50,000 using a calculator.

SC: 50000 $\boxed{x^2}$ --> $\boxed{2.5 \quad 09}$

GC: 50000 $\boxed{x^2}$ $\boxed{\text{ENTER}}$ --> $\boxed{\begin{array}{r} 50000^2 \\ 2500000000 \end{array}}$

Using the GC we obtain 2,500,000,000, which is easy to see as being the correct answer. However, the SC display gives 2.5 09. What does this mean? Notice that there are 10 digits in the answer, and the SC only has an 8 digit display. The SC has given the answer in an alternative form known as *scientific notation.* The number in the display stands for

$$2.5 \times 10^9 = 2.5 \times 1{,}000{,}000{,}000 = 2{,}500{,}000{,}000.$$

The space between 2.5 and 09 in the display calls our attention to the fact that the number has been written in scientific notation and 09 or 9 is the power on 10 that is multiplied times 2.5.

> If a number is written as a product of a power of 10 and another number that is between 1 and 10 (possibly equal to 1 itself), the number is in **scientific notation.**

Simply remember that if the display on your calculator gives an answer that has a gap in the digits, this is a reminder that the calculator has converted the answer to scientific notation. You can write the answer by multiplying the decimal number on the left by 10 raised to the power given by the number on the right.

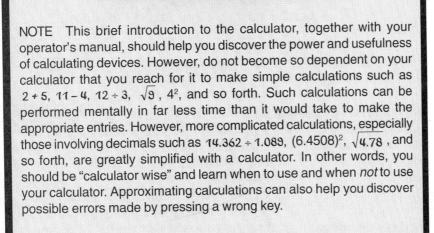

NOTE This brief introduction to the calculator, together with your operator's manual, should help you discover the power and usefulness of calculating devices. However, do not become so dependent on your calculator that you reach for it to make simple calculations such as $2 + 5$, $11 - 4$, $12 \div 3$, $\sqrt{9}$, 4^2, and so forth. Such calculations can be performed mentally in far less time than it would take to make the appropriate entries. However, more complicated calculations, especially those involving decimals such as $14.362 \div 1.089$, $(6.4508)^2$, $\sqrt{4.78}$, and so forth, are greatly simplified with a calculator. In other words, you should be "calculator wise" and learn when to use and when *not* to use your calculator. Approximating calculations can also help you discover possible errors made by pressing a wrong key.

4.8 EXERCISES

Answers to these exercises are given on page 648.

In Exercises 1–16, what calculation is made by pressing the keys as shown from left to right, and what is the result?

1. $\boxed{1}\boxed{0}\boxed{+}\boxed{3}\boxed{5}\boxed{=}$

2. $\boxed{6}\boxed{2}\boxed{-}\boxed{3}\boxed{1}\boxed{=}$

3. $\boxed{3}\boxed{8}\boxed{\times}\boxed{2}\boxed{4}\boxed{=}$

4. $\boxed{5}\boxed{5}\boxed{\div}\boxed{1}\boxed{1}\boxed{=}$

5. $\boxed{2}\boxed{.}\boxed{3}\boxed{+}\boxed{1}\boxed{.}\boxed{4}\boxed{=}$

6. $\boxed{4}\boxed{.}\boxed{7}\boxed{+}\boxed{.}\boxed{9}\boxed{=}$

7. $\boxed{6}\boxed{.}\boxed{2}\boxed{\times}\boxed{5}\boxed{.}\boxed{3}\boxed{=}$

8. $\boxed{1}\boxed{.}\boxed{3}\boxed{\div}\boxed{4}\boxed{.}\boxed{5}\boxed{=}$

9. $\boxed{6}\boxed{2}\boxed{.}\boxed{3}\boxed{4}\boxed{\div}\boxed{4}\boxed{.}\boxed{3}\boxed{6}\boxed{=}$

10. ① . ⑤ + ③ . ⑥ ② + ⑤ . ④ ⑦ + . ⑧ ① ＝

11. ① . ⑥ x^2

12. ② ⑤ . ③ ⑦ √

13. ① ① y^x ④ ＝

14. ⑥ ÷ ⓪ ② + ① ⓪ ＝

15. ⑥ ÷ ② + ① ＝

16. ② ⑤ √ + ③ x^2 ＝

In Exercises 17–41, perform the calculations using your calculator.

17. 15.2
    +1.03

18. 402.11
     +6.85

19. 542.309
     +62.155

20. 18.6
     − 9.2

21. 703.12
     − 41.35

22. 625.157
     −142.668

23. 21.7
     ×4.2

24. 62.37
     ×4.71

25. 603.97
     ×78.56

26. $3.2\overline{)8.2}$

27. $6.21\overline{)0.467613}$

28. $40.3\overline{)209.765}$

29. $\dfrac{1}{4} - 0.05$

30. $7 + \dfrac{5}{16}$

31. $\dfrac{2}{5} \div 1.2$

32. $0.2 + 5.8 - 3.1$

33. $2.6 \times 5.3 \div 1.2$

34. $5 \div 1.2 + 6.5$

35. $(6.98)^2$

36. $\sqrt{4.29}$

37. $(10.3)^5$

38. $4.8 \div (3.2 - 1.7)$

39. $(2.6 + 4.3) \times (1.3 - 0.8)$

40. $(7.04)^2 - \sqrt{8.15}$

41. $(3.8)^8 \div (6.3 + 10.4)$

Solve each applied problem in Exercises 42–45. Use your calculator.

42. **TAX**　The sales tax on an item is found by multiplying the cost by 0.0775. How much tax would be charged on a new car which costs $6745.83?

43. **FINANCE**　A stock broker finds the fee for making a transaction by multiplying the value of the transaction by 0.0125. Find the fee on a transaction of $148,425.40.

44. **CONSTRUCTION**　A slab for a foundation of a house is a rectangle that is 24.36 meters long and 13.92 meters wide. What is the area of the slab to the nearest hundredth of a square meter.

45. **CONSUMER**　To find the monthly interest which must be paid on his home mortgage, Carlos must multiply the mortgage balance by 0.007285. If his balance in June is $38,276.55, how much interest must he pay?

CRITICAL THINKING

Solve each applied problem in Exercises 46–49. Use your calculator.

46. **GEOMETRY**　The area of a rectangle is 106.005 square yards, and its width is 9.25 yards. Divide the area by the width to find the length of the rectangle.

47. **BUSINESS**　During five consecutive weeks, Ms. Whorton discovered that the overhead expenses on her business were $497.36, $643.21, $825.13, $503.07, and $601.58. What were the total expenses and the average expense per week?

48. **GEOMETRY**　In a certain triangle, two sides are 4.28 cm and 7.15 cm. The third side is given by

$$\sqrt{(4.28)^2 + (7.15)^2}.$$

Find the third side, correct to the nearest hundredth of a centimeter.

49. **INVESTMENT** The amount of money in a certain savings account at the end of 10 years when $1500 is invested initially is given by $(1.02)^{40}(1500)$. Find the amount.

50. Most calculators have a $\boxed{1/x}$ key. Explore the use of this key and describe in detail how you could use it in this course.

51. When Burford used his scientific calculator to find $(65,000)^2$, he gave 422,509 for the answer. Can you explain to Burford why this is incorrect? What is the correct answer?

REVIEW AND PREVIEW

52. Arrange the given numbers in order of size with the smallest on the left.

$$3.1, \ \frac{3}{10}, \ 0.31, \ 0.013, \ \frac{1}{3}$$

53. **CONSUMER** A 12-ounce bottle of soda sells for 45¢. What is the price per ounce (unit price)?

54. **SALARY** Janet earns $12.30 an hour. How much will she be paid for working $8\frac{3}{4}$ hours?

55. **CONSUMER** Karen bought 2 sweaters at $12.95 each and a pair of shoes for $31.90. The sales tax on her purchases amounted to $2.76. She put the items on layaway by paying $\frac{1}{3}$ down. How much must she pay when she picks up the items?

56. **CONSUMER** It costs $18.50 a day to rent a paint sprayer. If paint costs $12.95 a gallon and four gallons will be required, how much will it cost Juan to paint his fence if he uses the sprayer for $1\frac{1}{2}$ days?

4.8 PARALLEL EXERCISES

Answers to these exercises are not given in the text.

In Exercises 1–16, what calculation is being made by pressing the keys as shown left to right, and what is the result?

1. $\boxed{2}\boxed{0}\boxed{+}\boxed{4}\boxed{6}\boxed{=}$
2. $\boxed{8}\boxed{2}\boxed{-}\boxed{7}\boxed{3}\boxed{=}$
3. $\boxed{4}\boxed{1}\boxed{\times}\boxed{3}\boxed{5}\boxed{=}$
4. $\boxed{5}\boxed{6}\boxed{\div}\boxed{8}\boxed{=}$
5. $\boxed{6}\boxed{.}\boxed{5}\boxed{+}\boxed{2}\boxed{.}\boxed{9}\boxed{=}$
6. $\boxed{9}\boxed{.}\boxed{8}\boxed{+}\boxed{.}\boxed{3}\boxed{=}$
7. $\boxed{4}\boxed{.}\boxed{3}\boxed{5}\boxed{\times}\boxed{1}\boxed{.}\boxed{2}\boxed{=}$
8. $\boxed{5}\boxed{.}\boxed{2}\boxed{\div}\boxed{1}\boxed{.}\boxed{3}\boxed{=}$
9. $\boxed{9}\boxed{0}\boxed{.}\boxed{0}\boxed{4}\boxed{3}\boxed{8}\boxed{5}\boxed{-}\boxed{2}\boxed{8}\boxed{.}\boxed{4}\boxed{0}\boxed{3}\boxed{=}$
10. $\boxed{5}\boxed{.}\boxed{6}\boxed{-}\boxed{3}\boxed{.}\boxed{0}\boxed{5}\boxed{+}\boxed{2}\boxed{.}\boxed{9}\boxed{9}\boxed{=}$
11. $\boxed{4}\boxed{.}\boxed{2}\boxed{8}\boxed{x^2}$
12. $\boxed{3}\boxed{.}\boxed{4}\boxed{0}\boxed{9}\boxed{\sqrt{\ }}$
13. $\boxed{8}\boxed{.}\boxed{5}\boxed{y^x}\boxed{4}\boxed{=}$
14. $\boxed{1}\boxed{8}\boxed{\div}\boxed{(}\boxed{3}\boxed{+}\boxed{6}\boxed{)}\boxed{=}$
15. $\boxed{1}\boxed{8}\boxed{\div}\boxed{3}\boxed{+}\boxed{6}\boxed{=}$
16. $\boxed{7}\boxed{x^2}\boxed{-}\boxed{4}\boxed{.}\boxed{2}\boxed{\sqrt{\ }}\boxed{=}$

In Exercises 17–41, perform the following calculations using your calculator.

17. $\begin{array}{r} 19.3 \\ + 1.08 \\ \hline \end{array}$

18. $\begin{array}{r} 709.44 \\ + 5.87 \\ \hline \end{array}$

19. $\begin{array}{r} 652.993 \\ + 43.875 \\ \hline \end{array}$

20. $\begin{array}{r} 19.3 \\ - 5.7 \\ \hline \end{array}$

21. $\begin{array}{r} 204.53 \\ - 54.88 \\ \hline \end{array}$

22. $\begin{array}{r} 476.259 \\ -341.563 \\ \hline \end{array}$

23. $\begin{array}{r} 42.8 \\ \times 6.5 \\ \hline \end{array}$

24. $\begin{array}{r} 59.47 \\ \times 2.38 \\ \hline \end{array}$

25. $\begin{array}{r} 705.84 \\ \times 23.75 \\ \hline \end{array}$

26. $6.5\overline{)30.55}$

27. $4.58\overline{)0.273884}$

28. $20.7\overline{)109.36224}$

29. $\dfrac{1}{5} - 0.19$

30. $12 + \dfrac{15}{16}$

31. $\dfrac{3}{8} \div 2.5$

32. $0.9 + 4.07 - 2.58$

33. $4.7 \times 2.9 \div 1.02$

34. $6 \div 2.4 + 7.3$

35. $(4.09)^2$ 36. $\sqrt{11.37}$ 37. $(21.4)^6$

38. $6.3 \times (1.7 + 2.5)$ 39. $(4.3 - 1.9) \times (8.5 + 2.7)$

40. $(21.08)^2 - \sqrt{14.3}$ 41. $(2.18)^6 \div (9.2 - 4.7)$

Solve each applied problem in Exercises 42–45. Use your calculator.

42. **TAX**   The sales tax on a purchase can be found by multiplying the selling price by 0.0425. How much tax would be charged on a new boat which sells for $24,325.65?

43. **FINANCE**   The Bond House calculates the fee for a transaction by multiplying the amount of the transaction by 0.0095. Find the fee for a transaction of $58,912.50.

44. **CONSTRUCTION**   If insulation costs $0.25 per square foot, how much will it cost to insulate a wall that is 16.44 feet long and 9.06 feet high?

45. **CONSUMER**   To find the amount of interest paid in a given month, multiply the monthly balance by 0.008275. How much interest will Daphne pay in August if her loan balance is $42,179.85?

CRITICAL THINKING

Solve each applied problem in Exercises 46–49 using your calculator.

46. **GEOMETRY**   The area of a rectangle is 94.869 square feet, and its length is 12.45 feet. Divide the area by the length to find the width.

47. **TRAVEL**   During five consecutive weeks, a salesman drove 1324.7 miles, 1445.8 miles, 987.3 miles, 554.3 miles, and 1556.9 miles. How many total miles did he drive during this period?

48. **GEOMETRY**   In a triangle with two sides measuring 5.36 cm and 6.18 cm, the third side is given by $\sqrt{(5.36)^2 + (6.18)^2}$. Find the length of the third side correct to the nearest hundredth of a centimeter.

49. **INVESTMENT**   If $2500 is invested in an account at an annual interest rate of 6%, compounded annually, the amount in the account at the end of 15 years is given by $(1.06)^{15}(2500)$. Find the amount correct to the nearest cent.

50. Many calculators have a $\boxed{\%}$ key. When a number is entered and this key is pressed, the number is changed to a decimal corresponding to the given percent. For example, entering 20 and pressing $\boxed{\%}$ gives 0.2. We will work more with percent in Chapter 6, but for now can you see how this might be a useful key in this course?   Explain.

51. When Burford used his scientific calculator to find (23,000)(90,000), he gave 2.0709 for the answer. He was somewhat confused since, although most of the time he doesn't have a clue, he did realize that the product must be a number much larger than a number close to 2. Can you explain to Burford why his answer is incorrect?   What is the correct answer?

GROUP PROJECT

Scientific notation is usually covered in detail in later courses. In this section we showed how to write very large numbers in scientific notation. Can you figure out how to write very small numbers? Try to learn more about this special way of writing numbers and summarize your findings in a report to the class.

CHAPTER 4 REVIEW

KEY WORDS

🗝 4.1

- A **decimal fraction** is a fraction with denominator a power of 10. Decimal fractions are usually called simply **decimals.** The period used in a decimal is called a **decimal point.**

🗝 4.2

- If the division process ends with a remainder of zero, the decimal is a **terminating decimal.**
- If the division process does not end, there is a repeating block of digits, and the decimal is a **repeating decimal.**

🗝 4.3

- The number of digits to the right of the decimal point is called the number of **decimal places** in the number.

🗝 4.8

- On a calculator, the **display** shows numbers, the **register** stores numbers used in computations, the **number keys** are the buttons for the ten digits and the decimal point, and the **operation keys** are used to perform operations, such as adding, subtracting, multiplying, and dividing. If a number is written as a product of a power of 10 and another number that is between 1 and 10 (possibly equal to 1 itself), the number is in **scientific notation.**

KEY CONCEPTS

🗝 4.1

1. Each decimal has a fractional form and a decimal form.
2. A decimal point separates the ones digit from the tenths digit.

🗝 4.2

Every fraction can be written as a decimal that either terminates or repeats.

🗝 4.3

When rounding a decimal, if the first digit to the right of the desired position is less than 5, drop it and all digits to the right of it. If the first digit to the right is greater than or equal to 5, increase the digit in the desired position by one and drop all digits to the right of it. *Never* round off one digit at a time.

🗝 4.4

1. To add decimals, line up the decimal points and add like whole numbers.
2. To subtract decimals, line up the decimal points and subtract like whole numbers.

🗝 4.5

1. The product of two decimals has the same number of decimal places as the sum of the decimal places in the two factors.

2. To multiply by a power of 10, move the decimal point to the *right* the same number of decimal places as the number of zeros in the power of 10.
3. To multiply by 0.1, 0.01, or 0.001. move the decimal point to the *left* the same number of decimal places as decimal places in 0.1, 0.01, or 0.001.

🗝 4.6

1. When dividing a decimal by a decimal. move the decimal point in the divisor and dividend the same number of places to obtain a whole number divisor. The decimal point in the quotient is directly above the new decimal point in the dividend.
2. To divide by a power of 10, move the decimal point to the *left* the same number of decimal places as the number of zeros in the power of 10.
3. To divide by 0.1, 0.01, or 0.001, move the decimal point to the *right* the same number of decimal places as decimal places in 0.1, 0.01, 0.001.

🗝 4.7

The unit price of an item is

$$\text{unit price} = \frac{\text{total price}}{\text{number of units}}.$$

🗝 4.8

Only use a calculator for complex problems; do not become so dependent on it that you use it for simple calculations that can be found mentally.

CHAPTER 4 REVIEW EXERCISES

PART I

Answers to these exercises are given on page 648.

4.1

💡1. What do we call fractions that have a power of 10 in the denominator?

Give the formal *word name for each decimal in Exercises 2–3.*

💡2. 23.4   3. 7.0005

4.2

In Exercises 4–6, write each number in decimal notation.

💡4.   four and seven hundredths

5.   two hundred thirty-three and three hundred two ten thousandths

6.   Write $27.16 using a word name as it would appear on a check.

In Exercises 7–9, change each decimal to a fraction (or mixed number).

7. 0.63   8. 2.7   9. 5.125

In Exercises 10–12, change each fraction to a decimal.

10. $\dfrac{1}{9}$ 11. $\dfrac{5}{3}$ 12. $\dfrac{3}{16}$

4.3

Give the number of decimal places in each number in Exercises 13–15.

13. 2.103   14. 4.003   15. 0.01010

In Exercises 16–23, round each decimal to the given number of decimal places or position.

16. 3.255; two   17. 6.4908; thousandth   18. 26.05; tenth   19. $37.51; dollar

20. $0.\overline{84}$; tenth   21. $0.\overline{84}$; hundredth   22. $0.\overline{84}$; three   23. $0.426; cent

4.4

Solve each applied problem in Exercises 24–25.

24. **CONSUMER** Early in the season, peaches sell for $1.98 per pound. Estimate the cost of 6.12 pounds of these peaches.

25. **MONTHLY PAYMENTS** Alvin has a new car loan in the amount of $7895.60. If he plans to pay off the loan in 40 equal monthly payments, what is the approximate amount he must pay each month?

Solve each problem in Exercises 26–29.

26. Find the sum.

$$6.1 + 6.01 + 0.601 + 0.0601 + 60.1$$

27. **BUSINESS** The daily receipts for one week at Tony's Tastee Tacos were $421.36, $347.20, $289.17, $655.27, and $504.08. What was the total for the week?

28. **BANKING**   Find the total deposit on the following portion of a deposit slip.

DEPOSIT		
	Dollars	Cents
CASH	*371*	*05*
CHECKS	*480*	*77*
	19	*40*
	2037	*06*
TOTAL		

29. **RANCHING** The figure below gives the distance in miles around a ranch. How much would it cost to fence this property if fencing cost $2540.00 per mile?

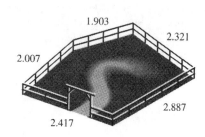

Find each difference in Exercises 30–32.

30. $42.6 - 3.08$

31. $100 - 74.36$

32. $2 - 1.003$

Solve each applied problem in Exercises 33–34.

33. **SCIENCE** A technician started out with 35.28 liters of acid. If he used 13.94 liters for one reaction and 9.62 liters for another, how much acid did he have left?

34. **CONSUMER** Becky bought a lobster dinner for $18.35 and a bottle of wine for $8.29. The sales tax on her purchases amounts to $1.07. How much change will she receive if she pays with two $20 bills?

4.5

Find each product in Exercises 35–37.

35. $\begin{array}{r} 13.06 \\ \times 2.7 \\ \hline \end{array}$

36. $\begin{array}{r} 3.1108 \\ \times 2.06 \\ \hline \end{array}$

37. $\begin{array}{r} 0.4001 \\ \times 1.3 \\ \hline \end{array}$

Solve each applied problem in Exercises 38–39.

38. **GAS MILEAGE** The EPA-estimated miles per gallon for a car is 23.7 mpg. Its gas tank capacity is 11.6 gallons. To the nearest mile, what is the driving range of the car?

39. **SALARY** Mr. Swokowski is paid $11.37 per hour. His time card for one week is shown in the figure. How much was he paid that week?

Day	Hours Worked
M	8.1
T	5.3
W	4.7
T	10.3
F	7.8

Without making the actual computation in Exercise 40, use an estimate to decide which of the given answers is correct.

40. 2.9×24.007 (a) 0.696   (b) 6.96   (c) 69.6   (d) 696

Solve each applied problem in Exercises 41–42.

41. **TRAVEL** A car gets 28.9 mpg and has a gas tank with capacity 12.2 gallons. What is the approximate driving range of the car? The exact driving range? Isn't the exact driving range also an *approximate* driving range?

42. **SHIPPING** A shipping company received 409.5 feet of pipe that weighs 2.94 pounds per foot. What is the approximate weight of the pipe? What is the exact weight?

Find the products in Exercises 43–45.

43. 10.785×1000

44. 10.785×0.1

45. 10.785×0.01

4.6

Find each quotient in Exercises 46–50.

46. $2.9\overline{)6.177}$

47. $42\overline{)222.6}$

48. $0.032\overline{)1.3312}$

49. $4.13\overline{)15.6}$ (to the nearest tenth)

50. $0.089\overline{)4.62}$ (to the nearest hundredth)

Solve each applied problem in Exercises 51–54.

51. **GAS MILEAGE** Terry drove 746.2 miles and used 34.9 gallons of gas. To the nearest tenth, how many miles per gallon did he get?

52. **EDUCATION** The table shows Betty's grades during one quarter. Complete the table and calculate her GPA correct to the nearest hundredth.

Course	Credits	Grade	Value	Course Value
Math	4	B	3	
French	1	F	0	
Biology	4	C	2	
English	3	A	4	
Russian	3	D	1	

53. **CONSUMER** What is the approximate cost per pound of 9 pounds of candy selling for $18.45? The exact cost?

54. **CONSUMER** The Morins plan to carpet their master bedroom. If the room is rectangular in shape and measures 4.8 yards long by 3.9 yards wide, and the total cost of the job is $383.76, what is the approximate cost of one square yard of carpet? The exact cost?

💡 *Without making actual computations in Exercise 55, use an estimate to decide which of the given answers is correct.*

55. $401.87 \div 39.6$ (a) 1.015   (b) 10.15   (c) 101.5   (d) 1015

Find the quotients in Exercises 56–58.

56. $43.89 \div 100$ 57. $1.497 \div 1000$ 58. $286.1 \div 10$

4.7

In Exercises 59–61, find the sums (to the nearest hundredth).

59. $\dfrac{2}{3} + 7.25$ 60. $6\dfrac{1}{4} + 8.39$ 61. $\dfrac{1}{6} + 3.78$

Solve each applied problem in Exercises 62–66.

62. **CONSTRUCTION** There are $16\dfrac{2}{5}$ boards left at a construction site. If each board weighs 8.32 pounds, what is the total weight of these boards to the nearest hundredth of a pound?

63. **CONSUMER** If the box of cereal below sells for $1.09, what is the price per ounce (the unit price) to the nearest tenth of a cent?

64. **CONSUMER** The Meyers paid $113,750 for their house. If the house has 2000 sq ft, how much did they pay per sq ft?

65. Arrange 0.74, 7.04, 7.4, 0.074, and 70.4 in order of size with the smallest on the left.

66. **CONSUMER** Complete the unit price column in the table and determine which item is the best buy.

Brand	Pounds	Total Price	Unit Price
X	7	$2.99	
Y	11	$4.71	
Z	8	$3.32	

Perform the indicated operations in Exercises 67–68.

67. $6.3 \div \dfrac{1}{3} - 1\dfrac{1}{2}$ 68. $(2.6)^2 - \dfrac{7}{8} \times \dfrac{3}{14}$

4.8

💡 *In Exercises 69–78, what calculation is made by pressing the keys as shown from left to right, and what is the result?*

69. ⑧•⑦⊖①②⊜

70. ②①•⑥⊖④•③⑦⊜

71. ①•⓪⓪⑨⊗③•⑤⊜

72. ⑥⊕②•⑤⊖④⊜

73. ②•③⊗⑥⊕⑧•⑨⊜

74. ⑨⊗⑨⊗⑨⊜

75. ④•②ⓧ²

76. ③•②⑦ √

77. ①•⑤ⓨˣ⑥⊜

78. ⑥÷⓪②⊕③⓪⊖①⊜

📱 *Solve each applied problem in Exercises 79–80.*

79. **TAX** The sales tax on an item is found by multiplying the cost by 0.0425. How much tax would be charged on a new motor home which costs $14,137.58?

80. **GARDENING** A rectangular garden is 4.85 meters long and 3.66 meters wide. If fertilizer costs $1.22 per square meter, how much will it cost to fertilize the garden?

PART II

Perform the indicated operations in Exercises 81–92.

81. 4.1035
     $\underline{\times 2.3}$

82. 6.15
     12.034
     $\underline{+\ 9.2}$

83. 142.75
     $\underline{-\ 38.016}$

84. 1.1596×100

85. $1.1596 \div 100$

86. 1.1596×0.1

87. $1.1596 \div 0.001$

88. $53\overline{)113.42}$

89. $0.35\overline{)4.68}$ (to the nearest tenth)

90. $3\dfrac{3}{4} + 2.48$

91. $4.67 - 1\dfrac{1}{5}$

92. $(2.6)^2 \times 4\dfrac{1}{2}$

93. Round 6.485 to the nearest (a) hundredth, (b) tenth, and (c) unit.

94. Change $\frac{11}{3}$ to a decimal.

95. Change 0.85 to a fraction.

96. Write $102.38 using a word name as it would appear on a check.

97. Estimate the product 6098.5×41.89.

📱 *Solve each applied problem in Exercises 98–103. A calculator may be helpful.*

98. **TAX** For every $1000 of assessed value on a store, the owner must pay $4.89 in real estate taxes. How much tax must be paid on a store with an assessed value of $125,600?

99. **BUSINESS** A business has $1473.95 left in an expense account. If purchases of $47.54, $1.06, and $289.53 are made, how much is left in the account?

100. **CONSUMER** Jackie bought 3 books for $8.95 each and paid with two $20 bills. How much change did she get back?

101. **CONSUMER** Which is a better buy, a 24-ounce bottle of soap for $1.20 or a 38-ounce bottle for $2.28?

102. **GAS MILEAGE** Jeff traveled 55 mph for $5\frac{1}{2}$ hours. If he used 12.8 gallons of gas during this time, what was his mileage per gallon, to the nearest tenth?

103. **CONSUMER** What is the approximate cost of 40 pounds of steak at $4.95 per pound? What is the exact cost?

💡*Without making the actual computation in Exercise 104, use an estimate to decide which of the given answers is correct.*

104. $398.097 \div 49.7$ (a) 0.801   (b) 8.01   (c) 80.1   (d) 801

📱*Use a calculator to perform the operations in Exercises 105–110.*

105. 62.308×401.375

106. $0.0435\overline{)2.6513}$

107. $(3.4)^2 \div 1.7$

108. $(1.05)^5 \times 1050$

109. $6.35 \times (4.1 - 3.8)$

110. $\sqrt{6.9 \times 11.4}$

Use the related addition, subtraction, multiplication, or division equation to solve each equation in Exercises 111–116.

111. $x + 3.6 = 5.8$

112. $y - 4.7 = 8.9$

113. $\dfrac{z}{6.3} = 1.1$

114. $3.2x = 28.8$

115. $y + \frac{1}{2} = 7.85$

116. $5z = 3\frac{1}{5}$

CHAPTER 4 TEST

Answers to the chapter test are given on page 649.

1. Give the formal word name for 73.005.

    1. _____
       _____

2. Write "ninety-two and six hundredths" in decimal notation.

    2. _____

3. Change 0.16 to a fraction reduced to lowest terms.

    3. _____

4. Change $\frac{7}{16}$ to a decimal.

    4. _____

5. Round 6.355 to two decimal places.

    5. _____

6. Round 45.05 to the nearest tenth.

    6. _____

7. Round $0.\overline{74}$ to the nearest hundredth.

    7. _____

Perform the indicated operations.

8. $9.1 + 0.91 + 9.01 + 91.0$

    8. _____

9. $11 - 5.003$

    9. _____

Solve.

10. Sally and Mark Forbes stayed at the Sands Hotel in Reno. Their room cost $126.87 and they charged $48.53 in food and beverages to their room account. If Ms. Forbes paid the bill with two $100 bills, how much change did she receive?

    10. _____

11. What is the *approximate* cost per pound of dog food if a 32-pound sack sells for $15.36? What is the *exact* cost per pound?

    11. _____

Perform the indicated operations.

12. 71.05
    $\times 1.8$

13. $4.7\overline{)47.376}$

14. 6.357×100

15. 6.357×0.1

16. $6.357 \div 1000$

17. $6.357 \div 0.1$

    12. _____
    13. _____
    14. _____
    15. _____
    16. _____
    17. _____

Solve.

18. Cynthia Yates ordered 2.15 tons of stream stones and 1.39 tons of cinders to use in landscaping her lawn. If the stones cost $59.75 per ton and the cinders $19.75 a ton, how much did Cynthia have to pay for the order?

    18. _____

CHAPTER 4 TEST

19. Charles Dawkins recorded his odometer reading when he left for a business trip to be 38,196.8. When he returned the reading was 39,301.2. If he used 42.1 gallons of gasoline on the trip, to the nearest tenth, how many miles per gallon did he get?

19. _____

20. A bricklayer uses 415 bricks at a cost of 9.3¢ per brick. What is the approximate cost of the bricks? The exact cost (to the nearest cent)?

20. _____

21. Perform the indicated operations.

$$(3.5)(4.1) - \left(\frac{1}{2}\right)^2$$

21. _____

22. What calculation is being made by pressing the keys shown from left to right? Determine the answer.

⑧ ⊙ ⓪ ③ ÷ ② ⊙ ⑤ ⊜

22. _____

23. Write seventy-five thousandths, six hundredths, and six hundred thirty-five ten thousandths in decimal notation, and arrange the numbers in order with the smallest first.

23. _____

24. A metal machine part was measured while hot and found to be 7.21 inches long. After the part cooled it measured 7.1985 inches. What was the total decrease in length?

24. _____

25. What is the effect on the decimal point if a number is divided by 100 and then multiplied by 0.001?

25. _____

_____

CUMULATIVE REVIEW CHAPTERS 1–4

Answers to these exercises are given on page 649.

Perform the indicated operations in Exercises 1–12.

1. $\left(\dfrac{3}{4}\right)^2$

2. $\sqrt{\dfrac{25}{16}}$

3. $\dfrac{2}{3}+\dfrac{4}{9}$

4. 4.649×10

5. $4.649 \div 10$

6. $7.832 + 0.441$

7. $2\dfrac{1}{2} \times 3\dfrac{1}{3}$

8. $3\dfrac{3}{5} \div 1\dfrac{1}{5}$

9. $\dfrac{8}{9}-\dfrac{5}{6}$

10. $\dfrac{3}{2}\cdot\left(\dfrac{1}{2}+\dfrac{1}{3}\right) \quad \frac{5}{4}$

11. $6\dfrac{1}{4}-3\dfrac{3}{8} \quad 2\frac{7}{8}$

12. $\dfrac{9}{5}+4.25$

💡*Answer* true *or* false *in Exercises 13–15.*

13. $2\dfrac{2}{3} < 2\dfrac{3}{4}$

14. $0.0601 < 0.0610$

15. $3\dfrac{1}{5} > 3.25$

Solve each applied problem in Exercises 16–19.

16. **ENGINEERING** A tank holds 18 gallons when it is full. How many gallons are in the tank when it is $\dfrac{2}{3}$ full?

17. **ENGINEERING** A gasoline tank had 24 gallons in it before $\dfrac{1}{4}$ of the gasoline was used. How many gallons were left in the tank?

18. **SPORTS** On opening day of fall practice, 123 football players were present. If only 65 can eventually make the team, how many players must be cut from the squad?

19. **MONEY** Mike has $25 and Jim has $43. Larry has $12 more than Jim, and Henri has $9 less than Mike and Jim together. How much money do the four men have together?

💡 20. Is 147 divisible by 2?

💡 21. Is 285 divisible by 5?

💡 22. Is 4332 divisible by 3?

💡*Round each decimal to the nearest hundredth in Exercises 23–25.*

23. 3.7461

24. 0.4955

25. $92.\overline{73}$

26. **RECREATION** On a four-day vacation, a family spent a total of $1123.06. They spent $418.19 on the first day, $176.43 on the second day, and $212.05 on the third day.

(a) How much did they spend on the fourth day?
(b) What is the answer to (a) rounded to the nearest dollar?
(c) What is the answer to (a) if all amounts are rounded to the nearest dollar before making any calculations?
(d) Compare the answers to (b) and (c).

CHAPTER *f·i·v·e*

RATIO, PROPORTION, AND MEASUREMENT

The term *ratio* is commonly used to describe certain fractions in many practical situations. Using the fact that two ratios are equal, a *proportion,* allows us to solve a variety of applications. Just as important, however, is the use of ratios to simplify changes made in the measurement units that we use today. The system of measurement that is commonly used in the United States, the English System, uses standards taken from measurements of the human body (foot, inch, yard, etc.). The metric system, based on the decimal system and the number 10, uses standards taken from nature or the earth itself. For example, the unit of length, the meter, was first proposed by Gabriel Mouton around 1670, and is based on the length of an arc of a great circle on the surface of the earth. Unlike the English System, in the metric system, units of measure for length, weight, and volume are all interrelated. Although we are probably more familiar with the English System, it is much easier to convert units in the metric system because often the change can be made simply by multiplying or dividing by powers of 10, that is, by moving the decimal point right or left. Ratios are often used to compare information and to give us a better understanding of a complex problem. This is illustrated in the following example which is solved in Example 4 in Section 5.1.

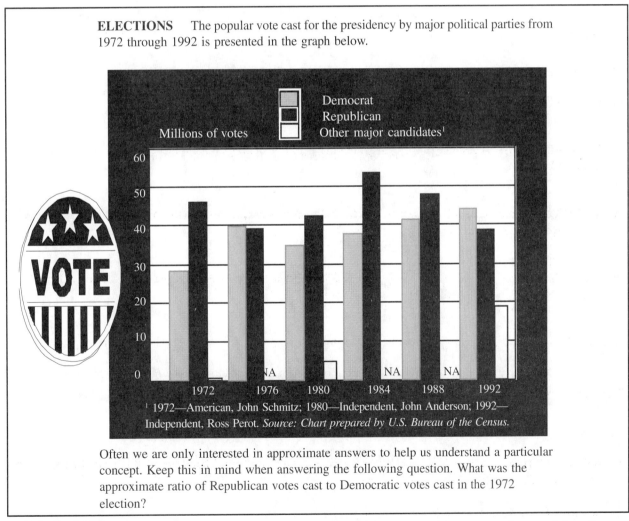

ELECTIONS   The popular vote cast for the presidency by major political parties from 1972 through 1992 is presented in the graph below.

Democrat
Republican
Other major candidates[1]

Millions of votes

[1] 1972—American, John Schmitz; 1980—Independent, John Anderson; 1992— Independent, Ross Perot. *Source: Chart prepared by U.S. Bureau of the Census.*

Often we are only interested in approximate answers to help us understand a particular concept. Keep this in mind when answering the following question. What was the approximate ratio of Republican votes cast to Democratic votes cast in the 1972 election?

We begin this chapter by considering the idea of a ratio and a proportion, learn to solve proportions, and then discuss various rates in terms of ratios. Next we review the English system of measurement and discuss operations with measurement numbers. Finally, we develop the metric system of measurement and investigate ways to convert a measure given in one system to the corresponding measure in the other.

5.1 RATIO AND PROPORTION

STUDENT GUIDEPOSTS
1   DEFINING RATIO
2   DEFINING PROPORTION
3   SOLVING PROPORTIONS

1 RATIO

We first used the term *ratio* in Section 1.7 as one of the terms used for the division process. The **ratio** of one number a to another number b is the quotient

$$a \div b \text{ or } \frac{a}{b}.$$

Sometimes the ratio $\frac{a}{b}$ is expressed using the notation $a{:}b$ and is read "the ratio of a to b." Thus, the ratio $\frac{2}{3}$ can be written 2:3 and read "the ratio of 2 to 3."

PRACTICE EXERCISE 1

Write each ratio in fraction form.

(a) The ratio of 5 to 11

(b) The ratio 4:12

Answers: (a) $\frac{5}{11}$ (b) $\frac{4}{12}$ or $\frac{1}{3}$ (reduced)

PRACTICE EXERCISE 2

There are 200 floor-level seats and 120 balcony seats in an auditorium.

(a) What is the ratio of balcony seats to floor seats?

(b) What is the ratio of floor seats to the total number of seats?

Answers: (a) $\frac{3}{5}$ or 3 to 5 or 3:5 (b) $\frac{5}{8}$ or 5 to 8 or 5:8

PRACTICE EXERCISE 3

Find the ratio of the length of the longest side to the length of the next longest side in the triangle in Figure 5.1.

WRITING RATIOS   EXAMPLE 1

Write each ratio in fraction form.

(a) The ratio of 7 to 10 $\dfrac{7}{10}$

(b) The ratio 10:5 $\dfrac{10}{5}$ which reduces to $\dfrac{2}{1}$ (See Chapter 2.)

A ratio can sometimes be used to provide a more descriptive relationship between two groups of people or between two sets of objects in general. This is illustrated in the next example.

WRITING RATIOS INVOLVING PEOPLE   EXAMPLE 2

A company employs 18 women and 12 men.

(a) What is the ratio of men to women in the company?

$$\frac{12 \text{ men}}{18 \text{ women}} = \frac{12}{18} = \frac{2}{3}$$

The ratio of men to women is $\frac{2}{3}$ or 2 to 3 or 2:3.

(b) What is the ratio of women employed to the total number of employees?
There are $18 + 12 = 30$ total employees.

$$\frac{18 \text{ women}}{30 \text{ employees}} = \frac{18}{30} = \frac{3}{5}$$

The ratio of women to total employees is $\frac{3}{5}$ or 3 to 5 or 3:5.

Ratios are used frequently in geometry. Considering ratios of the sides of triangles can be very useful in many applications.

USING RATIOS IN A GEOMETRY PROBLEM   EXAMPLE 3

Consider the triangle in Figure 5.1. Find the ratio of the length of the shortest side to the length of the longest side.

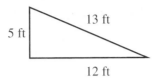

FIGURE 5.1

Since the shortest side is 5 ft and the longest side is 13 ft, the desired ratio is $\frac{5}{13}$ or 5 to 13 or 5:13.

In Example 4 of Section 3.6 we compared oil production by dividing the production of one country by the production of another. We were finding the ratio of one number in a table to another. The next example solves the application given in the chapter introduction by taking the ratio of numbers read from a bar graph.

E X A M P L E 4	FINDING APPROXIMATE RATIOS IN A BAR GRAPH

PRACTICE EXERCISE 4

The popular vote cast for the presidency by major political parties from 1972 through 1992 is presented in the graph below.

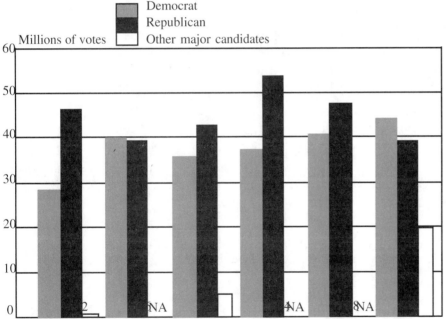

¹ 1972—American, John Schmitz; 1980—Independent, John Anderson; 1982—Independent, Ross Perot. *Source: Chart prepared by U.S. Bureau of the Census.*

Use the graph given in Example 4 to answer the following question. What was the approximate ratio of Republican voters to independent voters (for Ross Perot) in 1992?

Often we are only interested in approximate answers to help us understand a particular concept. Keep this in mind when answering the following question. What was the approximate ratio of Republican votes cast to Democratic votes cast in the 1972 election?

It would appear that slightly less than 30 million votes were cast for the Democratic candidate in 1972 whereas slightly more than 45 million were cast for the Republican candidate. It would be reasonable to say that the ratio of Republican votes to Democratic votes was about 45 to 30. Since $\frac{45}{30} = \frac{3 \cdot \cancel{15}}{2 \cdot \cancel{15}} = \frac{3}{2}$, the approximate ratio is 3 to 2. In actuality, the ratio is probably more like 47 to 29, but 3 to 2 is easier to comprehend.

2 | PROPORTION

An equation which states that two ratios are equal is called a **proportion.** For example,

$$\frac{1}{2} = \frac{4}{8}$$

is a proportion. When a pair of numbers such as 1 and 2 has the same ratio as a pair such as 4 and 8, the numbers are called **proportional.** Recall from Section 2.2 that two fractions (ratios) are equal whenever their cross products are equal. The cross products in the above proportion are:

$$2 \cdot 4 \longleftarrow - - - \frac{1}{2} \times \frac{4}{8} - - - \longrightarrow 1 \cdot 8$$

Since $2 \cdot 4 = 1 \cdot 8$, we know that the fractions are equal.

Proportions can be used to solve many problems. For example, if 3 hours are required to travel 165 miles, we might ask: "How many hours will be required to travel 275 miles?" The proportion

$$\textbf{First time} \xrightarrow{\text{in hours}} \frac{3}{165} = \frac{a}{275} \xleftarrow{\text{in hours}} \textbf{Second time}$$
$$\textbf{First distance} \xrightarrow{\text{in miles}} \qquad\quad \xleftarrow{\text{in miles}} \textbf{Second distance}$$

completely describes this problem. That is, the ratio of the first time to the first distance must equal the ratio of the second time to the second distance. We need to find the unknown value (represented by the variable a). Since

$$\frac{3}{165} = \frac{a}{275},$$

we know that the cross products are equal. Thus,

$$3 \cdot 275 = 165 \cdot a \qquad \text{Cross products are equal}$$
$$825 = 165 \cdot a \qquad \text{Multiply 3 and 275}$$
$$\frac{825}{165} = a \qquad \text{Related division equation}$$
$$5 = a. \qquad \text{Divide 825 by 165}$$

We see that 5 is indeed the desired number since

$$\frac{3}{165} = \frac{5}{275}. \qquad \text{Both cross products are 825}$$

3 | SOLVING PROPORTIONS

The process of finding the unknown value in a given proportion is called **solving the proportion.** The preceding discussion suggests a method for doing this.

TO SOLVE A PROPORTION INVOLVING AN UNKNOWN VALUE a
1. Set the cross products equal to each other (that is, **equate** the cross products).
2. Then a is equal to the numerical cross product divided by the multiplier of a. That is, the related division equation gives the desired value of a.

EXAMPLE 5	SOLVING PROPORTIONS

Solve the proportions.

(a) $\dfrac{a}{4} = \dfrac{12}{16}$

$16 \cdot a = 4 \cdot 12$ Cross products are equal
$16 \cdot a = 48$ Simplify

$a = \dfrac{48}{16}$ Divide by 16, the multiplier of a; this is the related division equation

$a = 3$

Thus, the missing value is 3, and

$\dfrac{3}{4} = \dfrac{12}{16}.$ To check, find the cross products:
$3 \cdot 16 = 48$ and $4 \cdot 12 = 48$

(b) $\dfrac{2}{a} = \dfrac{4}{10}$

$2 \cdot 10 = 4 \cdot a$ Equate cross products
$20 = 4 \cdot a$ Simplify

$\dfrac{20}{4} = a$ Divide 20 by 4

$5 = a$

Thus, the missing value is 5, and

$\dfrac{2}{5} = \dfrac{4}{10}.$ To check, find the cross products:
$2 \cdot 10 = 20$ and $5 \cdot 4 = 20$

Solve the proportions.

(a) $\dfrac{a}{2} = \dfrac{15}{10}$

(b) $\dfrac{6}{21} = \dfrac{2}{a}$

Answers: (a) 3 (b) 7

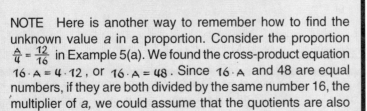

NOTE   Here is another way to remember how to find the unknown value a in a proportion. Consider the proportion $\frac{A}{4} = \frac{12}{16}$ in Example 5(a). We found the cross-product equation $16 \cdot A = 4 \cdot 12$, or $16 \cdot A = 48$. Since $16 \cdot A$ and 48 are equal numbers, if they are both divided by the same number 16, the multiplier of a, we could assume that the quotients are also equal. That is,

$$\frac{16 \cdot A}{16} = \frac{48}{16}.$$

Since $\frac{16 \cdot A}{16} = \frac{16}{16} \cdot \frac{A}{1} = 1 \cdot A = A$, by dividing both sides of the cross-product equation by 16 we obtain the related division sentence $A = \frac{48}{16} = 3$. We will study this process in more detail in Chapter 9.

| PRACTICE EXERCISE 6 | USING A PROPORTION IN POLITICS | EXAMPLE 6 |

In Professor Walter's algebra class, the ratio of women to men is 4 to 3. If there are 18 men in the class, how many women are there?

Let a represent the number of women in the class.

$$\frac{4}{3} = \frac{a}{18}$$

In a recent election for the position of mayor of Cedar City, Andy Hurd defeated Harry Payne by a ratio of 5 to 4. If Mayor Hurd received 600 votes, how many votes did Mr. Payne receive?

If a represents the number of votes received by Harry Payne, the proportion

Winning ratio $\longrightarrow \dfrac{5}{4} = \dfrac{600}{a}$ $\longleftarrow$ Votes for Hurd
$\longleftarrow$ Votes for Payne

describes the problem.

$5 \cdot a = 4 \cdot 600$ Equate cross products

$5 \cdot a = 2400$ Simplify

$a = \dfrac{2400}{5}$ Divide by 5

$a = 480$ Simplify

Answer: 24 women

Thus, Mr. Payne received 480 votes.

5.1 EXERCISES

Answers to these exercises are given on page 649.

💡 *Write the fraction form for each ratio in Exercises 1–6.*

1. 1 to 8 $\frac{1}{8}$

2. 2 to 7 $\frac{2}{7}$

3. 6 to 4 $\frac{6 \div 2}{4 \div 2} = \frac{3}{2}$

4. 12 to 3 $\frac{12}{3} = \frac{3}{1} = \frac{4}{1}$

5. 6 to 1 $\frac{6}{1}$

6. 4 to 4 $\frac{4}{4}$

💡 *Write the ratio that is indicated by each fraction in Exercises 7–12.*

7. $\dfrac{1}{4}$ 1 to 4

8. $\dfrac{3}{5}$ 3 to 5

9. $\dfrac{5}{2}$

10. $\dfrac{13}{6}$

11. $\dfrac{6}{13}$

12. $\dfrac{9}{9}$

Solve each proportion in Exercises 13–20.

13. $\dfrac{a}{3} = \dfrac{14}{21}$

14. $\dfrac{9}{a} = \dfrac{3}{1}$

15. $\dfrac{4}{7} = \dfrac{a}{28}$

16. $\dfrac{40}{35} = \dfrac{2}{a}$

17. $\dfrac{a}{13} = \dfrac{3}{39}$

18. $\dfrac{12}{a} = \dfrac{4}{1}$

19. $\dfrac{60}{72} = \dfrac{a}{6}$

20. $\dfrac{2}{1} = \dfrac{1}{a}$ $\frac{1}{2}$

Solve each applied problem in Exercises 21–28.

21. **SALES** There were 500 people who shopped in a department store one day and 380 of them made at least one purchase. How many people would be expected to make a purchase if 850 people shop the next day? *646*

22. **POLITICS** Representative Wettaw won an election by a ratio of 8 to 5. If he received 10,400 votes, how many votes did his opponent receive?

23. **CONSTRUCTION** If a wire 70 ft long weighs 84 pounds, how much will 110 ft of the same wire weigh?

24. **MAP READING** If $\frac{1}{2}$ inch on a map represents 10 miles, how many miles are represented by $6\frac{1}{2}$ inches?

25. **TRAVEL** If a car can travel 420 miles on 25 gallons of gasoline, how far can it go on 105 gallons of gasoline?

26. **GAME MANAGEMENT** A ranger wishes to estimate the number of antelope in a preserve. He catches 58 antelope, tags their ears, and returns them to the preserve. Some time later, he catches 29 antelope and discovers that 7 of them are tagged. Estimate the number of antelope in the preserve.

27. **SPORTS** A baseball pitcher gave up 60 earned runs in 180 innings. Estimate the number of earned runs he will give up every 9 innings. This number is called his *earned run average.*

28. **ENVIRONMENT** It has been estimated that a family of four will produce 115 pounds of garbage in one week. Estimate the number of pounds of garbage produced by 7 such families in one week.

In Exercises 29–30 read numbers from the bar graph to calculate the ratios. For the years 1988 and 1994 the numbers are given. For all other years, read the bar graph to the nearest thousand.

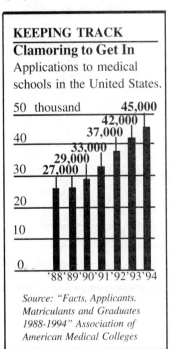

KEEPING TRACK
Clamoring to Get In
Applications to medical schools in the United States.

50 thousand   **45,000**
                     42,000
             37,000
40   33,000
      29,000
30 27,000

20

10

0
   '88 '89 '90 '91 '92 '93 '94

Source: "Facts, Applicants. Matriculants and Graduates 1988-1994" Association of American Medical Colleges

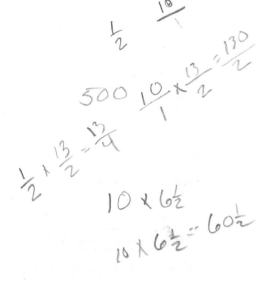

29. Compare the number of applicants in 1988 to the number in 1993 by taking the ratio of the number in 1988 to the number in 1993.

30. Determine the ratio of the number of applicants in 1991 to the number in 1988.

CALCULATOR EXERCISES

There were 3726 females and 2548 males in a survey of 6274 adults. In Exercises 31–32 find the ratio and use a calculator to express the fraction as a decimal rounded to the nearest hundredth.

31. What is the ratio of males to total adults in the survey?

32. What is the male-to-female-ratio?

33. A car travels 468.9 miles on 21.7 gallons of gas. Traveling at the same rate, how many gallons of gas would the car need to go 750 miles (to the nearest tenth)?

CRITICAL THINKING

34. Burford's solution to the following applied problem is given below. Explain what Burford is doing wrong, and show him that his answer is not even reasonable. What is the correct solution?

A 10-foot piece of steel reinforcing rod weighs 24 pounds. What would be the weight of a 15-foot section of the rod?

If *a* represents the weight of a 15-foot section of the rod, then:

$$\frac{10}{24} = \frac{a}{15}$$
$$10 \cdot 15 = 24 \cdot a$$
$$150 = 24 \cdot a$$
$$\frac{150}{24} = a$$
$$6.25 = a$$

Thus, the 15-foot section weighs 6.25 pounds.

35. Discuss the terms *ratio* and *proportion* and give examples of each.

36. Outline the steps used to *solve a proportion.*

REVIEW OR PREVIEW

Exercises 37–40 review topics from Sections 1.8 and 4.6. They will help you prepare for the next section.

37. **CONSUMER** Randee Wire bought a 20-pound box of detergent for $9.20. What was the price per pound; that is, what was the unit price of the detergent?

38. **CONSUMER** Alphonse bought a 20-pound bag of cat food for $7.20. What was the price per pound; that is, what was the unit price of the cat food?

39. Find the quotient rounded to the nearest tenth.

$$18\overline{)440}$$

40. Find the quotient rounded to the nearest hundredth

$$24\overline{)658}$$

5.1 PARALLEL EXERCISES

Answers to these exercises are not given in the text.

💡 *Write the fraction form for each ratio in Exercises 1–6.*

1. 1 to 12

2. 3 to 7

3. 9 to 3

4. 15 to 6

5. 13 to 1

6. 6 to 6

💡 *Write the ratio that is indicated by each fraction in Exercises 7–12.*

7. $\dfrac{1}{5}$

8. $\dfrac{4}{7}$

9. $\dfrac{7}{2}$

10. $\dfrac{1\,5}{4}$

11. $\dfrac{4}{1\,5}$

12. $\dfrac{8}{8}$

Solve each proportion in Exercises 13–20.

13. $\dfrac{a}{2} = \dfrac{11}{22}$

14. $\dfrac{7}{a} = \dfrac{14}{10}$

15. $\dfrac{3}{11} = \dfrac{a}{22}$

16. $\dfrac{50}{45} = \dfrac{10}{a}$

17. $\dfrac{a}{14} = \dfrac{28}{56}$

18. $\dfrac{15}{a} = \dfrac{3}{5}$

19. $\dfrac{56}{64} = \dfrac{a}{8}$

20. $\dfrac{3}{1} = \dfrac{1}{a}$

Solve each applied problem in Exercises 21–28.

21. **SALES** When 80 people shopped at a specialty shop, they bought $3600 worth of merchandise. How many customers would be needed to spend $9000?

22. **POLITICS** Peter Horn won a city council election by a ratio of 7 to 4. If he received 4522 votes, how many votes did his opponent receive?

23. **GEOMETRY** If a tree 15 ft tall casts a shadow 4 ft long, how long will the shadow of a 40 ft building be at the same instant?

24. **MAP READING** If $\frac{1}{4}$ inch on a map represents 20 miles, how many inches are required to represent 150 miles?

25. **TRAVEL** A pickup truck will travel 900 miles on 42 gallons of gasoline. How many gallons of gasoline would the truck use to go 2250 miles?

26. **GAME MANAGEMENT** A game and fish officer wishes to estimate the number of trout in a lake. He catches 94 trout, tags their fins, and returns them to the lake. Some time later, he catches 50 trout and discovers that 12 of them are tagged. Estimate the number of trout in the lake.

27. **SPORTS** A softball pitcher gave up 24 earned runs in 210 innings. The number of earned runs given up every 9 innings is called a pitcher's earned run average. Calculate her earned run average (to the nearest hundredth).

28. **ENVIRONMENT** It has been estimated that a family of three will produce 85 pounds of garbage in one week. Estimate the number of pounds of garbage produced by 10 such families in one week.

Refer to the bar graph given above Exercises 29–30 to find the following.

29. Compare the number of applicants in 1989 to the number in 1994 by taking the ratio of the number in 1989 to the number in 1994.

30. Determine the ratio of the number of applicants in 1994 to the number in 1991.

CALCULATOR EXERCISES

There were 3726 females and 2548 males in a survey of 6274 adults. In Exercises 31–32 find the ratio and use a calculator to express the fraction as a decimal rounded to the nearest hundredth.

31. What is the ratio of females to total adults in the survey?

32. What is the female-to-male-ratio?

33. A car travels 468.9 miles on 21.7 gallons of gas. Traveling at the same rate, how far can the car go on 17.4 gallons of gas (to the nearest tenth)?

CRITICAL THINKING

34. Burford wanted the variable in the numerator so he gave the following solution to the proportion.

$$\frac{2}{a} = \frac{4}{7}$$

$$\frac{a}{2} = \frac{4}{7}$$

$$7a = 2 \cdot 4$$

$$a = \frac{8}{7}$$

Is this answer the solution to the original proportion? Could he have solved it this way?

$$\frac{2}{a} = \frac{4}{7}$$

$$\frac{a}{2} = \frac{7}{4}$$

$$4a = 2 \cdot 7$$

$$a = \frac{14}{4} = \frac{7}{2}$$

Explain.

35. Explain what is meant by the phrase *two pairs of numbers are proportional.*

36. Explain why the proportion $\frac{a}{5} = \frac{3}{20}$ can be solved by multiplying both sides by 5.

GROUP PROJECT

In Example 4 and Exercises 29–30 we read numbers from a bar graph to compare data using ratios. Discuss the accuracy of the process. Are the ratios accurate enough for the comparisons we are making? Does the graph itself give an idea of the relationship of the data? Discuss the presentation of data in graphs and tables with the advantages and uses.

5.2 RATES

STUDENT GUIDEPOSTS

1 DEFINING RATE
2 USING UNIT RATES

1 DEFINITION OF A RATE

When a ratio is used to compare two quantities that involve different units or different measures, the result is called a rate. For example, suppose that 1510 gallons of water flow through a pipe in 20 minutes. The ratio of gallons to time is the rate

$$\frac{1510 \, gallons}{20 \, minutes}.$$

Notice that the units (gallons and minutes in this case) are given as part of the rate. A rate is said to be **simplified** when all common factors of the numbers in the rate have been divided out. For example,

$$\frac{1510 \text{ gallons}}{20 \text{ minutes}} = \frac{\cancel{10} \cdot 151 \text{ gallons}}{\cancel{10} \cdot 2 \text{ minutes}} = \frac{151 \text{ gallons}}{2 \text{ minutes}}$$

is now in simplified form.

2 UNIT RATES

A rate is more useful and descriptive when it is written with the number in the denominator equal to 1. Such rates are called **unit rates.** Any rate can be transformed into a unit rate by dividing the number in the numerator by the number in the denominator. For example, the rate given above could be written as the unit rate

$$\frac{151 \text{ gallons}}{2 \text{ minutes}} = \frac{151}{2} \frac{\text{gallons}}{\text{minutes}} = 75.5 \frac{\text{gallons}}{\text{minutes}}$$

which is often expressed in one of the forms

75.5 gallons per minute   or   75.5 gal/min   or   75.5 gpm.

Notice that the word *per* stands for the words "for each," or *per* can be thought of as division and written using the symbol /.

If a trucker drives 400 miles in 8 hours, we could form the rate

$$\frac{400 \text{ miles}}{8 \text{ hours}} = \frac{50 \text{ miles}}{1 \text{ hour}} = 50 \frac{\text{miles}}{\text{hour}} = 50\text{mi} / \text{hr} = 50\text{mph}.$$

Rates such as this that involve a ratio of distance traveled to time of travel are called **speed.**

EXAMPLE 1 USING (UNIT) RATES

Express each of the following as a rate.

(a) 100 miles driven on 5 gallons of gas.

$$\frac{100 \text{ miles}}{5 \text{ gallons}} = \frac{20 \text{ miles}}{1 \text{ gallon}} = 20 \frac{\text{miles}}{\text{gallon}} = 20\text{mi} / \text{gal} = 20\text{mpg}$$

EXPLORATION GUIDE

When the string on a guitar is plucked, the string begins to vibrate and a sound is heard. The number of times the string vibrates per second, called the *pitch,* gives us an interesting example of a rate. The measurement used for determining a pitch is cycles per second (cps). The human ear can detect sounds in the range from about 16 cps up to 20,000 cps. The string on a piano that corresponds to middle C vibrates at 261 cps. The string corresponding to the note one octave higher is half as long and vibrates twice as fast. The ratio of the frequencies of the adjacent keys on a piano (white and black) is a constant; that is, these ratios are all proportional. Are you surprised to learn that the music you enjoy depends on concepts from mathematics? Try to discover more about musical notes and this interesting relationship.

PRACTICE EXERCISE 1

(a) 150 kilometers driven on 3 liters of gas

(b) $8 for 4 pounds of meat

(b) $170 earned for 20 hours of work

$$\frac{\$170}{20 \text{ hours}} = \frac{\$17}{2 \text{ hours}} = \frac{17}{2}\frac{\$}{\text{hour}} = 8.5\frac{\$}{\text{hour}} = \$8.50 \text{ per hour}$$

Answers: (a) 50 kilometers/
liter (b) $2 per pound

NOTE   Notice that we have introduced several standard abbreviations thus far. We have used *gpm* for "gallons per minute," *mph* for "miles per hour," and *mpg* for "miles per gallon."

In Section 1.8 we introduced the concept of *unit pricing,* the price per unit of an item. We can see now that a unit price is simply a unit rate. For example, if a 14-ounce can of baked beans costs 49¢, the unit price of the beans is simply the unit rate

$$\frac{49¢}{14 \text{ ounces}} = \frac{49}{14}\frac{¢}{\text{ounces}} = 3.5\frac{¢}{\text{ounce}} = 3.5¢ \text{ per ounce.}$$

Many grocery stores now give the unit price of each item in their displays to assist shoppers in making decisions about better buys. The symbol oz is used to represent "ounce."

PRACTICE EXERCISE 2

Assuming equal quality, which is the better buy: 10 ounces of oat bran for $1.99 or 14 ounces of oat bran for $2.95?

COMPARING UNIT PRICES   EXAMPLE 2

Which of the boxes of detergent shown below is the better buy?

FIGURE 5.2

The unit price of the smaller box of detergent is:

$$\frac{\$1.29}{32 \text{ oz}} = \frac{1.29}{32}\frac{\$}{\text{oz}} \approx 0.0403\frac{\$}{\text{oz}} = 4.03¢ \text{ per oz}$$

The unit price of the larger box is:

Answer: 10 ounces at $1.99
is a better buy at 0.199¢ per
ounce than 14 ounces for
$2.95 at 0.211¢ per ounce

$$\frac{\$1.79}{46 \text{ oz}} = \frac{1.79}{46}\frac{\$}{\text{oz}} \approx 0.0389\frac{\$}{\text{oz}} = 3.89¢ \text{ per oz}$$

Thus, the larger box is the better buy in this case.

5.2 EXERCISES

Answers to these exercises are given on page 650.

💡 *In Exercises 1–4, write as a simplified rate.*

1. 44 feet traveled in 6 seconds

2. 18 children in 8 families

3. 54 gallons in 15 seconds

4. $40 for 6 boards

💡 *In Exercises 5–16, write as a unit rate.*

5. 44 feet traveled in 6 seconds

6. 18 children in 8 families

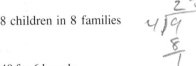

7. 54 gallons in 15 seconds

8. $40 for 6 boards

9. 107 miles driven on 5 gallons of gas

10. 840 trees planted on 12 acres

11. $10 for 5 pounds of candy

12. 88 ounces in 11 glasses

13. 750 television sets in 500 households

14. 10 cups of flour in 4 cakes

15. 2700 words on 12 pages

16. $1350 earned in 3 weeks

Solve each applied problem in Exercises 17–22.

17. **CONSUMER** The material required to make a dress costs $52.50 for 6 yards. Find the unit price; that is, find the price per yard.

18. **TRAVEL** An Air Force fighter jet flew 2337.5 miles in 4.25 hours. Find the speed of the jet.

19. **CONSUMER** A 13-ounce can of coffee sells for $2.89. Find the unit price in cents per ounce, correct to the nearest tenth of a cent.

20. **CONSUMER** A six-pack of 12-ounce cans of soda costs $1.50. Find the unit price of the soda in cents per ounce, correct to the nearest tenth of a cent.

21. **CONSUMER** Assuming equal quality, which brand of tissues is the better buy: Kleen, which has 200 tissues for 89¢, or WipeOff, which has 140 tissues for 65¢?

22. **CONSUMER** The same brand of jam comes in two sizes: a 14-ounce jar for $1.29 and a 32-ounce jar for $2.89. Which jar is the better buy?

CRITICAL THINKING

💡 23. **PHYSICS** Jeff's friend is 1 mile (5280 feet) from Jeff when he fires a gun. Jeff hears the sound of the shot 4.8 seconds after he sees the flash. What is the speed of sound in feet per second? [*Hint:* Assume that the speed of light is instantaneous compared to the speed of sound.]

🖋 24. What is the difference between a *rate* and a *ratio?*

🖋 25. Look for examples of rates and unit rates in newspaper and magazine articles and write a report of your findings.

REVIEW OR PREVIEW

💡 26. Write the fraction form for the ratio 7 to 8

💡 27. Write the ratio indicated by $\frac{12}{11}$.

Solve the proportions in Exercises 28–29

28. $\dfrac{12}{a} = \dfrac{6}{2}$

29. $\dfrac{7}{1} = \dfrac{1}{a}$

Solve each applied problem in Exercises 30–33.

30. **GARDENING** If it takes 8 pounds of fertilizer to cover 3000 square feet of lawn, how many pounds will be necessary to cover 7500 square feet?

31. **GARDENING** If it takes 8 pounds of fertilizer to cover 3000 square feet of lawn, how many square feet can be covered by 35 pounds of fertilizer?

32. **BUSINESS** If it takes 9 ribbon cartridges to type 3500 pages of a manuscript, how many cartridges will be needed to type 700 pages?

33. **BUSINESS** If it takes 9 ribbon cartridges to type 3500 pages of manuscript, how many pages can be typed using 3 cartridges?

5.2 PARALLEL EXERCISES

Answers to these exercises are not given in the text.

In Exercises 1–4, write as a simplified rate.

1. 250 miles traveled in 4 hours

2. 16 cars in 10 families

3. 150 gallons in 21 minutes

4. $56 for 12 books

In Exercises 5–16, write as a unit rate.

5. 250 miles traveled in 4 hours

6. 16 cars in 10 families

7. 150 gallons in 21 minutes

8. $56 for 12 books

9. 720 kilometers traveled on 60 liters of gas

10. 320 fish in 16 aquariums

11. $7 for 4 tubes of toothpaste

12. 360 gallons in 3 tanks

13. 18 hours to split 4 cords of wood

14. $12 for 4 pounds of nuts

15. 250 chairs for 150 people

16. $2700 in 4 savings accounts

Solve each applied problem in Exercises 17–22.

17. **CONSUMER** A 12-ounce bottle of shampoo costs $4.20. Find the unit price in cents per ounce; that is, find the price per ounce.

18. **TRAVEL** A dog that was left when a family stopped for gas traveled 8 miles to its home in 3.2 hours. At what speed did the dog travel?

19. **CONSUMER** A 12-ounce package of cheese costs $2.29. Find the unit price in cents per ounce, correct to the nearest tenth of a cent.

20. **CONSUMER** Two one dozen cartons of eggs cost $1.89. Find the unit price in cents per egg, correct to the nearest tenth of a cent.

21. **CONSUMER** Assuming equal quality, which brand of chile is the better buy: 12 ounces of Wolfy Brand at 69¢ or 20 ounces of Hornel at $1.19?

22. **CONSUMER** The same brand of orange juice concentrate comes in two sizes: a 16-ounce can for 79¢ and a 21-ounce can for $1.07. Which can is the better buy?

CRITICAL THINKING

23. **PHYSICS** The distance from the sun to the earth is approximately 93,000,000 miles. If it takes $8\frac{1}{3}$ minutes for light from the sun to reach the earth, what is the speed of light in miles per minute?

24. Define what is meant by a *unit rate* and discuss why unit rates might be more appropriate to use than a simplified rate.

25. Explain why knowledge of unit pricing is important for every consumer.

GROUP PROJECT

Rates are sometimes described using a table or a bar graph. Consider the information given below which appeared in the January 30, 1995 edition of Time. Notice that each number in the table on the left is used to give a rate formed by dividing the number by 1000. Also, in the bar graph, each bar itself represents a ratio, in this case, a number of people per 100,000 people. Write a paragraph giving some of the possible conclusions that could be reached by studying this information, and explain why a basic knowledge of rates and ratios is important in today's world. Discuss your conclusions in a group.

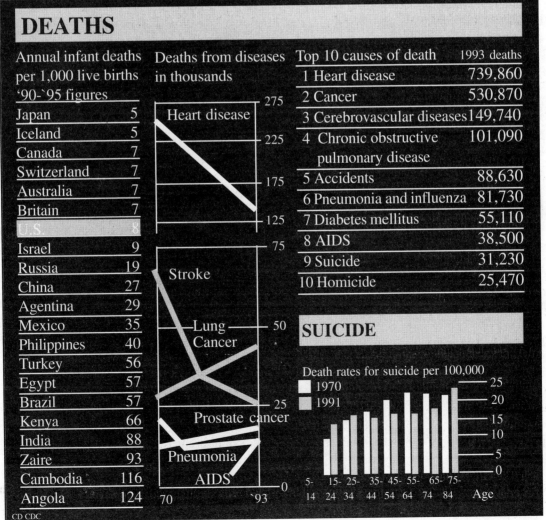

5.3 THE ENGLISH SYSTEM OF MEASUREMENT

STUDENT GUIDEPOSTS

1 DEFINING THE ENGLISH UNITS OF MEASURE
2 DEFINING UNIT FRACTIONS
3 USING HOUSEHOLD UNITS
4 WORKING WITH COMPOUND UNITS

1 | ENGLISH UNITS OF MEASURE

A standard system of units of measure is a necessary tool for people who are living and working together. The remainder of this chapter discusses two such systems, the English system and the metric system. While many countries in the world use the metric system, the United States continues to use the English system. We begin by summarizing the basic units used for length, volume, weight, and time.

UNITS OF MEASURE: ENGLISH SYSTEM

Length	1 foot (ft) = 12 inches (in)
	1 yard (yd) = 3 feet (ft)
	1 mile (mi) = 5280 feet (ft)
Volume	1 pint (pt) = 16 fluid ounces (fl oz)
	1 quart (qt) = 2 pints (pt)
	1 gallon (gal) = 4 quarts (qt)
Weight	1 pound (lb) = 16 ounces (oz)
	1 ton = 2000 pounds (lb)
Time	1 minute (min) = 60 seconds (sec)
	1 hour (hr) = 60 minutes (min)
	1 day (da) = 24 hours (hr)
	1 week (wk) = 7 days (da)
	1 year (yr) = 365 days (da)
	= 52 weeks (wk)
	= 12 months (mo)

[handwritten notes:] 3 tsp = 1 Tbs, 16 Tbs = 1 C, 1 C = 8 fl oz, 2 C = 1 pt, 2 pt = 1 qt, 52 wks = 1 yr

As the table shows, each type of measurement (length, volume, and so on) has several units in the English system. The weight of this book might be given in ounces, while the weight of a student would usually be given in pounds.

2 | UNIT FRACTIONS

When working with units of measure, we need to be able to convert from one unit to another. To do this, we use a special type of rate called a **unit fraction,** a fraction that has a value of 1. Some examples of unit fractions are

$$\frac{12\,in}{1\,ft}, \frac{1\,ft}{12\,in}, \frac{4\,qt}{1\,gal}, \frac{1\,gal}{4\,qt}, \frac{16\,oz}{1\,lb}, \frac{1\,lb}{16\,oz}.$$

Each of the fractions has value 1 because the numerator and denominator are equal. It is important to show the unit of measure as well as the number. Obviously, $\frac{12}{1}$ *is not* 1, but $\frac{12\,in}{1\,ft}$ *is* 1 since

$$1\,ft = 12\,in.$$

Thus, to change 4 yd to feet, write

$$4 \text{ yd} = 4 \text{ yd} \times \mathbf{1}$$ Multiply by 1

$$= \frac{4 \text{ yd}}{1} \times \frac{\mathbf{3 \text{ ft}}}{\mathbf{1 \text{ yd}}}$$ Replace 1 with the unit fraction and divide out yards

$$= 4 \times 3 \text{ ft}$$

$$= 12 \text{ ft}$$

With this method, the yards are divided out as if they were numbers.

NOTE   The fact that the yards do divide out tells us that we were right to multiply by 3 ft instead of dividing by 3 ft. If we had tried to multiply

$$\frac{4 \text{ YD}}{1} \times \frac{1 \text{ YD}}{3 \text{ FT}},$$

the yards would not have divided out and the change of units could not be made.

EXAMPLE 1   CONVERTING FEET TO INCHES

Convert 16 feet to inches (16 ft = _____ in).

Since

$$1 \text{ ft} = 12 \text{ in,}$$

we need to use one of the unit fractions

$$\frac{12 \text{ in}}{1 \text{ ft}} \quad \text{or} \quad \frac{1 \text{ ft}}{12 \text{ in}}.$$

To divide out the ft in 16 ft, use $\frac{12 \text{ in}}{1 \text{ ft}}$.

$$16 \text{ ft} = 16 \text{ ft} \times \mathbf{1}$$ Multiply by 1

$$= \frac{16 \text{ ft}}{1} \times \frac{\mathbf{12 \text{ in}}}{\mathbf{1 \text{ ft}}}$$ Divide out ft

$$= 16 \times 12 \text{ in}$$

$$= 192 \text{ in}$$

EXAMPLE 2   CONVERTING INCHES TO FEET

Convert 72 inches to feet (72 in = _____ ft).

For this problem use the unit fraction $\frac{1 \text{ ft}}{12 \text{ in}}$.

$$72 \text{ in} = 72 \text{ in} \times 1$$ Multiply by 1

PRACTICE EXERCISE 1

Convert 23 feet to inches.

$$\frac{23 \text{ ft}}{1} \times \frac{12 \text{ in}}{1 \text{ ft}} = 276 \text{ inc}$$

Answer: 276 in

PRACTICE EXERCISE 2

Convert 108 inches to feet.

$$\frac{108 \text{ in}}{1} \times \frac{1 \text{ ft}}{12 \text{ in}} = \frac{108}{12} =$$

9A

$$= \frac{72 \ \cancel{in}}{1} \times \frac{1 \ ft}{12 \ \cancel{in}} \qquad \text{Divide out inches}$$

$$= \frac{72}{12} \ ft$$

$$= 6 \ ft$$

Answer: 9 ft

| **PRACTICE EXERCISE 3** | **CONVERSION IN WEIGHT AND VOLUME** | **EXAMPLE 3** |

Complete the conversion in units.

(a) 15 lb = ____ oz.

$$\frac{15 \ \cancel{lbs}}{1} \times \frac{16 \ oz}{1 \ \cancel{lbs.}} \quad \frac{240}{1}$$

$$240 \ oz$$

Complete the conversion in units.

(a) 22 lb = _____ oz.

The unit fraction is $\frac{16 \ oz}{1 \ lb}$.

$$22 \ lb = 22 \ lb \times 1 \qquad \text{Multiply by 1}$$

$$= \frac{22 \ \cancel{lb}}{1} \times \frac{16 \ oz}{1 \ \cancel{lb}} \qquad \text{Divide out lb}$$

$$= 22 \times 16 \ oz$$

$$= 352 \ oz$$

(b) 144 fl oz = ____ pt.

$$\frac{144 \ \cancel{fl \ oz}}{1} = \frac{1 \ pt}{16 \ \cancel{fl \ oz}}$$

$$\frac{144}{16} \qquad 9 \ pt.$$

(b) 96 fl oz = _____ pt.

With the unit fraction $\frac{1 \ pt}{16 \ fl \ oz}$, the fl oz divide out.

$$96 \ fl \ oz = 96 \ fl \ oz \times 1$$

$$= \frac{96 \ \cancel{fl \ oz}}{1} \times \frac{1 \ pt}{16 \ \cancel{fl \ oz}}$$

$$= \frac{96}{16} \ pt$$

$$= 6 \ pt$$

(c) 9 pt = ____ qt.

$$\frac{9 \ pt}{1} = \frac{1 \ q}{2 \ pt} = \frac{9}{2}$$

$$4.5 \ qut$$

(c) 6 pt = _____ qt.

$$6 \ pt = 6 \ pt \times 1$$

$$= \frac{6 \ \cancel{pt}}{1} \times \frac{1 \ qt}{2 \ \cancel{pt}}$$

$$= \frac{6}{2} \ qt$$

$$= 3 \ qt$$

Answers: (a) 240 (b) 9
(c) 4.5

Parts (b) and (c) of Example 3 together change 96 fl oz to 3 qt. Some unit conversions may need two or more unit fractions.

E X A M P L E 4 — **USING SEVERAL UNIT FRACTIONS**

Complete the change in units.

$5 \text{ wk} = \underline{\hphantom{XXX}} \text{ min.}$

$$5 \text{ wk} = 5 \text{ wk} \times \mathbf{1}$$

$$= \frac{5 \text{ wk}}{1} \times \frac{\mathbf{7\ da}}{\mathbf{1\ wk}} \qquad \text{Convert 5 wk to 35 da}$$

$$= 35 \text{ da}$$

$$= \frac{35 \text{ da}}{1} \times \frac{\mathbf{24\ hr}}{\mathbf{1\ da}} \qquad \text{Convert 35 da to 840 hr}$$

$$= 840 \text{ hr}$$

$$= \frac{840 \text{ hr}}{1} \times \frac{\mathbf{60\ min}}{\mathbf{1\ hr}} \qquad \text{Convert 840 hr to 50,400 min}$$

$$= 50{,}400 \text{ min.}$$

The steps can be combined.

$$5 \text{ wk} = \frac{5 \text{ wk}}{1} \times \frac{\mathbf{7\ da}}{\mathbf{1\ wk}} \times \frac{\mathbf{24\ hr}}{\mathbf{1\ da}} \times \frac{\mathbf{60\ min}}{\mathbf{1\ hr}}$$

$$= 5 \times 7 \times 24 \times 60 \text{ min}$$

$$= 50{,}400 \text{ min.}$$

Complete the change in units.

$8 \text{ wk} = \underline{\hphantom{XXX}} \text{ min}$

$$\frac{8 wk}{1} \times \frac{7\ days}{1\ wk} \quad \frac{56}{1}$$

$$\frac{56\ days}{1} \times \frac{24\ hrs}{1\ day}$$

$$\frac{1344\ hrs}{1} \times \frac{6\ min}{1\ hr}$$

$$80,640$$

Answer: 80,640

3 | **HOUSEHOLD UNITS**

Some units of measure used in the kitchen are given in this table.

HOUSEHOLD UNITS
1 tablespoon (tbsp) = 3 teaspoons (tsp)
1 cup = 16 tablespoons (tbsp)
= 8 fluid ounces (fl oz)
1 pint (pt) = 2 cups

E X A M P L E 5 — **CONVERTING HOUSEHOLD UNITS**

Complete the change in units.

(a) $7 \text{ tbsp} = \underline{\hphantom{XXX}} \text{tsp.}$

$$7 \text{ tbsp} = 7 \text{ tbsp} \times \mathbf{1}$$

$$= \frac{7 \text{ tbsp}}{1} \times \frac{\mathbf{3\ tsp}}{\mathbf{1\ tbsp}} \qquad \frac{3 \text{ tsp}}{1 \text{ tbsp}} \text{ is a unit fraction}$$

$$= 7 \times 3 \text{ tsp} = 21 \text{ tsp}$$

(b) $40 \text{ tbsp} = \underline{\hphantom{XXX}} \text{pt.}$

$$40 \text{ tbsp} = 40 \text{ tbsp} \times \mathbf{1} \times \mathbf{1}$$

Complete the change in units.

(a) $15 \text{ tbsp} = \underline{\hphantom{XXX}} \text{tsp.}$

$$\frac{15\ tbsp}{1} = \frac{3\ tsp}{1\ tbsp}$$

$$\underline{45\ tsp}$$

(b) $120 \text{ tbsp} = \underline{\hphantom{XXX}} \text{pt.}$

$$7.5\ cps = \frac{1\ pt.}{2\ cups} \times \frac{1\ cup}{16\ tbs}$$

$$= \frac{40 \ \cancel{tbsp}}{1} \times \frac{1 \ \cancel{cup}}{16 \ \cancel{tbsp}} \times \frac{1 \ pt}{2 \ \cancel{cups}}$$

$$= 40 \times \frac{1}{16} \times \frac{1}{2} \ pt = \frac{40}{(16)(2)} \ pt$$

$$= \frac{\cancel{2} \cdot \cancel{2} \cdot \cancel{2} \cdot 5}{\cancel{2} \cdot \cancel{2} \cdot \cancel{2} \cdot 2 \cdot 2} \ pt = \frac{5}{4} \ pt = 1\frac{1}{4} \ pt$$

Answers: (a) 45   (b) 3.75

4   COMPOUND UNITS

When two different types of measure are considered together, we form a *compound unit*. For example, we can consider length or distance units along with units of time to form a unit of speed. Recall from Section 5.2 that 50 miles per hour can be written in any of the forms

$$\frac{50 \ mi}{1 \ hr} = 50 \frac{mi}{hr} = 50 \ mi \ / \ hr = 50 \ mph.$$

Thus, one unit that can be used for speed is the compound unit *mph* or *miles per hour.* Another unit for speed might be *ft/sec* or *feet per second.* For example,

$$12 \ \text{feet per second} \quad \text{means} \quad \frac{12 \ ft}{sec} = 12 \frac{ft}{sec} = 12 \ ft \ / \ sec$$

A unit for measuring the flow of a liquid is *gal/min* or *gallons per minute.* For example,

$$8 \ \text{gallons per minute} \quad \text{means} \quad \frac{8 \ gal}{min} = 8 \frac{gal}{min} = 8 \ gal \ / \ min.$$

All of these units are examples of compound units that give us units of rate.

PRACTICE EXERCISE 6

CONVERTING UNITS OF RATE   EXAMPLE 6

Complete the change in units.

$$90 \frac{mi}{hr} = \underline{\hspace{1cm}} \frac{ft}{sec}$$

Complete the change in units.

$$30 \frac{mi}{hr} = \underline{\hspace{1cm}} \frac{ft}{sec}.$$

Combine the steps.

$$30 \frac{mi}{hr} = \frac{30 \ mi}{hr} = \frac{30 \ mi}{hr} \times 1 \times 1 \times 1$$

$$= \frac{30 \ \cancel{mi}}{\cancel{hr}} \times \frac{5280 \ ft}{1 \ \cancel{mi}} \times \frac{1 \ \cancel{hr}}{60 \ \cancel{min}} \times \frac{1 \ \cancel{min}}{60 \ sec} \quad \text{Divide out mi, hr, and min}$$

$$= \frac{30 \times 5280 \ ft}{60 \times 60 \ sec}$$

$$= \frac{44 \ ft}{sec} = 44 \frac{ft}{sec}$$

Answer: 132

| **EXAMPLE 7** | **CONVERTING UNITS IN A CONSUMER PROBLEM** |

Claudia wants to buy 15 inches of fringe which costs $1.08 per yard. How much must she pay?

First convert dollars per yard to dollars per foot, then convert dollars per foot to dollars per inch.

$$\frac{1.08 \text{ dollars}}{\text{yd}} = \frac{1.08 \text{ dollars}}{1 \text{ yd}} \times 1 \times 1$$

$$= \frac{1.08 \text{ dollars}}{1 \text{ yd}} \times \frac{1 \text{ yd}}{3 \text{ ft}} \times \frac{1 \text{ ft}}{12 \text{ in}} \qquad \text{Unit fractions}$$

$$= \frac{1.08 \text{ dollars}}{3 \times 12 \text{ in}}$$

$$= \frac{0.03 \text{ dollars}}{\text{in}}$$

Since Claudia wants 15 in of the fringe, multiply 15 in by $\frac{0.03 \text{ dollars}}{\text{in}}$.

$$\frac{15 \text{ in}}{1} \times \frac{0.03 \text{ dollars}}{\text{in}} = \$0.45$$

She must pay $0.45 for the fringe.

| **EXAMPLE 8** | **CONVERTING WATER-FLOW UNITS** |

Herman is filling a tank with water from a larger tank. If 2 pints per minute flow through the filling tube, how many gallons per minute flow through?

Change pints per minute to gallons per minute.

$$2\frac{\text{pt}}{\text{min}} = \frac{2 \text{ pt}}{\text{min}} = \frac{2 \text{ pt}}{1 \text{ min}} \times \frac{1 \text{ qt}}{2 \text{ pt}} \times \frac{1 \text{ gal}}{4 \text{ qt}}$$

$$= \frac{2 \text{ gal}}{2 \times 4 \text{ min}} = \frac{1 \text{ gal}}{4 \text{ min}} = \frac{1}{4} \frac{\text{gal}}{\text{min}}$$

Thus, $\frac{1}{4}$ of a gallon flows through the tube per minute.

PRACTICE EXERCISE 7

Metal tubing costs $3.60 per yard. How much must Larry pay for 28 inches?

Answer: $2.80

PRACTICE EXERCISE 8

Bernice is told that a machine can fill 120 pints in one minute. How many gallons per minute is this?

Answer: 15 gal per min

5.3 EXERCISES

Answers to these exercises are given on page 650.
Study the lists of equal units before completing each statement in Exercises 1–27.

1. 5 ft = _____ in

2. 72 in = _____ ft

3. 72 in = _____ yd

4. 21 da = _____ wk

5. 64 oz = _____ lb

6. 36 hr = _____ da

7. 72 fl oz = _____ pt

8. 4500 lb = _____ ton

9. 6 wk = _____ da

10. 3 mi = _____ ft

11. 18 qt = _____ gal

12. 16 mo = _____ yr

13. 1 hr = _____ sec

14. 5400 sec = _____ hr

15. 96 in = _____ yd

16. 7 yd = _____ in

17. 3 ton = _____ oz

18. 96 fl oz = _____ qt

19. 2 mi = _____ in

20. 3 wk = _____ min

21. 7200 sec = _____ da

22. $15 \dfrac{\text{mi}}{\text{hr}} = $ _____ $\dfrac{\text{ft}}{\text{sec}}$

23. $88 \dfrac{\text{ft}}{\text{sec}} = $ _____ $\dfrac{\text{mi}}{\text{hr}}$

24. $5 \dfrac{\text{cents}}{\text{in}} = $ _____ $\dfrac{\text{dollars}}{\text{yd}}$

25. $2 \dfrac{\text{gal}}{\text{min}} = $ _____ $\dfrac{\text{qt}}{\text{sec}}$

26. $200 \dfrac{\text{lb}}{\text{da}} = $ _____ $\dfrac{\text{ton}}{\text{wk}}$

27. $32 \dfrac{\text{oz}}{\text{hr}} = $ _____ $\dfrac{\text{lb}}{\text{min}}$

Solve each applied problem in Exercises 28–31.

28. **RECREATION** Karen Judd needs 80 inches of material to finish a model train layout. How much will the material cost if it is $4.28 per yard?

29. **TRAVEL** The speed limit is 55 miles per hour and Maria is driving at 5280 feet per minute. Is she driving over the speed limit? If so, by how much?

30. **AGRICULTURE** Richard is filling a tank with liquid fertilizer at the rate of 4 pints per minute. How many gallons per hour is this?

31. **RANCHING** A rancher needs to buy 3 miles of wire to build a fence. What is the total cost if the wire costs 20¢ per foot?

CALCULATOR EXERCISES

Use a calculator to find the change in units in Exercises 32–34. Give answers correct to the nearest tenth.

32. 627 in = _____ yd

33. $55 \dfrac{\text{mi}}{\text{hr}} = $ _____ $\dfrac{\text{ft}}{\text{sec}}$

34. 143 da = _____ yr

35. Mount McKinley in Alaska is the highest mountain in the United States at 20,320 feet above sea level. Give the height in miles to the nearest tenth.

CRITICAL THINKING

PHYSICS *Measurement units are sometimes combined in another way. Energy is defined as the capability of performing work. One measure of energy is a **foot-pound**, the energy required to lift 1 pound a distance of 1 foot. For example, to lift a 5-pound weight a distance of 3 feet would require $5 \cdot 3 = 15$ foot-pounds of energy. The abbreviation for this unit of measure is ft · lb. Use this information in Exercises 36–37.*

36. A worker at a construction site must carry blocks that weigh 2.5 pounds up a 12 foot flight of stairs. Find the number of foot-pounds of energy required to carry 500 blocks up the stairs.

37. Find the amount of energy in foot-pounds required to lift a 4200-pound elevator up 12 stories if each story measures 12 feet.

38. What is a *unit fraction,* and how is it used?

REVIEW OR PREVIEW

Exercises 39–44 review material from Chapter 3 to help prepare you for the next section.

39. $6\dfrac{1}{2}$
    $+9\dfrac{1}{3}$

40. $42\dfrac{2}{5}$
    $-16\dfrac{3}{4}$

41. $162\dfrac{5}{12}$
    $-117\dfrac{17}{18}$

42. $14\dfrac{5}{7}$
    $+8\dfrac{5}{14}$

43. $22\dfrac{1}{3}$
    $-11\dfrac{4}{5}$

44. $216\dfrac{29}{60}$
    $-129\dfrac{17}{20}$

5.3 PARALLEL EXERCISES

Answers to these exercises are not given in the text.

Complete the change in units in Exercises 1–27.

1. 9 ft = _____ in

2. 132 in = _____ ft

3. 132 in = _____ yd

4. 63 da = _____ wk

5. 88 oz = _____ lb

6. 96 hr = _____ da

7. 108 fl oz = _____ pt

8. 15,000 lb = _____ ton

9. 13 wk = _____ da

10. 10 mi = _____ ft

11. 27 qt = _____ gal

12. 37 mo = _____ yr

13. $\dfrac{1}{2}$ hr = _____ sec

14. 400 sec = _____ hr

15. 144 in = _____ yd

16. 12 yd = _____ in

17. 0.1 ton = _____ oz

18. 160 ft oz = _____ qt

19. 0.4 mi = _____ in

20. $\dfrac{1}{2}$ wk = _____ min

21. 86,400 sec = _____ da

22. $75\dfrac{\text{mi}}{\text{hr}} = _____\dfrac{\text{ft}}{\text{sec}}$

23. $11\dfrac{\text{ft}}{\text{sec}} = _____\dfrac{\text{mi}}{\text{hr}}$

24. $20\dfrac{\text{cents}}{\text{in}} = _____\dfrac{\text{dollars}}{\text{yd}}$

25. $30\dfrac{\text{gal}}{\text{min}} = _____\dfrac{\text{qt}}{\text{sec}}$

26. $700\dfrac{\text{lb}}{\text{da}} = _____\dfrac{\text{ton}}{\text{wk}}$

27. $640\dfrac{\text{oz}}{\text{hr}} = _____\dfrac{\text{lb}}{\text{min}}$

Solve each applied problem in Exercises 28–31.

28. **MEDICINE** A compound used to make medicine costs $2.55 per ounce. How much will a laboratory have to pay for 46 pounds of the compound? $\dfrac{2.55}{1 \text{ oz.}} = \dfrac{16 \text{ oz}}{1 \text{ lbs}}$ $40.80 \times 46 = \$1876.80$

29. **TRAVEL** Burt is driving at the rate of 55 feet per second. If he is driving where the speed limit is 40 miles per hour, how does his speed compare to the limit?

30. **HYDROLOGY** A water pump will deliver 210 gallons per minute. How many quarts per second is this? $\dfrac{1}{4}$

31. **ELECTRICITY** Electrical wiring costs 5¢ per inch. How much would 25 yards of this wire cost?

CALCULATOR EXERCISES

Use a calculator to find the change in units in Exercises 32–34. Give answers correct to the nearest tenth.

32. 0.0367 yd = _____ in

33. $102 \dfrac{\text{ft}}{\text{sec}} =$ _____ $\dfrac{\text{mi}}{\text{hr}}$

34. 0.0812 yr = _____ da

35. Mount Everest in the Himalayas is the highest mountain in the world at 29,028 feet above sea level. Give the height in miles to the nearest tenth.

69.5 ?

CRITICAL THINKING

PHYSICS   *Measurement units are sometimes combined in another way. Energy is defined as the capability of performing work. One measure of energy is a **foot-pound**, the energy required to lift 1 pound a distance of 1 foot. For example, to lift a 5-pound weight a distance of 3 feet would require $5 \cdot 3 = 15$ foot-pounds of energy. The abbreviation for this unit of measure is ft · lb. Use this information in Exercises 36–37.*

36. How many foot-pounds are required to lift 1200 bricks up 16 feet if each brick weighs 5.4 pounds?

37. A helicopter is required to lift a 2-ton vehicle up to the top of a mesa 1362 feet above the roadway. How much energy in foot-pounds is required?

38. When making a change of units by multiplying by a unit fraction, explain how you would know if you used the wrong fraction, for example, used the reciprocal of the correct fraction.

GROUP PROJECT

Each member of the group should look up an English unit of measurment to see how it originated. For example, try to discover why 1 foot is the length that it is and why it is called a *foot*.

5.4 ARITHMETIC OF MEASUREMENT NUMBERS

STUDENT GUIDEPOSTS
1   SIMPLIFYING MEASUREMENT UNITS
2   ADDING MEASUREMENT UNITS
3   SUBTRACTING MEASUREMENT UNITS
4   MULTIPLYING MEASUREMENT UNITS
5   DIVIDING MEASUREMENT UNITS

EXPLORATION GUIDE

Discuss why it is important to be able to change from one measurement to another. Consider, for example, why you might want to change 54,000 seconds to 15 hours.

1   SIMPLIFYING MEASUREMENT UNITS

Suppose the answer to a time-conversion problem is 64 minutes. When a time answer is more than 1 hour (60 min), the result is usually written in hours and minutes.

$$64 \text{ min} = \mathbf{60\ min} + 4 \text{ min}$$
$$= \mathbf{1\ hr}\ 4 \text{ min} \qquad \text{Plus sign left out}$$

This is read "one hour four minutes." This form of the answer gives a better idea of the size of some measurements, especially when the numbers are large. For example, we have a better idea of the time if we are told a job will take 8 hr rather than 480 min.

Other measurement units can also be simplified. For example, to change 32 inches to feet and inches, write 32 as the sum of a multiple of 12 and a number less than 12.

$$32 \text{ in} = \mathbf{24 \text{ in}} + 8 \text{ in}$$
$$= \mathbf{2 \text{ ft}} \text{ 8 in} \qquad \text{24 in = 2ft}$$

This is read "two feet eight inches."

E X A M P L E 1   **SIMPLIFYING UNITS**

Simplify the following measurements.

(a) 3 hr 92 min

To change 92 minutes to hours and minutes, write 92 as the sum of a multiple of 60 and a number less than 60.

$$3 \text{ hr } \mathbf{92 \text{ min}} = 3 \text{ hr} + \mathbf{60 \text{ min}} + \mathbf{32 \text{ min}} \qquad 92 = 60 + 32$$
$$= 3 \text{ hr} + 1 \text{ hr} + 32 \text{ min} \qquad 60 \text{ min} = 1 \text{ hr}$$
$$= 4 \text{ hr } 32 \text{ min} \qquad \text{Add 3 hr and 1 hr}$$

(b) 3 yd 8 ft

$$3 \text{ yd } \mathbf{8 \text{ ft}} = 3 \text{ yd} + \mathbf{6 \text{ ft}} + \mathbf{2 \text{ ft}} \qquad 8 = 6 + 2$$
$$= 3 \text{ yd} + 2 \text{ yd} + 2 \text{ ft} \qquad 6 \text{ ft} = 2 \text{ yd}$$
$$= 5 \text{ yd } 2 \text{ ft}$$

E X A M P L E 2   **EXPANDING UNITS**

Write 125 inches as yards, feet, and inches.

First, change 125 inches to feet and inches by writing it as the sum of a multiple of 12 and a number less than 12.

$$125 \text{ in} = \mathbf{120 \text{ in}} + 5 \text{ in} \qquad \text{120 is a multiple of 12}$$
$$= \mathbf{10(12)} \text{ in} + 5 \text{ in}$$
$$= \mathbf{10} \text{ ft } 5 \text{ in} \qquad \text{12 in = 1 ft}$$

Now change 10 ft to yards and feet.

$$\mathbf{10 \text{ ft}} \text{ 5 in} = \mathbf{9 \text{ ft}} + \mathbf{1 \text{ ft}} + 5 \text{ in} \qquad 10 = 9 + 1$$
$$= 3 \text{ yd } 1 \text{ ft } 5 \text{ in} \qquad \text{9 ft = 3 yd}$$

E X A M P L E 3   **SIMPLIFYING VOLUME UNITS**

Simplify 9 gal 18 qt 9 pt.

First change 9 pints to quarts and pints.

$$9 \text{ pt} = \mathbf{8 \text{ pt}} + 1 \text{ pt}$$
$$= \mathbf{4 \text{ qt}} \text{ 1 pt} \qquad \text{2 pt = 1 qt}$$

Adding 4 qt to 18 qt gives 22 qt. Now we have 9 gal 22 qt 1 pt. To change 22 qt to gallons and quarts, write 22 as the sum of a multiple of 4 and a number less than 4.

$$\mathbf{22 \text{ qt}} \text{ 1 pt} = \mathbf{20 \text{ qt}} + \mathbf{2 \text{ qt}} + 1 \text{ pt}$$

PRACTICE EXERCISE 1

Simplify the following measurements.

(a) 7 hr 116 min

(b) 5 yd 14 ft

Answers: (a) 8 hr 56 min
(b) 9 yd 2 ft

PRACTICE EXERCISE 2

Write 400 inches as yards, feet, and inches.

Answer:
11 yd 0 ft 4 in = 11 yd 4 in

PRACTICE EXERCISE 3

Simplify 4 gal 34 qt 23 pt.

$$= 5(4 \text{ qt}) + 2 \text{ qt} + 1 \text{ pt}$$
$$= 5 \text{ gal } 2 \text{ qt } 1 \text{ pt} \qquad 4 \text{ qt} = 1 \text{ gal}$$

Answer: 15 gal 1 qt 1 pt

Now we have 9 gal+5 gal 2 qt 1 pt. Since

$$9 \text{ gal} + 5 \text{ gal} = 14 \text{ gal},$$

the final answer is 14 gal 2 qt 1 pt.

2 | ADDING MEASUREMENT UNITS

In these simplifications, we have been adding measurements. In Example 3 we wrote

$$9 \text{ gal} + 5 \text{ gal} = 14 \text{ gal}.$$

Only measurements in the same unit can be added. Thus, 9 gal can be added to 5 gal, but 14 gal cannot be added to 2 qt without first converting one of the units to the other.

   In some cases, we need to add measurements such as 8 ft 5 in and 6 ft 4 in. This problem is like adding mixed numbers. We can change both to inches and add or we can add them as mixed measurement units.

PRACTICE EXERCISE 4

Add.

(a) 17 ft 7 in and 5 ft 2 in

ADDING UNITS — EXAMPLE 4

Add.

(a) 8 ft 5 in and 6 ft 4 in

$$\begin{array}{r} 8 \text{ ft} \quad 5 \text{ in} \\ + 6 \text{ ft} \quad 4 \text{ in} \\ \hline \end{array}$$

Add each unit separately.   **Sum of feet** ⟶ **14 ft   9 in** ⟵ **Sum of inches**

The sum is 14 ft 9 in.

(b) 14 hr 42 min and 5 hr 37 min

(b) 3 hr 28 min and 7 hr 54 min

$$\begin{array}{r} 3 \text{ hr} \quad 28 \text{ min} \\ + 7 \text{ hr} \quad 54 \text{ min} \\ \hline \end{array}$$

Sum of hours ⟶ **10 hr   82 min** ⟵ **Sum of minutes**

Since 82 min is more than 1 hr, simplify the sum.

$$10 \text{ hr } \mathbf{82 \text{ min}} = 10 \text{ hr} + \mathbf{60 \text{ min}} + \mathbf{22 \text{ min}}$$
$$= 10 \text{ hr} + 1 \text{ hr} + 22 \text{ min} \qquad 60 \text{ min} = 1 \text{ hr}$$
$$= 11 \text{ hr } 22 \text{ min}$$

Answers: (a) 22 ft 9 in
(b) 20 hr 19 min

The sum is 11 hr 22 min.

3 | SUBTRACTING MEASUREMENT UNITS

To subtract measurement units, subtract only like units.

PRACTICE EXERCISE 5

Subtract 10 ft 4 in from 14 ft 11 in.

SUBTRACTING UNITS — EXAMPLE 5

Subtract 6 ft 4 in from 8 ft 5 in.

$$\begin{array}{r} 8 \text{ ft} \quad 5 \text{ in} \\ - 6 \text{ ft} \quad 4 \text{ in} \\ \hline \end{array}$$

Difference of feet ⟶ **2 ft   1 in** ⟵ **Difference of inches**

The difference is 2 ft 1 in.

Answer: 4 ft 7 in

   As with subtraction of mixed numbers, sometimes we need to borrow. With measurement units, this means changing one unit of the larger measure to units of the smaller.

EXAMPLE 6 — **SUBTRACTING WITH BORROWING**

Subtract.

$$17 \text{ ft } 2 \text{ in}$$
$$- \ 9 \text{ ft } 8 \text{ in}$$

Subtract.

$$25 \text{ ft } 1 \text{ in}$$
$$- \ 11 \text{ ft } 9 \text{ in}$$

Since 2 inches is less than the 8 inches to be subtracted, borrow 1 ft (12 in) from 17 ft.

$$\mathbf{17 \text{ ft}} \ 2 \text{ in} = \mathbf{16 \text{ ft}} + \mathbf{1 \text{ ft}} + 2 \text{ in}$$
$$= 16 \text{ ft} + 12 \text{ in} + 2 \text{ in} \qquad 1 \text{ ft} = 12 \text{ in}$$
$$= 16 \text{ ft } 14 \text{ in}$$

Now subtract.

$$\begin{array}{rll} 17 \text{ ft } 2 \text{ in} = & 16 \text{ ft} & 14 \text{ in} \\ - \ \ 9 \text{ ft } 8 \text{ in} = & - \ 9 \text{ ft} & 8 \text{ in} \\ \hline & 7 \text{ ft} & 6 \text{ in} \end{array}$$

The difference is 7 ft 6 in.

Answer: 13 ft 4 in

4 — MULTIPLYING MEASUREMENT UNITS

Some multiplication problems involve measurement units. For example, suppose it requires 2 yd 1 ft 7 in of material to make one suit. To learn how much material is required for 4 suits, multiply 2 yd 1 ft 7 in by 4. As with addition and subtraction, all units could be converted to inches and multiplied by 4, but the same result can be reached by multiplying 2 yd by 4, 1 ft by 4, and 7 in by 4, and then simplifying the result.

$$4 \times (2 \text{ yd } 1 \text{ ft } 7 \text{ in}) = 4(2 \text{ yd} + 1 \text{ ft} + 7 \text{ in})$$
$$= 8 \text{ yd} + 4 \text{ ft} + 28 \text{ in} \qquad \text{Distributive property}$$

Now simplify. First change 28 in to feet: $28 \text{ in} = 24 \text{ in} + 4 \text{ in} = 2 \text{ ft} + 4 \text{ in}$. Then, rewrite the product.

$$8 \text{ yd} + 4 \text{ ft} + \mathbf{28 \text{ in}} = 8 \text{ yd} + 4 \text{ ft} + \mathbf{2 \text{ ft}} + \mathbf{4 \text{ in}} \qquad \text{Replace 28 in by 2 ft} + 4 \text{ in}$$
$$= 8 \text{ yd} + \mathbf{6 \text{ ft}} + 4 \text{ in} \qquad \text{Add 4 ft and 2 ft}$$
$$= 8 \text{ yd} + \mathbf{2 \text{ yd}} + 4 \text{ in} \qquad 3 \text{ ft} = 1 \text{ yd}$$
$$= 10 \text{ yd } 4 \text{ in}$$

Thus, 10 yd 4 in is needed for the 4 suits. This could be written as 10 yd 0 ft 4 in.

EXAMPLE 7 — **MULTIPLYING BY A NON-MEASUREMENT NUMBER**

If a tank holds 7 gal 3 qt 1 pt of liquid, how much would be used to fill 6 tanks of the same size?

Multiply 7 gal 3 qt 1 pt by 6.

$$6 \times (7 \text{ gal } 3 \text{ qt } 1\text{pt})$$
$$= 6(7 \text{ gal} + 3 \text{ qt} + 1\text{pt})$$
$$= 42 \text{ gal} + 18 \text{ qt} + \mathbf{6 \text{ pt}}$$
$$= 42 \text{ gal} + 18 \text{ qt} + \mathbf{3 \text{ qt}} \qquad 2 \text{ pt} = 1 \text{ qt}$$

For a survival test each person was given 1 gal 2 qt 1 pt of water. How much water was needed to supply the 15 people taking the test?

$$= 42 \text{ gal} + \textbf{21 qt} \qquad \text{\small 18 qt + 3 qt = 21 qt}$$
$$= 42 \text{ gal} + \textbf{20 qt} + \textbf{1 qt} \qquad \text{\small 21 q = 20 qt + 1 qt}$$
$$= 42 \text{ gal} + \textbf{5 gal} + \textbf{1 qt} \qquad \text{\small 4 qt = 1 gal, 20 qt = 5(4 qt) = 5 gal}$$
$$= 47 \text{ gal 1 qt} \qquad \text{\small 42 gal + 5 gal = 47 gal}$$

As shown in the next example, it is possible to multiply measurement units by measurement units.

MULTIPLYING MEASUREMENT UNITS	EXAMPLE 8

Find the area of a rectangle which is 4 ft wide and 6 ft long.

Recall from Chapter 1 that

$$\text{area} = \textbf{length} \times \textbf{width}$$
$$= \textbf{6 ft} \times \textbf{4 ft}$$

To work the problem find not only 6×4 but also $\text{ft} \times \text{ft}$.

$$\text{area} = 6 \text{ ft} \times 4 \text{ ft}$$
$$= (6 \times 4)(\text{ft} \times \text{ft})$$
$$= 24 \text{ ft}^2$$
$$= 24 \text{ sq ft}$$

The area is 24 sq ft. (The unit sq ft was used in Chapter 1. The unit ft^2 is also used for area. We will say more about it in Chapter 8.)

5	DIVIDING MEASUREMENT UNITS

To divide a measurement by an ordinary number, first divide the largest unit by the number. If there is a remainder, add it to the next unit and divide again.

DIVIDING BY A NON-MEASUREMENT NUMBER	EXAMPLE 9

Divide 17 lb 6 oz by 3.

First divide 17 lb by 3.

$$\begin{array}{r} 5 \text{ lb} \\ 3\overline{)17 \text{ lb}} \\ \underline{15} \\ 2 \ \ \text{lb} \end{array}$$

Thus, $17 \text{ lb} \div 3 = 5 \text{ lb}$ with a remainder of 2 lb. Change 2 lb to ounces.

$$2 \text{ lb} = 2(\textbf{1 lb}) = 2(\textbf{16 oz}) = 32 \text{ oz}$$

Add the 6 oz from the original measurement to 32 oz.

$$32 \text{ oz} + 6 \text{ oz} = 38 \text{ oz}$$

Now divide 38 oz by 3.

$$\begin{array}{r} 12 \text{ oz} \ \frac{2}{3} \\ 3\overline{)38 \text{ oz}} \\ \underline{3} \\ 8 \\ \underline{6} \\ 2 \end{array}$$

PRACTICE EXERCISE 8

Find the area of a rectangular garden which is 10 yd wide and 17 yd long.

PRACTICE EXERCISE 9

Divide 42 lb 13 oz by 5.

The answer to this division is 12 oz with remainder 2 or $12\frac{2}{3}$ oz. The final answer to the problem $(17\text{ lb }6\text{ oz})\div 3$ is

$$5\text{ lb }12\frac{2}{3}\text{ oz}$$

Some problems involve division of a measurement by a measurement. Suppose you want to know how many shirts costing $16 each can be bought for $48.

$$\frac{48\text{ dollars}}{16\text{ dollars}}=\frac{3\times\cancel{16\text{ dollars}}}{\cancel{16\text{ dollars}}}=3$$

The dollars cancel and the answer is the whole number (with no measurement unit) 3. You can buy 3 shirts for $48.

DIVIDING MEASUREMENT UNITS   EXAMPLE 10

PRACTICE EXERCISE 10

How many 4-ft shelves can be cut from a board 16 ft long?

Divide 16 ft by 4 ft.

$$\frac{16\text{ ft}}{4\text{ ft}}=\frac{4\times\cancel{4\text{ ft}}}{\cancel{4\text{ ft}}}=4$$

Thus, 4 shelves can be cut from the board.

One uniform can be made from 3 yd of material. How many uniforms can be made from 51 yd of the material?

5.4 EXERCISES

Answers to these exercises are given on page 650.

Simplify each measurement in Exercises 1–6.

1. 83 min

2. 3 hr 92 min

3. 5 yd 8 ft

4. 8 gal 17 qt

5. 14 lb 73 oz

6. 4 yd 7 ft 23 in

Perform the indicated operations and simplify in Exercises 7–24.

7. $\begin{array}{r}8\text{ lb }\ \ 3\text{ oz}\\+4\text{ lb }10\text{ oz}\\\hline\end{array}$

8. $\begin{array}{r}5\text{ hr }52\text{ min}\\+13\text{ hr }41\text{ min}\\\hline\end{array}$

9. $\begin{array}{r}3\text{ gal }3\text{ qt}\\+4\text{ gal }2\text{ qt}\\\hline\end{array}$

10. $\begin{array}{r}6\text{ yd }2\text{ ft }11\text{ in}\\+7\text{ yd }1\text{ ft }\ 9\text{ in}\\\hline\end{array}$

11. $\begin{array}{r}7\text{ yd }2\text{ ft}\\-3\text{ yd }1\text{ ft}\\\hline\end{array}$

12. $\begin{array}{r}8\text{ hr }30\text{ min}\\-2\text{ hr }26\text{ min}\\\hline\end{array}$

13. $\begin{array}{r}8\text{ gal }1\text{ qt}\\-4\text{ gal }3\text{ qt}\\\hline\end{array}$

14. $\begin{array}{r}5\text{ da }3\text{ hr }\ 8\text{ min}\\-4\text{ da }6\text{ hr }40\text{ min}\\\hline\end{array}$

15. $\begin{array}{r}9\text{ yd }2\text{ ft }\ 3\text{ in}\\-2\text{ yd }2\text{ ft }10\text{ in}\\\hline\end{array}$

16. $3\times(5\text{ hr }16\text{ min})$

17. $5\times(4\text{ gal }3\text{ qt})$

18. $4\times(2\text{ yd }2\text{ ft }11\text{ in})$

19. $6\times(2\text{ hr }18\text{ min }14\text{ sec})$

20. $3\text{ in}\times12\text{ in}$

21. $7\text{ yd}\times12\text{ yd}$

22. $(5\text{ lb }12\text{ oz})\div 2$

23. $(7\text{ hr }33\text{ min})\div 3$

24. $18\text{ ft}\div 3\text{ ft}$

Solve each applied problem in Exercises 25–30.

25. **CONSUMER** Julie Davis found ski caps on sale for $12.50 each. How many of these can she buy if she has $62.50?

26. **CHEMISTRY** A chemist has 5 gal 3 qt of one liquid to be mixed with 4 gal 2 qt of another. How much will he have after he mixes them?

27. **RECREATION** Henry took 6 gal 2 qt of water on a camping trip. After using 2 gal 4 qt, how much water did he have left?

28. **BAKING** If it takes 1 lb 12 oz of flour to make one loaf of bread, how much will it take to make 7 loaves?

29. **GARDENING** How many square feet are available for planting flowers if a rectangular garden is 14.5 feet long and 13.4 feet wide?

30. **BAKING** If it takes 1 lb 12 oz of flour to make one loaf of bread, how much will it take to make a loaf one half the size?

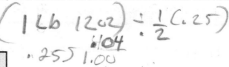

CRITICAL THINKING

31. **RECREATION** If the material for a fanny pack costs $2.70 per yard, how much does 8 feet of the material cost?

32. When Burford was asked to add 2 miles and 4000 ft, he gave 4002 miles for the answer. Explain to Burford what he is doing wrong.

33. Discuss the concepts of *carrying* and *borrowing* as they relate to the operations of addition and subtraction of measurement numbers.

34. Explain why multiplying measurement numbers often results in a product that has a different measure. For example, when multiplying 4 ft by 5 ft, why is the product in *square feet?*

REVIEW OR PREVIEW

Complete each unit conversion in Exercises 35–40.

35. 4.25 da = ____ hr

36. 126 in = _____ yd

37. 62 pt = _____ gal

38. 16 tons = _____ lb

39. $44 \dfrac{\text{ft}}{\text{sec}} =$ _____ $\dfrac{\text{mi}}{\text{hr}}$

40. $50 \dfrac{\text{cents}}{\text{in}} =$ _____ $\dfrac{\text{dollars}}{\text{ft}}$

5.4 PARALLEL EXERCISES

Answers to these exercises are not given in the text.

Simplify each measurement in Exercises 1–6.

1. 137 min

2. 7 hr 72 min

3. 4 yd 19 ft

4. 2 gal 25 qt

5. 6 lb 105 oz

6. 5 yd 14 ft 42 in

Perform the indicated operations and simplify in Exercises 7–24.

7. 9 lb 11 oz
   +5 lb 1 oz

8. 12 hr 39 min
   +10 hr 32 min

9. 9 gal 3 qt
   +7 gal 3 qt

10. 12 yd 1 ft 5 in
   +18 yd 2 ft 10 in
   _____

11. 4 yd 2 ft
   −1 yd 1 ft
   _____

12. 19 hr 49 min
   −15 hr 32 min
   _____

13. 17 gal 1 qt
   −13 gal 2 qt
   _____

14. 22 da 2 hr 36 min
   −21 da 22 hr 48 min
   _____

15. 6 yd 1 ft 1 in
   −3 yd 2 ft 2 in
   _____

16. $4 \times (3 \text{ hr } 10 \text{ min})$

17. $10 \times (3 \text{ gal } 2 \text{ qt})$

18. $6 \times (7 \text{ yd } 1 \text{ ft } 8 \text{ in})$

19. $3 \times (5 \text{ hr } 40 \text{ min } 25 \text{ sec})$

20. $14 \text{ in} \times 22 \text{ in}$

21. $5 \text{ yd} \times 9 \text{ yd}$

22. $(7 \text{ lb } 8 \text{ oz}) \div 3$

23. $(10 \text{ hr } 20 \text{ min}) \div 4$

24. $33 \text{ ft} \div 11 \text{ ft}$

Solve each applied problem in Exercises 25–30.

25. **CONSUMER** Glen Wilson has $9.90 to spend on ground beef for a cookout. How many pounds can he buy if it is $1.80 per pound?

26. **RECREATION** For a company picnic, Ward brought 7 gal 2 qt of iced tea. If Sarah brought 10 gal 3 qt, how much tea did they have?

27. **RECREATION** If the people at the picnic in Exercise 26 drank 15 gal 3 qt of the tea, how much was left?

28. **COOKING** Billy Joe has a chili recipe that requires 2 lb 6 oz of ground beef. How much meat should he buy to make 5 times his recipe?

29. **CONSTRUCTION** How many square feet must be painted on a wall that is 8.5 feet high and 16.2 feet long?

30. **BAKING** A cookie recipe requires 1 lb 2 oz of flour. How much flour would be used if only one third of the recipe is to be made?

CRITICAL THINKING

31. **ELECTRICITY** Electrical wire costs $13.85 per yard. How much does the wire cost per foot (to the nearest cent)?

32. Burford's solution to a subtraction problem is given below. What did Burford do wrong, and what is the correct difference?

   8 ft 3 in
   2 ft 7 in
   _____
   6 ft 4 in

33. Operations on measurement numbers is sometimes compared to operations with mixed numbers studied in Chapters 2 and 3. Explain why this comparison is accurate.

34. Explain why dividing measurement numbers often results in a quotient that does not involve a measurement unit. For example, when dividing 12 ft by 3 ft, why is the quotient simply 4 (not 4 ft)?

The type of operations that we have done in this section are not seen as much in the metric system that we study next because more decimal parts of units are used. Discuss the advantages and disadvantages of using more decimal notation in the English system. For example, $2\,\text{yd}\,2\,\text{ft}\,3\,\text{in} = 8.25\,\text{ft}$. Think of the measuring instruments used with the various units of measurement. How would a ruler need to be modified? What about measuring time?

5.5 THE METRIC SYSTEM OF MEASUREMENT

STUDENT GUIDEPOSTS
1   MEASURING LENGTH IN METERS
2   MEASURING VOLUME IN LITERS
3   MEASURING WEIGHT IN GRAMS
4   RELATING UNITS OF MEASURE

Most of the world uses the metric system of measurement. It is a decimal system, and changes in units can be made by moving the decimal point. Thus, it is much easier to convert from one unit to another in the metric system than it is in the English system (just as easy as changing $1.27 to 127¢).

1 | LENGTH IN METERS

The standard of length in the metric system is the **meter**. The opening in a normal doorway is about 2 meters high. Thus, a meter is about half the height of an opening in a doorway. A twin bed is about a meter wide and most newborn babies are about $\frac{1}{2}$ meter tall.

The actual length of the scale in Figure 5.3 is 0.1 meter. The distance between each mark is 0.01 meter.

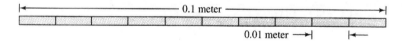

FIGURE 5.3

2 | VOLUME IN LITERS

If we make a box as shown in Figure 5.4 (not actual size), the box holds one **liter**. This is the standard unit for capacity in the metric system. If you are thirsty on a summer day, you can probably drink a liter of liquid. It is a little less than three cans of soft drink.

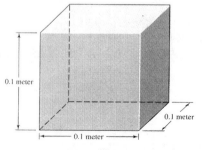

FIGURE 5.4

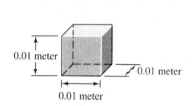

FIGURE 5.5

3 | WEIGHT IN GRAMS

The standard for mass or weight at sea level is the **gram.** Figure 5.5 shows a cube of side 0.01 meter. If this cube were filled with water, the weight of the water would be 1 gram. One large paper clip (or two small ones) weighs about one gram and a large steak might weigh 1000 grams.

4 | UNITS OF MEASURE

As with the English system, the various size units such as 1000 grams have names, and the naming is standard. For example, the names for 1000 meters, 1000 liters, and 1000 grams all start with the same prefix, *kilo.* Thus,

$$1000 \text{ meters} = 1 \text{ } kilometer,$$
$$1000 \text{ liters } = 1 \text{ } kiloliter,$$
$$1000 \text{ grams } = 1 \text{ } kilogram.$$

The following table lists the prefixes and symbols used in the metric system.

Number of units	1000	100	10	1	$\frac{1}{10}$ or 0.1	$\frac{1}{100}$ or 0.01	$\frac{1}{1000}$ or 0.001
Prefix	kilo	hecto	deka	**unit**	deci	centi	milli
Length	km	hm	dam	**meter(m)**	dm	cm	mm
Volume	kl	hl	dal	**liter(L)**	dl	cl	ml
Weight	kg	hg	dag	**gram(g)**	dg	cg	mg

The different size units are used in different applications. For example, the size of a room is given in meters, the distance between Miami and Washington, D.C., in kilometers, and bolt sizes in millimeters. In Figure 5.6, the paper clip and bolt are shown actual size.

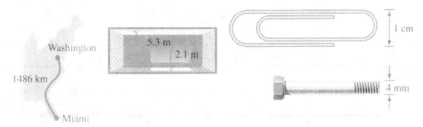

FIGURE 5.6

In Figure 5.7 (drawn to actual size), Figure 5.3 has been repeated using the new names we have learned and a few more details. This should give you a good idea of the sizes of some units of length and their relationship. A meter is 10 times the total length of the scale in Figure 5.7. A kilometer is about the length of five city blocks.

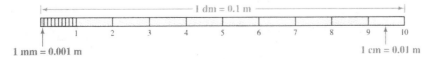

FIGURE 5.7

The most commonly used measures of length are the kilometer, meter, centimeter, and millimeter. These same prefixes—kilo, centi, and milli—are used for volume and weight also.

In volume units, the liter is used to measure gasoline and beverages. The kiloliter measures the capacity of large tanks, and the milliliter measures liquids in a laboratory.

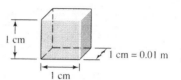

FIGURE 5.8

The cube in Figure 5.8, which is 1 cm on a side, has volume 1 ml and this much water weighs 1 g. Thus, the gram is a small unit of measurement. It is used in the laboratory where an even smaller unit, the milligram, is also needed. The unit that would suit many common weight applications is the kilogram. As has been mentioned, a large steak weighs about 1 kg (1000 g).

Now that we have some idea of the size of metric units, we turn to conversion problems. Instead of using decimal conversion units such as 1 mm = 0.001 m, it will be easier to write all unit fractions in terms of 10, 100, or 1000. The following table gives the equal units.

Length	*Volume*	*Weight*
1 km = 1000 m	1 kl = 1000 L	1 kg = 1000 g
1 hm = 100 m	1 hl = 100 L	1 hg = 100 g
1 dam = 10 m	1 dal = 10 L	1 dag = 10 g
1 m = 10 dm	1 L = 10 dl	1 g = 10 dg
1 m = 100 cm	1 L = 100 cl	1 g = 100 cg
1 m = 1000 mm	1 L = 1000 ml	1 g = 1000 mg

NOTE Remember that multiplying and dividing by powers of ten can be done by moving the decimal point. Consider these examples.

$16.2 \times 100 = 1620$ **Move two places to the right**

$16.2 \div 100 = 0.162$ **Move two places to the left**

PRACTICE EXERCISE 1

13.25 m = _____ cm.

Answer: 1325

EXAMPLE 1   CONVERTING METERS TO CENTIMETERS

5.2 m = ___ cm

Since 1 m = 100 cm, the unit fraction is $\frac{100 \text{ cm}}{1 \text{ m}}$.

$$5.2 \text{ m} = 5.2 \text{ m} \times \mathbf{1}$$
$$= \frac{5.2 \text{ m}}{1} \times \frac{\mathbf{100 \text{ cm}}}{\mathbf{1 \text{ m}}} \qquad \frac{100 \text{ cm}}{1 \text{ m}} \text{ is a unit fraction}$$
$$= 5.2 \times 100 \text{ cm}$$
$$= 520 \text{ cm}$$

5.2 is multiplied by 100 which moves the decimal point 2 places to the right. That is,

$$5.2 \text{ m} = 5\underset{2}{\underset{\smile}{20}}. \text{ cm.}$$

CONVERTING MILLILITERS TO DECILITERS   EXAMPLE 2

362 ml = _____ dl.

The unit fractions are $\dfrac{1 \text{ L}}{1000 \text{ ml}}$ and $\dfrac{10 \text{ dl}}{1 \text{ L}}$.

$$362 \text{ ml} = 362 \text{ ml} \times \mathbf{1} \times \mathbf{1}$$

$$= \frac{362 \text{ ml}}{1} \times \frac{\mathbf{1 \ L}}{\mathbf{1000 \ ml}} \times \frac{\mathbf{10 \ dl}}{\mathbf{1 \ L}}$$

$$= 362 \times \frac{1}{1000} \times \frac{10}{1} \text{ dl}$$

$$= 362 \times \frac{10}{1000} \text{ dl}$$

$$= 362 \times \frac{1}{100} \text{ dl}$$

$$= 3.62 \text{ dl}$$

362 is divided by 100 which moves the decimal point 2 places to the left.

In Example 2, multiplying by one unit fraction moved the decimal point 3 places to the left and multiplying by the other moved it 1 place to the right. The same change of units could have been made by moving the decimal point 2 places to the left. This method of conversion is shown in the next example.

CONVERTING BY MOVING DECIMAL PLACES   EXAMPLE 3

362 ml = _____ dl.

First show all the units in a diagram.

1000 L   100 L   10 L   **0.1 L**   0.01 L   **0.001 L**
                        1L
(kl)   **(hl)**   **(dal)**   **(dl)**   **(cl)**   **(ml)**

Start at **ml** and make 2 moves to the *left* to get to **dl.** Thus, to change ml to dl move the decimal point 2 places to the *left*.

$$362 \text{ ml} = 3.\underset{2}{\underset{\smile}{62}} \text{ dl} = 3.62 \text{ dl}$$

CONVERTING HECTOGRAMS TO CENTIGRAMS   EXAMPLE 4

0.0256 hg = _____ cg.

1000 g   **100 g**   10 g   0.1 g   **0.01 g**   0.001 g
                        1g
(kg)   **(hg)**   **(dag)**   **(dg)**   **(cg)**   **(mg)**

Start at hg and move 4 times to the *right* to get to cg. Thus, to change hg to cg, move the decimal point 4 places to the *right*.   0.0256 hg = 00256. cg = 256 cg

| PRACTICE EXERCISE 5 | CONVERTING MILLIMETERS TO HECTOMETERS | EXAMPLE 5 |

3280 mm = _____ hm.

426,000 mm = ___ hm.

1000 m	**100 m**	10 m		0.1 m	0.01 m	**0.001 m**
(km)	(hm)	(dam)	1 m	(dm)	(cm)	(mm)
	5	4	3	2	1

Start at mm and make 5 moves to the *left* to get to hm. Thus, to change mm to hm, move the decimal point 5 places to the *left*.

Answer: 4.26

$$3280 \text{ mm} = 0.03280 \text{ hm}$$

The time units for the metric system are the same as for the English system. However, the temperature scale is different. Both metric and English temperature will be discussed in the next section when we convert from one system to the other.

5.5 EXERCISES

Answers to these exercises are given on page 650.

💡 *Answer* true *or* false *in Exercises 1–6. If the answer is false, tell why.*

1. The system of measurement used in most of the world is the metric system.

2. The opening in a normal doorway is about 10 meters high.

3. A liter is the space in a box which is 0.1 meter or one decimeter on a side.

4. The weight of water that can be put in a box which is 0.01 meter (1 centimeter) on a side is one gram.

5. A large steak might weight about one gram.

6. To change units of length in the metric system, just move the decimal point.

Complete each statement in Exercises 7–33 by moving the decimal point as shown in the examples.

7. 1 km = _____ m

8. 1 hl = _____ L

9. 1 dag = _____ g

10. 1 m = _____ dm

11. 1 mg = _____ g

12. 1 g = _____ mg

13. 62 g = _____ kg

14. 3.2 cm = _____ m

15. 16 dal = _____ L

16. 10.3 cm = _____ hm

17. 0.00721 kg = _____ dag

18. 63,000 ml = _____ kl

19. 1700 dm = _____ hm

20. 16.25 cg = _____ mg

21. 0.000212 hl = _____ ml

22. 92.6 mm = _____ cm

23. 4728 dg = _____ hg

24. 5,000,000 cl = _____ dal

25. 0.0052 hm = _____ mm

26. 0.07 dag = _____ mg

27. 3200 dl = _____ kl

28. 0.0953 km = _____ dm

29. 42 kg = _____ hg

30. 7.2 hl = _____ cl

31. $30\dfrac{cm}{sec} =$ _____ $\dfrac{m}{hr}$

32. $20\dfrac{cg}{da} =$ _____ $\dfrac{g}{wk}$

33. $360\dfrac{kl}{hr} =$ _____ $\dfrac{ml}{min}$

Perform the indicated operations in Exercises 34–39.

34. 2.05 m
    +7.97 m

35. 382.6 ml
    + 23.8 ml

36. 983 kg
    −724 kg

37. 75.36 cm
    −28.71 cm

38. 16.3 m
    ×5

39. 16.3 m
    ×5 m

Solve each applied problem in Exercises 40–43.

40. **CHEMISTRY** For an experiment a technician needs 12.5-ml samples of a chemical. How many of the samples can he make up from a supply of 400 ml of this chemical?

41. **CONSUMER** If steak costs $6 per kilogram, how much would 600 grams of steak cost?

42. **TRAVEL** Gabi is traveling at $60\frac{km}{hr}$. How many meters per minute is this?

43. **RANCHING** A rancher needs 10 km of wire. How much will it cost him if the wire is 40¢ per meter?

CRITICAL THINKING

44. Complete: $50\dfrac{dl}{min} =$ _____ $\dfrac{hl}{hr}$

45. When Burford tried to convert 54.38 mg to hectograms, he realized that he must move the decimal point five places. When he did this he obtained an answer of 5,438,000 hg. What is Burford doing wrong?

46. Remembering the relative size of the various metric units can be very helpful when making conversions. For example, if you are to convert from km to cm, since km is a much larger unit of measure than cm, when converting a given number of km to cm, the result must be a much larger number. Use this concept and write a paragraph that would help Burford (in Exercise 5) remember which direction to move the decimal point.

47. Conversions in the metric system can be made simply by moving a decimal point. Explain why we cannot make the same statement for the English system.

48. Units of measure for length, volume, and weight in the metric system are very closely related. For example, a gram is the weight of the water in a cube that is 1 cm on a side. Give a discussion showing that a similar result does not follow for the English system.

REVIEW OR PREVIEW

Perform the indicated operations and simplify in Exercises 49–54.

49. 8 ft 11 in
    +1 ft 3 in

50. 8 lb 12 oz
    −3 lb 15 oz

51. 12 gal 2 qt 1 pt
    − 6 gal 3 qt 1 pt

52. $5 \times (7 \text{ yd } 2 \text{ ft } 10 \text{ in})$ 53. $(11 \text{ yd } 40 \text{ min}) \div 5$ 54. $42 \text{ ft} \div 7 \text{ ft}$

5.5 PARALLEL EXERCISES

Answers to these exercises are not given in the text.
Answer true or false in Exercises 1–6. If the answer is false, tell why.

1. The United States is one of the few countries in the world that uses the English system.

2. The opening in a normal doorway is about 2 meters high.

3. The liter is used to measure gasoline in the metric system.

4. One gram of meat is more than one pound of meat.

5. A large steak might weigh about one kilogram.

6. Units of weight in the metric system can be changed by moving the decimal point.

Complete each statement in Exercises 7–33 by moving the decimal point as shown in the examples.

7. $40 \text{ km} = \underline{\hspace{1cm}} \text{ m}$

8. $6 \text{ hl} = \underline{\hspace{1cm}} \text{ L}$

9. $0.05 \text{ dag} = \underline{\hspace{1cm}} \text{ g}$

10. $50 \text{ m} = \underline{\hspace{1cm}} \text{ dm}$

11. $0.061 \text{ mg} = \underline{\hspace{1cm}} \text{ g}$

12. $0.061 \text{ g} = \underline{\hspace{1cm}} \text{ mg}$

13. $420 \text{ g} = \underline{\hspace{1cm}} \text{ kg}$

14. $2300 \text{ cm} = \underline{\hspace{1cm}} \text{ m}$

15. $2.5 \text{ dal} = \underline{\hspace{1cm}} \text{ L}$

16. $6320 \text{ cm} = \underline{\hspace{1cm}} \text{ hm}$

17. $8.7 \text{ kg} = \underline{\hspace{1cm}} \text{ dag}$

18. $493,000 \text{ ml} = \underline{\hspace{1cm}} \text{ kl}$

19. $0.75 \text{ dm} = \underline{\hspace{1cm}} \text{ hm}$

20. $0.88 \text{ cg} = \underline{\hspace{1cm}} \text{ mg}$

21. $5.5 \text{ hl} = \underline{\hspace{1cm}} \text{ ml}$

22. $250 \text{ mm} = \underline{\hspace{1cm}} \text{ cm}$

23. $98,750 \text{ dg} = \underline{\hspace{1cm}} \text{ hg}$

24. $0.44 \text{ cl} = \underline{\hspace{1cm}} \text{ dal}$

25. $927 \text{ hm} = \underline{\hspace{1cm}} \text{ mm}$

26. $0.000082 \text{ dag} = \underline{\hspace{1cm}} \text{ mg}$

27. $200 \text{ dl} = \underline{\hspace{1cm}} \text{ kl}$

28. $0.000024 \text{ km} = \underline{\hspace{1cm}} \text{ dm}$

29. $0.081 \text{ kg} = \underline{\hspace{1cm}} \text{ hg}$

30. $4400 \text{ hl} = \underline{\hspace{1cm}} \text{ cl}$

31. $2 \dfrac{\text{cm}}{\text{sec}} = \underline{\hspace{1cm}} \dfrac{\text{m}}{\text{hr}}$

32. $500 \dfrac{\text{cg}}{\text{da}} = \underline{\hspace{1cm}} \dfrac{\text{g}}{\text{wk}}$

33. $0.06 \dfrac{\text{kl}}{\text{hr}} = \underline{\hspace{1cm}} \dfrac{\text{ml}}{\text{min}}$

Perform the indicated operations in Exercises 34–39.

34. $\begin{array}{r} 8.09 \text{ km} \\ +3.66 \text{ km} \\ \hline \end{array}$

35. $\begin{array}{r} 24.89 \text{ dl} \\ +13.77 \text{ dl} \\ \hline \end{array}$

36. $\begin{array}{r} 402 \text{ g} \\ -389 \text{ g} \\ \hline \end{array}$

37. $\begin{array}{r} 4.735 \text{ m} \\ -1.908 \text{ m} \\ \hline \end{array}$

38. $\begin{array}{r} 213.2 \text{ cm} \\ \times 8 \\ \hline \end{array}$

39. $\begin{array}{r} 213.2 \text{ cm} \\ \times 8 \text{ cm} \\ \hline \end{array}$

Solve each applied problem in Exercises 40–43.

40. **CHEMISTRY**   Each time a particular reaction takes place a technician collects 5.6 mg of a salt. How many times will the process have to be repeated to obtain 1.68 g of the salt?

41. **CONSUMER**   Peaches are marked at $1.20 per kilogram. How much will 4000 g of peaches cost?

42. **HYDROLOGY**   A water tank is being filled at the rate of 25 liters per minute. What is this in kiloliters per hour?

43. **CONSUMER**   A perfume is worth $2.60 per milliliter. How much would 5 liters cost?

CRITICAL THINKING

44. Complete: $120\dfrac{\text{cm}}{\text{hr}} = \underline{\qquad}\dfrac{\text{km}}{\text{sec}}$

45. Burford was asked to measure the diameter of a pencil and was pleased when he told his fellow classmates that the diameter was 7 meters. Was he even close? What units might be used to give a more reasonable answer?

46. Review the actual sizes of the units of mesurement in the metric system. Give Burford in Exercise 45 a written report that might keep him from making the same mistake again.

47 Give several advantages and disadvantages of both systems of measurement, the English system and the metric system. Which system do you prefer, and why?

48 Use your library, investigate the history of the metric system and consider how it has changed over the years. Also, determine precisely how the unit of length, the meter, came to be the length that we use today. Write a brief report of your findings.

GROUP PROJECT

In any number system the selection of the proper unit for a given measurement must be considered. For example, we would likely choose centimeters to measure the width of this page but certainly not the distance between cities. Of course, the idea is to choose a unit that gives the best "feel" for the measure. Have members of your group suggest a distance, weight, or volume to measure and discuss the most appropriate metric measurement unit. Can two different units work equally well?

5.6 CONVERSIONS BETWEEN MEASUREMENT SYSTEMS

STUDENT GUIDEPOSTS

1 CONVERTING UNITS OF LENGTH, VOLUME, AND WEIGHT
2 MEASURING SPEED IN BOTH SYSTEMS
3 MEASURING TEMPERATURE IN BOTH SYSTEMS

1 CONVERTING UNITS OF LENGTH, VOLUME, AND WEIGHT

If the United States ever changes to the metric system, it will not be necessary to change units from one system to another. But while both systems are in use it is important to know the relationship between the two.

In the table below are some useful conversion units of measure. Notice that these units are all approximations.

LENGTH, VOLUME, AND WEIGHT		
	Metric to English	*English to Metric*
Length units	1 km ≈ 0.621 mi	1 mi ≈ 1.61 km
	1 m ≈ 39.37 in	1 in ≈ 2.54 cm
Volume units	1 L ≈ 1.06 qt	1 qt ≈ 0.946 L
Weight units	1 kg ≈ 2.20 lb	1 lb ≈ 454 g

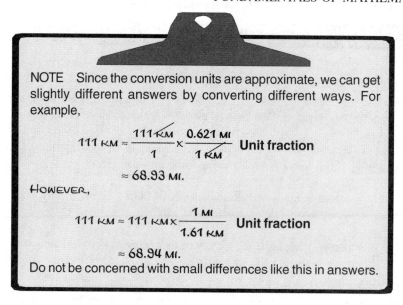

NOTE   Since the conversion units are approximate, we can get slightly different answers by converting different ways. For example,

$$111 \text{ KM} \approx \frac{111 \cancel{\text{ KM}}}{1} \times \frac{0.621 \text{ MI}}{1 \cancel{\text{ KM}}} \quad \textbf{Unit fraction}$$

$$\approx 68.93 \text{ MI.}$$

However,

$$111 \text{ KM} \approx 111 \text{ KM} \times \frac{1 \text{ MI}}{1.61 \text{ KM}} \quad \textbf{Unit fraction}$$

$$\approx 68.94 \text{ MI.}$$

Do not be concerned with small differences like this in answers.

Since we are familiar with the English units, these conversions will help us get a better idea of the size of the metric units. For example, on a quarter-mile track, a kilometer is about 2.5 times around. If two towns are 10 miles apart, they are about 16 km apart. A meter (39.37 in) is a little more than a yard (36 in). Figure 5.9 shows the relationship between centimeters and inches.

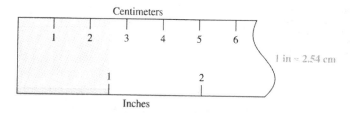

FIGURE 5.9

There is a little more milk in a liter container than there is in a quart, as shown in Figure 5.10.

FIGURE 5.10

We now know that the 1-kg steak mentioned in Section 5.5 weighs 2.2 lb. Figure 5.11 shows the relative sizes of 1 lb and 1 kg of the same material.

FIGURE 5.11

The following examples show some conversions between the two systems. In most of these problems a calculator is helpful.

EXPLORATION GUIDE

When converting from a metric measure to an English measure, or conversely, we must have knowledge of the basic conversion facts. However, it is also helpful if we have some idea of relative size in each system because then we can make approximations that will enable us to check our work. Discuss why this is true by considering, for example, that a liter is just a little more than a quart, that 5 kilometers is a little more than 3 miles, and that 5 kilograms is about 11 pounds.

E X A M P L E 1 CONVERTING MEASURES OF LENGTH

(a) 20 km = _____ mi.

Since $0.621 \text{ mi} \approx 1 \text{ km}$, the unit fraction is $\frac{0.621 \text{ mi}}{1 \text{ km}}$.

$$20 \text{ km} = \underline{\quad} 20 \text{ km} \times \mathbf{1}$$

$$\approx \frac{20 \cancel{\text{ km}}}{1} \times \frac{\mathbf{0.621 \text{ mi}}}{\mathbf{1 \cancel{\text{ km}}}}$$ Multiply by the unit fraction

$$= 20 \times (0.621) \text{ km}$$

$$\approx 12.4 \text{ mi}$$ Rounded to the nearest tenth

(a) 44 km = _____ mi.

(b) 35 mi = _____ km.

Multiply by the unit fraction $\frac{1.61 \text{ km}}{1 \text{ mi}}$.

$$35 \text{ mi} = 35 \text{ mi} \times \mathbf{1}$$

$$\approx \frac{35 \cancel{\text{ mi}}}{1} \times \frac{\mathbf{1.61 \text{ km}}}{\mathbf{1 \cancel{\text{ mi}}}}$$ Multiply by the unit fraction

$$= 35 \times 1.61 \text{ km}$$

$$\approx 56.4 \text{ km}$$ Rounded to the nearest tenth

(b) 120 mi = _____ km.

(c) $18\frac{3}{4}$ in = _____ cm.

The unit fraction is $\frac{2.54 \text{ cm}}{1 \text{ in}}$.

$$18\frac{3}{4} \text{ in} = 18.75 \text{ in} \times \mathbf{1}$$

$$\approx \frac{18.75 \cancel{\text{ in}}}{1} \times \frac{\mathbf{2.54 \text{ cm}}}{\mathbf{1 \cancel{\text{ in}}}}$$

$$= (18.75)(2.54) \text{ cm}$$

$$\approx 47.63 \text{ cm}$$ Rounded to the nearest hundredth

(c) $216\frac{1}{2}$ in = _____ cm.

E X A M P L E 2 CONVERTING MEASURES OF SPEED

Joe is driving at a rate of $95\frac{\text{km}}{\text{hr}}$. What is his speed in miles per hour?

$$95\frac{\text{km}}{\text{hr}} \approx \frac{95 \cancel{\text{ km}}}{\text{hr}} \times \frac{\mathbf{0.621 \text{ mi}}}{\mathbf{1 \text{ km}}}$$ Unit fraction

$$\approx 59\frac{\text{mi}}{\text{hr}}$$ Rounded to the nearest mile per hour

Vera is driving $50\frac{\text{km}}{\text{hr}}$ in a $30\frac{\text{mi}}{\text{hr}}$ zone. Approximately how many miles per hour is she traveling over the speed limit?

Answer: She is about $1\frac{\text{mi}}{\text{hr}}$ over the speed limit.

2 SPEED IN BOTH SYSTEMS

Figure 5.12 shows a comparison of some common speed limits. Approximations are to the nearest kilometer per hour. A speed of $55\frac{\text{mi}}{\text{hr}}$ is about $89\frac{\text{km}}{\text{hr}}$.

Kilometers per hour	24	40	56	72	89	105

$1\frac{\text{mi}}{\text{hr}} \approx 1.61 \frac{\text{km}}{\text{hr}}$

Miles per hour	15	25	35	45	55	65

FIGURE 5.12

| PRACTICE EXERCISE 3 | CONVERTING OF MILLILITERS TO QUARTS | EXAMPLE 3 |

PRACTICE EXERCISE 3

1020 ml = _____ qt.

CONVERTING OF MILLILITERS TO QUARTS — **EXAMPLE 3**

520 ml = _____ qt.

Since the unit fraction that we know is $\frac{1.06 \text{ qt}}{1 \text{ L}}$, first change 520 ml to liters.

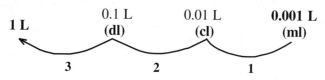

$$1 \text{ L} \qquad \begin{array}{c} 0.1 \text{ L} \\ (\text{dl}) \end{array} \qquad \begin{array}{c} 0.01 \text{ L} \\ (\text{cl}) \end{array} \qquad \begin{array}{c} \mathbf{0.001 \text{ L}} \\ (\mathbf{ml}) \end{array}$$

$$3 \qquad\qquad 2 \qquad\qquad 1$$

$$520 \text{ ml} = 0.520 \text{ L}$$

$$0.520 \text{ L} \approx \frac{0.52 \text{ L}}{1} \times \frac{\mathbf{1.06 \text{ qt}}}{\mathbf{1 \text{ L}}}$$

$$= (0.52)(1.06) \text{ qt}$$

Answer: 1.08

$$\approx 0.55 \text{ qt} \qquad \text{Rounded to the nearest hundredth}$$

PRACTICE EXERCISE 4

Deb has a foreign car with a 40-L gas tank. How many gallons does the tank hold?

CONVERTING GALLONS TO LITERS — **EXAMPLE 4**

The gasoline tank on Roberto's car holds 12.6 gal. How many liters will it hold?

$$12.6 \text{ gal} = \frac{12.6 \text{ gal}}{1} \times \frac{\mathbf{4 \text{ qt}}}{\mathbf{1 \text{ gal}}} \qquad \text{Change 12.6 gal to quarts}$$

$$= (12.6)(4) \text{ qt}$$

$$= 50.4 \text{ qt}$$

$$50.4 \text{ qt} \approx \frac{50.4 \text{ qt}}{1} \times \frac{\mathbf{0.946 \text{ L}}}{\mathbf{1 \text{ qt}}} \qquad \text{Change quarts to liters}$$

$$= (50.4)(0.946) \text{ L}$$

Answer: 10.6 gal

$$\approx 47.7 \text{ L} \qquad \text{To the nearest tenth}$$

PRACTICE EXERCISE 5

2240 dg = _____ lb.

CONVERTING HECTOGRAMS TO POUNDS — **EXAMPLE 5**

68.2 hg = _____ lb.

The unit fraction is $\frac{2.20 \text{ lb}}{1 \text{ kg}}$. First, change 62.8 hg to kilograms.

$$\begin{array}{cc} \mathbf{1000g} & \mathbf{100g} \\ (\mathbf{1kg}) & (\mathbf{1hg}) \end{array} \qquad 68.2 \text{ hg} = 6.82\text{kg}$$

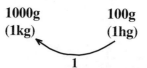

$$1$$

$$6.82 \text{ kg} \approx \frac{6.82 \text{ kg}}{1} \times \frac{\mathbf{2.20 \text{ lb}}}{\mathbf{1 \text{ kg}}} \qquad \text{Change kilograms to pounds}$$

Answer: 0.49

$$= (6.82)(2.20) \text{ lb}$$

$$= 15.0 \text{ lb} \qquad \text{To the nearest tenth}$$

E X A M P L E 6	CONVERTING POUNDS TO KILOGRAMS

A football team's starting fullback weighs 200 lb. How many kilograms does he weigh?

$$200 \text{ lb} \approx \frac{200 \text{ lb}}{1} \times \frac{454 \text{ g}}{1 \text{ lb}}$$

$$= (200)(454) \text{ g}$$

$$= 90{,}800 \text{ g}$$

A foreign basketball player trying to break into the NBA reported his weight as 97 kg. How many pounds does he weigh?

Change 90,800 g to kilograms.

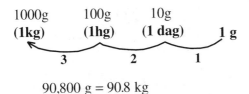

$$90{,}800 \text{ g} = 90.8 \text{ kg}$$

Answer: 213 lb

The following table gives comparisons of common weights of people in pounds and kilograms (to the nearest kilogram).

Pounds	Kilograms
100	45
125	57
150	68
175	79
200	91
225	102
250	114

3 TEMPERATURE IN BOTH SYSTEMS

The temperature scale used in the metric system is the **Celsius** (°C) scale. Water freezes at 0°C (32°F) and boils at 100°C (212°F). Figure 5.13 shows a comparison between degrees **Fahrenheit** (°F) and degrees Celsius. (In the past Celsius was called *centigrade*.)

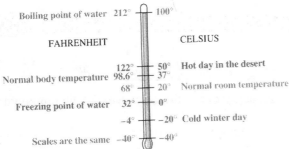

FIGURE 5.13

The equal temperatures on the scale in Figure 5.13 can be found once we know the relationship between the two scales. For example, using the following rules we can find that $20°C = 68°C$.

EXPLORATION GUIDE

The relationship between temperature measurements

$$F = 1.8C + 32$$

and

$$C = \frac{5}{9}(F - 32)$$

are referred to as rules in the text. Can you give them other names? As you begin to study algebra you will be able to give a more complete discussion of this topic.

TO CONVERT FROM °C TO °F

Multiply C, the temperature in °C, by $\frac{9}{5} = 1.8$ and add 32.

$$F = \frac{9}{5}C + 32 \quad \text{or} \quad F = 1.8C + 32$$

PRACTICE EXERCISE 7

$35°C = \underline{\quad\quad}°F.$

CONVERTING CELSIUS TO FAHRENHEIT   EXAMPLE 7

$20°C = \underline{\quad\quad}°F.$

$$F = \frac{9}{5}C + 32$$

$$F = \frac{9}{5}\mathbf{20} + 32 \qquad \text{Substitute 20 for } C$$

$$= \frac{9 \cdot 20}{5} + 32 \qquad \text{Multiply before adding}$$

$$= \frac{9 \cdot 4 \cdot 5}{5} + 32$$

$$= 36 + 32 = 68$$

Answer: 95

Thus, 20°C is 68°F.

TO CONVERT FROM °F TO °C

First subtract 32 from F, the temperature in °F, then multiply by $\frac{5}{9}$.

$$C = \frac{5}{9}(F - 32)$$

PRACTICE EXERCISE 8

$86°F = \underline{\quad\quad}°C.$

CONVERTING FAHRENHEIT TO CELSIUS   EXAMPLE 8

$122°F = \underline{\quad\quad}°C.$

$$C = \frac{5}{9}(F - 32)$$

$$= \frac{5}{9}(\mathbf{122} - 32) \qquad \text{Substitute 122 for } F$$

$$= \frac{5}{9}(90) \qquad \text{Subtract inside parentheses first}$$

$$= \frac{5 \cdot 9 \cdot 10}{9} = 50 \qquad \text{Then multiply}$$

Answer: 30

Thus, 122°F is 50°C.

PRACTICE EXERCISE 9

Would you go swimming in water which has a temperature of 25°C?

APPLYING TEMPERATURE CONVERSION   EXAMPLE 9

You are going to a ballgame and the weatherman says the temperature will be 30°C. What kind of clothes should you wear?

If you have a better understanding of °F, change °C to °F using

$$F = \frac{9}{5}C + 32$$

$$F = \frac{9}{5}\mathbf{30} + 32 \qquad C = 30$$

$$= \frac{9 \cdot 30}{5} + 32$$

$$= \frac{9 \cdot 5 \cdot 6}{5} + 32$$

$$= 54 + 32 = 86$$

Answer: 77°F water would be fine for swimming.

Thus, $30°C = 86°C$, and you should wear light clothing.

5.6 EXERCISES

Answers to these exercises are given on page 651.

1. Which is longer, 1 mi or 1 km?

2. Which is longer, 3 cm or 1 in?

3. Which is more, 1 qt or 1 L?

4. Which is more, 1 kg or 3 lb?

Complete each statement in Exercises 5–22.

5. 16 km = _____ mi $\frac{16 km}{1} = \frac{1 m}{1.61}$ 9.937

6. 128 mi = _____ km $128 mi \cdot \frac{1.61 km}{1}$

7. 2.6 m = _____ in

8. 72 in = _____ cm

9. 3 km = _____ ft

10. 3.2 ft = _____ cm

11. $80 \dfrac{km}{hr}$ = _____ $\dfrac{mi}{hr}$ $\frac{80 km}{1 hr} \cdot \frac{1 mi}{1.61}$

12. $20 \dfrac{mi}{hr}$ = _____ $\dfrac{km}{hr}$

13. 20 qt = _____ L

14. 40 L = _____ gal

15. 50 kg = _____ lb $\frac{50 kg}{1} \cdot \frac{2.20}{1}$

16. 5 lb = _____ g

17. 0.25 kg = _____ oz

18. 625 lb = _____ kg

19. 40°C = _101_ °F

20. 50°F = _10_ °C

21. 200°C = _____ °F

22. 200°F = _____ °C

Solve each applied problem in Exercises 23-26.

23. **CONSUMER** Caralee Woods rented a car with a 13.7 gallon gas tank. How many liters will the tank hold?

24. **TRAVEL** Winston was driving in Mexico where the speed limit was $100 \dfrac{km}{kr}$. What is this in miles per hour?

25. **SPORTS** The average weight of the starting line of a football team is 258 lb. What is this in kilograms?

26. **TEMPERATURE** Would you put your hand in water at 95°C?

CALCULATOR EXERCISES

Use a calculator to complete each statement in Exercises 27–29. Give answers rounded to the nearest hundredth.

27. 17.65 pt = _____ L

28. $3\dfrac{1}{9}$ m = _____ in

29. 4.65 kg = _____ oz

CRITICAL THINKING

30. Burford and his best friend Chuck were asked to convert 100 miles to kilometers. Burford's work is shown below.

$$100 \text{ mi} = \frac{100 \text{ mi}}{1} \times \frac{1 \text{ km}}{0.621 \text{ mi}} = \frac{100}{0.621} \text{ km} = 161.0305958 \text{ km}$$

Chuck's work is shown on the following page.

$\dfrac{18}{1} \cdot \dfrac{5}{9} = \dfrac{90}{9}$

$$100 \text{ mi} = \frac{100 \text{ mi}}{1} \times \frac{1.61 \text{ km}}{1 \text{ mi}} = (100)(1.61) \text{ km} = 161 \text{ km}$$

Since their answers were different, they began to argue about which was correct. Can you explain to them that they are both correct before a fight breaks out?

REVIEW OR PREVIEW

Complete each statement in Exercises 31–33 using an appropriate diagram.

31. 720 mm = _____ cm

32. 0.45 g = _____ mg

33. 0.0021 kl = _____ ml

The following exercises will help you prepare for Chapter 6. Change each fraction or mixed number in Exercises 34–36 to a decimal.

34. $\dfrac{13}{4}$

35. $2\dfrac{5}{11}$

36. $\dfrac{4}{5}$

Change each decimal in Exercises 37–39 to a fraction or mixed number.

37. 0.3

38. 0.14

39. 5.6

40. Change $\dfrac{4}{7}$ to a decimal, rounded to the nearest hundredth.

5.6 PARALLEL EXERCISES

Answers to these exercises are not given in the text.

💡 1. Which is longer, 1 dm or 1 in?

💡 2. Which is longer, 10 mi or 17 km?

💡 3. Which is more, 1 gal or 4 L?

💡 4. Which is more, 500 g or 1 lb?

🖩 Complete each statement in Exercises 5–22.

5. 125 km = _____ mi

6. 48 mi = _____ km

7. 0.056 m = _____ in

8. 9.5 in = _____ cm

9. 0.05 km = _____ ft

10. 0.15 ft = _____ cm

11. $25\dfrac{\text{km}}{\text{hr}} =$ _____ $\dfrac{\text{mi}}{\text{hr}}$

12. $100\dfrac{\text{mi}}{\text{hr}} =$ _____ $\dfrac{\text{km}}{\text{hr}}$

13. 0.5 qt = _____ L

14. 8.5 L = _____ gal

15. 0.2 kg = _____ lb

16. $\dfrac{1}{2}$ lb = _____ g

17. 0.0046 kg = _____ oz

18. 85 lb = _____ kg

19. 15°C = _____ °F

20. 77°F = _____ °C

21. 1000°C = _____ °F

22. 1000°F = _____ °C

🖩 Solve each applied problem in Exercises 23–26.

23. **CONSUMER** Joseph Seniw knows that a car that he is considering buying has a 45.6-liter gas tank. How many gallons will the tank hold?

24. **TRAVEL** Patricia's speedometer reads in kilometers per hour. How fast can she legally drive where the speed limit is $45\dfrac{\text{mi}}{\text{hr}}$?

25. **SPORTS** Willy must have his weight down to 82 kg to compete in Europe. What is this in pounds?

26. **TEMPERATURE** Instructions call for a temperature control to be at 65°C. What is this in °F?

CALCULATOR EXERCISES

 Use a calculator to complete each statement in Exercises 27–29. Give answers rounded to the nearest hundredth.

27. $75\dfrac{km}{hr} =$ _____ $\dfrac{ft}{sec}$

28. $77.2°C =$ _____ °F

29. $15.5°F =$ _____ °C

CRITICAL THINKING

30. Burford and his friend Chuck were working together on converting 5°F to the Celsius scale. Here is their work.

$$C = \frac{5}{9}(F - 32)$$

$$= \frac{5}{9}(5 - 32)$$

$$= \frac{5}{9}(-27) = -15$$

After step two Burford began to object and refused to do any more. He said that there was no such temperature as −15°C. Can you help Chuck explain to him that there are signed numbers such as −15?

GROUP PROJECT

 When we are asked, "About how much water is in 5 liters?", most of us will try to think in terms of quarts when we give our answer. We might think: *A little more than 5 quarts.* Consider how a student in a European country would respond to this same question. Explain why we normally relate metric measures back to the English system. If the European student were asked, "About how much water is in 5 quarts?", discuss what might be his/her thought process.

CHAPTER 5 REVIEW

KEY WORDS

 5.1

- A **ratio** is a comparison of two numbers using division.
- An equation which states that two ratios are equal is a **proportion.**
- When two pairs of numbers have the same ratio, the numbers are **proportional.**
- **Solving a proportion** is the process of finding a missing number in a proportion.

5.2

- A **rate** is a ratio used to compare two quantities that involve different units or different measures.
- A rate is called **simplified** when all common factors of the numbers in the rate have been divided out.
- A **unit rate** is a rate with the number in the denominator equal to 1.

5.3

- The **English system** is the measurement system used in the United States.
- A **unit fraction** is a fraction which has value 1 and is used to make measurement conversions.

5.5

- The **metric system** is the system of measurement used in most of the countries of the world. The **meter** is the basic unit for length, the **liter** is the basic unit for volume, and the **gram** is the basic unit for weight.

5.6

- The **Celsius** scale is the temperature scale used in the metric system.
- The **Fahrenheit** scale is the temperature scale used in the English system.

KEY CONCEPTS

5.1

1. Ratios can be expressed in three ways, 2:3 or 2 to 3 or $\frac{2}{3}$. The latter form is the fractional form of the ratio.
2. To solve a proportion involving a missing number a, equate the cross products and divide the numerical cross product by the multiplier of a.

5.2

Two excellent examples of the use of rates are speed and unit pricing.

5.5

1. In the metric system, conversions in units can be made by moving the decimal point.
2. A meter is about half the height of a doorway opening. A liter is the volume of a cube 0.1 m (1 dm) on a side. A gram is the weight of water that can be put in a cube 0.01 m (1 cm) on a side.

5.6

1. To change °C to °F, use $F = \frac{9}{5}C + 32$.
2. To change °F to °C, use $C = \frac{5}{9}(F - 32)$.

CHAPTER 5 REVIEW EXERCISES

PART I

Answers to these exercises are given on page 651.

 5.1

💡 1. Write the fraction form for the ratio 8 to 5.

💡 2. Write the ratio which is indicated by the fraction $\frac{1}{8}$.

Solve each proportion in Exercises 3–4.

3. $\dfrac{a}{8} = \dfrac{1}{2}$

4. $\dfrac{7}{21} = \dfrac{6}{a}$

5. **POLITICS** Before the election 330 out of 600 voters who were surveyed said that they would vote for Joe Lingerfelt for state representative. If the survey accurately predicted the vote and 21,520 people voted in the election, how many voted for Joe?

6. **MAP READING** If $\frac{1}{2}$ inch on a map represents 20 miles, how many miles will be represented by $5\frac{1}{2}$ inches?

7. Write $\frac{364 \text{ miles}}{8 \text{ hours}}$ as a simplified rate.

8. Write $\frac{364 \text{ miles}}{8 \text{ hours}}$ as a unit rate.

In Exercises 9-10, write as a unit rate.

9. 20 computer disks for $30

10. 28 hours to split 8 cords of wood

11. **CONSUMER** A 21-ounce package of longhorn cheese costs $4.29. Find the unit price in cents per ounce, correct to the nearest tenth of a cent.

5.3

Complete each statement in Exercises 12–17.

12. 7 ft = _____ in

13. 30 in = _____ ft

14. 48 fl oz = _____ pt

15. 90 min = _____ hr

16. 3 ton = _____ lb

17. 18 pt = _____ gal

5.4

Perform the indicated operation and simplify in Exercises 18–27.

18.
   10 ft 3 in
   + 7 ft 2 in

19.
   10 ft 3 in
   − 7 ft 2 in

20.
   18 hr 22 min
   + 5 hr 56 min

21.
   18 hr 22 min
   − 5 hr 56 min

22.
   12 yd 2 ft 2 in
   + 6 yd 2 ft 8 in

23.
   12 yd 2 ft 2 in
   − 6 yd 2 ft 8 in

24. $3 \times (5 \text{ gal } 3 \text{ qt } 1 \text{ pt})$

25. $8 \text{ ft} \times 3 \text{ ft}$

26. $(8 \text{ lb } 13 \text{ oz}) \div 3$

27. $18 \text{ dollars} \div 3 \text{ dollars}$

5.5

Complete each statement in Exercises 28–33.

28. 860 m = _____ km

29. 0.582 m = _____ cm

30. 483 ml = _____ dl

31. 48,300 mg = _____ kg

32. 0.00035 km = _____ dm

33. 5.6 L = _____ cl

Perform the indicated operation in Exercises 34–36.

34.
   15.2 m
   + 75.3 m

35.
   831.6 L
   − 416.9 L

36.
   42.8 g
   × 7

5.6

Complete each statement in Exercises 37–42.

37. 12 km = _____ mi

38. 420 in = _____ m

39. $50\dfrac{mi}{hr}$ = _____ $\dfrac{km}{hr}$

40. 22 qt = _____ L

41. 18 L = _____ gal

42. 16 lb = _____ g

43. **TEMPERATURE** Would water at 65°C feel cool to your hand?

44. **CONSUMER** If your Italian car has a 54-liter gas tank, how many gallons will it hold?

PART II

Complete each statement in Exercises 45–53.

45. 0.032 kg = _____ oz

46. 7.8 ft = _____ cm

47. 114° F = _____ °C

48. 6.35 dg = _____ dag

49. 9900 ml = _____ hl

50. 0.0008 g = _____ cg

51. 1 hr = _____ sec

52. 3200 oz = _____ ton

53. $22\dfrac{ft}{sec}$ = _____ $\dfrac{mi}{hr}$

Solve each applied problem in Exercises 54–57

54. **MEDICINE** A compound used to make a medicine costs $39.95 per gram. How much will a company be billed for 3.25 kilograms of the compound?

55. **ELECTRICITY** An electrician needs 60 yd of wire. What will be the total cost if the wire is 50¢ per foot?

56. **BAKING** If it takes 2 lb 4 oz of flour to make a loaf of bread, how much will it take to make 5 loaves?

57. **TRAVEL** A car can go 450 miles on 18 gallons of gas. How far can the car go on 32 gallons of gas?

58. Write $\dfrac{42 \text{ gallons}}{15 \text{ seconds}}$ as a simplified rate.

59. Write $\dfrac{42 \text{ gallons}}{15 \text{ seconds}}$ as a unit rate.

60. In which measurement system can conversions be made by simply moving a decimal point?

In Exercises 61–64 determine the ratios from the data given in the table below. Give answers as a decimal fraction correct to two decimal places.

Value of Privately Owned Nonresidential Building Projects, by Construction Status, 1986 to 1994, and by Type of Project, 1994

[In billions of dollars]

CONSTRUCTION STATUS	1986	1987	1988	1989	1990	1991	1992	1993	1994				
									Total	Indus-trial	Office Build-ing	Other Com-mer-cial	Other[1]
Value of projects-- Started	97.1	95.7	107.7	109.9	89.5	72.9	81.3	81.3	91.8	16.3	17.2	32.0	26.2
Completed	107.5	91.4	101.6	107.7	114.0	109.5	100.1	94.8	103.5	23.9	18.2	31.7	29.6

[1] Privately owned hotels and motels, religious, educational, hospital and institutional, and miscellaneous nonresidential building projects.
Source: U.S. Bureau of the Census, *Current Construction Reports,* series C30

61. Determine the ratio of the value of building projects started in 1986 to the value of those completed in 1986.

62. Determine the ratio of the value of building projects completed in 1990 to the value of those completed in 1992.

63. Determine the ratio of the value of office buildings started in 1994 to the value of industrial projects started in 1994.

64. Determine the ratio of the value of other commercial projects completed in 1994 to the value of the total completed in 1994.

CHAPTER 5 TEST

Answers to this test are given on page 651.

1. Write the fractional form for the ratio 13 to 7.

    1. _____

2. Write the ratio that is indicated by the fraction $\frac{13}{5}$.

    2. _____

3. Solve the proportion. $\dfrac{12}{a} = \dfrac{72}{18}$

    3. _____

4. A steel cable 35 feet long weighs 105 pounds. How much will 93 feet of the same cable weigh?

    4. _____

5. Write as a unit rate.

    400 pages printed in 80 minutes

    5. _____

6. If a tree 18 ft tall casts a shadow 3 ft long, how tall is a building that casts a shadow 51 ft long at the same instant?

    6. _____

7. If $\frac{1}{2}$ inch on a map represents 50 miles, how many miles are represented by $3\frac{1}{4}$ inches on the map?

    7. _____

Complete the change in units.

8. 40 oz = ___?___ lb

    8. _____

9. 2800 ml = ___?___ hl

    9. _____

10. 6.5 kg = ___?___ lb

    10. _____

11. 65°C = ___?___ °F

    11. _____

12. 30 qt = ___?___ L

    12. _____

13. 450 mi = ___?___ km

    13. _____

14. Perform the indicated operation and simplify. $\begin{array}{r} 12\,\text{yd}\,2\,\text{ft}\,3\,\text{in} \\ -\ 3\,\text{yd}\,2\,\text{ft}\,8\,\text{in} \\ \hline \end{array}$

    14. _____

15. If 9 inches of ribbon cost $3.15, how much would 3 m of the ribbon cost?

    15. _____

16. The following is the statement of a proportion problem: If 11 feet of cable weighs 6 pounds, how much would 132 feet of the same cable weigh? Which of the following proportions describe this problem?

    $$\frac{a}{132} = \frac{6}{11}; \quad \frac{132}{a} = \frac{11}{6}; \quad \frac{a}{6} = \frac{132}{11}; \quad \frac{6}{a} = \frac{11}{132}$$

    16. _____

Answer true *or* false. *If the answer is false, tell why.*

17. The meter would be the best metric measure to use to report distance between cities.

    17. _____

18. A kilogram is more than 2 pounds

    18. _____

19. One gallon is less than four liters.

    19. _____

20. If the temperature were 50°C, it would be a very hot day.

    20. _____

CUMULATIVE REVIEW: CHAPTERS 1–5

Answers to these exercises are given on page 651.

Find the LCM of the numbers in Exercises 1–3.

1. 60 and 9

2. 35 and 14

3. 10, 16, and 24

Solve each proportion in Exercises 4–6

4. $\dfrac{3}{5} = \dfrac{a}{20}$

5. $\dfrac{7}{22} = \dfrac{a}{11}$

6. $\dfrac{15}{a} = \dfrac{3}{4}$

Reduce each fraction in Exercises 7–9.

7. $\dfrac{144}{24}$

8. $\dfrac{135}{155}$

9. $\dfrac{2000}{840}$

In Exercises 10–12 change each improper fraction to a mixed number.

10. $\dfrac{21}{4}$

11. $\dfrac{100}{3}$

12. $\dfrac{32}{14}$

In Exercises 13–18 perform the indicated operations.

13. 8 ft 7 in
    +9 ft 11 in

14. 12 ft 9 in
    − 3 ft 10 in

15. 1672.41
    − 419.86

16. $\sqrt{\dfrac{50}{8}} - \left(\dfrac{3}{2}\right)^2$

17. $\dfrac{3}{8} - \dfrac{1}{4}$

18. $\dfrac{1}{2} \div \left(6 - \dfrac{1}{4}\right)$

19. Write $\dfrac{240 \text{ miles}}{4 \text{ hours}}$ as a unit rate.

20. Complete: $230\,\text{cm} = $ _____ mm

21. Complete: 20 lb = _____ g

22. Complete: $122°\,\text{F} = $ _____ °C

Solve each applied problem in Exercises 23–24.

23. **BUSINESS** Antwine bought a coat on sale. If the original price of the coat was $185 and it was discounted $40, how much change did he receive if he paid with two $100 bills?

24. **TRAVEL** At the start of a trip, the odometer on a car read 48,263 miles. At the end of the trip it read 51,191 miles. What distance was traveled on the trip?

In Exercises 25-26, add on the number line.

25. $4 + 4 + 7$

26. $1 + 5 + 1$

CHAPTER *s·i·x*

PERCENT

Another common way to represent fractions or ratios is to use percent. The word *percent* is derived from the Latin words *per centum,* which literally mean *by the hundred.* Thus, a percent is really a fraction with denominator 100. Percents have been used since the fifteenth century in various business and interest problems. The percent sign, %, is thought to have evolved from the manuscript of an unknown Italian author in the early 1400s. By about 1650, the abbreviation for percent was "per $\frac{0}{0}$" Later on the "per" was deleted and $\frac{0}{0}$ eventually became %. We will consider two approaches to solving problems involving percent: the basic percent equation and the basic percent proportion. Many applied problems today make use of percent, and we see many references to percent in daily newspapers and magazines. One such application is presented below.

STATE AND LOCAL TAXES An average family of four (two wage earners and two children of school age), owning their own home and living in cities that collect taxes on state and local sales, automobile registration, and real estate must pay a certain portion of their income for these taxes. The tax amount is related to the income level of the family as well as where the family lives in the United States. The estimated state and local taxes paid by a family with an annual income of $50,000 who lived in several selected cities in 1992 is presented in the table below.

CITY	TOTAL TAXES PAID BY A FAMILY WITH INCOME OF $50,000	TOTAL TAXES PAID AS A PERCENT OF INCOME
Aluquerque, NM	$3434	6.9%
Atlanta, GA	$5593	11.2%
Charlotte, NC	$4412	8.8%
Columbus, OH	$4713	
Memphis, TN	$2896	5.8%
Newark, NJ	$11,445	
Virginia Beach, VA	$4423	8.8%

Source: Government of the District of Columbia, Department of Finance and Revenue

Although the actual amount of tax paid is interesting to note, it is also revealing to consider the taxes paid as a percent of annual income (the right hand column of the table). We will complete this column in both Example 6 and Practice Exercise 6 in Section 6.3.

We begin this chapter by considering the basic concept of percent and examining various percent conversions. We then describe two methods for solving percent problems, and illustrate these techniques by considering consumer and business applications that involve taxes, commission, discounts, interest, percent increase and decrease, and markup and markdown. In each example we will present parallel solutions using both approaches to percent so that you can choose the technique with which you feel more comfortable.

6.1 PERCENT AND PERCENT CONVERSIONS

STUDENT GUIDEPOSTS	
1	INVESTIGATING THE MEANING OF PERCENT
2	CHANGING A PERCENT TO A FRACTION
3	CHANGING A PERCENT TO A DECIMAL
4	CHANGING A DECIMAL TO A PERCENT
5	CHANGING A FRACTION TO A PERCENT

1 THE MEANING OF PERCENT

The idea of percent and the percent symbol (%) are used widely in our society. We may pay a five-percent (5%) sales tax, read that Mr. Gomez won the election with 52% of the vote, or hear that a basketball player hit 80% of his free throws.

The word **percent** means "per hundred." That is, it refers to the number of parts in each one hundred parts. For example, when the tax rate is 5%, we pay 5¢ tax on each 100¢ purchase.

$$\text{Percent: } 5\% \qquad \text{Fraction or ratio: } \frac{5}{100}$$

In Figure 6.1, the five shaded coins (5¢) correspond to 5% tax on the one hundred coins (100¢).

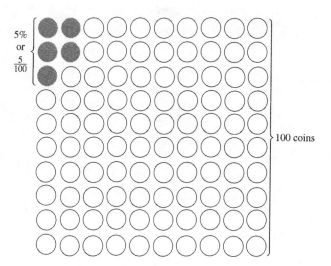

FIGURE 6.1

Thus, $\quad$ **5% is** $\dfrac{5}{100}$ **or** $5 \times \dfrac{1}{100}$ **or** $5 \times 0.01.$

2 CHANGING A PERCENT TO A FRACTION

If Mr. Gomez received 52 out of every 100 votes, then he got 52% of the vote.

$$\text{Percent: } 52\% \qquad \text{Fraction or ratio: } \frac{52}{100}$$

> **NOTE** The words "out of" can be replaced with a division bar. Notice above how "52 out of every 100 votes" became the fraction $\frac{52}{100}$.

A basketball player could have hit 8 out of 10 (or 80 out of 100) free throws which we shall see is 80%.

Percent: 80%   Fraction or ratio: $\dfrac{80}{100} = \dfrac{8}{10}$

We also hear on the news that the price of gasoline is 250% of its price several years ago.

Percent: 250%   Fraction or ratio: $\dfrac{250}{100} = 2.5$

Thus, 250% means that the price of gasoline is 2.5 times what it was several years ago.

There are also percents less than 1%. For example, the cost of living might increase 0.8% during the month of December.

Percent: 0.8%   Fraction or ratio: $\dfrac{0.8}{100} = \dfrac{(0.8)(10)}{(100)(10)} = \dfrac{8}{1000}$

In each of these examples, the percent was changed to a fraction by removing the percent symbol (%) and dividing by 100. Since dividing by 100 is the same as multiplying by $\dfrac{1}{100}$, we can form the following rule.

TO CHANGE A PERCENT TO A FRACTION

1. Replace the % symbol with either $\left(\times \dfrac{1}{100} \right)$ or $(\div 100)$.

2. Evaluate and then reduce the fraction.

EXAMPLE 1 **CHANGING PERCENTS TO FRACTIONS**

Change each percent to a fraction.

(a) $38\% = 38 \times \dfrac{1}{100} = \dfrac{38}{100} = \dfrac{\cancel{19} \cdot 2}{\cancel{50} \cdot 2} = \dfrac{19}{50}$ Replace % with ($\times$ 1/100) and reduce the fraction

(b) $500\% = 500 \times \dfrac{1}{100} = \dfrac{500}{100} = \dfrac{5 \cdot \cancel{100}}{1 \cdot \cancel{100}} = \dfrac{5}{1} = 5$

(c) $0.3\% = \dfrac{3}{10}\% = \dfrac{3}{10} \times \dfrac{1}{100} = \dfrac{3}{1000}$

(d) $2\dfrac{3}{4}\% = \left(2\dfrac{3}{4} \right)\left(\dfrac{1}{100} \right)$

$= \dfrac{11}{4} \cdot \dfrac{1}{100} = \dfrac{11}{400}$ Note: $2\dfrac{3}{4} = \dfrac{4 \cdot 2 + 3}{4} = \dfrac{11}{4}$

(e) $66\dfrac{2}{3}\% = \left(66\dfrac{2}{3} \right)\left(\dfrac{1}{100} \right)$

$= \left(\dfrac{200}{3} \right)\left(\dfrac{1}{100} \right)$ Note: $66\dfrac{2}{3} = \dfrac{3 \cdot 66 + 2}{3} = \dfrac{200}{3}$

$= \dfrac{2 \cdot \cancel{100}}{3 \cdot \cancel{100}} = \dfrac{2}{3}$

(f) $100\% = 100 \div 100 = \dfrac{100}{100} = 1$

PRACTICE EXERCISE 1

Change each percent to a fraction.

(a) 25%

(b) 300%

(c) 0.5%

(d) $3\dfrac{1}{5}\%$

(e) $33\dfrac{1}{3}\%$

(f) 1000%

Answers:

(a) $\dfrac{1}{4}$ (b) 3 (c) $\dfrac{1}{200}$

(d) $\dfrac{4}{125}$ (e) $\dfrac{1}{3}$ (f) 10

3 | **CHANGING A PERCENT TO A DECIMAL**

Percents are frequently given as decimals. Changing to a decimal fraction is exactly the same as changing to any other fraction; simply remove the % symbol and multiply by $\dfrac{1}{100}$, which is 0.01 in decimal form.

TO CHANGE A PERCENT TO A DECIMAL

Replace the % symbol with (× 0.01) and multiply.

NOTE   Multiplying a number by 0.01 is the same as moving the decimal point two places to the left. Thus, to change 5% to a decimal write 0.05.

PRACTICE EXERCISE 2

Change each percent to a decimal.

(a) 65%

(b) 26.5%

(c) 0.3%

(d) 550%

(e) $7\frac{3}{5}\%$

(f) 1%

Answers:
(a) 0.65   (b) 0.265
(c) 0.003   (d) 5.5
(e) 0.076   (f) 0.01

CHANGING PERCENTS TO DECIMALS — EXAMPLE 2

Change each percent to a decimal.

(a) $29\% = 29 \times \mathbf{0.01}$
$= 0.29. = 0.29$

Remember that 29. is the same as 29, then move the decimal point two places to the left

(b) $39.5\% = 39.5 \times \mathbf{0.01}$
$= 0.39.5 = 0.395$

Move the decimal point two places to the left

(c) $0.7\% = (0.7)(\mathbf{0.01})$
$= 0.00.7 = 0.007$

Put two zeros before 7

(d) $823\% = (823)(\mathbf{0.01}) = 8.23. = 8.23$

(e) $2\frac{3}{4}\% = 2.75\%$ $\frac{3}{4} = 0.75$

$= (2.75)(0.01)$

$= 0.02.75 = 0.0275$

(f) $0.01\% = (0.01)(\mathbf{0.01}) = 0.00.01 = 0.0001$

NOTE   Remember that the % symbol means "divide by 100 or multiply by $\frac{1}{100} = 0.01$." Thus, after the % symbol is removed and the change to decimal notation is made, you will have a smaller number. It may help if you keep in mind a simple example, such as

$50\% = 0.5$ OR 50% MEANS $\frac{1}{2}$.

---

4   CHANGING A DECIMAL TO A PERCENT

Some practical problems require changing from percent to fractions and decimals. Others require converting from a decimal or a fraction to a percent. To change a decimal to a percent we multiply by 100, the reverse of dividing by 100, which was used to change a percent to a decimal.

TO CHANGE A DECIMAL TO A PERCENT

Multiply the decimal by 100 and attach the % symbol.

NOTE   Multiplying a number by 100 is the same as moving the decimal point two places to the right. Thus, to change a decimal to a percent, move the decimal point two places to the right and attach the % symbol.

EXAMPLE 3   **CHANGING DECIMALS TO PERCENTS**

Change each decimal to a percent.

(a) $0.31 = (0.31)(100)\% = 31.\% = 31\%$ Move the decimal point two place to the right

(b) $3.25 = (3.25)(100)\% = 325.\% = 325\%$

(c) $1 = (1)(100)\% = 100.\% = 100\%$ Attach two zeros when moving the decimal point

(d) $0.01 = (0.01)(100)\% = 01.\% = 1\%$

(e) $0.007 = (0.007)(100)\% = 00.7\% = 0.7\%$

(f) $56.2 = (56.2)(100\%) = 5620.\% = 5620\%$

NOTE   To keep from moving the decimal point the wrong way, keep in mind a simple example, such as **0.5 = 50%** .

From percent to decimal,

move decimal point left

0.50   50.%

From decimal to percent,

move decimal point right

Consider the first letter of the words **D**ecimal and **P**ercent. Since **D** -comes before **P** in the alphabet, the letters **DP** can remind us that to change from **D**ecimal to **P**ercent, the decimal point is moved from left to right while to change from **P**ercent to **D**ecimal, it is moved from right to left.

5 | CHANGING A FRACTION TO A PERCENT

We change fractions to percents by multiplying the fraction by 100 and attaching the % symbol, just as was done with decimals.

TO CHANGE A FRACTION TO A PERCENT
Multiply the fraction by 100 and attach the % symbol.

PRACTICE EXERCISE 4

Change each fraction to a percent.

(a) $\dfrac{3}{10}$

(b) $\dfrac{5}{8}$

(c) $\dfrac{1}{3}$

Answers:
(a) 30%

(b) 62.5% or $62\frac{1}{2}\%$

(c) $33.\overline{3}\%$ or $33\frac{1}{3}\%$

CHANGING FRACTIONS TO PERCENTS   EXAMPLE 4

Change each fraction to a percent.

(a) $\dfrac{4}{5} = \dfrac{4}{5} \times \mathbf{100\%}$

$= \dfrac{4 \times \overset{20}{\cancel{100}}}{\cancel{5}}\%$

$= (4 \times 20)\% = 80\%$

(b) $\dfrac{1}{8} = \dfrac{1}{8} \times 100\% = \dfrac{100}{8}\%$

$= 12.5\%$ Divide 100 by 8

This could also be written as $12\frac{1}{2}\%$.

(c) $\dfrac{2}{3} = \dfrac{2}{3} \times 100\% = \dfrac{200}{3}\%$

$= 66.\overline{6}\%$ Divide 200 by 3

Since $0.\overline{6} = \frac{2}{3}$, we could also write this as $66\frac{2}{3}\%$.

In Example 4(c) we could have rounded the percent to 66.7% (correct to the nearest tenth of a percent) or to 66.67% (correct to the nearest hundredth of a percent) in a practical situation.

We may also convert a fraction to a decimal before changing it to a percent as in Example 5 below.

PRACTICE EXERCISE 5

Change $\frac{5}{7}$ to an approximate percent by rounding to the nearest percent, nearest tenth of a percent, and nearest hundredth of a percent.

CHANGING TO APPROXIMATE PERCENTS   EXAMPLE 5

Change $\frac{2}{7}$ to an approximate percent by rounding to the nearest percent, nearest tenth of a percent, and nearest hundredth of a percent.

$$7\overline{\smash{\big)}2.00000} \quad \text{.28571}$$

Divide 2 by 7

$$
\begin{array}{r}
.28571 \\
7\overline{\smash{)}2.00000} \\
\underline{1\ 4} \\
60 \\
\underline{56} \\
40 \\
\underline{35} \\
50 \\
\underline{49} \\
10 \\
\underline{7} \\
3
\end{array}
$$

$\dfrac{2}{7} \approx 0.29 = 29\%$ To the nearest percent

$\dfrac{2}{7} \approx 0.286 = 28.6\%$ To the nearest tenth of a percent

$\dfrac{2}{7} \approx 0.2857 = 28.57\%$ To the nearest hundredth of a percent

Some fractions, decimals, and percents which occur often are listed in the table. The numbers on each line are equal. You should memorize this table for use in the exercises.

Answer: 71%, 71.4%, 71.43%

Fraction	Decimal	Percent	Fraction	Decimal	Percent
$\dfrac{1}{20}$	0.05	5%	$\dfrac{1}{2}$	0.5	50%
$\dfrac{1}{10}$	0.1	10%	$\dfrac{3}{5}$	0.6	60%
$\dfrac{1}{8}$	0.125	12.5%	$\dfrac{5}{8}$	0.625	62.5%
$\dfrac{1}{6}$	$0.1\overline{6}$	$16.\overline{6}\% = 16\frac{2}{3}\%$	$\dfrac{2}{3}$	$0.\overline{6}$	$66.\overline{6}\% = 66\frac{2}{3}\%$
$\dfrac{1}{5}$	0.2	20%	$\dfrac{7}{10}$	0.7	70%
$\dfrac{1}{4}$	0.25	25%	$\dfrac{3}{4}$	0.75	75%
$\dfrac{3}{10}$	0.3	30%	$\dfrac{4}{5}$	0.8	80%
$\dfrac{1}{3}$	$0.\overline{3}$	$33.\overline{3}\% = 33\frac{1}{3}\%$	$\dfrac{5}{6}$	$0.8\overline{3}$	$83.\overline{3}\% = 83\frac{1}{3}\%$
$\dfrac{3}{8}$	0.375	37.5%	$\dfrac{7}{8}$	0.875	87.5%
$\dfrac{2}{5}$	0.4	40%	$\dfrac{9}{10}$	0.9	90%
			1	1.0	100%

Table of Equal Fractions, Decimals, and Percents

6.1 EXERCISES

Answers to these exercises are given on page 651.

1. The word *percent* means "per _____."

2. To change a percent to a fraction drop the % symbol and divide by 100 or multiply by _____.

3. To change a percent to a decimal replace the % symbol with (×0.01) and multiply. This is the same as moving the decimal point two places to the_____.

Change each percent in Exercises 4–11 to a fraction and reduce to lowest terms.

4. 87% 5. 16% 6. 125% 7. 1000%

8. $\frac{1}{4}$% 9. 0.7% $\frac{7}{10} \cdot \frac{1}{100} = \frac{7}{1000}$ 10. $16\frac{2}{3}$% $\frac{50}{3} \cdot \frac{1}{100} = \frac{50}{300}$ $\frac{1}{6}$ 11. 0.05% $\frac{5}{100} \cdot \frac{1}{100} = \frac{5}{10,000}$

Change each percent in Exercises 12–19 to a decimal.

12. 92% .92 13. 1% .01 14. 145% 1.45 15. 0.1%

16. 37.35% 17. $\frac{1}{4}$% .00.25 $4\overline{)100}$ $\frac{1}{20}$ 18. 4392.5% 19. $6\frac{3}{4}$% $\frac{27}{4}$ $4\overline{)27}$ $\frac{24}{30}$

20. **POLITICS** In a survey there were 76 out of 100 voters who favored the street improvements.
    (a) What fractional part of the voters favored the improvements? $\frac{76}{100}$
    (b) Write the fraction in (a) as a percent. 76%
    (c) Write the percent in (b) as a decimal. .76

21. **EDUCATION** On a recent placement exam, 45 students out of 100 who took the exam placed in algebra.
    (a) What fractional part of the students placed in algebra?
    (b) Write the fraction in (a) as a percent.
    (c) Write the percent in (b) as a decimal.

22. **SPORTS** Of all college basketball players, fewer than 0.8% will play in the NBA. Write 0.8% as a decimal.

Change each decimal in Exercises 23–30 to a percent.

23. 0.07 % 24. 0.375 37.5% 25. 3.75 375% 26. 37.5 %

27. 375 % 28. 0.009 9% 29. 0.0009 .09% 30. 0.032 03.2%

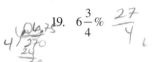Change *each fraction in Exercises 31–38 to a percent.*

31. $\frac{13}{10}$ 130% $10\overline{)130}$ $\frac{130}{30}$ 1.30 32. $\frac{7}{4}$ 33. $\frac{5}{3}$ 1.66 $\frac{2}{3}$ $3\overline{)5.0}$ 34. $\frac{7}{50}$

35. $\frac{1}{1000}$ 36. $\frac{100}{3}$ 37. $\frac{7}{2}$ $\frac{70}{20}$ 38. $\frac{106}{200}$

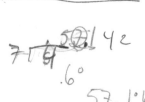Find *each approximate percent in Exercises 39–41 to the nearest tenth of a percent.*

39. $\frac{4}{7}$ $7\overline{)4}$ .57 142 .6 57.1% 40. $\frac{2}{9}$ 41. $\frac{15}{13}$

Complete the table in Exercises 42–53 given one value in each row.

	Fraction	Decimal	Percent			Fraction	Decimal	Percent
42.	$\frac{3}{10}$	_____	_____	43.	_____		0.6	_____
44.	_____	_____	62.5%	45.	1		_____	_____
46.	_____	0.875	_____	47.	_____		_____	$66\frac{2}{3}\%$
48.	$\frac{1}{20}$	_____	_____	49.	_____		$0.\bar{3}$	_____
50.	_____	_____	$83\frac{1}{3}\%$	51.	$\frac{1}{2}$		_____	_____
52.	_____	0.16	_____	53.	_____		_____	12.5%

Give the answers to Exercises 54–57 as a fraction, as a decimal, and as a percent.

54. **EDUCATION** On a geology test Valerie Alger got 42 points out of a possible 50. What portion of the points did she get?

55. **EDUCATION** What portion of the points did Valerie in Exercise 54 not get?

56. **CHEMISTRY** A chemist mixed 12 parts of acid with 13 parts of distilled water to obtain a particular solution. What part of the solution is acid?

57. **CHEMISTRY** What part of the solution in Exercise 56 is distilled water?

CALCULATOR EXERCISES

In Exercises 58–61 use a calculator to write each fraction as a percent rounded to the nearest hundredth of a percent.

58. $\frac{23}{41}$ 59. $\frac{7}{101}$ 60. $\frac{123}{477}$ 61. $\frac{853}{329}$

CRITICAL THINKING

62. **RETAILING** The price of a coat is reduced 35%.
   (a) What fractional part of the original price amounts to the reduction?
   (b) What fractional part of the original price is the new sale price?
   (c) What percent of the original price must a buyer pay?

63. **TAX** In Hood, Oregon the sales-tax rate is 5.25%. Write 5.25% as a decimal and as a fraction.

64. Burford can't seem to change a fraction with the denominator equal to 100 to percent. Can you give him a quick way to change this fraction to a percent?

65. Outline the method used to change a percent to a decimal.

66. Outline the method used to change a fraction to a percent.

REVIEW OR PREVIEW

Exercises 67–70 review topics covered in Section 2.4 to help you prepare for the next section. Solve.

67. **BUSINESS** If one-half of the number of coats in a clothing store is 225, find the number of coats in the store.

68. **TRAVEL** After driving 720 miles, the Blows had completed $\frac{3}{5}$ of their trip. How long was their trip?

69. **RETAILING** If one-fourth of the number of software packages in a store is 110, find the number of packages in the store.

70. **WORK** After working for 7 hours, Sarah had completed $\frac{2}{5}$ of a job. How long will it take to do the whole job?

6.1 PARALLEL EXERCISES

Answers to these exercises are not given in the text.

1. The word that means "per hundred" is_____.

2. To change a percent to a decimal, remove the % symbol and move the decimal point to the left_____ places.

3. To change a percent to a fraction multiply by 0.01 or divide by_____.

Change each percent in Exercises 4–11 to a fraction.

4. 98%   5. 22%   6. 375%   7. 2000%

8. $\frac{3}{4}$%   9. 0.2%   10. $83\frac{1}{3}$%   11. 0.15%

Change each percent in Exercises 12–19 to a decimal.

12. 73%   13. 8%   14. 235%   15. 0.8%

16. 62.45%   17. $\frac{3}{4}$%   18. 7325.4%   19. $10\frac{2}{5}$%

20. **MEDICINE** There were 5 of 100 patients at the clinic that could not take penicillin.
    (a) What fractional part of the patients cannot take penicillin?
    (b) Write the fraction in (a) as a percent.
    (c) Write the percent in (b) as a decimal.

21. **EDUCATION** Of 100 students in Weitzel Elementary School, 25 were found to have at least one cavity in a tooth.
    (a) What fractional part of the students had a cavity?
    (b) Write the fraction in (a) as a percent.
    (c) Write the percent in (b) as a decimal.

22. **BUSINESS** During the month of June, of the cars sold at Tyrrell Chevrolet-Buick, 42.5% were Buicks. Write 42.5% as a decimal.

Change each decimal in Exercises 23–30 to a percent.

23. 0.09   24. 0.435   25. 4.35   26. 43.5

27. 435   28. 0.008   29. 0.0008   30. 0.062

Change each fraction in Exercises 31–38 to a percent.

31. $\frac{25}{10}$ 32. $\frac{11}{4}$ 33. $\frac{4}{3}$ 34. $\frac{11}{50}$

35. $\frac{1}{2000}$ 36. $\frac{400}{3}$ 37. $\frac{13}{2}$ 38. $\frac{48}{200}$

Find each approximate percent in Exercises 39–41 to the nearest tenth of a percent.

39. $\dfrac{6}{7}$ 40. $\dfrac{5}{9}$ 41. $\dfrac{17}{13}$

Complete the table in Exercises 42-53 given one value in each row.

	Fraction	Decimal	Percent		Fraction	Decimal	Percent
42.	$\dfrac{3}{4}$	___	___	43.		0.2	___
44.	___	___	90%	45.	$\dfrac{1}{10}$	___	___
46.	___	0.8	___	47.	___	___	25%
48.	$\dfrac{1}{8}$	___	___	49.		0.7	___
50.	___	___	37.5%	51.	$\dfrac{5}{6}$	___	___
52.	___	0.4	___	53.	___	___	$33\dfrac{1}{3}\%$

Give the answers to Exercises 54–57 as a fraction, as a decimal, and as a percent.

54. **SALES** Of the 500 books that Mike and Sue had to sell, Mike sold 240 and Sue sold 260. What portion of the books did Mike sell?

55. **SALES** What portion of the books in Exercise 54 did Sue sell?

56. **EDUCATION** Of the 80 classes taught by the mathematics department at a community college, 55 were taught during the day and the rest were taught in the evening. What part of the classes was taught during the day?

57. **EDUCATION** What part of the classes in Exercise 56 was taught in the evening?

CALCULATOR EXERCISES

In Exercises 58–61 use a calculator to write each fraction as a percent rounded to the nearest hundredth of a percent.

58. $\dfrac{16}{31}$ 59. $\dfrac{14}{281}$ 60. $\dfrac{613}{729}$ 61. $\dfrac{1032}{418}$

CRITICAL THINKING

62. **TAX** There was a 24% reduction in the school tax.
(a) What fractional part of the original tax amounts to the reduction?
(b) What fractional part of the original tax is the new tax?
(c) What percent of the original tax must the homeowner pay?

63. **INVESTMENT** Each employee in the State Retirement System must contribute 6.35% of his/her salary to the retirement fund. Write 6.35% as a decimal and as a fraction.

64. Burford is having trouble changing a natural number to a percent. Can you tell him an easy way to do it?

65. Outline the method used to change a percent to a fraction.

66. Outline the method used to change a decimal to a percent.

GROUP PROJECT

Discuss the graph below, taking note of the use of percent. What kind of information does the graph present? What questions could you ask that would require calculating other percentages? (For example, what percent of total protestants are black?) Discuss this method of presentation of data in relation to other ways data is presented.

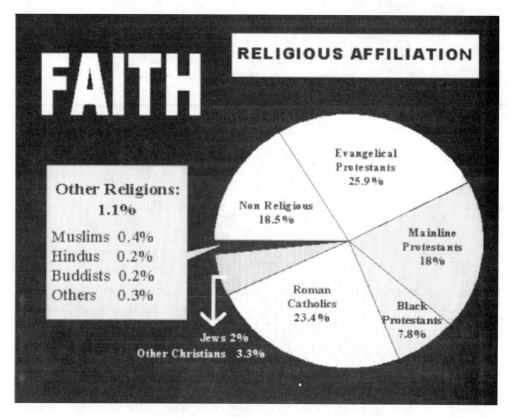

6.2 PROBLEM SOLVING WITH PERCENT

STUDENT GUIDEPOSTS
1   SOLVING THE BASIC PERCENT PROBLEM
2   SOLVING PERCENT PROBLEMS (METHOD 1)
3   USING PROPORTIONS TO SOLVE PERCENT PROBLEMS (METHOD 2)
4   WORKING WITH APPLICATIONS OF PERCENT

1 | THE BASIC PERCENT PROBLEM

In Section 2.4 we solved problems of the type:

On a two-day trip of 440 miles, Rob drove $\frac{1}{2}$ the distance the first day. How far did he drive the first day?

Letting the variable a represent the distance driven the first day, and recalling that the word "of" translates to multiplication, and the word "is" translates to equals,

$$\boxed{\text{distance 1st day}} \quad \text{is} \quad \frac{1}{2} \quad \text{of} \quad 440$$

$$\downarrow \qquad\qquad \downarrow \quad \downarrow \quad \downarrow$$

$$a \qquad\qquad = \left(\frac{1}{2}\right) \cdot (440).$$

Thus,

$$a = \frac{1}{2} \cdot 440 = 220 \text{ miles.}$$

Using the notion of percent, the same problem might be stated as follows:
On a two-day trip of 440 miles, Rob drove 50% of the distance the first day. How far did he drive the first day?

By changing 50% to the fraction $\frac{1}{2}$, this problem can be solved as above. Similarly, 50% could be changed to the decimal 0.5.

distance 1st day	is	50%	of	440
↓		↓	↓	↓
a		$=(0.5)$	$\cdot$	(440)

Thus,

$$a = (0.5)(440) = 220 \text{ miles.}$$

This problem is an example of the basic percent problem that takes the form

*A*mount is *P*ercent of *B*ase   or   *P*ercent of *B*ase is *A*mount.

Thus, the **basic percent equation** is

$$A = P\% \cdot B \quad \text{or} \quad P\% \cdot B = A.$$

2 | SOLVING PERCENT ROBLEMS (METHOD 1)

We now illustrate the first method for solving a basic percent problem, "*A* is *P*% of *B*," by finding the amount *A* when the percent *P* and base *B* are given.

EXAMPLE 1 — SOLVING FOR THE AMOUNT *A*

Solve by using the basic percent equation $A = P\% \cdot B$.
(a) What is 5% of $22.40?

In this case, *A* is the unknown, $P = 5$, and $B = 22.40$. Thus we have

What number	is	5%	of	22.40?
↓		↓	↓	↓
A		$= P\%$	$\cdot$	B
↓		↓		↓
A		$=(0.05)$	$\cdot$	22.40

Notice that *is* translates to =, *of* translates to · (times or multiplication), and 5% has been changed to decimal form, 0.05. To find *A* we simply multiply.

$$A = (0.05) \cdot (22.40) = 1.12$$

Thus, *A* is $1.12, that is, $1.12 is 5% of $22.40.

(b) 120% of 450 is what number?

This translates as follows:

120%	of	450	is	what number	?
↓	↓	↓		↓	
$P\%$	$\cdot$	B	$=$	A	
↓		↓		↓	
1.2	$\cdot$	450	$=$	A	
		540	$=$	A	

Multiply 1.2 by 450

Thus, *A* is 540, that is, 120% of 450 is 540.

PRACTICE EXERCISE 1

Solve.

(a) What is 10% of $120.20?

(b) 210% of 70 is what number?

Answers: (a) $12.02 (b) 147

> CAUTION   In any percent problem, $P\%$ must always be changed to a decimal or fraction form in order to carry out the necessary calculations. When you remove the % symbol, be sure to multiply by 0.01. For instance, in Example 1(a) it would have been wrong to write
>
> $A = (5) \cdot (22.40).$

Solving for $P\%$ or B requires that we solve the percent equation by dividing both sides by the coefficient of the unknown. For example, consider

8 is 40% of what number?

This sentence can be translated to the basic percent equation $A = P\% \cdot B$ just like we did before.

$$
\begin{array}{ccccc}
\textbf{8} & \text{is} & \textbf{40\%} & \text{of} & \boxed{\textbf{what number}} \; ? \\
\downarrow & \downarrow & \downarrow & \downarrow & \downarrow \\
A & = & P\% & \cdot & B \\
\downarrow & & \downarrow & & \downarrow \\
\textbf{8} & = & \textbf{0.40} & \cdot & B
\end{array}
$$

$A = 8$, and $P\% = 40\%$, which becomes 0.4

We must solve the equation $8 = 0.40B$ for the base B.

$$8 = 0.40\,B \qquad \text{Equation to be solved}$$

$$\frac{8}{0.04} = \frac{0.04\,B}{0.04} \qquad \text{Divide both sides by 0.04}$$

$$20 = B \qquad \tfrac{8}{0.04} = 20$$

Thus, 8 is 40% of 20.

PRACTICE EXERCISE 2

Solve.

(a) 392 is 70% of what number?

SOLVING FOR THE BASE B   EXAMPLE 2

Solve by using the basic percent equation $A = P\% \cdot B$.

(a) 60 is 20% of what number?

In this case, B is the unknown, $P = 20$, and $A = 60$. Thus, we have

$$
\begin{array}{ccccc}
\textbf{60} & \text{is} & \textbf{20\%} & \text{of} & \boxed{\textbf{what number}} \; ? \\
\downarrow & \downarrow & \downarrow & \downarrow & \downarrow \\
A & = & P\% & \cdot & B \\
\downarrow & & \downarrow & & \downarrow \\
\textbf{60} & = & \left(\textbf{0.2}\right) & \cdot & B
\end{array}
$$

We must solve the equation $60 = 0.2B$.

$$0.2B = 60$$

$$\frac{0.2B}{0.2} = \frac{60}{0.2} \qquad \text{Divide both sides by 0.2}$$

$$B = 300 \qquad \tfrac{60}{0.2} = 300$$

Thus, 60 is 20% of 300. Does this seem reasonable?

(b) 2.5% of what number is 12.5?

Although the order of wording has been reversed, this is the same type of problem.

$$
\begin{array}{ccccc}
\textbf{2.5\%} & \text{of} & \boxed{\textbf{what number}} & \text{is} & \textbf{12.5?} \\
\downarrow & \downarrow & \downarrow & \downarrow & \downarrow \\
P\% & \cdot & B & = & A \\
\downarrow & & \downarrow & & \downarrow \\
(0.025) & \cdot & B & = & 12.5
\end{array}
$$

To solve the equation divide both sides by 0.025.

$$B = \frac{12.5}{0.025} = 500$$

Thus, 2.5% of 500 is 12.5. Is this reasonable?

Finally, we consider finding the percent $P\%$ when the amount A and base B are given. For example, suppose we are asked:

What percent of 30 is 6?

First we translate to the basic percent equation $A = P\% \cdot B$, or in this case $P\% \cdot B = A$.

$$
\begin{array}{ccccc}
\boxed{\textbf{What percent}} & \text{of} & \textbf{30} & \text{is} & \textbf{6 ?} \\
\downarrow & & \downarrow & \downarrow & \downarrow \\
P\% & \cdot & B & = & A \\
\downarrow & & \downarrow & & \downarrow \\
P\% & \cdot & 30 & = & 6
\end{array}
$$

We must solve the equation $P\%(30) = 6$.

$$\frac{P\%(30)}{30} = \frac{6}{30} \qquad \text{Divide both sides by 30}$$

$$P\% = 0.2$$

Thus, $P\%$ is 20%, and 20% of 30 is 6.

EXAMPLE 3 — SOLVING FOR THE PERCENT $P\%$

Solve by using the basic percent equation $P\% \cdot B = A$.

(a) What percent of 300 is 4.5?

Find the following:

$$
\begin{array}{ccccc}
\boxed{\textbf{What percent}} & \text{of} & \textbf{300} & \text{is} & \textbf{4.5?} \\
\downarrow & & \downarrow & \downarrow & \downarrow \\
P\% & \cdot & B & = & A \\
\downarrow & & \downarrow & & \downarrow \\
P\% & \cdot & (300) & = & 4.5
\end{array}
$$

The equation to solve is $P\%(300) = 4.5$ or $300P\% = 4.5$.

$$\frac{300P\%}{300} = \frac{4.5}{300} \qquad \text{Divide both sides by 300}$$

$$P\% = 0.015$$

(b) 10.5% of what number is 89.25?

PRACTICE EXERCISE 3

Solve.

(a) What percent of 150 is 7.5?

Thus, $P\%$ is 1.5%, and 1.5% of 300 is 4.5. Does this seem reasonable?

(b) 280 is what percent of 112?

(b) 320 is what percent of 240?

Translate the following:

$$
\begin{array}{ccccc}
\textbf{320} & \text{is} & \boxed{\textbf{what percent}} & \text{of} & \textbf{240 ?} \\
\downarrow & \downarrow & \downarrow & \downarrow & \downarrow \\
A & = & P\% & \cdot & B \\
\downarrow & & \downarrow & & \downarrow \\
\textbf{320} & = & P\% & \cdot & \textbf{240}
\end{array}
$$

Solve the equation $240P\% = 320$.

$$\frac{240P\%}{240} = \frac{320}{240} \qquad \text{Divide both sides by 240}$$

$$P\% = 1.\overline{3} = 1.\overline{333}$$

Answers: (a) 5%   (b) 250%

Thus, $P\%$ is $133.\overline{3}\%$ or $133\frac{1}{3}\%$. Since 320 was larger than 240, it is reasonable to assume that the desired percent should be greater than 100%.

NOTE When solving

A is what percent of B?,

part (a) of Example 3 shows that the percent must be *less than* 100% when *A* is *less than B,* and part (b) shows that the percent must be *greater than 100%* when *A is greater than B*. This fact can be very helpful when determining whether an answer to a percent problem is reasonable.

---

3 | USING PROPORTIONS TO SOLVE PERCENT PROBLEMS (METHOD 2)

We now consider a second method that can be used to solve percent problems. Since percent is the number of parts per hundred, a percent such as 60% can be written as a ratio in the following way:

$$\frac{60}{100} \quad \begin{array}{l} \leftarrow \textbf{Sixty parts} \\ \leftarrow \textbf{Per hundred} \end{array}$$

Also, the fraction $\frac{3}{5}$, changed to percent, is 60% (dividing 3 by 5 and converting to percent). We may express this fact by writing the proportion

$$\frac{3}{5} = \frac{60}{100}.$$

Suppose we are asked to solve the following percent problem:

What is 60% of 5?

Since, as shown above,

$$\frac{3}{5} = \frac{60}{100},$$

we know that 3 is 60% of 5. If we did not know the answer, we could solve the proportion

$$\frac{A}{5} = \frac{60}{100}$$

for A, the amount, to obtain 3.

Now we ask another question:

3 is 60% of what number?

This can be written as the proportion

$$\frac{3}{B} = \frac{60}{100},$$

where B, the base, is now the number to be found. (Of course, in this case we know it is 5.)

Finally, consider the question:

What percent of 5 is 3?

In this case we have the proportion

$$\frac{3}{5} = \frac{P}{100},$$

where P, the percent, is what we are looking for (the 60 in 60%).

In general, combining what we have learned from these three percent questions, we have

$$\text{Amount} \rightarrow \frac{A}{B} = \frac{P}{100}. \leftarrow \textbf{Percent}$$
$$\textbf{Base} \rightarrow$$

We call this the **basic percent proportion.** Every percent problem can be stated using this proportion where either A, B, or P is missing.

NOTE   When reading a percent problem, notice that the amount, A, is next to the word *is* and the base, B, is next to the word *of.* Thus, the percent proportion

$$\frac{A}{B} = \frac{P}{100}$$

can be remembered by writing

$$\frac{IS}{OF} = \frac{\%}{100}.$$

We now solve the percent problems in Examples 1, 2, and 3 using percent proportions.

EXAMPLE 4 **SOLVING FOR THE AMOUNT A**

Solve by using the basic percent proportion.

(a) What is 5% of $22.40?

Start with the basic percent proportion $\dfrac{A}{B} = \dfrac{P}{100}$

with A the unknown, $B = 22.40$, and $P = 5$.

$$\frac{A}{22.40} = \frac{5}{100}$$

$100A = (5)(22.40)$ Equate cross products

$A = \dfrac{(5)(22.40)}{100}$ Divide by the multiplier of A, 100

$A = 1.12$ Simplify

Thus, A is $1.12.

PRACTICE EXERCISE 4

Solve.

(a) What is 10% of $120.20?

(b) 210% of 70 is what number?   (b) 120% of 450 is what number?

Substitute 120 for P and 450 for B in the percent proportion

$$\frac{A}{B} = \frac{P}{100} \cdot$$

$$\frac{A}{450} = \frac{120}{100}$$

$100A = (120)(450)$ Equate cross products

$$A = \frac{(120)(450)}{100}$$ Divide by 100

$A = 540$ Simplify

Answers: (a) $12.02   (b) 147

Thus, 120% of 450 is 540.

> CAUTION   When using the percent proportion *do not* write the percent as a decimal or a fraction. This is a difference between the percent proportion and the percent equation.

PRACTICE EXERCISE 5

SOLVING FOR THE BASE B   EXAMPLE 5

Solve.

Solve by using the basic percent proportion.

(a) 392 is 70% of what number?

(a) 60 is 20% of what number?

Substitute 60 for A and 20 for P in the basic percent proportion

$$\frac{A}{B} = \frac{P}{100} \cdot$$

$$\frac{60}{B} = \frac{20}{100}$$

$(60)(100) = (20)B$ Equate cross products

$$\frac{(60)(100)}{20} = B$$ Divide by 20

$300 = B$

Thus, 60 is 20% of 300.

(b) 10.5% of what number is 89.25?

(b) 2.5% of what number is 12.5?

Substitute 12.5 for A and 2.5 for P in the basic percent proportion.

$$\frac{12.5}{B} = \frac{2.5}{100}$$

$(12.5)(100) = (2.5)B$ Equate cross products

$$\frac{(12.5)(100)}{2.5} = B$$ Divide by 2.5

$500 = B$

Answers: (a) 560   (b) 850

Thus, 2.5% of 500 is 12.5.

EXAMPLE 6 — SOLVING FOR THE PERCENT P %

Solve by using the basic percent proportion.

Solve.

(a) What percent of 300 is 4.5?

(a) What percent of 150 is 7.5?

Substitute 4.5 for A and 300 for B in the percent proportion

$$\frac{A}{B} = \frac{P}{100}.$$

$$\frac{4.5}{300} = \frac{P}{100}$$

$(4.5)(100) = (300)P$ Equate cross products

$$\frac{(4.5)(100)}{300} = P$$ Divide by 300

$$1.5 = P$$

Thus, 1.5% of 300 is 4.5.

(b) 320 is what percent of 240?

(b) 280 is what percent of 112?

Substitute 320 for A and 240 for B in the percent proportion.

$$\frac{320}{240} = \frac{P}{100}$$

$(320)(100) = (240)P$ Equate cross products

$$\frac{(320)(100)}{240} = P$$ Divide by 240

$$133.\overline{3} = P$$

Thus, P% is $133.\overline{3}$% or $133\frac{1}{3}$%.

> **NOTE** Consider both the equation method (Method 1) and the proportion method (Method 2) for solving percent problems and use the one that you prefer or that your instructor recommends. In the examples that follow, we present both methods in a side-by-side approach to help you decide which to use.

4 | APPLICATIONS OF PERCENT

We conclude this section with three examples of typical percent applications.

EXAMPLE 7 — SOLVING AN APPLICATION IN CHEMISTRY

If 14 g (grams) of pure sulfuric acid is mixed with water and the resulting solution is 28% acid, what is the total weight of the solution?

Minnie spends $120 a week to feed her family. If this is 24% of the total weekly family income, what is the weekly income of her family?

We know that 14 g is 28% of the solution. Thus, we must answer the question:
14 is 28% of what number?

Method 1 (Equation Method)

$$A = P\% \cdot B$$
$$14 = (0.28)B$$

Method 2 (Proportion Method)

$$\frac{A}{B} = \frac{P}{100}$$

$$\frac{14}{0.28} = B$$

$$\frac{14}{B} = \frac{28}{100}$$

$$50 = B$$

$$(14)(100) = (28)B$$

$$\frac{(14)(100)}{28} = B$$

$$50 = B$$

Thus, 14 g is 28% of 50 g of the solution.

Answer: $500

PRACTICE EXERCISE 8

At a recent concert attended by 840 people, 45% of those in attendance were children. How many children were at the concert?

SOLVING AN APPLICATION IN FAMILY BUDGETING EXAMPLE 8

The income of the Ross family is $1250 per month. If they spend 22% of their income for food, how much do they pay for food each month?

We must find 22% of the income, $1250. Thus the question is:
What is 22% of $1250?

Method 1

$$A = P\% \cdot B$$

$$A = (0.22)(1250)$$

$$A = 275$$

Method 2

$$\frac{A}{B} = \frac{P}{100}$$

$$\frac{A}{1250} = \frac{22}{100}$$

$$100A = (22)(1250)$$

$$A = \frac{(22)(1250)}{100} = 275$$

Thus, $275 is 22% of $1250, and the family spends $275 for food each month. If we come up with $2750 for an answer, since $2750 is more than $1250 but 22% is less than 100%, we would have known we had made an error.

Answer: 378 children

PRACTICE EXERCISE 9

During the World Series, Reggie Jackson had 10 hits in 30 times at bat. What was his batting percentage in the series?

SOLVING AN APPLICATION IN SPORTS EXAMPLE 9

A basketball player hit 16 out of 20 free throws in a game. What was her shooting percent?

The question to answer is 16 is what percent of 20?

Method 1

$$A = P\% \cdot B$$

$$16 = (P\%) \cdot (20)$$

$$\frac{16}{20} = \frac{P\%(20)}{20}$$

$$0.80 = P\%$$

Method 2

$$\frac{A}{B} = \frac{P}{100}$$

$$\frac{16}{20} = \frac{P}{100}$$

$$(16)(100) = (20)P$$

$$\frac{(16)(100)}{20} = P = 80$$

Answer: 33.3% (Batting percentages or averages are often expressed as three-place decimals so we might give 0.333 for the answer.)

Thus, her shooting percent was 80%. That is, 16 is 80% of 20.

6.2 EXERCISES

Answers to these exercises are given on page 652.

Solve the percent problems in Exercises 1–18. Before checking, ask yourself if your answer seems reasonable.

1. What is 20% of 150?

2. What is 140% of 20?

3. 70% of 600 is what number?

4. 10 is 20% of what number?

5. 200 is 40% of what number?

6. 4.5 is 150% of what number?

7. What percent of 50 is 10?

8. What percent of 10 is 50?

9. 75 is what percent of 225?

10. What is 35% of 70?

11. 6.2 is what percent of 24.8?

12. 0.15 is 60% of what number?

13. **ENVIRONMENT** In a survey of 2200 people, 85% were in favor of recycling newspapers. How many people were in favor of the recycling?

14. **METEOROLOGY** Flagstaff, Arizona, received 120 inches of snow one year. This was 150% of the normal snowfall. What is the normal annual snowfall in Flagstaff? [*Hint:* 120 is 150% of what number?]

15. **BUSINESS** It is estimated that 70% of the people at a baseball game will buy refreshments. If 24,530 people were at Saturday's game, how many people would need to be served refreshments?

16. **CHEMISTRY** In an acid solution weighing 120 g there are 35 g of acid. To the nearest percent, what is the percent of acid in the solution?

17. **POLITICS** Ms. McShane received 2860 of the votes in an election. This was about 58% of the votes cast. Approximately how many votes were cast?

18. **EDUCATION** A student answered 22 questions correctly on a test having 30 questions. To the nearest percent, what percent of her answers were correct?

CALCULATOR EXERCISES

Use a calculator in Exercises 19–22 and give answers to the nearest hundredth or nearest hundredth of a percent.

19. What is 12.7% of 257?

20. 27 is 6.3% of what number?

21. What percent of 83 is 122?

22. **RECREATION** During one year the Browns spent 10.3% of their income on entertainment and vacations. If they spent $3485.20 on these two items, to the nearest cent, what was their income?

Use the table below in Exercises 23–25. Give answers to the nearest tenth of a percent.

Textiles and Apparel Products—U.S. Exports and Imports: 1992 to 1994

[In millions of dollars. Excludes glass fibers, rubber and leather apparel, and clothing donated for charity. Minus sign (-) indicates deficit]

PRODUCT	EXPORTS			GENERAL IMPORTS			MERCHANDISE TRADE BALANCE		
	1992	1993	1994	1992	1993	1994	1992	1993	1994
Total	10,120	10,977	12,208	39,070	42,225	45,952	–28,950	–31,248	–33,744
Textile yarn fabrics	5,911	6,025	6,592	7,844	8,438	9,208	–1,933	–2,413	–2,616
Textile yarn	1,179	1,045	1,213	955	1,146	1,335	224	–101	–122
Cotton fabric, woven	591	641	725	1,493	1,522	1,498	–902	–911	–773
Woven fabric of manmade textiles	825	883	925	1,206	1,261	1,291	–381	–378	–366
Woven fabric of textile material	185	210	236	666	682	695	–481	–452	–459
Special yarns	1,335	1,418	1,588	797	878	977	538	540	611
Other	1,796	1,828	1,905	2,727	2,939	3,412	–931	–1,111	–1,507
Apparel	4,209	4,952	5,616	31,226	33,787	36,744	–27,017	–28,835	–31,128

Source: U.S. Bureau of the Census, *U.S. Merchandise Trade: Exports, General Imports, and Imports for Consumption,* Report FT925, monthly.

23. What percent of the total exports in 1994 were textile yarn fabrics?

24. What percent of the exports of textile yarn fabrics in 1994 were textile yarn?

25. What percent of the total imports in 1992 was apparel?

CRITICAL THINKING

26. Burford does not know how to show that if $P=80$ then $P\%=0.8$. Can you help him?

27. Discuss the *basic percent equation* and explain what each of the variables A, B, and $P\%$ represents.

28. Discuss how approximating the answer to a percent problem can help prevent making major errors. For example, if we are asked, *What percent of 50 is 25?*, explain why the answer must be a percent **less than** 100%. On the other hand, if asked, *What percent of 25 is 50?*, explain why the answer must be a percent **greater than** 100%.

REVIEW OR PREVIEW

29. Change 35% to a fraction.   30. Change 13.5% to a decimal.

31. **INVESTMENT** Tonya has deposited $2000 in a savings account which earns 8.75% interest. Write 8.75% as a decimal.

Change to percents in Exercises 32–37.

32. 0.17   33. 0.005   34.   0.05

35. 0.5   36. $\dfrac{3}{8}$ 37. $\dfrac{7}{9}$

38. **POLITICS** In a two-person school board election, Dr. Yard received 2130 votes out of a total of 3360 votes cast.
    (a) What fractional part of the votes did Dr. Yard receive?
    (b) Express the fraction in (a) as a decimal rounded to the nearest thousandth.
    (c) Express the decimal in (b) as a percent rounded to the nearest tenth of a percent.
    (d) What percent of the votes (to the nearest tenth of a percent) did Dr. Yard's opponent receive?

39. **RECREATION** Of the 1092 hours of prime-time television programming in a recent year, it was estimated that 648 hours were viewed by children under the age of 16.
    (a) What fractional part of the total prime-time hours was viewed by children?
    (b) Express the fraction in (a) as a decimal rounded to the nearest thousandth.
    (c) Express the decimal in (b) as a percent rounded to the nearest tenth.
    (d) What percent of the total hours (to the nearest tenth of a percent) was not viewed by children?

6.2 PARALLEL EXERCISES

Answers to these exercises are not given in the text.

Solve the percent problems in Exercises 1–18. Before checking, ask yourself if your answer seems reasonable.

1. What is 16% of 400?   2. What is 420% of 5?

3. 35% of 900 is what number?   4. 30 is 5% of what number?

5. 120 is 0.2% of what number?   6. 12.5 is 625% of what number?

7. What percent of 80 is 24?   8. What percent of 520 is 130?

9. 15 is what percent of 8?   10. 55% of 4000 is what number?

11. 0.6 is 12% of what number?   12. 9.8 is 280% of what number?

Chapter 6 PERCENT

13. **HYDROLOGY** If there is a 0.05% impurity rate in a water sample of 820 grams, how many grams of impurities are in the sample?

14. **METEOROLOGY** During one year Phoenix had a total of 168 days when the temperature exceeded 100°. This was 120% of normal. Normally how many days per year does the temperature exceed 100° in Phoenix?

15. **POLITICS** There were 38,600 people who voted in the state race for senator. If Karen La Bonte won with 50.5% of the votes, how many votes did Karen receive?

16. **CHEMISTRY** If 6 liters of acid are mixed with 9 liters of water, what is the percent of acid in the solution?

17. **EDUCATION** Diana Denlinger got 182 points on a final exam. If this was 91% of the points, how many points were possible on the final?

18. **RECREATION** At a recent campus sold-out showing of the movie *Rambo First Blood Part II,* 485 members of the audience were under 30 years of age. If the theater seats 615, to the nearest tenth of a percent, what percent of those present was under 30 years old?

CALCULATOR EXERCISES

Use a calculator in Exercises 19–22 and give answers to the nearest hundredth or nearest hundredth of a percent.

19. 6.9 is what percent of 72.7?

20. 27.3 is 14.2% of what number?

21. What is 102.6% of 38.5?

22. **TAXES** The Hendersons paid $1120.17 in county taxes on their house. If the tax rate was 0.639%, what is the value of their house to the nearest hundred dollars?

Use the table given above Exercises 23–25 in 6.2 Exercises to answer the following questions. Give answers to the nearest tenth of a percent.

23. What percent of the total exports in 1994 were apparel?

24. What percent of the exports of textile yarn fabrics in 1994 were special yarns?

25. What percent of the total imports in 1994 were textile yarn fabrics?

CRITICAL THINKING

26. Burford knows that $P\% = 0.2$. Can you show him how to show that $P = 20$?

27. Discuss the *basic percent proportion* and explain what each of the letters A, B, and P represents.

28. One major difference between using the basic percent equation and the basic percent proportion is in the way we write the percent. What is this difference? Explain.

GROUP PROJECT

When solving applied problems that involve percent, parallel solutions using both the basic percent equation and the basic percent proportion have been presented. Discuss the advantages and disadavantages of each of these equations. What are some of the differences that might cause you to prefer one over the other? (For example, the percent equation uses the variable $P\%$ that is always in decimal or fraction form while the proportion uses the variable P that gives the percent number itself.) Does the solution of one equation generally require more steps than the other?

6.3 TAX PROBLEMS

<table>
<tr><td colspan="2">STUDENT GUIDEPOSTS</td></tr>
<tr><td>1</td><td>WORKING WITH SALES TAX PROBLEMS</td></tr>
<tr><td>2</td><td>SOLVING SOCIAL SECURITY TAX PROBLEMS</td></tr>
<tr><td>3</td><td>SOLVING INCOME TAX PROBLEMS</td></tr>
<tr><td>4</td><td>INVESTIGATING STATE AND LOCAL TAXES</td></tr>
</table>

In the next five sections we will study a variety of applications of percent all of which can be translated into the basic percent equation

or the basic percent proportion
$$A = P\% \cdot B$$
$$\frac{A}{B} = \frac{P}{100}.$$

We will give a dual presentation in many of the examples. Use the method you prefer.

1 SALES TAX PROBLEMS

In most states a tax is charged on purchases made in retail stores. The rate of this tax, called a **sales tax,** varies from location to location. In a state with a **sales-tax rate** of 5%, the tax on a purchase of $10.00 is given by

sales tax = **5%** of **$10.00**.   Use $A = P\% \cdot B$

= **(0.05)** · **$(10.00)**

= $0.50

When you buy an item for $10.00, you must pay a

total price = **price before tax + sales tax.**

= **$10.00** + **$0.50**

= $10.50

We now present a summary of the necessary concepts related to a sales-tax problem.

TO SOLVE A SALES-TAX PROBLEM

1. Use the basic percent equation
$$A = P\% \cdot B$$
sales tax = tax rate · price before tax

or use the basic percent proportion
$$\frac{A}{B} = \frac{P}{100}$$
$$\frac{\text{sales tax}}{\text{price before tax}} = \frac{\text{tax rate}}{100}.$$

2. The total price is given by
total price = price before tax + sales tax .

EXAMPLE 1 — FINDING SALES TAX AND TOTAL PRICE

If the sales-tax rate is 5% in Tucson, Arizona, what is the sales tax on a TV with a marked selling price of $625.40? What is the total price including the tax?

Find the sales tax. Note that $P = 5$ and $P\% = 5(0.01) = 0.05$.

Method 1

$$A = P\% \cdot B$$
$$\text{tax} = \text{rate} \cdot \text{price}$$
$$= (0.05) \cdot (\$625.40)$$
$$= \$31.27$$

Method 2

$$\frac{A}{B} = \frac{P}{100}$$
$$\frac{\text{tax}}{\text{price}} = \frac{\text{rate}}{100}$$
$$\frac{\text{tax}}{\$625.40} = \frac{5}{100}$$
$$(\text{sales tax})(100) = (5)(\$625.40)$$
$$\text{sales tax} = \frac{(5)(\$625.40)}{100}$$
$$= \$31.27$$

Now add the price before tax and the sales tax to obtain the total price.

$$\text{total price} = \textbf{price before tax} + \textbf{sales tax}$$
$$= \qquad \textbf{\$625.40} \ + \ \textbf{\$31.27}$$
$$= \$656.67$$

Thus, one must pay a total of $656.67 for the TV set.

> **CAUTION** Always check to see if your answer seems reasonable. A 5% tax is $5 for each $100. If we had found the tax to be $312.70 in Example 1, we would have realized that this was much too big. (The decimal point is too far to the right.) Similarly, we know that an answer of $3.13 is wrong because the decimal point is too far to the left.

The sales-tax rate in a particular city can be found if we know the price before tax and the amount of sales tax paid.

EXAMPLE 2 — FINDING THE SALES-TAX RATE

What is the sales-tax rate if the tax is $2.50 on the purchase of a $62.50 sport coat?

The question asked is: $2.50 is what percent of $62.50?

Method 1

$$A = P\% \cdot B$$
$$\$2.50 = P\% \cdot \$62.50$$
$$2.50 = P\% \cdot 62.50$$
$$\frac{2.50}{62.50} = P\%$$

Method 2

$$\frac{A}{B} = \frac{P}{100}$$
$$\frac{\$2.50}{\$62.50} = \frac{P}{100}$$
$$(2.50)(100) = (62.50)P$$

PRACTICE EXERCISE 1

If the sales-tax rate is 4% in Blue Key, Florida, what is the sales tax on a pair of water skis selling for $315.50? What is the total price including tax?

Answer: $12.62; $328.12

PRACTICE EXERCISE 2

What is the sales-tax rate in Denver if the tax is $24.77 on the purchase of a desk with a selling price of $495.40?

$$0.04 = P\%$$

$$\frac{(2.50)(100)}{62.50} = P$$

Thus, the sales-tax rate is 4%. Since

$$4 = P$$

$$(0.04)(62.50) = 2.50, 4\% \text{ does check.}$$

Finally, when the sales-tax rate and the sales tax are given, we can find the price of an item before tax.

Answer: 5%

PRACTICE EXERCISE 3

A tax of $5.76 was charged on a purchase of a pair of boots in Dallas where the tax rate is 4.5%.

(a) What was the selling price (price before tax) of the boots?

| **FINDING THE PRICE OF AN ITEM** | **EXAMPLE 3** |

A tax of $1.26 was charged on a purchase of cosmetics in a city where the tax rate is 3.5%.

(a) What was the price of the cosmetics before tax?
   The question asked is: $1.26 is 3.5% of what number?

Method 1

$$A = P\% \cdot B$$

$$\$1.26 = (3.5)(0.01)B$$

$$1.26 = (0.035)B$$

$$\frac{1.26}{0.035} = B$$

$$36 = B$$

Method 2

$$\frac{A}{B} = \frac{P}{100}$$

$$\frac{\$1.26}{B} = \frac{3.5}{100}$$

$$(1.26)(100) = (3.5)B$$

$$\frac{(1.26)(100)}{3.5} = B = 36$$

The cosmetics sold for $36.00 before tax.

(b) What was the total price paid?

(b) What was the total price paid?

$$\text{total price} = \text{price before tax} + \text{sales tax}$$
$$\downarrow \qquad \qquad \downarrow$$
$$= \quad \$36.00 \quad + \quad \$1.26 \quad = \$37.26$$

Answers:
(a) $128.00 (b) $133.76

---

2 | SOCIAL SECURITY TAX PROBLEMS

The Social Security tax is used by the federal government to provide income for retired people. In 2004 the tax rate was 6.2% on the first $87,900 of earnings. A wage earner who made $87,900 or more in 2004 paid 6.2% of $87,900, which was

$$(0.062)(\$87,900) = \$5449.80$$

in Social Security taxes. A person who made less than $87,900 paid 6.2% of whatever was earned. We summarize this in the following rule.

TO FIND THE AMOUNT OF SOCAL SECURITY TAX (2004)

1. If total earnings are less than $87,900: Use the percent equation

$$A = P\% \cdot B$$

$$\text{Social Security tax} = 0.062 \cdot \text{total earnings}$$

or use the percent proportion $\dfrac{A}{B} = \dfrac{P}{100}$.

$$\frac{\text{Social Security tax}}{\text{total earnings}} = \frac{6.2}{100}$$

2. If total earnings are $87,900 or more, the Social Security tax is fixed at $5449.80

EXAMPLE 4 — FINDING SOCIAL SECURITY TAX

Clara earned $39,600 in 2004. How much Social Security tax did she pay?

Since Clara made less than $87,900, use Method 1 or Method 2.

Benito earned $22,480 in 2004. How much Social Security tax did he pay?

Method 1	Method 2

Method 1

$$A = P\% \cdot B$$

$$\text{S. S. tax} = (0.062) \cdot \text{earnings}$$

$$= (0.062)(\$39,600)$$

$$= \$2455.20$$

Method 2

$$\frac{A}{B} = \frac{P}{100}$$

$$\frac{\text{S. S. tax}}{\text{earnings}} = \frac{6.2}{100}$$

$$\frac{\text{S. S. tax}}{\$39,600} = \frac{6.2}{100}$$

$$(\text{S. S. tax})(100) = (6.2)(\$39,600)$$

$$\text{S. S. tax} = \frac{(6.2)(\$39,600)}{100}$$

$$= \$2455.20$$

Thus, Clara had to pay $2455.20 in Social Security tax in 2004. Clearly a calculator is helpful in solving problems like this.

Answer: $1393.76

3 | INCOME TAX PROBLEMS

Income tax is usually the biggest tax that a person pays each year. Many taxpayers find the tax by looking up their taxable income (total earnings less deductions) in a table and reading the tax. However, for some, determining federal or state income taxes requires use of percent.

The following tax rate schedule for single taxpayers is from the 2004 federal income tax form. (You can obtain other tables at your post office.) Suppose your taxable income was $29,580. Look down the two columns on the left until you find the two numbers between which your income falls. In this case, $29,580 is between $29,050 and $70,350. The tax is calculated by adding 25% of the difference between $29,580 and $29,050 to $4000.00. First subtract $29,050 from $29,580.

$$\$29,580 - \$29,050 = \$530$$

Take 25% of $530,

$$(0.25)(\$530) = \$132.50$$

and add this amount to $4000.00 to obtain the total income tax to be paid.

$$\$4000.00 + \$132.50 = \$4132.50$$

Thus, $4132.50 was your income tax in 2004.

2004 Tax Rate Schedule

Schedule X—Use if your filing status is **Single**

If your taxable income is: Over—	But not over—	Then your tax is	of the amount over—
$0	$ 7,150	...........10%	$0
7,150	29,050	$ 715.00 + 15%	7,150
29,050	70,350	4,000.00 + 25%	29,050
70,350	146,750	14,325.00 + 28%	70,350
146,750	319,100	35,717.00 + 33%	146,750
319,100	....	92,592.50 + 35%	319,100

FINDING INCOME TAX   EXAMPLE 5

Paul is a single taxpayer who uses the tax rate schedule. In 2004 his taxable income was $9800. How much income tax did he pay?

Paul's taxable income, $6900, was between $0 and $22,750. He paid 10% of his taxable income which was

$$(0.10)($6900) = $690$$

4   STATE AND LOCAL TAXES

We now use the applied problem from the chapter introduction to look at state and local taxes.

INVESTIGATING VARIOUS STATE AND LOCAL TAXES   EXAMPLE 6

An average family of four (two wage earners and two children of school age), owning their own home and living in cities that collect taxes on state and local sales, automobile registration, and real estate must pay a certain portion of their income for these taxes. The tax amount is related to the income level of the family as well as where the family lives in the United States. The estimated state and local taxes paid by a family with an annual income of $50,000 who lived in several selected cities in 1992 is presented in the table below.

CITY	TOTAL TAXES PAID BY A FAMILY WITH INCOME OF $50,000	TOTAL TAXES PAID A PERCENT OF INCOME
Albuquerque, NM	$3434	6.9%
Atlanta, GA	$5593	11.2%
Charlotte, NC	$4412	8.8%
Columbus, OH	$4713	
Memphis, TN	$2896	5.8%
Newark, NJ	$11,445	
Virginia Beach, VA	$4423	8.8%

Source: Government of the District of Columbia, Department of Finance and Revenue

Although the actual amount of tax paid is interesting to note, it is also revealing to consider the taxes paid as a percent of annual income (the right hand column of the table). What percent of a family's income was paid in state and local taxes if the family lived in Columbus, OH in 1992?

The question asked is: $4713 is what percent of $50,000?

Method 1   Method 2

$$A = P\% \cdot B$$ $$\frac{A}{B} = \frac{P}{100}$$

$$$4713 = P\% \cdot $50,000$$ $$\frac{$4713}{$50,000} = \frac{P}{100}$$

$$4713 = P\%(50,000)$$ $$(4713)(100) = (50,000)P$$

$$\frac{4713}{50,000} = P\%$$ $$\frac{(4713)(100)}{50,000} = P$$

$$0.094 = P\%$$ $$9.4 = P$$

Thus, the percent of income for state and local taxes in Columbus was about 9.4% (to the nearest tenth) in 1992.

6.3 EXERCISES

Answers to these exercises are given on page 652.

Solve the applied problems in Exercises 1–12. Before making a final calculation, estimate the answer for a reasonable approximation.

1. **SALES TAX** The sales-tax rate in Upstate, New York is 6%. How much sales tax should be charged on a purchase of $182.50? What is the total cost?

2. **SALES TAX** In Silverville, Colorado the sales-tax rate is 5.5%. How much tax would be charged on a silver necklace that is priced at $1500? What is the total cost?

3. **SALES TAX** Find the tax and total price of a shirt if the price before tax is $15.20, and the tax rate is 2.5%.

4. **SALES TAX** If $0.43 tax is charged on a price of $21.50, what is the tax rate?

5. **SALES TAX** Janet LaMott was charged a sales tax of $8.82 in a city where the sales-tax rate is 7%. What was the price that was marked on the coat that she purchased?

6. **SALES TAX** Sandy Morales found a toaster on sale for a price of $32.40. If she was charged a sales tax of $1.62, what is the tax rate in the city where she made the purchase?

7. **SALES TAX** The tax rate in Hudson, New York, is 5% and the tax charged on an item is $12.50. What is its price before tax?

8. **SALES TAX** A used car lists for $6827.50. If the sales-tax rate is 4.5%, find the tax and the total price.

9. **SOCIAL SECURITY TAX** Susan had an income from wages of $15,800 in 2004. How much Social Security tax did she pay?

10. **SOCIAL SECURITY TAX** Toni made $93,000 in 2004. What Social Security tax did she pay?

11. **INCOME TAX** Mark was a single taxpayer with a taxable income of $29,200 in 2004. What income tax did he pay?

12. **INCOME TAX** On total wages of $20,800 in 2004, Jim had a taxable income of $16,600. How much income tax did he pay on his taxable income? How much Social Security tax did he pay on his total wages?

In Exercises 13–14, refer to the table given in Example 6. Give answers correct to the nearest tenth of a percent.

13. **TAXES** If a typical family with income of $50,000 in Albuquerque pays $950 for real estate taxes, what percent of their income is for these taxes? What percent of the total taxes paid is the real estate tax?

14. **TAXES** If a typical family with income of $50,000 in Atlanta pays $4000 for all taxes except sales tax, what percent of their income is for sales taxes?

CRITICAL THINKING

Solve each applied problem in Exercises 15–16.

15. **SALES TAX** A washer normally selling for $389.95 is put on sale at 20% off the regular price. If the sales-tax rate is 4.5%, to the nearest cent, how much will the washer cost including the sales tax?

16. **SALES TAX** Burford had $15.50 in his pocket, and he wanted to buy a calculator priced at $15.00. The sales-tax rate in Burford's city is 6%. He decided to figure the price of the calculator plus sales tax before going to pay, and he concluded that since the tax was only 9¢, he had enough to make the purchase. Why was Burford embarrassed when he tried to buy the calculator?

17. What is the difference between the *Social Security tax* and the *income tax* for an individual?

REVIEW OR PREVIEW

Solve each percent problem in Exercises 18–24.

18. What is 18% of 245?

19. 5.2 is 8% of what number?

20. 676 is what percent of 520?

21. **POLLING** In a recent poll, 52% of those contacted were female. If 182 females were in the poll, how many were contacted?

22. **EDUCATION** Maria answered 76 of 88 questions correctly on a test. What was her percent score to the nearest percent?

23. **STATISTICS** It has been estimated that 18% of the residents of a county cannot read or write. If there are 26,580 people living in the county, about how many of them cannot read or write?

24. **WORK** Because of illness, Troy could only work 27 hours of his normal 40-hour work week. What percent of the normal week did he work?

6.3 PARALLEL EXERCISES

Answers to these exercises are not given in the text.

Solve the applied problems in Exercises 1–12. Before making a final calculation, estimate the answer for a reasonable approximation.

1. **SALES TAX** The sales-tax rate in Pacific, California, is 7%. How much tax should be charged on jeans that are priced at $68.00? What will be the total cost?

2. **SALES TAX** In Wheat, Kansas, the sales-tax rate is 4.5%. How much tax will be charged on a refrigerator that is marked at $940.00? What is the total cost?

3. **SALES TAX** Neal Newton bought a part for his motor home that was priced at $128.00. If the sales-tax rate is 6.5%, how much tax did he have to pay? What was the total cost?

4. **SALES TAX** While on vacation Red and Teddy Phillips bought an antique doll. If the marked price on the doll was $250.00 and they were charged a sales tax of $13.75, what is the sales-tax rate in the city where they made the purchase?

5. **SALES TAX** The sales-tax rate in Mountain, Colorado, is 4%. If the tax on a pair of ski boots was $3.58, what was the price before tax?

6. **SALES TAX** The tax on a sofa costing $685.50 before tax is $41.13. What is the tax rate?

7. **SALES TAX** The tax rate in Pacifica, California, is 6%, and the tax charged on an item is $33.63. What is the price before tax of the item?

8. **SALES TAX** A new boat lists for $17,435.75. If the sales-tax rate is 5.5%, find the tax and the total cost of the boat.

9. **SOCIAL SECURITY TAX** The Social Security tax rate was 6.2% in 2004. How much Social Security tax did Claude pay on a salary of $18,200?

10. **SOCIAL SECURITY TAX** Margie had an income of $97,500 in 2004. How much Social Security tax did she pay?

11. **INCOME TAX** Ms. West was a single taxpayer with a taxable income of $33,200 in 2004. How much income tax did she pay?

12. **INCOME TAX** On total wages of $31,200 in 2004, Kent had a taxable income of $21,400. How much income tax did he pay on his taxable income? How much Social Security tax did he pay?

In exercises 13–14 refer to the table given in Example 6. Give answers correct to the nearest tenth of a percent.

13. **TAXES** If a typical family with income of $50,000 in Charlotte pays $1150 for real estate taxes, what percent of their income is for these taxes? What percent of the total taxes paid is the real estate tax?

14. **TAXES** If a typical family with income of $50,000 in Memphis pays $2000 for all taxes except sales tax, what percent of their income is for sales taxes?

CRITICAL THINKING

Solve each applied problem in Exercises 15–16.

15. **SALES TAX** Paul buys a typewriter for $459.95 and a desk for $189.98. If the sales tax on the purchase of these items is $26.65, to the nearest tenth of a percent, what is the sales-tax rate?

16. **SOCIAL SECURITY TAX** Burford told his rich uncle that he could determine the amount of Social Security tax that he paid in 2004 by taking 6.2% of his annual earnings. Burford's uncle made $90,000 in 2004. Was Burford's advice correct?

17. Explain the difference between the terms *sales tax* and *sales-tax rate*.

GROUP PROJECT

Politicians talk about simplifying the process of determining income tax. Investigate the currrent system and discuss the advantages and disadvantages of various proposals to simplify. Would you want your income tax determined simply by calculating a percent of your gross income?

6.4 COMMISSION AND DISCOUNT PROBLEMS

STUDENT GUIDEPOSTS

1   SOLVING COMMISSION PROBLEMS
2   WORKING WITH DISCOUNT PROBLEMS

We next look at two quantities which, like sales tax, are calculated by taking a percent of the selling price.

1 | COMMISSION PROBLEMS

Some salespersons receive all or part of their income as a percent of their sales. This is called a **commission.** The **commission rate** is the percent of the sales that the person receives.

TO SOLVE A COMMISSION PROBLEM

Use the percent equation

$$A \quad = \quad P\% \quad \cdot \quad B$$

commission = commission rate · total sales

or use the percent proportion $\dfrac{A}{B} = \dfrac{P}{100}$

$$\frac{\text{commission}}{\text{total sales}} = \frac{\text{commission rate}}{100}.$$

EXAMPLE 1 | FINDING A COMMISSION

Elaine sells furniture and receives a 20% commission on the selling price. In April, her sales totaled $8360. What was her commission?

Method 1

$$A \quad = \quad P\% \quad \cdot \quad B$$
$$\text{commission} = \quad \text{rate} \quad \cdot \quad \text{sales}$$
$$= \quad 0.20 \quad \cdot \$8360$$
$$= (0.20)(\$8360)$$
$$= \$1672$$

Method 2

$$\frac{A}{B} = \frac{P}{100}$$
$$\frac{\text{commission}}{\text{sales}} = \frac{\text{rate}}{100}$$
$$\frac{\text{commission}}{\$8360} = \frac{20}{100}$$
$$(100)\text{commission} = (20)(\$8360)$$
$$\text{commission} = \frac{(20)(\$8360)}{100}$$
$$= \$1672$$

Thus, Elaine received a commission of $1672.00 for April.

As with sales-tax problems, we can find the commission rate if we know the total sales and the commission.

PRACTICE EXERCISE 1

Rich receives a 3% commission on all life insurance policy sales. In September his sales totaled $195,400. What was his commission?

Answer: $5862

PRACTICE EXERCISE 2

Adrienne received a commission of $98.75 on sales of $790 in an appliance store. What was her commission rate?

$$\frac{98.75}{790} \quad \overline{100}$$

Answer: 12.5%

PRACTICE EXERCISE 3

If Louis received a commission of $46.04 working in a hardware store where he is paid at a commission rate of 8%, what were his total sales?

$$\frac{46.04}{\$575.50} = \frac{8}{100}$$

1875
850
750

Answer: $575.50

PRACTICE EXERCISE 4

A real estate salesman receives a monthly salary of $850 plus 0.75% of the first $100,000 in sales and 1.5% of sales above $100,000. How much did he earn in a month when he sold $225,000 worth of property?

FINDING A COMMISSION RATE — EXAMPLE 2

Shane received a $123 commission on sales of $820 in men's clothing. What was his commission rate?

The question to answer is: $123 is what percent of $820?

Method 1

$$A = P\% \cdot B$$

commission = rate · sales

$$\downarrow \qquad \downarrow \qquad \downarrow$$

$$123 = \text{rate} \cdot (820)$$

$$123 = \text{rate } (820)$$

$$\frac{123}{820} = \text{rate}$$

$$0.15 = \text{rate}$$

Method 2

$$\frac{A}{B} = \frac{P}{100}$$

$$\frac{\text{commission}}{\text{sales}} = \frac{\text{rate}}{100}$$

$$\frac{123}{820} = \frac{\text{rate}}{100}$$

$$(123)(100) = (820)\text{rate}$$

$$\frac{(123)(100)}{820} = \text{rate}$$

$$15 = \text{rate}$$

Shane's commission rate is 15%.

FINDING TOTAL SALES — EXAMPLE 3

What are the total sales on which Mario received a commission of $336 if his commission rate is 12%?

Since the commission is known but not the amount of the sales, the question is: $336 is 12% of what number?

Method 1

$$A = P\% \cdot B$$

commission = rate · sales

$$\downarrow \qquad \downarrow \qquad \downarrow$$

$$\$336 = 0.12 \cdot \text{sales}$$

$$\$336 = (0.12)\text{sales}$$

$$\frac{\$336}{0.12} = \text{sales}$$

$$\$2800 = \text{sales}$$

Method 2

$$\frac{A}{B} = \frac{P}{100}$$

$$\frac{\text{commission}}{\text{sales}} = \frac{\text{rate}}{100}$$

$$\frac{\$336}{\text{sales}} = \frac{12}{100}$$

$$(\$336)(100) = (12)\text{sales}$$

$$\frac{(\$336)(100)}{12} = \text{sales}$$

$$\$2800 = \text{sales}$$

The sales total is $2800.

MONTHLY INCOME INVOLVING A COMMISSION — EXAMPLE 4

An automobile salesperson receives a monthly salary of $500 plus 2% of the first $20,000 sales and 4% of sales above $20,000. What is the monthly income on sales of $38,000?

First, calculate 2% of $20,000.

$$(0.02)(\$20,000) = \$400$$

Next, calculate 4% of the difference $38,000 - $20,000 = $18,000.

$$0.04(\$18,000) = \$720$$

The total income is $500 plus the two commissions.

$$\$500 + \$400 + \$720 = \$1620$$

The total income for the month is $1620.

2 DISCOUNT PROBLEMS

A **discount** is a reduction in the regular price of an item when it is put on sale. The **discount rate** is the percent of the regular price that the item is reduced. The **sale price** is the price after the discount. For example, if an appliance store reduces a $600 refrigerator to a sale price of $450, the discount is $600 − $450 = $150.

The discount rate relative to the original price is $\dfrac{150}{600} = \dfrac{1 \cdot \cancel{150}}{4 \cdot \cancel{150}} = \dfrac{1}{4} = 0.25$

which is 25%. We are usually given the regular price and the discount rate and are asked to find this discount. In this problem, given the $600 and the 25%, we could have calculated the discount.

$$(0.25)(\$600) = \$150$$

TO SOLVE A DISCOUNT PROBLEM

1. Use the percent equation

$$A = P\% \cdot B$$

discount = discount rate · regular price

or use the percent proportion $\dfrac{A}{B} = \dfrac{P}{100}$

$$\dfrac{\text{discount}}{\text{regular price}} = \dfrac{\text{discount rate}}{100}.$$

2. The sale price is given by

sale price = regular price − discount.

EXAMPLE 5 FINDING A DISCOUNT

What is the discount and the sale price of a coat which is regularly priced $69.50 if the discount rate is 20%?

First find the discount.

Method 1

$$A = P\% \cdot B$$

$$\text{discount} = \text{rate} \cdot \text{reg. price}$$

$$\downarrow \qquad \downarrow$$

$$= 0.20 \cdot \$69.50$$

$$= (0.20)(\$69.50)$$

$$= \$13.90$$

Method 2

$$\dfrac{A}{B} = \dfrac{P}{100}$$

$$\dfrac{\text{discount}}{\text{reg. price}} = \dfrac{\text{rate}}{100}$$

$$\dfrac{\text{discount}}{\$69.50} = \dfrac{20}{100}$$

$$(100)\text{discount} = (20)(\$69.50)$$

$$\text{discount} = \dfrac{(20)(\$69.50)}{100}$$

$$= \$13.90$$

Then

$$\text{sale price} = \textbf{reg. price} - \textbf{discount}$$

$$\downarrow \qquad \downarrow \qquad \downarrow$$

$$= 69.50 - 13.90$$

$$= 55.60.$$

During the sale, the coat can be bought for $55.60.

PRACTICE EXERCISE 6

A jeweler put a diamond ring on sale at 15% off the regular price of $850.00. A week later he discounted it again 20% of the sale price. What was the final sale price and the overall rate of discount?

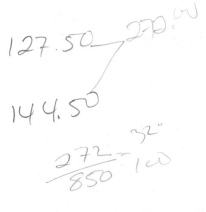

Answer: $578; 32% [Note that the overall discount is not the sum of the two discounts which is 35%.]

EXAMPLE 6 — FINDING A SALE PRICE

A retailer first discounted a $450 computer printer 10%. When the printer was not purchased, he discounted it 30% of the sale price. What was the second sale price and the overall rate of discount?

The first discount is

$$(0.10)(\$450) = \$45,$$

and the first sale price is

$$\$450 - \$45 = \$405.$$

Since the second discount is taken on the sale price of $405, find 30% of $405.

$$(0.30)(\$405) = \$121.50$$

The second discount is $121.50, and the second sale price is

$$\$405.00 - \$121.50 = \$283.50.$$

Since the second discount was taken on $405 and not on $450, the discount rates cannot be added. Add the discounts.

$$\$45.00 + \$121.50 = \$166.50$$

The total discount is $166.50 on a regular price of $450. The discount rate is given by:

$$\$166.50 = \text{discount rate} \cdot \$450$$

$$\frac{\$166.50}{\$450} = \text{discount rate}$$

$$0.37 = \text{discount rate}$$

The overall discount rate is 37%, which is less than the 40% obtained by adding 10% and 30%. The reason for the difference is that the 30% discount was taken on $405 instead of on $450.

6.4 EXERCISES

Answers to these exercises are given on page 652.

Solve each applied problem in Exercises 1–16. Estimate the answer before solving.

1. **COMMISSION** If Marsha Mildred receives a commission of 1.5% on the sale of each new car, how much will she be paid for selling a $17,200 car?

2. **COMMISSION** Mary receives a 15% commission on all clothing sales. If her sales were $3872.16 during the month of April, what was her commission?

3. **COMMISSION** Catherine Konradt received a commission of $279.00 on the sale of $1860.00 worth of books. What was the commission rate?

4. **COMMISSION** Angela received a commission of $639.12 on her furniture sales for the month of June. If the commission rate is 12%, what were her total sales?

5. **COMMISSION** The Sun Realty Company receives a 6% commission on all real estate sales. On July 16 the company sold a house for $82,560 and a lot for $21,320. What was the total commission on these sales?

6. **COMMISSION** Lynne receives a 1.5% commission each month on all farm equipment sales of $20,000 or less. For all sales over $20,000, she is paid a 3% commission on the amount over $20,000. What is her commission on sales of $45,280 during the month of May?

7. **COMMISSION** Considering the total commission that Lynne received in Exercise 6, what is her overall commission rate?

8. **BUSINESS** A retailer discounted all the coats in her shop by 25%. What is the discount and the sale price on a coat regularly priced $128.60?

9. **BUSINESS** A refrigerator normally sells for $720, but an appliance dealer put it on sale at an 18% discount. What is the discount and the sale price?

10. **BUSINESS** Dick Walker was considering a pair of shoes that were priced at $120.00 but were on sale for $84.00. What was the discount rate?

11. **BUSINESS** The Popular Shirt Shop has shirts that are discounted by $8.75. If the discount rate is 25%, what was the price before the discount?

12. **BUSINESS** In a closeout sale, a carpet dealer has reduced all carpet prices by 40%. If the normal price of a pattern is $16.90 per square yard, how much would it cost to buy the carpet for a room which is 4 yards wide and 5 yards long?

13. **BUSINESS** Vern's Vintage Autos has a 1954 Ford that was originally priced at $13,500 but now can be bought for $10,800. What is the discount rate?

14. **BUSINESS** In the spring a department store reduced the price of coats at a discount rate of 25%. When some coats were left, the store reduced their price 20% of the sale price. What was the second sale price of a coat that was originally priced $142.80?

15. **BUSINESS** What was the overall rate of discount on the coat in Exercise 14?

16. **BUSINESS** A toaster normally selling for $42.50 is on sale for 12% off the normal price. What total price must Sean pay if, after the discount is made, a 5% sales tax is added?

CRITICAL THINKING

17. **BUSINESS** A sofa was first discounted 25%. When it did not sell, it was reduced again by 30% of the sale price. When again it did not sell, it was reduced a third time by 40% of the second sale price. What was the third sale price if the sofa originally was priced at $785.50? To the nearest tenth of a percent, what was the overall rate of discount?

18. **CONSUMER** Burford decided to buy a new mountain bike valued at $500. He went to a store where the dealer had previously discounted all bikes by 10%. Presently the dealer was offering a clearance sale by taking an additional 20% off any bike on sale. When the dealer quoted a price of $360, Burford complained that he should only pay $350, 30% off the original price of $500. Explain why Burford is wrong.

19. What is the difference between a *commission* and a *commission rate?*

REVIEW OR PREVIEW

20. **SALES TAX** The sales-tax rate in Twin Falls, Idaho, is 4%. How much tax will Paula pay on the purchase of three posters each selling for $2.98 before tax? What is the total price of the posters?

21. **SALES TAX** Jeff was charged $3.29 in sales tax on the purchase of a pair of basketball shoes. What is the sales-tax rate if the before tax selling price of the shoes was $65.80?

22. **SOCIAL SECURITY TAX** Maria had an income from wages of $19,600 in 1994, How much Social Security tax did she pay if the rate was 6.2% that year?

23. **INCOME TAX** In 1994 Juanita had a taxable income of $15,743. If she used the tax table given in Section 6.3, how much income tax did she pay?

6.4 PARALLEL EXERCISES

Answers to these exercises are not given in the text.
Solve each problem in Exercises 1–16. Estimate the answer before solving.

1. **COMMISSION** Best Homes Inc. receives a commission of 7% on the sale of any property. How much did they receive for selling a house that was priced at $148,620?

2. **COMMISSION** Beth receives a 12% commission on all sales. If her sales totaled $2475.50 one week, what was her commission?

3. **COMMISSION** Earl Karn received a commission of $314.00 on the sale of $12,560.00 worth of books. What was his commission rate?

4. **COMMISSION** Art received a commission of $9817.50 on sales of computer hardware for the month of December. If his commission rate is 15%, what were his total sales?

5. **COMMISSION** The Vacation Center pays its employees an 8% commission on all sales. During June Shannon sold a motorhome for $36,580 and a travel trailer for $14,230. What was her total commission on these sales?

6. **COMMISSION** Wayne receives a 2% commission on sales of $24,000 or less. For sales over $24,000, he receives 4% of the amount over $24,000. What is his total commission on sales of $36,200?

7. **COMMISSION** Considering the total commission that Wayne receives in Exercise 6, what is his overall commission rate (to the nearest tenth of a percent)?

8. **BUSINESS** Dana put all swim suits in her store on sale at 40% off the regular price. What is the discount and sale price of a suit normally priced at $35.00?

9. **BUSINESS** A video recorder normally sells for $650, but it is put on sale at a 20% discount. What is the discount and the sale price?

10. **BUSINESS** The Discount Appliance Company claims to have high discount rates. If they discounted an electric stove from $480.00 to $300.00, what was the discount rate?

11. **BUSINESS** Gloria Smith got a discount of $5.83 on a book for keeping accounting records. If this was a 22% discount, what was the normal price of the book?

12. **BUSINESS** Carpet normally selling for $19.80 per square yard is being reduced by 30%. How much would it cost to carpet a room which is 3 yards wide and 4 yards long?

13. **BUSINESS** The Light Truck Company put a $17,750 pickup on sale for $16,330. What was the discount rate?

14. **BUSINESS** A set of dishes was first discounted 20%. When the dishes did not sell, they were reduced by 30% of the sale price. What was the second sale price if the dishes originally sold for $160.50?

15. **BUSINESS** What is the overall rate of discount on the dishes in Exercise 14?

16. **BUSINESS** A jacket normally selling for $35 is on sale for 15% off the normal price. What total price must Amber pay if, after the discount is made, a 4% sales tax is added?

 CRITICAL THINKING

17. **COMMISSION**   Jeff sold a sweater for $39.95, a pair of pants for $34.50, and a jacket for $79.98. If he received a commission of $19.30 on these sales, to the nearest tenth of a percent, what is the commission rate?

18. **BUSINESS**   When Burford bought a shirt at a 25% discount, he expected the clerk to multiply the marked price by 0.25 and subtract the result from the marked price. When the clerk multiplied by 0.75 and asked that price, Burford was upset. Can you explain to Burford why his price and the clerk's price are the same?

19. What is the difference between *discount* and *discount rate*?

GROUP PROJECT

Discuss the similarities and difference between commission and discount problems. Investigate connections between all types of percent problems, those we have studied and the ones in the next sections. Look at how the problems are stated and the techniques used to solve each type.

6.5 INTEREST PROBLEMS

STUDENT GUIDEPOSTS

1   DETERMINING SIMPLE INTEREST
2   MAKING EQUAL PAYMENTS ON A LOAN
3   USING COMPOUND INTEREST

1 SIMPLE INTEREST

The money paid for the use of money is called **interest**. When we borrow money, we pay interest to the lender. When we invest money in a bank account we receive interest from the bank. The money borrowed or invested is called the **principal** and the money paid for the use is a percent of the principal. This percent is called the **rate of interest.** For example, suppose you borrow $500 for one year and the interest rate is 12% per year. To find the interest charged, find 12% of $500.

$$(0.12)(\$500) = \$60$$

At the end of the year you must return the $500 plus the interest, $60, for a total of

$$\$500 + \$60 = \$560.$$

If you had needed the $500 for two years, the interest rate would have been

$$2(0.12) = 0.24 = 24\%.$$

The total interest for two years is

$$(0.24)(\$500) = \$120.$$

At the end of two years you would pay

$$\$500 + \$120 = \$620.$$

Interest calculated this way is called **simple interest.** Interest is charged only on the principal, and not on the interest earned. In general, the following formula is used to calculate simple interest. Remember that the interest rate must always be changed from a percent to a decimal. (**Simple interest is sometimes used by individuals but institutions use** *compound interest* **that we study later in this section.)**

SIMPLE INTEREST

If P represents a principal, R is a yearly rate of interest converted to a decimal, T is the time in years, and I is simple interest, then

$$I = P \cdot R \cdot T.$$

In addition, if A is the amount to be repaid or amount in the account, then

$$A = P + I.$$

EXAMPLE 1   FINDING THE AMOUNT TO REPAY ON A LOAN

Find the interest on $1500 for 2 years if the interest rate is 9% per year. How much must be repaid at the end of the 2-year period?

First find the simple interest. We are given that
$P = \$1500$, $R = 9\% = 0.09$, and $T = 2$. Substitute these values.

$$I = \quad P \quad \cdot \quad R \quad \cdot \quad T$$
$$\quad\quad \downarrow \quad\quad \downarrow \quad\quad \downarrow$$
$$= (\$1500) \cdot (0.09) \cdot (2)$$
$$= \$270$$

The interest is $270. Next we find A, the amount to be repaid.

PRACTICE EXERCISE 1

Find the interest on $3500 for 3 years if the interest rate is 12% per year. How much must be repaid at the end of the 3-year period?

$420 \times 3 = \$1260$
$4,760$

$$A = \quad P \quad + \quad I$$
$$\qquad \downarrow \qquad \downarrow$$
$$= \$1500 + \$270$$
$$= \$1770$$

At the end of 2 years, $1770 must be repaid.

PRACTICE EXERCISE 2

| FINDING INTEREST ON TIME LESS THAN A YEAR | EXAMPLE 2 |

What interest must be paid on an 8-month loan of $1400 if the interest rate is 9% per year? What amount must be repaid in 8 months?

Since 8 months is $\frac{8}{12}$ or $\frac{2}{3}$ of a year, use $\frac{2}{3}$ for the number of years when finding the simple interest.

What interest must be paid on a 6-month loan of $2800 if the interest rate is 16% per year? What amount must be repaid in 6 months?

Since 6 months is half of a year, we use 0.5 for T, along with $2800 for P, and $16\% = 0.16$ for R.

$$I = \quad P \quad \cdot \quad R \quad \cdot \quad T$$
$$\qquad \downarrow \qquad \downarrow \qquad \downarrow$$
$$= (\$2800) \cdot (0.16) \cdot (0.5)$$
$$= \$224$$

The interest for 6 months is $224. Next we find A, the amount to be repaid.

$$A = \quad P \quad + \quad I$$
$$\qquad \downarrow \qquad \downarrow \qquad \downarrow$$
$$= \$2800 \quad + \quad \$224$$
$$= \$3024$$

Answer: $84; $1484

Thus, in 6 months, $3024 must be repaid.

PRACTICE EXERCISE 3

| FINDING THE INTEREST RATE | EXAMPLE 3 |

Wally put $4150.15 in a savings account and after two months he had earned $124.50. What was the yearly interest rate?

Heather put $3622.16 in a savings account for one month. If the interest paid was $27.17, what was the yearly interest rate?

Since 1 month is $\frac{1}{12}$ of a year, use $\frac{1}{12}$ for T, along with $3622.16 for P, and $27.17 for I. We must solve the interest equation for R.

$$I = \quad P \quad \cdot \quad R \cdot T$$
$$\qquad \downarrow \qquad \downarrow \qquad \downarrow \qquad \downarrow$$
$$\$27.17 = \$3622.16 \quad \cdot R \cdot \left(\frac{1}{12}\right)$$

$$\frac{(\$27.17)(12)}{\$3622.16} = \frac{(\$3622.16)R(12)}{(\$3622.16)(12)}$$

Divide by $3622.16 and multiply 12

$$0.090 = R$$

The yearly interest rate is 9.0%.

Answer: 18%

---

2   EQUAL PAYMENTS ON A LOAN

On some purchases the customer pays the amount of the purchase, together with simple interest charged, in monthly payments. For example, suppose you buy a refrigerator costing $750, pay $50 down, and wish to pay off the rest, with interest, over 18 months.

The amount after the down payment is

$$\$750 - \$50 = \$700.$$

If the interest rate R is $12\% = 0.12$ per year and you have 18 months to pay, then $T = 1.5$ (18 months is 12 months + 6 months = 1 year + 0.5 year = 1.5 years), and the principal is $P = \$700$.

$$
\begin{array}{ccccc}
I = & P & \cdot & R & \cdot & T \\
 & \downarrow & & \downarrow & & \downarrow \\
 = & (\$700) & \cdot & (0.12) & \cdot & (1.5)
\end{array}
$$

$$= \$126$$

Add the principal and interest to obtain the amount A to be repaid.

$$
\begin{array}{ccccc}
A = & P & + & I \\
 & \downarrow & & \downarrow \\
 = & \$700 & + & \$126
\end{array}
$$

$$= \$826$$

Thus, the amount to be paid in 18 equal payments is $826. To find the amount of each payment, divide $826 by 18.

$$\frac{\$826}{18} = \$45.89 \quad \text{Monthly payment, rounded to nearest cent}$$

TO FIND THE AMOUNT OF EACH PAYMENT ON A LOAN

1. Find the total interest over the period.
2. Add the amount borrowed to the interest to find the total due.
3. Divide the total due by the number of payments.

EXAMPLE 4 — FINDING A MONTHLY PAYMENT

Sam buys a television set for $587.50. He pays 10% down and the rest in 24 equal monthly payments. If the simple interest is 16%, what are his monthly payments?

First, find his down payment by taking 10% of $587.50.

$$(0.10)(\$587.50) = \$58.75$$

The balance due is found by subtracting the down payment from the price of the set.

$$\$587.50 - \$58.75 = \$528.75 \quad \text{Balance due}$$

Use the balance due, $528.75 as the principal P, $16\% = 0.16$ as R, and 2 for T (T is always in years and 24 months is 2 years).

$$
\begin{array}{ccccc}
I = & P & \cdot & R & \cdot & T \\
 & \downarrow & & \downarrow & & \downarrow \\
 = & (\$528.75) & \cdot & (0.16) & \cdot & (2)
\end{array}
$$

$$= \$169.20$$

Then the total due to be paid in the monthly payments is

$$\$528.75 + \$169.20 = \$697.95.$$

Divide the total due by 24 to find the amount of each monthly payment.

$$\text{monthly payment} = \frac{\$697.95}{24} = \$29.08 \quad \text{Rounded to nearest cent}$$

Sam must pay $29.08 each month for 24 months to pay off the television set.

EXPLORATION GUIDE

Savings institutions often quote various compounding periods using the same annual rate of interest to give consumers the impression that earnings will increase substantially when the number of compounding periods increases. Although there is some truth to this argument, the increase may not be quite what you would expect. Suppose you deposit $100 in an account that pays 12% interest compounded over various periods. Calculate the amount in the account at the end of 1 year if compounding is (a) annually, (b) semiannually, (c) quarterly, (d) monthly, and (e) daily (use 365 days in a year with the interest per period 12/365). Discuss what you have discovered.

3 | COMPOUND INTEREST

For many loans or savings accounts, interest is paid on interest as well as the principal. This type of interest is called **compound interest.** For example, if you borrow $1000 for a year at 10% per year simple interest, the interest paid is

$$(0.10)(\$1000) = \$100.$$

If the 10% per year is compounded every 6 months (semiannually), the interest is calculated every 6 months and added to the principal. Since there are 2 compounding periods every year, the yearly interest rate 10% is divided by 2 to obtain an interest rate of

$$\frac{10\%}{2} = 5\%$$

for every 6-month period. The interest on $1000 for the first 6 months is

$$(0.05)(\$1000) = \$50.$$

With compound interest, the principal on which interest is paid for the second 6 months is the original principal plus the first 6-month interest,

$$\$1000 + \$50 = \$1050.$$

The interest on $1050 for the second 6 months is

$$(0.05)(\$1050) = \$52.50.$$

The total interest for the year is the sum of the interests on the first and second 6-month periods.

$$\$50.00 + \$52.50 = \$102.50.$$

Notice that the compound interest amounted to $2.50 more than the simple interest.

This process could be continued to find the interest compounded semiannually over more than one year.

TO SOLVE A COMPOUND INTEREST PROBLEM

1. Determine the interest rate for a compounding period by dividing the yearly rate by the number of periods per year.
2. Find the interest for the first period.
3. Use the sum of the interest found in Step 2 and the principal as the principal for the next period.
4. Continue until all periods have been accounted for.

Interest can be compounded over different periods. The most common types are shown in the table below where R is the annual or yearly interest rate.

Type of Compounding	Number of Compounding Periods Each Year	Interest Rate per Period
compounded annually	1	R
compounded semiannually	2	$\dfrac{R}{2}$
compounded quarterly	4	$\dfrac{R}{4}$
compounded monthly	12	$\dfrac{R}{12}$

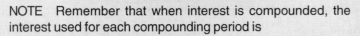

NOTE Remember that when interest is compounded, the interest used for each compounding period is

$$\frac{\text{ANNUAL INTEREST RATE}}{\text{NUMBER OF PERIODS PER YEAR}}.$$

For example, if the annual interest rate is 12%, and compounding is semiannually, quarterly, or monthly, use 6%, 3%, or 1%, respectively, as the interest rate each period.

EXAMPLE 5 — FINDING INTEREST COMPOUNDED ANNUALLY

Richard invests $5000 in an account which pays 8% compounded annually. How much will he have in his account at the end of 2 years?

Calculate the interest for the first year. Since there is only one period per year, the interest rate is 8% = 0.08.

$$(0.08)(\$5000) = \$400$$

The principal on which the second year interest is calculated is thus

$$\$5000 + \$400 = \$5400.$$

The interest for the second year is

$$(0.08)(\$5400) = \$432.$$

The total in the account at the end of 2 years is

$$\$5400 + \$432 = \$5832.$$

EXAMPLE 6 — FINDING INTEREST COMPOUNDED SEMIANNUALLY

Joe borrowed $600 for $1\frac{1}{2}$ years. Interest is 12% per year compounded semiannually. What amount must he pay back in $1\frac{1}{2}$ years?

Since semiannually means twice a year, the interest rate for a compounding period is

$$\frac{12\%}{2} = 6\%,$$

and the number of periods is 3. Interest for the first 6 months (the first period) is

$$(0.06)(\$600) = \$36.$$

The principal to be used for the second period is

$$\$600 + \$36 = \$636.$$

Interest for the second period is

$$(0.06)(\$636) = \$38.16.$$

The principal to be used for the third period is

$$\$636.00 + \$38.16 = \$674.16.$$

Interest for the third period is

$$(0.06)(\$674.16) = \$40.45.$$ To the nearest cent

The final amount to be paid is

$$\$674.16 + \$40.45 = \$714.61.$$

6.5 EXERCISES

Answers to these exercises are given on page 652.

▣ *Solve each applied problem in Exercises 1–12. Be sure your answer seems reasonable.*

1. **LOANS** Kevin Connors borrowed $8000 for one year at a bank where the interest rate was 10.5%. How much interest did he have to pay at the end of the year?

2. **SAVINGS** Cyndi Keen put $6200 into a savings account and after one year had $6603.00 in the account. What was the interest rate?

3. **CONSUMER** Julie Rislov bought a lawn mower for $675 and paid $75 dollars down. She paid the remaining amount at the end of 9 months. If interest was 12% per year (9% for 9 months), what was the total that she paid at the end of 9 months?

4. **CONSUMER** Dick Walker borrowed $1200 and after 3 months paid $1230 to pay off the loan. What was the yearly interest rate?

5. **CONSUMER** Harold bought a $2526.50 compact disc system and paid 10% down. The remaining money plus interest was to be paid at the end of 2 years. If interest is 14% per year simple interest, how much interest (to the nearest cent) did Harold have to pay?

6. **LOANS** Lynn borrowed $5482.50 for 2 years at 12% simple interest. What did she have to pay at the end of the period to pay off the loan?

7. **MONTHLY PAYMENTS** If Lynn in Exercise 6 had paid off the loan in 24 equal monthly payments, what would her monthly payment have been (to the nearest cent)?

8. **MONTHLY PAYMENTS** Robert will pay off a $1213.40 debt in 18 monthly payments. Simple interest is 16% per year. What are his payments (to the nearest cent)?

9. **LOANS** Susan borrowed $500 from a loan shark who charges 15% per month simple interest. What interest did she have to pay for one year? What was her monthly payment if she paid off the loan in 12 months?

10. **SAVINGS** Sylvester invests $2500 in an account which pays 7% per year compounded annually. What does he have in the account at the end of 2 years?

11. **LOANS** Maria borrows $625.50 at 12% compounded semiannually. What must she pay (to the nearest cent) to pay off the loan at the end of 18 months?

12. **SAVINGS** Patricia has $7000 to invest in an account which pays 10% compound interest. How much is in her account at the end of one year if the interest is compounded semiannually? How much is in her account at the end of one year if the compounding is quarterly (4 times per year)?

CALCULATOR EXERCISES

▣ *It can be shown that the amount A in an account if a principal P is deposited at 12% interest compounded monthly for 5 years is given by*

$$A = P(1.01)^{60}.$$

Use a scientific calculator with a ☐ y^x *key or* ☐ ^ *key on a graphing calculator and this formula to find the amount in an account with the value of P given in Exercises 13–15.*

13. *P* = $1000

14. *P* = $5000

15. *P* = $10,000

▣ 16. **SAVINGS** Ling Lee invests $8575 in an account which pays 11.5% interest compounded semiannually. How much is in his account at the end of 18 months?

CRITICAL THINKING

💡17. **SAVINGS** Burford deposited $100 in an account that pays 10% interest compounded semiannually. He decided to calculate the value of his account at the end of 1 year. His work is shown below. What is Burford doing wrong? What will be the correct amount in the account?

$$(\$100)(0.10) = \$10 \quad \textit{Interest after 6 months}$$

$$\$100 + \$10 = \$110 \quad \textit{Principal for next 6 months}$$

$$($110)(0.10) = $11 \quad \textit{Interest for next 6 months}$$

$$$110 + $11 = $121 \quad \textit{Value of account at end of 1 year}$$

✎ 18. Write a paragraph explaining the difference between *simple interest* and *compound interest.* Is it fair to say that using simple interest, you obtain interest on the principal only; however, for compound interest, you receive interest on your interest?

REVIEW OR PREVIEW

19. **EARNINGS** Joseph receives a 20% commission on all appliances he sells. His total sales for June were $7218.50. What was his commission?

20. **BUSINESS** Michael's, a shop for men, put suits on sale at a 33% discount. What is the sale price of a $285 suit?

21. **EARNINGS** Bridgette earned $123.65 in commissions on sales in a dress shop. If she works on a 10% commission rate, what were her total sales?

22. **CONSUMER** Mr. Miller, a senior citizen, receives a discount of 15% on all bills for food at the Village Waffle Shoppe. If the bill comes to $123.40 when he takes his family out to eat, how much must he pay?

6.5 PARALLEL EXERCISES

🖩 *Solve each applied problem in Exercises 1–12. Be sure your answer seems reasonable.*

1. **LOANS** The interest rate for loans at the State Credit Union is 9%. How much interest would be charged on a loan of $2400 that is paid back after one year?

2. **SAVINGS** Paul Sadler put $3250 in a savings account and after a year had $3493.75 in the account. What was the yearly interest rate?

3. **CONSUMER** Juan Garcia purchased a TV for $1250 and put $150 down. The remaining amount was financed at a rate 10% per year. If he paid off the loan in 9 months, how much did he have to pay?

4. **CONSUMER** Pam Johnson took out a short term loan of $2250. After 4 months she paid off the loan with a check for $2317.50. What was the yearly interest rate?

5. **CONSUMER** Colleen bought a lawn mower for $252.20 and paid 20% down. The remaining amount is to be paid off at the end of 6 months. If the simple interest rate is 10% per year, what will she have to pay to pay off the loan?

6. **LOANS** Calvin borrowed $628 for 2 years. If the simple interest rate is 12% per year, what amount will he have to pay at the end of the 2-year period?

7. **MONTHLY PAYMENTS** If Calvin in Exercise 6 pays off the loan in 24 equal monthly payments, how much will he pay each month?

8. **MONTHLY PAYMENTS** Bruce will pay off a $782.50 debt in 18 monthly payments. If simple interest is 14% per year, what is his monthly payment?

9. **LOANS** Vinnie, the loan shark, charges 20% *per month* simple interest. How much interest will he collect on a loan of $1000 which is paid off in one year? If Vinnie collects the loan with interest in 12 equal monthly payments, how much does he receive each month?

10. **SAVINGS** Maria Vasquez invests $5800 in an account that pays 8% per year compounded semiannually. How much is in her account at the end of a year?

11. **LOANS** Virgil borrows $840.50 at 10% interest compounded semiannually. What must he pay (to the nearest cent) to pay off the loan at the end of 30 months?

12. **LOANS** William borrows $540.00 at 12% compound interest per year. What total amount must he pay at the end of the year if the compounding is semiannually? How much if the compounding is quarterly?

CALCULATOR EXERCISES

Use the formula given above Exercises 13-15 to find the amount in the account with the value of P given.

13. $P = 1500

14. $P = 4500

15. $P = $12,500$

🖩 16. **SAVINGS** Find the simple interest earned on $13,455 at 11.25% per year for 20 months.

CRITICAL THINKING

17. **LOANS** Burford's loan was for 5 years at 12% interest compounded monthly. He used the formula from Exercises 13 – 15 to determine the amount. Since he was to make monthly payments, he divided the amount by 60, the number of months in five years. His number for amount of payment was higher than the number given to him by the bank. Can you explain why?

18. Historically simple interest was used before compound interest. Explain the changes in society that may have caused the spread of the use of compound interest.

GROUP PROJECT

In Exercises 13–15 we used the compound interest formula, $A = P(1.01)^{60}$, when the interest rate was 12% and the period was 5 years. Can you explain the meaning of the 1.01 and the 60? Investigate compound interest and discuss it's use. Can you find a general compound interest formula? See if your group can use the formula on a problem of interest to one of you.

6.6 PERCENT INCREASE AND DECREASE PROBLEMS

The percent by which a quantity increases is called the **percent increase.** Similarly, the percent by which a quantity decreases is called the **percent decrease.** For example, if a salary increased 7%, we find the increase by taking 7% of the *original* salary. Thus, if you earn $20,000 a year and receive a 7% raise, the increase in salary or your raise is

$$(0.07)(\$20,000) = \$1400$$

and your new salary will be

new salary = **former salary + raise**
$$\downarrow \qquad\qquad \downarrow$$
=   **\$20,000   + \$1400**

$$= \$21,400.$$

If school enrollment decreases by 6%, we find the decrease by taking 6% of the *original* number of students. For example, if BSU had 10,500 students last year and enrollment went down 6% this year, the decrease in enrollment was

$$(0.06)(10,500) = 630 \text{ students}$$

The enrollment this year is

this year's enrollment = **last year's enrollment − decrease**
$$\downarrow \qquad\qquad \downarrow$$
=   **10,500   − 630**

$$= 9870 \text{ students.}$$

These are examples of percent increase and percent decrease problems.

TO SOLVE A PERCENT INCREASE (DECREASE) PROBLEM

1. Use the percent equation

$$A \quad = \quad P\% \quad \cdot \quad B$$

increase (decrease) = percent increase (decrease) · original amount

or use the percent proportion $\dfrac{A}{B} = \dfrac{P}{100}$

$$\frac{\text{increase (decrease)}}{\text{original amount}} = \frac{\text{percent increase (decrease)}}{100}.$$

2. The new amount is given by

new amount = original amount + increase

or

new amount = original amount − decrease.

EXAMPLE 1 SOLVING A PERCENT DECREASE APPLICATION

A labor union votes to take a 5% decrease in wages in order to keep the company from going bankrupt. If the average salary before the decrease was $17,500 per year, what is the new salary?

First find the decrease in salary.

Method 1

$$A \quad = \quad P\% \quad \cdot \quad B$$

decrease = % decrease · original salary

$$= \quad (0.05) \quad \cdot \quad (\$17,500)$$

$$= \$875$$

Method 2

$$\frac{A}{B} = \frac{P}{100}$$

$$\frac{\text{decrease}}{\text{original salary}} = \frac{\% \text{ decrease}}{100}$$

$$\frac{\text{decrease}}{\$17,500} = \frac{5}{100}$$

$$\text{decrease}(100) = (5)(\$17,500)$$

$$\text{decrease} = \frac{(5)(\$17,500)}{100}$$

$$= \$875$$

Thus, the decrease in salary is $875. Next find the new salary.

new salary = **original salary − decrease in salary**

$$= \quad \$17,500 \quad - \quad \$875$$

$$= \$16,625$$

The new average salary is $16,625.

EXAMPLE 2 SOLVING A PERCENT INCREASE APPLICATION

State University expects an increase in enrollment of 2.5% next year. If the present enrollment is 15,276, what will be the approximate number of students next year?

First find the increase in enrollment.

PRACTICE EXERCISE 1

Due to declining enrollments, teachers in the Kachina District are faced with a 3% decrease in wages. If the average salary before the decrease is $14,700, what will be the new average salary?

Answer: $14,259

402 FUNDAMENTALS OF MATHEMATICS

PRACTICE EXERCISE 2

The placement director expects an increase of 3.5% in the number of students taking the placement exam in mathematics during the fall semester. If 2480 students took the exam last fall, what will be the approximate number of students tested this fall?

Answer: 2567 students

Method 1

$$A = P\% \cdot B$$

increase = % increase · enrollment

$$= (0.025) \cdot (15{,}276)$$

$$= 381.9$$

Method 2

$$\frac{A}{B} = \frac{P}{100}$$

$$\frac{\text{increase}}{\text{enrollment}} = \frac{\%\ \text{increase}}{100}$$

$$\frac{\text{increase}}{15{,}276} = \frac{2.5}{100}$$

$$\text{increase}(100) = (2.5)(15{,}276)$$

$$\text{increase} = \frac{(2.5)(15{,}276)}{100}$$

$$= 381.9$$

We must round to the nearest whole number so the increase will be approximately 382 students. The new enrollment is found by adding this year's enrollment to the increase.

$$\text{New enrollment} = \textbf{Original enrollment} + \textbf{Enrollment increase}$$

$$= 15{,}276 + 382$$

$$= 15{,}658$$

Thus, there will be approximately 15,658 students next year.

NOTE Remember that percent increase or decrease is always taken on the original quantity. To find the new quantity *add* the increase to the *original* amount or *subtract* the decrease from the *original* amount.

PRACTICE EXERCISE 3

The price of a six-pack of soda dropped from $2.25 to $1.85. What was the percent decrease, to the nearest tenth of a percent?

Answer: 17.8%

FINDING A PERCENT DECREASE EXAMPLE 3

The price of a dozen eggs dropped from 75¢ to 67¢. What was the percent decrease?

First find the amount of the decrease.

$$75¢ - 67¢ = 8¢$$

Since 8¢ is the amount of the decrease, and 75¢ is the original price, we must find the percent decrease, *P*.

Method 1

$$A = P\% \cdot B$$

decrease = % decrease · original price

$$8 = P\% \cdot (75)$$

$$8 = P\%(75)$$

$$\frac{8}{75} = P\%$$

Method 2

$$\frac{A}{B} = \frac{P}{100}$$

$$\frac{\text{decrease}}{\text{original price}} = \frac{\%\ \text{decrease}}{100}$$

$$\frac{8}{75} = \frac{P}{100}$$

$$(8)(100) = (75)P$$

$$0.10\overline{6} = P\%$$

$$\frac{(8)(100)}{75} = P$$

$$10.\overline{6} = P$$

Thus, the percent decrease was $10.\overline{6}\%$ or $10\frac{2}{3}\%$.

FINDING AN ORIGINAL PRICE

The price of gasoline increased 10%. The amount of this increase was 12¢ per gallon. What was the original price of a gallon of gasoline?

We know the percent increase and the amount of the increase, so we must find the original price.

Method 1

$$A = P\% \cdot B$$

increase = % increase · price

$$\downarrow \qquad \downarrow \qquad \downarrow$$

$$12 = (0.10) \cdot \text{price}$$

$$\frac{12}{0.10} = \text{price}$$

$$120 = \text{price}$$

Method 2

$$\frac{A}{B} = \frac{P}{100}$$

$$\frac{\text{increase}}{\text{price}} = \frac{\% \text{increase}}{100}$$

$$\frac{12}{\text{price}} = \frac{10}{100}$$

$$(12)(100) = (10)\text{price}$$

$$\frac{(12)(100)}{10} = \text{price}$$

$$120 = \text{price}$$

Thus, the original price of a gallon of gasoline was 120¢ or $1.20.

FINDING A PERCENT INCREASE

The Smith family bought a house two years ago for $85,000. It is now valued at $102,680. To the nearest percent, what is the percent increase in value?

To find the amount of the increase, subtract the original value from the new value.

$$\$102,680 - \$85,000 = \$17,680 \quad \text{Increase in value}$$

We must find the percent increase, P.

Method 1

$$A = P\% \cdot B$$

increase = % increase · original value

$$\downarrow \qquad \downarrow \qquad \downarrow$$

$$17,680 = P\% \cdot 85,000$$

$$17,680 = P\%(85,000)$$

$$\frac{17,680}{85,000} = P\%$$

$$0.208 = P\%$$

Method 2

$$\frac{A}{B} = \frac{P}{100}$$

$$\frac{\text{increase}}{\text{original value}} = \frac{\% \text{increase}}{100}$$

$$\frac{17,680}{85,000} = \frac{P}{100}$$

$$(17,680)(100) = (85,000)P$$

$$\frac{(17,680)(100)}{85,000} = P$$

$$20.8 = P$$

$$\frac{1300}{2400} = \frac{54.2}{100}$$

Thus, to the nearest percent, the percent increase is about 21%.

CAUTION   In problems such as the one in Example 5, be sure to compare the increase in value to the *original* value, not the new value. In such cases always ask:

increase is what percent of *original value*?

An interesting application of percent increase and decrease has to do with changes in automobile fuel economy. Such things as temperature, humidity, wind conditions, and road conditions have an effect on the amount of fuel used.

Suppose we assume the percent increases and decreases in the following tables for the given conditions. An increase in fuel economy means more miles per gallon (mpg) and a decrease means fewer mpg.

Condition	% Increase	Condition	% Decrease
Tailwind	15%	Headwind	17%
Smooth road	12%	Rough road	25%
High humidity	6%	Low temperature	10%

SOLVING APPLICATIONS OF FUEL ECONOMY

EXAMPLE 6

(a) If Michael's car normally gets 30 mpg, what should it get with a tailwind?

First use the table to find that a tailwind increases economy by 15%. Find 15% of 30 mpg.

$$(0.15)(30) = 4.5$$

A tailwind gives Michael an additional 4.5 mpg for a total of

$$30 + 4.5 = 34.5 \text{ mpg.}$$

Thus, Michael's car gets about 34.5 mpg with a tailwind.

(b) Suppose Mary drives on a rough road under high humidity conditions. What is the percent change in economy? If her normal mileage is 20 mpg, what is her mileage under the given conditions?

Since the rough road means a 25% decrease and high humidity means a 6% increase, find the difference:

$$25\% - 6\% = 19\%.$$

Under these conditions there is a 19% decrease in economy. Taking 19% of 20,

$$(0.19)(20) = 3.8 \text{ mpg,}$$

the amount of decrease is 3.8 mpg. The mileage under these conditions is

$$20 - 3.8 = 16.2 \text{ mpg.}$$

Thus, Mary's mileage is approximately 16.2 mpg.

PRACTICE EXERCISE 6

(a) If Michael's car normally gets 30 mpg, what should it get when he drives on a smooth road?

(b) If Mary drives against a headwind but on a smooth road, what is the percent change in economy? What is her mileage under these conditions if normally she gets 20 mpg?

Answers: (a) 33.6 mpg (b) 5% decrease; 19 mpg

6.6 EXERCISES

Answers to these exercises are given on page 653.

Solve each applied problem in Exercises 1–16. First estimate the answer.

1. **SALARY** Beth Miller had a salary of $42,500 before she got a 6.5% raise. What was her salary after the raise?

2. **SALARY** All State University employees got a 2.5% raise. What would be the new salary of a professor who was making $38,500 before the raise?

3. **SALARY** The executives of the Paper Corporation agree to take an 8% salary cut in order to help the financial situation of the company. If the president was making $125,300 per year, what is her new salary?

4. **EDUCATION** City College expects a decrease in enrollment of 3.5% next year. If the current enrollment is 23,254, what will be the approximate enrollment next year?

5. **POPULATION** The population of a small community on the coast of Maine increased from 2460 to 2890 in one year. What was the percent increase to the nearest tenth of a percent?

6. **CONSUMER** Over a period of years, the price of a gallon of gasoline increased from $0.32 to $1.27. To the nearest percent, what was the percent increase?

7. **BUSINESS** As the harvest season progressed the price of tomatoes dropped from 59¢ per pound to 42¢ per pound. What was the percent decrease to the nearest tenth of a percent?

8. **SALARY** Forrest received a 15% increase in salary. The amount of the increase was $1824. What was his original salary?

9. **HEALTH** By attending a weight-control class, Mary lost 24 pounds. If she now weighs 115 pounds, what was her original weight and her percent decrease to the nearest tenth of one percent?

10. **CONSUMER** The value of a new car decreases 27% the first year. If the decrease amounted to $2300, what was the original value?

Refer to the mileage tables in this section for Exercises 11–14.

11. **GAS MILEAGE** The normal gasoline mileage of a car is 25 mpg. What is its mileage on a smooth road?

12. **GAS MILEAGE** Henry normally gets 8 mpg with his truck. If he drives on a rough road, what mileage will he get?

13. **GAS MILEAGE** Jane is driving with a tailwind but the temperature is low. What will be her mileage if she normally gets 42 mpg?

14. **GAS MILEAGE** Sue is driving into a headwind under conditions of high humidity. She has a decrease of 4.4 mpg in her mileage. What is her normal mileage?

15. **GAS MILEAGE** Driving at high speeds reduces your mileage. Michael normally gets about 33 mpg, but by driving fast, he only got 27 mpg. To the nearest tenth of a percent, what was his percent decrease? *18.2%*

16. **GAS MILEAGE** By keeping his car in good mechanical condition, Arnie can get an increase in mileage of 13%. Good driving habits will give a 9% increase in mileage. By keeping his car in good condition and driving correctly, what mileage can Arnie get if his normal rate is 30 mpg?

CRITICAL THINKING

In Exercises 17–18 use the following graph that appeared in the November 3, 1995 issue of The New York Times. Give approximate answers to the nearest tenth of a percent.

17. What was the percent decrease in factory orders from January, 1995 to April, 1995?

18. What was the percent increase in factory orders from April, 1994 to April, 1995?

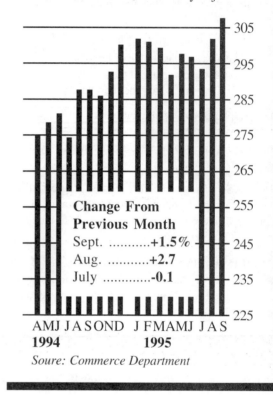

Factory Orders
Manufacturers' total new orders, in billions of dollars, seasonally adjusted.

Change From Previous Month
Sept. ....+1.5%
Aug. ....+2.7
July ....-0.1

AMJ J A S O N D J F M A M J J A S
1994   **1995**

Soure: Commerce Department

In Exercises 19–20 use the following table. Give answers correct to the nearest tenth of a percent.

Recent Trends in Computers and Peripherals (SIC 3571,2,5,7): 1988 to 1994

[Census reclassified some parts for electronic computers (3571) to component industries (367) for 1989–1990]

ITEM	UNIT	1988	1989	1990	1991	1992	1993[1]	1994[1]
INDUSTRY DATA								
Value of shipments[2]	Mil. dol ..	62,773	59,758	58,981	54,703	61,385	65,900	70,500
Total employment	1,000	290	263	248	227	219	201	191
Production workers	1,000	105.0	96.8	89.6	76.2	73.3	68.0	67.0
Average hourly earnings .	Dollar	10.93	11.68	11.72	12.52	12.47	12.59	13.01
Capital expenditures	Mil. dol ..	2,213	2,148	1,993	1,813	2,123	(NA)	(NA)
PRODUCT DATA								
Value of shipments[3]	Mil. dol ..	53,230	54,891	52,628	49,144	54,342	58,700	62,900
TRADE DATA								
Value of imports	Mil. dol ..	(NA)	21,714	23,323	26,424	32,137	38,636	46,833
Value of exports.	Mil. dol ..	(NA)	22,360	24,138	25,182	26,304	26,696	30,393

NA Not available.   [1]Estimate, except exports and imports.   [2] Value of all products and services sold by establishments in the computers and peripherals industry.   [3]Value of products classified in the computers and peripherals industry produced by all industries.

Source: U.S. Department of Commerce: Bureau of the Census, International Trade Administration (ITA). Estimates by ITA.

19. What was the percent decrease in the total employment from 1988 to 1994?

20. What was the percent increase in the value of imports from 1989 to 1994?

21. **CONSUMER** A new car decreases in value by approximately 27.5% each year. If a car is purchased for $12,685.35, what is its approximate value two years later?

22. Burford is still upset when he sees signed numbers. In the insert on the graph used for Exercises 17–18, he saw +1.5%, +2.7%, and –0.1%. Can you explain these numbers to Burford?

23. What is the difference between *increase* and *percent increase?*

REVIEW OR PREVIEW

24. **MONTHLY PAYMENTS** Sara buys a stereo for $728.50 and puts 10% down, paying the rest in 18 monthly payments. If the simple interest is 16%, what are her payments (to the nearest cent)?

25. **INVESTMENT** Henry puts $1500 in a savings account which pays 8% compounded semiannually. What will be the value of his account at the end of 2 years?

26. **MONTHLY PAYMENTS** Den bought a set of tools for $565.50 by putting 20% down and paying the rest in 12 monthly payments. If he is charged 14% simple interest, what are his payments?

27. **INVESTMENT** Montana plans to put $3000 into a savings account for two years. She can choose one account which pays 11% simple interest or another which pays 10% interest compounded semiannually. Which account will return the most interest?

6.6 PARALLEL EXERCISES

Answers to these exercises are not given in the text.

Solve each applied problem in Exercises 1–16. First estimate the answer.

1. **SALARY** Joseph Tsosie has a salary of $42,360. How much will he make if he gets the 8.5% raise that he is expecting?

2. **SALARY** The employees of The Motor Works are getting a 5.5% raise. What will be the new salary of a mechanic who is currently making $36,420?

3. **CONSUMER** Several years ago, the price of gasoline was $0.40 per gallon. What was the price after a 190% increase?

4. **BUSINESS** A major corporation is forced to decrease its number of employees by 4.5% next year. If it now employs 3540 workers, how many will be employed next year?

5. **ENVIRONMENT** On an island in the Pacific Ocean the bird population increased from an estimated 1280 to 1570. What was this percent increase to the nearest percent?

6. **BUSINESS** Due to overstocking, a retailer is forced to decrease the price of an item from $1.85 to $1.25. To the nearest tenth of a percent, what is the percent decrease?

7. **BUSINESS** Because of slow sales Foreign Cars, Inc. lowered the price of an import from $28,650 to $24,990. What was this percent decrease to the nearest tenth of a percent?

8. **CONSUMER** A new car decreased in value a total of $1920 the first year. If this was a 24% decrease, what was the original value?

9. **MILTARY** After six weeks of basic training, a new recruit in the army lost 14 pounds. If he now weighs 176 pounds, what was his original weight and the percent decrease in weight (to the nearest tenth of a percent)?

10. **INVESTMENT** The value of a Navajo Indian rug increased 15% during the first year. If the increase amounted to $114.87, what was the original price?

Refer to the mileage tables in this section for Exercises 11–14.

11. **GAS MILEAGE** The normal gasoline mileage for a motorhome is 12 mpg. What is the mileage with a tailwind?

12. **GAS MILEAGE** Danielle normally gets 26 mpg with her car. If she drives during a period of low temperature, what mileage will she get?

13. **GAS MILEAGE** Rufus is driving with a headwind on a smooth road. What will his mileage be if he usually gets 18 mpg?

14. **GAS MILEAGE** Randy is driving into a headwind, on a rough road, and at a low temperature. If he has a decrease of 13 mpg in his mileage, what is his normal mileage?

15. **GAS MILEAGE** By driving at the speed limit, you can improve your mileage from what would be obtained by driving over the limit. If Marla got 14 mpg while exceeding the limit and 19 mpg while driving at the speed limit, what was the percent increase (to the nearest tenth of a percent)?

16. **GAS MILEAGE** When a car is tuned properly, its gas mileage can be improved by 5%. If Ronnie was getting 24 mpg before a tune-up, what mileage can he expect to get after the car has been serviced?

 CRITICAL THINKING

Refer to the bar graph given above Exercises 17–18 to answer the following. Give approximate answer to the nearest tenth of a percent.

17. What was the percent decrease in factory orders from December, 1994 to July, 1995?

18. What was the percent increase in factory orders from August, 1994 to August, 1995?

In Exercises 19–20 use the table given above Exercise 19. Give answers correct to the nearest tenth of a percent.

19. What was the percent decrease in the production workers from 1988 to 1994?

20. What was the percent increase in the value of exports from 1989 to 1994?

21. **CONSUMER** By decreasing the thermostat from 72° to 68°, a company can reduce its heating bill by 35.5%. If the bill last month, prior to turning down the thermostat, was $478.63, what can the company expect to pay for heat this month?

22. **SALARY** Burford was asked to solve the following problem. After receiving a 5% raise, Mary's new salary is $15,000. What was her former salary? Burford's solution is given below. What is wrong with his work? Can you solve this problem? The correct answer is about $14,285.71. Check this.

$$\$15,000 - 0.05(\$15,000) = \$15,000 - \$750 = \$14,250$$

23. What is the difference between *decrease* and *percent decrease*?

 **GROUP PROJECT**

In Chapter 5 we compared data by taking ratios. Determine ratios of data from a magazine or newspaper and calculate percent increase and decrease on the same data. Discuss the two ways of comparing data. Is there a relationship between the two techniques. (For example, is there a percent increase or decrease that means the same as a ratio of 2 to 1?) Give examples of applications that might be best understood by each comparison.

6.7 MARKUP AND MARKDOWN PROBLEMS

A special type of percent increase problem involves marking up prices in a business. Any wholesale or retail business must sell an item for more than its cost. This extra amount goes to pay operating expenses and give the owners a return on their investment. In many businesses, the difference between the cost and selling price is a fixed percent of the cost.

The amount by which the selling price is increased over the cost is called the **markup** on the item. The markup is divided by the cost to get the **percent markup.** For example, if the cost of an item is $4 and the selling price is $5, then the markup on the item is

$$\$5 - \$4 = \$1.$$

The percent markup is found by dividing $1 (markup) by $4 (cost).

$$\frac{\text{markup}}{\text{cost}} = \frac{1}{4} = 0.25 = 25\%$$

Thus, the percent markup is 25%.

In most businesses, the percent markup is given and the amount of the markup must be found. Suppose a 30% markup is needed to make a business prosper. When a pair of shoes costing $20 is to be sold, the sales staff can calculate the markup as follows:

$$(0.30)(\$20) = \$6.$$

The markup is $6 and the selling price is

$$\$20 + \$6 = \$26.$$

Thus, the store will sell the pair of shoes for $26.

On the other hand, suppose a wholesaler bought too many of a particular item. He might have to reduce his selling price to sell them. This is a percent decrease or a discount problem, and the **percent markdown** is based on the selling price of the item. For example, a 30% reduction would be found by taking 30% of the selling price. The amount of the price reduction is called the **markdown.**

TO SOLVE A MARKUP (MARKDOWN) PROBLEM

1. Use the percent equation

$$A \quad = \quad P\% \quad \cdot \quad B$$

$$\textbf{markup}\,(\textbf{markdown}) = \textbf{percent markup}\,(\textbf{markdown}) \cdot \textbf{cost}\,(\textbf{price})$$

or use the percent proportion $\dfrac{A}{B} = \dfrac{P}{100}$

$$\frac{\textbf{markup}\,(\textbf{markdown})}{\textbf{cost}\,(\textbf{price})} = \frac{\textbf{percent markup}\,(\textbf{markdown})}{\textbf{100}}$$

2. To find the new selling price use

$$\textbf{selling price} = \textbf{cost} + \textbf{markup}$$

or

$$\textbf{new selling price} = \textbf{old selling price} - \textbf{markdown.}$$

NOTE   In a markup problem, the markup is always a percent of the original cost, *not* a percent of the new selling price.

In order to stay in business, the owner of a clothing store must have a percent markup of 85%. If he buys a suit for $125.00 what is the selling price of the suit?

The Sun and Surf Sports Shop uses a 25% markup rate on all its sports equipment. A slalom water ski is purchased from the wholesale supplier for $285. Determine the markup and the selling price of the ski. If the sales-tax rate is 5%, how much will Sherri have to pay for the water ski, including the tax?

Method 1

$$A = P\% \cdot B$$

$$\text{markup} = \%\ \text{markup} \cdot \text{cost}$$

$$\text{markup} = (0.25) \cdot \$285$$

$$= \$71.25$$

Method 2

$$\frac{A}{B} = \frac{P}{100}$$

$$\frac{\text{markup}}{\text{cost}} = \frac{\%\ \text{markup}}{100}$$

$$\frac{\text{markup}}{\$285} = \frac{25}{100}$$

$$\text{markup}(100) = (25)(\$285)$$

$$\text{markup} = \frac{(25)(\$285)}{100}$$

$$= \$71.25$$

The markup is $71.25, and the selling price is the sum of the markup and the cost.

$285.00	**Cost**
+ 71.25	**Markup**
$356.25	**Selling price**

The dealer must sell the ski for $356.25. Since the sales-tax rate is 5%, the tax on the purchase of the ski is:

$$(0.05)(\$356.25) = \$17.81 \quad \text{To the nearest cent}$$

Thus, Sherri will have to pay a total of $356.25 + $17.81 = $374.06

Answer: $231.25

A retailer buys a radio for $34.50 and sells it for $48.30. What is the markup and the percent markup?

The Shoe Store buys one type of shoe for $26.50 per pair and sells them for $34.45. What is the markup and the percent markup?

Find the markup first by finding the difference between the selling price and the cost.

$$\begin{array}{r} \$34.45 \\ -\ 26.50 \\ \hline \$\ 7.95 \end{array} \quad \text{Selling price} - \text{cost} = \text{markup}$$

The markup is $7.95. The percent markup is found by answering the question: $7.95 is what percent of $26.50? Let P be the percent markup.

Method 1

$$A = P\% \cdot B$$

$$\text{markup} = \%\ \text{markup} \cdot \text{cost}$$

$$7.95 = P \cdot 26.50$$

$$7.95 = P\%(26.50)$$

$$\frac{7.95}{26.50} = P\%$$

$$0.30 = P\%$$

The percent markup is 30%.

Method 2

$$\frac{A}{B} = \frac{P}{100}$$

$$\frac{\text{markup}}{\text{cost}} = \frac{\%\ \text{markup}}{100}$$

$$\frac{7.95}{26.50} = \frac{P}{100}$$

$$(7.95)(100) = (26.50)P$$

$$\frac{(7.95)(100)}{26.50} = P$$

$$30 = P$$

Answer: $13.80; 40%

EXAMPLE 3 — FINDING THE COST AND SELLING PRICE

PRACTICE EXERCISE 3

A clothing wholesaler has a 40% markup. If the markup on a suit is $86.50, what is the cost? What is the selling price?

A store owner operates on a 45% markup. If the markup on a stereo is $108, what is the cost? What is the selling price?

Method 1

$$A = P\% \cdot B$$

markup = % markup · cost

$$\downarrow \qquad \downarrow \qquad \downarrow$$

$$86.50 = (0.40) \cdot cost$$

$$\frac{86.50}{0.40} = cost$$

$$216.25 = cost$$

Method 2

$$\frac{A}{B} = \frac{P}{100}$$

$$\frac{markup}{cost} = \frac{\% \ markup}{100}$$

$$\frac{86.50}{cost} = \frac{40}{100}$$

$$(86.50)(100) = cost(40)$$

$$\frac{(86.50)(100)}{40} = cost$$

$$216.25 = cost$$

The cost to the wholesaler is $216.25.

$$selling\ price = cost + markup$$

$$\downarrow \qquad \downarrow$$

$$= \$216.25 + \$86.50$$

$$= \$302.75$$

Thus, the selling price is $302.75.

$$\frac{108}{240} \qquad \frac{45}{100} \qquad \frac{240}{1 \cdot 108}$$
$$\overline{348}$$

Answer: $240; $348

EXAMPLE 4 — USING MARKDOWN TO FIND A NEW SELLING PRICE

PRACTICE EXERCISE 4

The wholesale dealer in Example 3 must reduce the selling price of his suits by 30% in order to make room for new suits. What is the markdown and the new selling price of the suit that sold for $302.75?

When the stereo did not sell, the owner in Practice Exercise 3 was forced to reduce the selling price by 30%. What was the markdown and the new selling price of the stereo which sold for $348?

Method 1

$$A = P\% \cdot B$$

markdown = % markdown · price

$$\downarrow \qquad \downarrow \qquad \downarrow$$

$$markdown = (0.30) \cdot \$302.75$$

$$= \$90.83 \quad \text{Nearest cent}$$

Method 2

$$\frac{A}{B} = \frac{P}{100}$$

$$\frac{markdown}{price} = \frac{\% \ markdown}{100}$$

$$\frac{markdown}{\$302.75} = \frac{30}{100}$$

$$markdown = \frac{(\$302.75)(30)}{100}$$

$$= \$90.83$$

Then we have

$$new\ selling\ price = old\ selling\ price - markdown.$$

$$= \$302.75 - \$90.83$$

$$= \$211.92$$

The suit now sells for $211.92.

104.4

Answer: $104.40; $243.60

EXPLORATION GUIDE

Explain why a 100% markup on the cost of an item followed by a 50% markdown on the selling price results in a no-profit situation when the item is sold. If an item is marked up 50%, what markdown rate would be required if the item is to be sold for no profit?

Notice that the new selling price in Example 4 is actually less than the cost given in Example 3.

$$216.25 - 211.92 = 4.33$$

The suit was sold for $4.33 less than the cost. (The dealer lost on the sale.) This means that the 30% markdown ($90.83) is more than the 40% markup ($86.50). That is,

30% of $302.75   ($90.83)

is more than

40% of $216.25   ($86.50).

This shows that we need to keep in mind the amount on which the percent is taken as well as the percent rate when working with markup and markdown problems.

USING MARKUP AND MARKDOWN TOGETHER   EXAMPLE 5

The Green Grocery Company bought lettuce for 30¢ per head. The markup on the cost was 80%. After a few days, the price of the remaining lettuce was reduced by 60% of the selling price.

(a) What was the markup and the first selling price?
    To find the markup, take 80% of 30¢.

$$(0.80)(30¢) = 24¢$$

The first selling price was

$$30¢ + 24¢ = 54¢.$$

(b) What was the markdown and the second selling price?
    The markdown is 60% of 54¢ (selling price).

$$(0.60)(54¢) = 32¢ \text{ (to the nearest cent)}$$

To find the second selling price, subtract 32¢ from 54¢.

$$54¢ - 32¢ = 22¢$$

(c) What was the loss on the lettuce sold after the markdown?
    In order to sell the lettuce before it spoiled, the grocer sold it for 22¢. This was a loss of

$$30¢ - 22¢ = 8¢$$

per head. The grocer sold at an 8¢ loss to prevent a loss of 30¢ on each head spoiled.

(d) What percent of the cost was the loss?
The question we must answer is:

8¢ is	what percent	of 30¢?
↓ ↓	↓	↓ ↓
A =	$P\%$ ·	B
↓	↓	↓
8 =	$P\%$ ·	30
8 =	$P\%(30)$	

$$\frac{8}{30} = P\% \qquad \text{Divide by 30}$$

$$0.26\overline{6} = P\%$$

Thus, the percent loss based on the cost of the lettuce was 26.6%.

PRACTICE EXERCISE 5

Booker's Books bought a book for $3.00. The markup on cost was 75%. When the book did not sell, it was reduced 40% of the selling price.

(a) What was the markup and the first selling price?

2.25

(b) What was the markdown and the second selling price?

2.10

(c) What was the profit on the book sold after the markdown?

.15 ¢

(d) What percent of the cost was the profit?

.15 / 3.00   5%

Answers:
(a) $2.25; $5.25 (b) $2.10; $3.15
(c) $0.15 (d) 5%

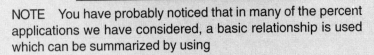

NOTE   You have probably noticed that in many of the percent applications we have considered, a basic relationship is used which can be summarized by using

$$A = P\% \cdot B \text{ OR } \frac{A}{B} = \frac{P}{100}$$ in the following forms.

CHANGE = PERCENT · ORIGINAL AMOUNT

or

$$\frac{\text{CHANGE}}{\text{ORIGINAL AMOUNT}} = \frac{\text{PERCENT}}{100}$$

Now that you have experience with the basic terminology used in the various applications, you may want to remember this one formula and use it to cover a multitude of situations. For example, in a markup problem, *change is markup, percent is percent markup,* and *original amount* is *cost.*

6.7 EXERCISES

Answers to these exercises are given on page 653.

Solve each applied problem in Exercises 1–12. First estimate the answer.

1. **BUSINESS** The Glass Shop has a markup of 25% on their merchandise. What would be the selling price of a set of glasses that was purchased for $64.60?

2. **BUSINESS** Auto Plus bought a used sedan for $2690 and sold it for $4842. What was the markup and the percent markup?

3. **BUSINESS** Roberta's Interior Design made $3.50 per yard on carpet sold to a customer. If the markup was 40%, what was the cost and what was the selling price?

4. **BUSINESS** To raise money for a project, the Student Club bought flowers for $2.00 per dozen and sold them on campus for $5.00 per dozen. What was the percent markup?

5. **BUSINESS** Because of a high spoilage rate, the markup on fruit must be 120%. What is the selling price (to the nearest cent) of peaches that cost 22¢ per pound?

6. **BUSINESS** Fred's TV Shop bought a color television set for $582 and sold it for $727.50. What was the percent markup?

7. **BUSINESS** The Fashion Place put a $192.50 dress on sale at a markdown (discount) rate of 40%. What was the reduced selling price?

8. **BUSINESS** The Fashion Place sold a sports coat for $195 that was originally priced at $250. What was the percent markdown?

9. **BUSINESS** The markdown on a loaf of bread is 36¢ and the markdown rate is 40%. What was the old selling price? What is the new selling price?

10. **BUSINESS** The Tough Tool Company bought a set of tools for $120. The markup was 20%. When the set did not sell, the price was reduced at a markdown rate of 15%. What was the first selling price and what was the second selling price?

11. **BUSINESS** If the tool set in Exercise 10 sold at the second price, what was the profit? What percent of the cost was the profit?

12. **BUSINESS** Mario's Men's Shop bought a suit for $180. The markup was 30%. Because of changing styles, the suit was sold at a discount of 25%. What was the loss? What percent of the cost was the loss?

CRITICAL THINKING

13. **BUSINESS** Some store owners operate on a 50%-10% markup rate. The cost of an item is first marked up 50%, and the resulting price is marked up an additional 10% to obtain the selling price. Under these conditions, what would be the selling price of a man's suit which costs the owner $105?

Complete each statement in Exercise 14.

14. The amount by which the selling price of an item is increased over the cost is called ____, and the percent used to calculate this increase is the ____.

15. Burford was told to use a markup rate of 50% on light fixtures. When one fixture did not sell, he was told to sell it at cost. Since Burford did not remember the cost, he tried to find the markdown rate that would erase the 50% markup. Can you help him?

REVIEW OR PREVIEW

16. **GAS MILEAGE** Under normal conditions, Martha's car gets 28.5 mpg. While driving against a headwind, the mileage was 25.3 mpg. To the nearest tenth, what was the percent decrease?

17. **SALARY** Jenny got a 12% raise. If her old salary was $16,250, what is her new salary?

18. **GAS MILEAGE** By driving at high speeds, Mark reduced his mileage by 18%. However, a tailwind gave him a 5% increase in mileage. Under these conditions, what was his mileage if normally it is 30 mpg?

19. **SALARY** Last year Bill earned $42,560.00, and this year his salary will be $47,241.60. What was the percent raise that Bill received?

6.7 PARALLEL EXERCISES

Answers to these exercises are not given in the text.

Solve each applied problem in Exercises 1–12. First estimate the answer.

1. **BUSINESS** Appliances Unlimited purchased a refrigerator for $930.00. If the markup is 35%, what is the selling price?

2. **BUSINESS** Asparagus is purchased during the off season for $2.90 per pound. If the markup is 80%, what is the selling price?

3. **BUSINESS** The Farmers Market bought a load of watermelons for 10¢ per pound and sold them for 22¢ per pound. What was the percent markup?

4. **BUSINESS** With a 25% markup Books New and Old made $6.05 on the sale of a new book. What was the purchase price and the selling price?

5. **BUSINESS** Fast Eddie bought a watch for $8.70 and sold it at a markup rate of 250%. What was the selling price of the watch?

6. **BUSINESS** The Fan Shop buys a ceiling fan for $125 and sells it for $195. What is the percent markup?

7. **BUSINESS** The selling price of a washer is $345.80. It is put on sale at a markdown rate of 35%. What is the reduced selling price?

8. **BUSINESS** A camera which sells for $289.75 is put on sale for $195.50. To the nearest tenth of a percent, what is the markdown rate?

9. **BUSINESS** The markup on books is 25%. There was a $2.05 markup on a novel. What was the original cost?

10. **BUSINESS** Lettuce was bought for 30¢ per head and sold at an 80% markup. The lettuce that did not sell the first day was reduced at a markdown rate of 50%. What was the first selling price and what was the second selling price?

11. **BUSINESS** If the lettuce in Exercise 10 sold at the second price, what was the loss? What percent of the cost was the loss?

12. **BUSINESS** A ball costing $10 has a markup rate of 40% and is then put on sale at a markdown of 20%. What is the profit? What is the percent profit based on the cost?

CRITICAL THINKING

♀13. **BUSINESS** A lamp that was purchased by a dealer for $28.70 was to be sold at a 70.5% markup. When it did not sell, the dealer reduced the price at a markdown rate of 50%. Did the dealer make a profit or take a loss when the lamp was then sold? What was the percent profit or loss (to the nearest tenth of a percent)?

Complete each statement in Exercise 14.

♀14. The ____ of an item is the price reduction based on the ____ applied to the selling price of the item.

♀15. Burford was told to use a markdown rate of 50% on light fixtures. When the boss changed his mind, he told Burford to put the original price back on each fixture. Since Burford did not remember the prices, he tried to find the markup rate that would erase the 50% markdown. Can you help him?

GROUP PROJECT

In Exercise 15 Burford was asked to find a markdown that erased a given markup and a markup to erase a markdown. Discuss a general way to do this. That is, if *u* is a variable representing the markup rate as a decimal and *d* represents the markdown rate as a decimal, can you find a formula relating the two variables?

CHAPTER 6 REVIEW

KEY WORDS

 6.1

- The word **percent** means "per hundred" and refers to the number of parts in one hundred parts.

6.2

- In the basic percent problem "*A* is *P%* of *B*," *A* is the **amount**, *P* is the **percent**, and *B* is the **base**.

6.3

- A tax charged on purchases is a **sales tax** and the percent of tax is the **sales-tax rate.**

6.4

- Income received as a percent of total sales is called a **commission** and the percent used is the **commission rate.**

- A **discount** is a reduction in the regular price of an item based on a **discount rate** which is a percent of the *regular* price. The **sale price** is the price after the discount.

6.5

- Money paid for the use of money is called **interest.** The money borrowed or invested is the **principal,** and the **rate of interest** is the percent applied to the principal.

- Interest found using only the principal and not using previous interest along with the principal is called **simple interest.**

- Interest earned or paid on previous interest along with the principal is called **compound interest.**

6.6

- The percent by which a quantity increases (decreases) is called the **percent increase (decrease).**

6.7

- The amount by which the selling price of an item is increased over the cost is called **markup,** and the percent used to calculate this increase is the **percent markup.**

- The **markdown** of an item is the price reduction based on the **markdown rate** applied to the selling price of the item.

KEY CONCEPTS

🔑 6.1

1. To change a percent to a fraction, replace the % symbol with either ($\times \frac{1}{100}$) or ($\div 100$). Then evaluate and reduce the fraction.

2. To change a percent to a decimal, replace the % symbol with ($\times 0.01$) and multiply. This is the same as moving the decimal point two places to the left.

3. To change a decimal to a percent, multiply the decimal by 100 and attach the % symbol. This is the same as moving the decimal point two places to the right.

4. To change a fraction to a percent, multiply the fraction by 100 and attach the % symbol.

🔑 6.2

1. The basic percent equation is
$$A = P\% \cdot B.$$
To solve for P or B, use the related division sentences
$$P\% = \frac{A}{B} \qquad \text{or} \qquad B = \frac{A}{P\%}.$$

2. The basic percent proportion is
$$\frac{A}{B} = \frac{P}{100}.$$
Solve for any of A, B, or P by solving the proportion.

🔑 6.3

1. sales tax = tax rate · price before tax
or
$$\frac{\text{sales tax}}{\text{price before tax}} = \frac{\text{tax rate}}{100}$$
and
total price = price before tax + sales tax

2. In 2004, the Social Security-tax rate was 6.2% on the first $87,900 of earnings.
Social Security tax = 0.062 · total earnings
or
$$\frac{\text{Social Security tax}}{\text{total earnings}} = \frac{6.2}{100}$$

3. Use the tax-rate schedule given in Section 6.3 to calculate income taxes paid in 2004 by a single taxpayer.

🔑 6.5

1. If P is a principal, R is a yearly rate of interest converted to a decimal, T is the time in years, and I is simple interest, then $I = P \cdot R \cdot T$. If A is the amount to be repaid or the amount in the account, then $A = P + I$.

2. To find the amount of each payment on a loan, divide the sum of the principal and interest by the number of payments.

3. In a compound interest problem, the interest rate used for each period is
$$\frac{\text{Annual Interest Rate}}{\text{Number of Periods Per Year}}.$$
For example, if the annual interest rate is 10%, if we compound annually (1 time a year), semiannually (2 times a year), or quarterly (4 times a year), the interest rate per period is 10%, 5%, and 2.5%, respectively.

4. In a compound interest problem, the principal for the second period is the original principal plus the interest charged for the first period. This process continues over each period.

🔑 6.6

1. increase (decrease) =
percent increase (decrease) · original amount
or
$$\frac{\text{increase (decrease)}}{\text{original amount}} = \frac{\text{percent increase (decrease)}}{100}$$
and
new amount = original amount + increase
or
new amount = original amount − decrease

2. Remember that in a percent increase (decrease) problem, the percent is taken on the original amount *not* the new amount.

🔑 6.7

1. markup (markdown) =
percent markup (markdown) · cost (price)
or
$$\frac{\text{markup (markdown)}}{\text{cost (price)}} = \frac{\text{percent markup (markdown)}}{100}$$
and
selling price = cost + markup
or
new selling price = price − markdown

2. Percent markup is based on cost.

3. Percent markdown is based on selling price.

CHAPTER 6 REVIEW EXERCISES

PART I

Answers to these exercises are given on page 653.

 6.1

♀ 1. *Percent* means "per _____ ."

Change from percents to fractions in Exercises 2–5.

2. 23%

3. 324%

4. 0.6%

5. $6\frac{1}{4}\%$

Change from percents to decimals in Exercises 6–9.

6. 84%

7. 267%

8. $\frac{3}{4}\%$

9. 0.3%

Change to percents in Exercises 10–13.

10. 0.63

11. 0.032

12. 3.2

13. $\frac{3}{5}$

 6.2

▦ *Solve each percent problem in Exercises 14–33.*

14. What is 30% of 620?

15. 6 is 0.5% of what number?

16. What percent of 72 is 9?

17. **EDUCATION** On a test with 300 questions, Susan got 86% correct. How many did she answer correctly?

18. **SPORTS** During the regular season the State University basketball team won 38 out of 44 games. What percent of their games did they win to the nearest tenth of a percent?

19. **POLITICS** In an election for president of the Chess Club the winning candidate got 24 votes. If this was 60% of the votes, how many club members participated in the election?

 6.3

20. **SALES TAX** What is the sales tax and total cost of a $17.50 shirt if the tax rate is 6%?

21. **SALES TAX** If a sales tax of $13.97 is charged on the purchase of a $254 dryer, what is the sales-tax rate?

22. **SOCIAL SECURITY TAX** Raymond had an income from wages of $17,350 in 2004. The Social Security tax rate was 6.2% on all wages up to $87,900 that year. What Social Security tax did Raymond pay?

23. **INCOME TAX** Diane had a taxable income of $47,300 in 2004. Use the tax table in Section 6.3 to determine how much income tax she paid.

6.4

24. **COMMISSION** The price of a 1956 Chevrolet was $12,720. If Garth Smith got a commission of $2289.60 for selling the car, what was the commision rate?

25. **COMMISSION** Wanda receives 2% commission on all car sales of $25,000 or less. She receives 3% commission on all sales above $25,000. What is her commission on sales of $42,500?

26. **BUSINESS** A lawn mower normally sells for $216. At the end of the summer, it was put on sale at a 30% discount. What was the sale price?

27. **BUSINESS** The Art Dealer put a $2700 painting on sale for $1755. What was the discount rate?

6.5

28. **LOANS**   Phillip bought a watch for $285. He paid 10% down and paid the remaining amount, plus interest, at the end of 6 months. If simple interest is 14% per year, how much did he pay at the end of 6 months?

29. **INVESTMENT**   William invests $3500 in an account which pays 8% compounded semiannually. How much will he have in the account at the end of 2 years?

 6.6

30. **EDUCATION**   Golden State Community College had a 1.5% decrease in students after the opening of another college in another county. If there were 22,400 students before the decrease, how many students are now at Golden State?

31. **BUSINESS**   When the Local Bread Company was forced to stop production, the price of a loaf of bread increased from $1.39 to $1.49. To the nearest tenth of a percent, what was this percent increase?

 6.7

32. **BUSINESS**   A dealer bought a microwave oven for $682.50 and sold it for $819.00. What was the percent markup?

33. **BUSINESS**   An electric blanket which normally sells for $42.00 is put on sale for $29.40. What is the markdown rate?

PART II

Solve each applied problem in Exercises 34 –43.

34. **GAS MILEAGE**   Sam's car usually gets 28 mpg. He is driving on a rough road which will decrease his mileage by 14%, but a tailwind is increasing his mileage by 9%. What mileage should he get?

35. **BUSINESS**   University Books and Supplies is required by law to keep their markup at 20% or less. Is a calculator that was purchased for $22.50 and marked with a selling price of $27.90 within the state law?

36. **SALARY**   The average salary of the workers at Steel, Incorporated, was $19,280. After the union negotiated an 11% increase, what was the average salary?

37. **LOANS**   Shelley borrowed $722.50 to buy a stereo. If simple interest is 15% per year, what are her monthly payments if she pays for 18 months?

38. **COMMISSION**   Faye receives a commission of 20% on clothing sales. She sold $2868.50 worth of clothing during the month of May. What was her commission?

39. **SALES TAX**   The sales-tax rate in Newton, Vermont, is 4%. If a tax of $2.58 is charged on a dress, what is the price of the dress?

40. **BUSINESS**   The Shirt Shop bought one type of shirt for $14.50. The markup was 28%. Because of oversupply, the shirts were put on sale at a markdown of 25%. What was the percent of profit or loss based on the original cost?

41. **SALARY**   Bernadine makes $428 a week as a secretary. Her boss told her that starting next week she will receive a raise of $8\frac{1}{2}\%$ per week. What will be her new weekly salary?

42. **INVESTMENT**   If $1000 increased to $1120 in a savings account one year, what was the simple interest rate for the year?

43. **SALES TAX**   If the sales-tax rate in Stephentown, New York, is 6%, what tax would be charged on a purchase of $12.50?

Complete the table given one value in each row.

	Fraction	Decimal	Percent		Fraction	Decimal	Percent
44.	$\frac{1}{4}$	____	____	45.	____	0.42	____
46.	____	____	35%	47.	____	1.3	____
48.	$\frac{4}{3}$	____	____	49.	____	____	0.5%

50. 6 is what percent of 20?   51. What is 12% of 37?   52. 80.75 is 85% of what number?

The bar graph shown below was taken from the October 24, 1994 issue of Time. Use it in Exercises 53–56

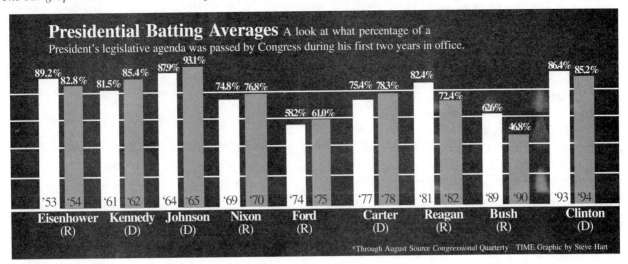

Presidential Batting Averages A look at what percentage of a President's legislative agenda was passed by Congress during his first two years in office.

89.2% 82.8% 81.5% 85.4% 87.9% 93.1% 74.8% 76.8% 58.2% 61.0% 75.4% 78.3% 82.4% 72.4% 62.6% 46.8% 86.4% 85.2%

'53 '54 | '61 '62 | '64 '65 | '69 '70 | '74 '75 | '77 '78 | '81 '82 | '89 '90 | '93 '94

Eisenhower (R) | Kennedy (D) | Johnson (D) | Nixon (R) | Ford (R) | Carter (D) | Reagan (R) | Bush (R) | Clinton (D)

*Through August Source Congressional Quarterly   TIME Graphic by Steve Hart

53. What was the percent decrease in percentage of legislation passed between the first and second years of the Eisenhower administration?

54. What was the percent increase in percentage of legislation passed between the first and second years of the Carter administration?

55. What was the percent decrease from the most successful of all years to the least successful of all years?

56. What was the percent increase from the least successful of all years to the most successful of all years?

The table below appeared in the January 30, 1995 issue of Time. Use the data in Exercises 57–59, and give all percents correct to the nearest unit.

HOUSING

Median cost of a house, 1994

	Most expensive		Least expensive	
1	Honolulu	$368,000	Waterloo/Cedar Falls. IA	$55,500
2	San Francisco	250,200	Saginaw/Bay City/Midland, MI	60,400
3	Orange County. CA	217,000	South Bend/Mishawaka, IN	60,900
4	Los Angeles	189,000	Youngstown/Warren, OH	62,100
5	Boston	188,200	Topeka, KS	62,300
6	New York (metro)	177,400	Ocala, FL	62,800
7	San Diego	175,400	Amarillo, TX	63,900
8	Washington (VA/MD)	160,000	Beaumont/Port Arthur, TX	65,400
9	Seattle	158,400	Oklahoma City. OK	66,500
10	Chicago	150,200	Mobile. AL	68,300

Source: National Association of Realtors   TIME Graphics by Joe Lertola. Steve Hart and Paul Pugtiese

57. If Jean McGhee moves from the Waterloo/Cedar Falls area to Honolulu, what percent increase in housing costs can she expect?

58. If Peter Horn moves from Honolulu to the Waterloo/Cedar Falls area, what percent decrease in housing costs can he expect?

59. Explain why the answers to Exercises 57 and 58 are so different.

CHAPTER 6 TEST

Answers to this test are given on page 653.

1. Change 95% to a fraction in lowest terms.

2. Change 0.8% to a decimal.

3. Change 5.06 to a percent.

4. Change $\frac{9}{5}$ to a percent.

5. Change $\frac{5}{11}$ to an approximate percent, to the nearest tenth of a percent.

Solve.

6. 12 is what percent of 60?

7. What number is 18% of 120?

8. 160 is 400% of what number?

9. A toaster with a normal price of $29.50 is to be discounted 30%. What is the sale price?

10. Howard bought a TV for $720 and paid 25% down. If simple interest is 13%, how much will he have to pay at the end of a year to pay off the debt?

Solve.

11. The Social Security tax rate in 2004 was 6.2%. How much Social Security tax did Jennifer pay on a salary of $27,480?

12. While driving with a headwind, Terry's car got 22.8 mpg instead of the normal 27.9 mpg. To the nearest tenth, what was the percent decrease?

13. A refrigerator cost a dealer $820 and was put on sale at a markup rate of 20%. It was then reduced at a markdown rate of 15%. What was the percent profit or loss based on the cost?

14. Wylie Smith, sports information director, makes a profit for NAU of 40¢ on the sale of each basketball program. If the markup rate is 25%, what is the cost of each program? What is the selling price of each program?

15. It costs $29.90 for a tune-up at Zach's garage. If Zach offers a Saturday special at 30% off the regular price, how much will a tune-up cost on Saturday?

1. _____

2. _____

3. _____

4. _____

5. _____

6. _____

7. _____

8. _____

9. _____

10. _____

11. _____

12. _____

13. _____

14. _____

15. _____

CHAPTER 6 TEST

16. If $600 is invested in an account that pays 8% interest compounded semiannually, what will be the value of the account at the end of 1 year?

16. _____

17. State the basic percent equation.

17. _____

18. Wilma Young pays 1.5% interest per month on her credit card balance which was $1286.50 for the month. If she also had to pay an annual fee of $75.00 that month and thought that it was part of the interest, what would she calculate as the approximate monthly rate of interest?

18. _____

Answer true *or* false. *If the answer is false, tell why.*

19. A 30% markup followed by a markdown of 25% would result in selling the item at less than cost.

19. _____

20. An interest rate of 10% compounded semiannually is better for one year than a simple interest rate of 10.2%.

20. _____

CUMULATIVE REVIEW: CHAPTERS 1– 6

Answers to these exercises are given on page 653.

Complete each statement in Exercises 1–3.

1. 72 in = _____ ft

2. 4 ton = _____ lb

3. 28 pt = _____ gal

Change each mixed number to an improper fraction in Exercises 4–6.

4. $3\dfrac{1}{7}$

5. $10\dfrac{8}{9}$

6. $6\dfrac{5}{3}$

Solve each applied problem in Exercises 7–10.

7. **BUSINESS** What is the commission on a sale of $3600 if the commission rate is 8%?

8. **INVESTMENT** If an account worth $1500 increased to $1800 in one year, what was the interest rate for the year?

9. **SALARY** Wanda received an increase in salary of $2640. If this was a 12% raise, what was her original salary?

10. **HEALTH** Henry's weight decreased from 220 pounds to 187 pounds on a diet. What was the percent decrease in his weight?

Perform the indicated operations in Exercises 11–22.

11. 3.62×0.56

12. 0.12×1.5

13. 72.8×81.6

14. $5.6376 \div 0.72$

15. $5.61 \div 5.5$

16. $0.1 \div 0.01$

17. $\dfrac{9}{15} - \dfrac{7}{14}$

18. $1\dfrac{1}{3} + 2\dfrac{3}{4}$

19. $3\dfrac{3}{8} \times 2\dfrac{2}{3}$

20. $\left(\dfrac{3}{4}\right)^2 - \sqrt{\dfrac{1}{16}}$

21. $4 \cdot 1\dfrac{1}{2} \cdot \dfrac{1}{12}$

22. $2\dfrac{8}{9} \div \dfrac{4}{27}$

In Exercises 23–25, solve each proportion.

23. $\dfrac{21}{a} = \dfrac{7}{4}$

24. $\dfrac{6}{7} = \dfrac{a}{28}$

25. $\dfrac{60}{a} = \dfrac{15}{14}$

CHAPTER *s·e·v·e·n*

INTRODUCTION TO STATISTICS

Many people think of *statistics* as having to do with tables of numbers or charts and graphs that display numerical information. Although not entirely wrong, this is a somewhat narrow view of statistics. The statistician is more interested in trying to determine what these numbers, charts, or graphs mean. In this chapter we present a very brief introduction to the ways that numerical data can be presented with little emphasis on what conclusions might or might not be drawn from the presentations. We have been looking at tables and graphs throughout the text up to this point, but now we will concentrate on a more comprehensive discussion. Although the ancient Chinese and Egyptians used statistics for keeping various records of importance to the governing leaders, it is generally accepted that the father of modern statistics was an Englishman, John Graunt (1620-1674). Graunt studied the causes of death in several cities and published his results in a book entitled *Natural and Political Observations Upon the Bills of Mortality*. Using the data that he collected, he formulated numerous conclusions, one of which was that at the age of marriage, the number of men and women was approximately the same. As a result, Graunt believed that his study reinforced the concept of monogamy! Statistics can be used to analyze a variety of problems such as the one given below and solved in Example 2 in Section 7.2.

HEALTH CARE The graph below presents a summary of the average cost for personal health care for United States citizens in the years 1970-1993.

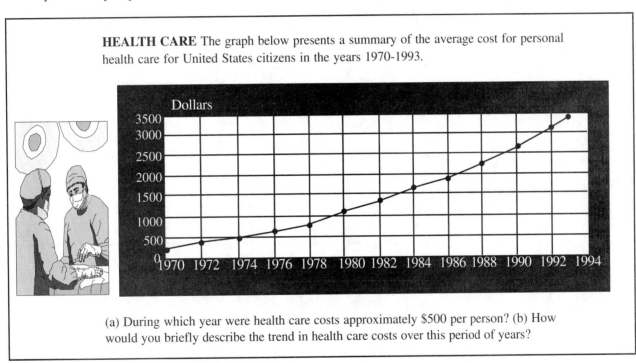

(a) During which year were health care costs approximately $500 per person? (b) How would you briefly describe the trend in health care costs over this period of years?

We will first consider the ways that numerical data can be presented using circle graphs, bar graphs, broken-line graphs, and histograms. The chapter concludes with a discussion of three important statistics: mean, median, and mode. These can be helpful when trying to interpret the meaning of large sets of numbers.

7.1 CIRCLE GRAPHS, BAR GRAPHS, AND PICTOGRAPHS

STUDENT GUIDEPOSTS	
1	USING STATISTICS AND NUMERICAL DATA
2	WORKING WITH CIRCLE GRAPHS
3	USING BAR GRAPHS
4	READING PICTOGRAPHS

1   STATISTICS AND NUMERICAL DATA

Statistics is the branch of mathematics that deals with collecting, organizing, and summarizing numerical data in order to describe or interpret it. The world of sports relies on statistics such as batting averages, pass completions, free-throw percentages, and points scored. The number of people under age 30 in the United States, the average study time of junior college students, and the Michigan election results are all statistics.

Tables provide one way to present data in a manner that is easy to interpret. Suppose Tanya, a college student, has decided to keep a record of her monthly expenses. She might summarize the data in the table.

Monthly Expenses	
Item	*Amount Spent*
Rent	$200
Food	$150
Entertainment	$100
Clothes	$ 35
Other	$ 15
TOTAL	$500

2   CIRCLE GRAPHS

Sometimes it is hard to interpret a large set of data. One way to simplify the process is to "picture" the data in some way. **A circle graph** is often used to represent parts of a whole unit. For example, the data collected by Tanya and presented in the table above could be organized and displayed in a circle graph. The circle graph in Figure 7.1 represents her entire budget, and each pie-shaped part, or sector, represents the number of dollars she spent on each item.

By reading information from a circle graph, various comparisons can be made in the form

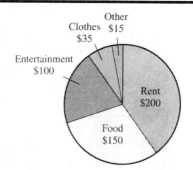

FIGURE 7.1

Circle Graph

of ratios. Consider the circle graph in Figure 7.1 again. Since the total amount Tanya spent during the month was $500, the ratio of rent to total expenses is

$$\frac{\$200}{\$500} = \frac{2}{5},$$

and the ratio of clothing expenses to total expenses is

$$\frac{\$35}{\$500} = \frac{7}{100}.$$

Converting these ratios to percents, Tanya sees that she spent 40% of her budget on rent and 7% on clothes.

Tanya can also find the ratio of one expense to another. For example, the ratio of food expenses to entertainment expenses is

$$\frac{\$150}{\$100} = \frac{3}{2},$$

and the ratio of rent to clothing expenses is

$$\frac{\$200}{\$35} = \frac{40}{7}.$$

Thus, for every $3 spent on food, Tanya spends $2 on entertainment, and for every $40 spent on rent, she spends $7 on clothes.

EXAMPLE 1	READING A CIRCLE GRAPH

PRACTICE EXERCISE 1

The circle graph in Figure 7.2 shows the distribution of the $9 billion in state lottery proceeds in 1993.

Use the circle graph in Figure 7.2 to answer the following.

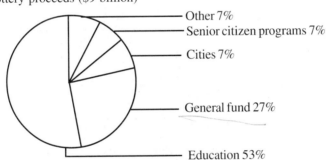

Percent distribution of 1993
State lottery proceeds ($9 billion)

- Other 7%
- Senior citizen programs 7%
- Cities 7%
- General fund 27%
- Education 53%

Source: Chart prepared by U.S. Bureau of the Census.

FIGURE 7.2

(a) Determine the amount of the proceeds that was spent on education.

The graph shows that 53% went to education.

$$53\% \text{ of } \$9,000,000,000$$
$$\downarrow \quad \downarrow \qquad \downarrow$$
$$0.53 \cdot \$9,000,000,000 = \$4,770,000,000$$

Thus, of the total funds collected from lotteries, $4,770,000,000 went for education.

(b) What was the ratio of the amount going to senior citizen programs to the amount that went to education?

We could determine the amount going to senior citizen programs and then divide by the amount to education. However, we get the same result by dividing the percent to senior citizen programs by the percent to education.

$$\frac{0.07}{0.53} \approx 0.132 = 13.2\%$$

Thus, 13.2% as much is spent on senior citizen programs as on education.

(a) Determine the amount of the proceeds that was spent on general funds.

(b) What was the ratio of the amount going to cities to the amount that went to general funds?

Answers: (a) $2,430,000,000
(b) 25.9%

3 | BAR GRAPHS

Another way to present data is with a **bar graph.** Suppose 100 people have been polled regarding their preference among four brands of toothpaste, Brand A, Brand B, Brand C, and Brand D. The results of the poll are given in the bar graph in Figure 7.3.

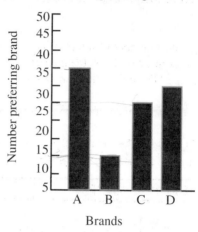

FIGURE 7.3

Bar Graph

The graph shows that 35 people chose Brand A, 10 chose Brand B, 25 chose Brand C, and 30 chose Brand D.

Bar graphs are quite useful when comparing data. It is easy to see at a glance which brand was most preferred (Brand A) and which was least preferred (Brand B). Also, Brand A was preferred to Brand B by a ratio of

$$\frac{35}{10} = \frac{7}{2}.$$

That is, for every 7 people who chose Brand A, 2 people chose Brand B.

| READING A BAR GRAPH | EXAMPLE 2 |

Use the bar graph in Figure 7.3 to determine the ratio of people preferring Brand C to those preferring Brand B.

Since 25 people preferred Brand C and 10 people preferred Brand B, the ratio is $\frac{25}{10} = \frac{5}{2}$.

A double-bar graph is often used to compare two sets of data. The doublebar graph in Figure 7.4 shows the total enrollment in beginning algebra classes compared to intermediate algebra classes at a community college during a four-year period.

PRACTICE EXERCISE 2

Use the bar graph in Figure 7.3 to determine the ratio of those preferring Brand A over Brand C.

Answer: $\frac{7}{5}$

$\frac{35 \div 5}{25 \div 5} = \frac{7}{5}$

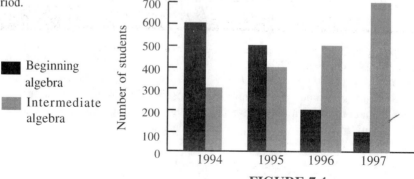

FIGURE 7.4

Double Bar Graph

READING A DOUBLE-BAR GRAPH   **EXAMPLE 3**

Use the double-bar graph in Figure 7.4 to answer the following.

(a) What was the number of beginning algebra students in 1995?

Since the bar on the left in 1995 rises to the 500 level, there were 500 students in beginning algebra in 1995.

(b) Which year had the greatest number of intermediate algebra students?

The right bar rises highest in 1997. Thus, the greatest number of students in intermediate algebra occurred in 1997. In fact, that number was 700 students.

(c) What could you say about the number of beginning algebra students over the four-year period?

Since the number went from 600 to 500 to 200 to 100, we can see that the number of beginning algebra students declined over the four-year period.

4   PICTOGRAPHS

A **pictograph** uses pictures that relate to the subject to accomplish about the same result as a bar graph. Each picture represents a given number of people, cars, barrels of oil, or whatever is being discussed. For example we might see the graph in Figure 7.5 in a newspaper or magazine.

Number of tires sold	⬤ = 1000 tires
1993	⬤ ⬤ ⬤ ⬤
1994	⬤ ⬤ ⬤
1995	⬤ ⬤ ⬤ ⬤ ◖
1996	⬤ ⬤ ⬤ ⬤ ⬤ ◖
1997	⬤ ⬤ ⬤ ⬤ ⬤ ⬤ ⬤ ⬤

FIGURE 7.5

The pictograph shows that 4000 tires were sold in 1993 and 3000 in 1994. In 1995 we have four whole tires and a half of a tire. This means that about 4500 tires were sold in 1995. In 1996 approximately 6500 tires were sold and in 1997 there were 8000 sold.

Notice that we use the word *approximately* because a pictograph is not designed to give exact numbers but is good for making comparisons. For example, we observe that sales went down from 1993 to 1994 but have increased every year since then. Also notice that twice as many tires were sold in 1997 as in 1993.

READING A PICTOGRAPH   **EXAMPLE 4**

The pictograph in Figure 7.6 gives the number of acres of wheat harvested in each of the counties indicated.

Number of acres harvested	🌾 = 10,000 acres
Adams	🌾 🌾 🌾 🌾 🌾
Lincoln	🌾 🌾 🌾 🌾 🌾 🌾
Smith	🌾 🌾 🌾
Warren	🌾 🌾 🌾 🌾

FIGURE 7.6

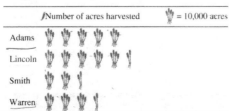

(a) What is the difference between the largest number of acres harvested and the smallest number harvested?

(b) The number of acres harvested in Warren County is what percent of the number of acres in Adams County?

Answers: (a) 30,000 acres (b) 70%

(a) How many more acres were harvested in Lincoln County than in Adams County?

Since 55,000 acres were harvested in Lincoln County and 50,000 acres in Adams County, there were 5000 acres more in Lincoln County.

(b) What is the ratio of the number of acres harvested in Smith County to the number harvested in Warren County?

This ratio is found by dividing 25,000 acres by 35,000 acres.

$$\frac{25,000}{35,000} = \frac{25}{35} = \frac{5 \cdot 5}{5 \cdot 7} = \frac{5}{7}$$

7.1 EXERCISES

Answers to these exercises are given on page 653.

Exercises 1–8 refer to the circle graph at the right which shows a breakdown of the amounts spent by the Warrens on an addition to their house

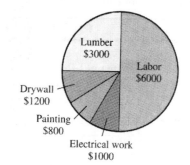

1. What was the total cost of the addition?

2. What was the largest expense item on the project?

3. What was the ratio of the cost of labor to the cost of lumber?

4. What was the ratio of the cost of painting to the cost of drywall?

5. What was the ratio of the cost of lumber to the cost of electrical work?

6. Lumber accounted for what percent of the total cost?

7. Labor accounted for what percent of the total cost?

8. Electrical work accounted for what percent of the total cost?

Exercises 9–20 refer to the circle graph below which shows the distribution of the 42,500 students enrolled in various schools in Coconino County.

9. Which sector represents the largest number of students?

10. Which sector represents the smallest number of students?

11. How many students are in grades K–8?

12. How many students are in high school?

13. How many students are enrolled in the community college?

14. How many students are enrolled in the university?

15. How many students are in grades K–8 and in high school?

16. How many students are in the community college and in the university?

17. What is the ratio of high school students to university students?

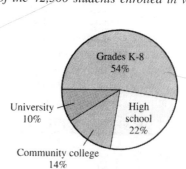

18. What is the ratio of students in grades K–8 to students in high school?

19. What is the ratio of high school students to students in the university and the community college?

20. How many students are in school beyond the high school level?

Exercises 21–32 refer to the bar graph below, which shows the number of students by major course of study in the College of Arts and Science.

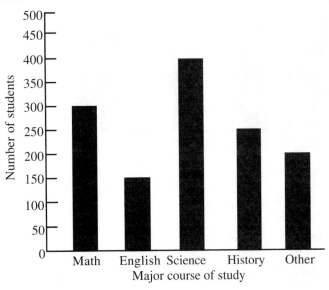

21. How many students are in the College of Arts and Science?

22. What is the ratio of math majors to the total number of students in the college?

23. What percent of students in the college are math majors (to the nearest tenth of a percent)?

24. What is the ratio of science majors to the total number of students in the college?

25. What percent of students in the college are science majors (to the nearest tenth of a percent)?

26. What percent of students are math and science majors (to the nearest tenth of a percent)?

27. What is the ratio of science majors to history majors?

28. What is the ratio of English majors to math majors?

29. What percent of students have a major other than math, science, English, or history (to the nearest tenth of a percent)?

30. What is the total of math and English majors?

31. What percent of the students are math and English majors (to the nearest tenth of a percent)?

32. What is the ratio of math and science majors to English and history majors?

Exercises 33–40 refer to the double-bar graph below, which shows the number of male and female athletes at a university over a four-year period.

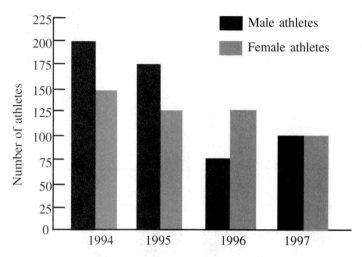

33. Which year had the greatest number of male athletes?

34. Which year had the smallest number of male athletes?

35. Which year had the greatest number of female athletes?

36. Which year had the smallest number of female athletes?

37. What was the ratio of male athletes to female athletes in 1994?

38. What was the ratio of female athletes to male athletes in 1996?

39. Which year had the same number of male and female athletes?

40. Would it be fair to conclude from the graph that some athletics programs were forced to be dropped? Explain.

Exercises 41–45 refer to the pictograph which shows the amount of money spent by each family last year on entertainment.

41. What was the total amount spent by all four families?

42. What amount was spent by the two families who spent the same amount?

43. To the nearest tenth of a percent what was the percent that the Dawson family spent of the total spent by the four families?

44. What was the ratio of the least amount spent to the most spent?

45. The Carroll family spent what percent of the total amount spent?

CRITICAL THINKING

A die was rolled 600 times and the number of times that each number (1, 2, 3, 4, 5, or 6) came up was recorded. The results of this experiment are shown in the bar graph at the right. The statistical probability of obtaining a particular number is defined as the ratio of the number of times that number came up on the die to the total number of times the die is rolled. Use this information in Exercises 46–48 to give the statistical probability of rolling the particular number.

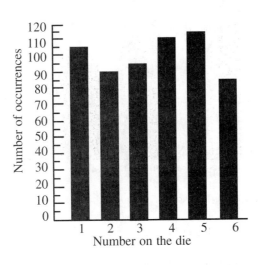

46. 1   47. 3   48. 5

The bar graph and circle graph below give information an military safety. Use these graphs in Exercises 49–50.

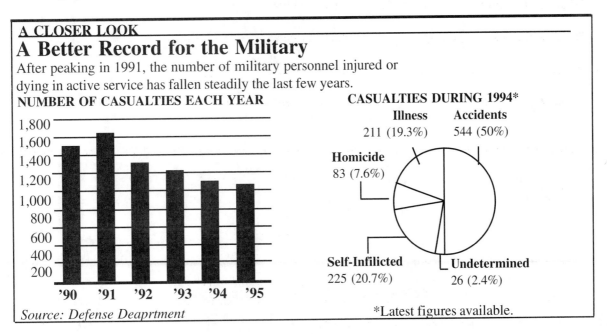

49. Use the bar graph to determine the percent decrease from 1991 to 1995.

50. Read the total from the bar graph for 1994. Use the data on illness from the circle graph to calculate the total. Do you think that the two numbers agree closely enough to be within the accuracy of reading the bar graph?

7.1 PARALLEL EXERCISES

Answers to these exercises are not given in the text.

Exercises 1–8 refer to the circle graph below, which gives the approximate land area of the seven continents in millions of square miles.

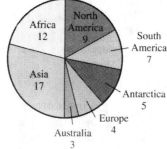

1. What is the approximate total land area of the seven continents?
2. What is the largest continent by area?
3. What is the ratio of the area of Africa to the area of North America?
4. What is the ratio of the area of Australia to the area of South America?
5. What is the ratio of the area of Europe to the area of Asia?
6. To the nearest tenth of a percent, the area of Asia is what percent of the total land area?
7. To the nearest tenth of a percent, the area of North America is what percent of the total land area?
8. North and South America together account for what percent of the total land area (to the nearest tenth of a percent)?

Exercises 9–20 refer to the circle graph below which shows how a university spends its funds totalling $25,000,000 in a given year.

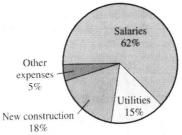

9. Which sector represents the greatest expenditure?
10. Which sector represents the smallest expenditure?
11. How much was spent on salaries?
12. How much was spent on utilities?
13. How much was spent on new construction?
14. How much was spent on other expenses?
15. How much was spent on salaries and utilities?
16. How much was spent on utilities and new construction?
17. What is the ratio of utility expenses to new-construction expenses?
18. What is the ratio of salaries to utilities?
19. What is the ratio of salaries to the expenses for new construction and utilities?
20. How much was spent in all categories besides salaries?

Exercises 21–32 refer to the bar graph at the right, which shows the number of new cars sold by a dealer during a five-month period.

21. How many cars were sold in this five-month period?

22. What is the ratio of cars sold in March to the total number sold in the five-month period?

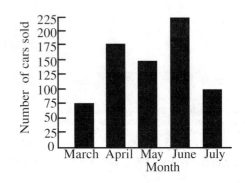

23. What percent of the cars sold in the five-month period were sold in March (to the nearest tenth of a percent)?

24. What is the ratio of cars sold in June to the total number sold in the five-month period?
25. What percent of the cars sold in the five-month period were sold in June (to the nearest tenth of a percent)?

26. What percent of the cars sold in the five-month period were sold in June and July (to the nearest tenth of a percent)?
27. What is the ratio of cars sold in June to cars sold in May?
28. What is the ratio of cars sold in March to cars sold in July?
29. What percent of the cars sold in the five-month period were sold in a month other than July (to the nearest tenth of a percent)?
30. What is the total of the cars sold in March and April?
31. What percent of the cars sold in the five-month period were sold in March and April (to the nearest tenth of a percent)?

32. What is the ratio of the cars sold in March, April, and May to the cars sold in June and July?

Exercises 33–40 refer to the double-bar graph at the right which shows the quarterly profits for a large corporation in millions of dollars for the years 1992 and 1993.

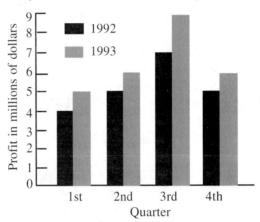

33. Which quarter showed the greatest profit in 1992?
34. Which quarter showed the smallest profit in 1992?
35. Which quarter showed the greatest profit in 1993?
36. Which quarter showed the smallest profit in 1993?
37. What was the profit in the 2nd quarter of 1992?
38. What was the profit in the 3rd quarter of 1993?
39. What was the total profit in all four quarters in 1993?
40. Would it be fair to say that during both years there was a steady increase in profits through the first three quarters and a decline during the fourth quarter? Explain.

Exercises 41–45 refer to the pictograph below which shows the number of clocks produced last month by a company's factories in the given cities.

41. How many clocks were produced by the companies four factories?
42. What is the difference between the most produced by a factory and the least produced?
43. To the nearest tenth of a percent what was the percent that the Dallas factory produced of the total number produced by the four factories?
44. What was the ratio of the least number produced to the greatest number produced?
45. The Mobile factory produced what percent of the number that the Atlanta factory produced?

CRITICAL THINKING

Refer to the bar graph given above Exercises 46–48 to give the probability of rolling the given number on a die.

46. 2   47. 4   48. 6

49. Use the bar graph given above Exercises 49-50 to determine the percent increase from 1990 to 1991.

50. Read the total from the bar graph for 1994. Use the data on accidents from the circle graph to calculate the total. Do you think that the two numbers agree closely enough to be within the accuracy of reading the bar graph?

GROUP PROJECT

 Discuss the relative merit of circle graphs, bar graphs, and pictographs. Collect examples of each for your discussion. Is the data well presented by the graph? Are the graphs understandable and accurate? As an example, consider the following pictograph.

COMPARISON

Guarding Prisoners

The number of prisoners per correctional officer in 1994 in various states.

Guards to Inmates

CALIF.	7.0
TEXAS	4.0
FLA.	3.9
N.Y.	3.3
National average	4.4

Source: Bureau of Justice Statistics

The sentence uses the phrase "prisoners per correction officer." The graph has "Guards to Inmates." What do the numbers on the right side represent?

7.2 BROKEN-LINE GRAPHS AND HISTOGRAMS

STUDENT GUIDEPOSTS

1 USING BROKEN-LINE GRAPHS
2 STUDYING HISTOGRAMS
3 WORKING WITH FREQUENCY POLYGONS

1 | BROKEN-LINE GRAPHS

A **broken-line graph** is often used to show a trend in data collected over a period of time. For example, the broken-line graph in Figure 7.7 shows the number of traffic citations issued by a police department over a six-month period. Each dot shows the number of tickets given during that month.

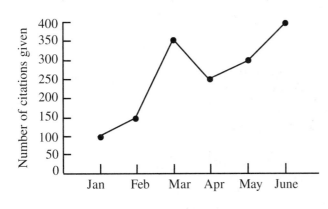

FIGURE 7.7
Broken-Line Graph

READING A BROKEN-LINE GRAPH   EXAMPLE 1

Refer to the broken-line graph in Figure 7.7.

(a) In which month were 350 tickets given out?

Since the dot above March is at the 350 level, 350 tickets were issued in March.

(b) How would you briefly describe the trend in giving out tickets over the six-month period?

Basically the number of tickets given increased from month-to-month with the exception of March to April.

We now solve the applied problem given in the chapter introduction.

OBTAINING HEALTH CARE INFORMATION   EXAMPLE 2

The graph in Figure 7.8 presents a summary of the average cost for personal health care for United States citizens in the years 1970-1993.

PRACTICE EXERCISE 1

Refer to the broken-line graph in Figure 7.7.

(a) How many citations were issued in April?

(b) How many tickets were given out during the six-month period?

Answers: (a) 250 (b) 1550

PRACTICE EXERCISE 2

Refer to the graph in Example 2 to answer the following questions.

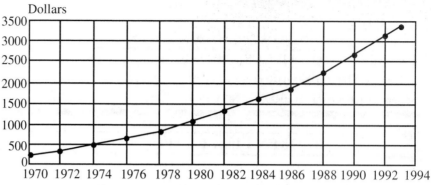

Source: U.S. Health Care Financing Administration

FIGURE 7.8

(a) During which year were health care costs approximately $2000 per person?

(b) Health costs approximately doubled (from $400 to $800) in the period from 1970 to 1978. In what year did costs double again to about $1600 per person?

Answers: (a) 1987 (b) 1984

(a) During which year were health care costs approximately $500 per person?

Since the dot above the year 1974 is at about the $500 level, the average cost of health care in 1974 was approximately $500 per person.

(b) How would you briefly describe the trend in health care costs over this period of years?

Since the graph rises from left to right, this indicates that the cost of health care has increased from year-to-year during this period of time.

Two broken-line graphs in the same figure are often used to show a comparison between two sets of data. For example, the broken-line graphs in Figure 7.9 show the quarterly profits realized by a company during the years 1996 and 1997. By showing both graphs together, it is easy to see at a glance how one year compared with the other.

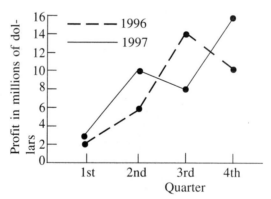

FIGURE 7.9
Double-Line Graph

PRACTICE EXERCISE 3

EXAMPLE 3   **READING A DOUBLE-LINE GRAPH**

Refer to the graph in Figure 7.9.

(a) What was the profit made during the 3rd quarter of 1996?
(b) Between which two consecutive quarters in 1997 did the profit increase the most?

Refer to the graph in Figure 7.9.

(a) What was the profit made during the first quarter of 1997?

Since the dot on the solid line is halfway between the 2 and 4 million marks, the profit this quarter was 3 million dollars.

(b) Between which two consecutive quarters in 1996 was there a decrease in profit?

The dashed line graph goes down from 14 million dollars to 10 million dollars between the 3rd and 4th quarters of 1996.

(c) In which year did the company show the greater profit?

Adding up the quarterly profits in 1996 we obtain

$$2 + 6 + 14 + 10 = 32 \text{ million dollars.}$$

Adding up the quarterly profits in 1997 we obtain

$$3 + 10 + 8 + 16 = 37 \text{ million dollars.}$$

Thus, the greater profit was made in 1997.

2 HISTOGRAMS

Suppose sixty men in an organization list their heights in inches. The resulting data might be somewhat difficult to understand due to the large number of heights. To make the data easier to interpret, the heights could be divided into groups called **class intervals.** We might use 66 inches–68 inches as one interval, 68 inches–70 inches as another, and so forth. The number of heights in each class interval is called the class frequency. The table below summarizes the data collected.

Height in Inches (Class Intervals)	Number of Men (Class Frequency)
66–68	4
68–70	12
70–72	24
72–74	18
74–76	2

Suppose we assume that a person whose height is exactly 68 inches is in the class interval $68 - 70$ and not in $68 - 68$, and similarly for persons whose height is 70 inches, 72 inches, and 74 inches. Then each of the sixty men has his height in exactly one of the class intervals. A special type of bar graph, a **histogram** shown in Figure 7.10, is used to picture the information in the table. The width of each bar represents the range of values in that class interval, and the length or height of the bar corresponds to the **class frequency.**

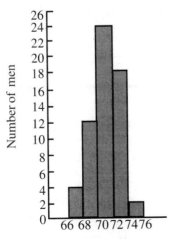

FIGURE 7.10

Histogram

(c) Which year had the better profit change between the 3rd and 4th quarters?

Answers: (a) 14 million dollars (b) between the 3rd and 4th quarters (c) 1997

EXPLORATION GUIDE

Collect your own data by making a number of measurements of some kind. Decide on class intervals and construct a histogram. What kind of information is best presented in this way?

**PRACTICE
EXERCISE 4**

READING A HISTOGRAM   **EXAMPLE 4**

Use the histogram in Figure 7.10 to answer the following.

(a) How many men are 70 inches or taller?

Use the histogram in Figure 7.10 to answer the following.

(a) How many men are shorter than 72 inches?

We must add the class frequencies for the class intervals

$$70 - 72, \ 72 - 74, \ \text{and} \ 74 - 76.$$

$$24 + 18 + 2 = 44$$

There are 44 men 70 inches or taller.

(b) Find the ratio of men with heights between 66 and 68 inches to those between 74 and 76 inches.

(b) Find the ratio of men 68 to 70 inches tall to those 72 to 74 inches tall.

Since there are 12 men with heights between 68 and 70 inches and 18 men with heights between 72 and 74 inches, the ratio is

$$\frac{12}{18} = \frac{2}{3} \quad \text{or 2 to 3.}$$

(c) What percent of the men in the organization are between 68 and 74 inches in height?

(c) What percent of the men in the organization are between 68 and 70 inches in height?

Since there are 12 men 68 to 70 inches tall out of a total of 60 men in the organization, the question is: 12 is what percent of 60?

Method 1 (Equation Method)	Method 2 (Proportion Method)
$A = P\% \cdot B$	$\dfrac{A}{B} = \dfrac{P}{100}$
$\downarrow \quad \downarrow \quad \downarrow$	
$\mathbf{12} = P\% \cdot \mathbf{60}$	$\dfrac{\mathbf{12}}{\mathbf{60}} = \dfrac{P}{100}$
$12 = P\% \cdot 60$	
divide by 60	$12(100) = 60(P)$
$P = \dfrac{12}{60}$	divide by 60
$P = 0.20$	$P = \dfrac{12(100)}{60}$
	$P = 20$

Answers: (a) 40 (b) $\frac{2}{1}$ or 2
to 1 (c) 90%

Thus, 20% of the men are between 68 and 70 inches tall.

3   **FREQUENCY POLYGONS**

Sometimes data that is divided into class intervals is displayed using a special kind of broken-line graph. For instance, suppose we find the midpoint of each class interval, called the **class midpoint,** in the example above. The class midpoint of the class interval 66-68 inches is 67 inches, and the remaining class midpoints are 69 inches, 71 inches, 73 inches, and 75 inches. Locate the class midpoints in the histogram in Figure 7.10, and place a dot at the corresponding point on the top of each bar. When these dots are connected, as shown in Figure 7.11, the resulting broken-line graph is called a **frequency polygon.**

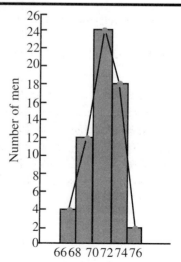

FIGURE 7.11

Frequency Polygon

NOTE   Histograms and frequency polygons are used when data collected consists of a wide range of values such as numbers obtained by measurements.

7.2 EXERCISES

Answers to these exercises are given on page 654.

The number of personal comput-ers sold by a dealer in a six-week period is shown in the broken-line graph at the right. Use this graph in Exercises 1–10.

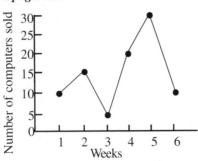

1. How many computers were sold in week 2?

2. During which week(s) were 10 computers sold?

3. How many computers were sold during the six-week period?

4. What was the ratio of computers sold in week 5 to week 3?

5. During which week did the dealer sell the most computers?

6. During which week did the dealer sell the least computers?

7. Between which two consecutive weeks did the sales increase the most?

8. Between which two consecutive weeks did the sales decrease the most?

9. What percent of the total sales were made during week 5?

10. What percent of the total sales were made during week 1?

The double-line graph at the right shows the comparison between new subscribers signed up for cable television during a four-month pe-riod in 1996 and 1997. Use this graph in Exercises 11–18

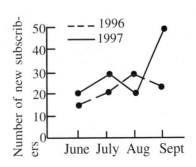

11. How many new subscribers were there in June of 1996?

12. How many new subscribers were there in August of 1997?

13. How many new subscribers were there in the four months of 1996?

14. How many new subscribers were there in the four months of 1997?

15. To the nearest percent, what was the percent increase or decrease in new subscribers from 1996 to 1997 during the four-month period?

16. What was the ratio of new subscribers in June 1996 to June 1997?

17. What was the ratio of new subscribers in July 1997 to August 1997?

18. Between which two consecutive months of 1997 did the company have the greatest increase in new subscribers?

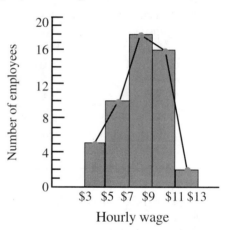

The hourly wages of all the employees of Mutter Manufacturing Company are presented in the histogram at the right. Use this information in Exercises 19–28. Assume that $5 is in the class interval $5–$7 not in $3–$5, similarly for $7, $9, and $11.

19. How many employees earn at least $3 and less than $5 an hour?

20. How many employees earn at least $7 and less than $9 an hour?

21. How many employees earn $7 an hour or more?

22. How many employees earn less than $9 an hour?

23. How many employees are there in Mutter Manufacturing Company?

24. What is the ratio of employees earning $9 or more an hour to the total number of employees?

25. What percent of the employees earn $9 or more an hour (to the nearest tenth of a percent)?

26. What is the ratio of employees earning less than $7 an hour to those who earn $9 or more an hour?

27. What values would be used as the class midpoints of the class intervals to construct the frequency polygon for this data?

28. Draw the frequency polygon in the figure above.

CRITICAL THINKING

The line graphs below are drawn using data from the table. Note that the graph on the left gives the number in thousands and the one on the right gives the value in billions of dollars. In Exercises 29–32 read from the appropriate graph and before making the required calculations check the numbers by refering to the table.

Mergers and Acquisitions: 1985 to 1993

Number

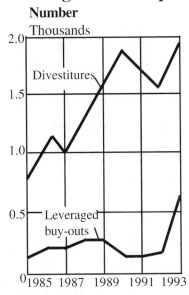

Value

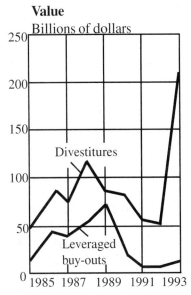

Source: Chart prepared by U.S. Bureau of the Census.

No. 869. Mergers and Acquisitions—Summary: 1985 to 1993

ITEM	Unit	1985	1986	1987	1988	1989	1990	199	1992	1993
All activity: Number	Number..	1,719	2,497	2,479	2,970	3,752	4,239	3,446	3,502	(NA)
Value	Bil dol..	149.6	223.1	198.8	281.8	316.8	205.6	141.5	125.3	(NA)
Divestitures: Number	Number..	780	1,090	1,004	1,274	1,615	1,907	1,759	1,598	1,993
Value	Bil dol..	51	84.7	77.8	115.8	94.9	90.8	61.4	57.2	213.4
Leveraged buyouts: Number.	Number..	154	233	208	291	293	177	171	199	621
Value	Bil dol..	16.3	46.5	40.5	55.2	75.5	17.6	73	7.2	16.4

NA Not available.

Source: Securities Data Company, Newark, NJ. Merger & Corporate Transactions Database (copyright).

29. What was the average value of each of the divestitures in 1987?

30. What was the average value of each of the leveraged buy-outs in 1993?

31. What was the ratio of the number of divestitures to the number of leveraged buy-outs in 1989?

32. What percent of the value of the divestitures was the value of the leveraged buy-outs in 1985?

REVIEW OR PREVIEW

Exercises 33–36 refer to the circle graph at the right which shows the distribution of Chuck's gross monthly income of $2500.

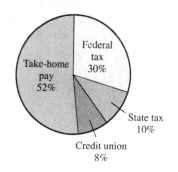

33. What is Chuck's monthly take-home pay?

34. How much federal tax does Chuck pay each month?

35. How much state tax does Chuck pay each month?

36. What is the ratio of federal tax to take-home pay?

Exercises 37–40 refer to the bar graph at the right which shows the number of students who preferred various cable television networks in a recent survey.

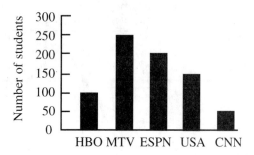

37. How many students preferred HBO?

38. How many students were in the survey?

39. To the nearest tenth of a percent, what percent of the students preferred ESPN?

40. What was the ratio of students preferring MTV to CNN?

The letters in our alphabet occur with different frequencies in the words that we use. The letter "e" occurs most frequently and the letter "z" occurs least frequently. In fact, it has been shown statistically that in a large sample of words, the words on a page in a text for example, approximately 13% of the letters will be "e", 7% will be "a", 6% will be "s", and 8% will be "n". Select a page in one of your textbooks (a page with many words), and count the number of times e, a, s, and n occur. Also, count the total number of letters on the page.

41. Make a table showing the number of times each of the four letters occurs.

42. Construct a bar graph that displays the data from the table in Exercise 41.

43. Construct a circle graph that displays the data from the table in Exercise 41. One of the sections of the graph will represent all letters except the four counted.

44. Which of the four letters occurred most frequently?

45. Which of the four letters occurred least frequently?

46. How do the percents of occurrence of the letters e, a, s, and n in your data compare to the percents given above?

7.2 PARALLEL EXERCISES

Answers to these exercises are not given in the text.

The number of yards gained passing by quarterback Greg Wyatt in five home games of the 1993 season is shown in the broken-line graph at the right. Use this graph in Exercises 1–10.

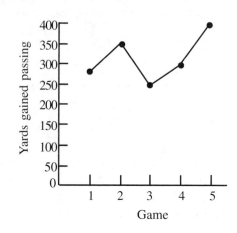

1. How many yards passing did Greg have in game 1?
2. During which game did Greg have 400 yards passing?
3. How many total yards passing did Greg have in the five home games?
4. What was the ratio of yards passing in game 2 to game 3?
5. In which game did Greg have the most yards passing?
6. In which game did Greg have the fewest yards passing?
7. Between which two consecutive home games did his yards passing increase the most?

8. Between which two consecutive home games did his yards passing decrease?
9. To the nearest tenth of a percent, what percent of Greg's total passing yards in the five home games was gained in week 5?
10. To the nearest tenth of a percent, what percent of Greg's total passing yards in the five home games was gained in week 1?

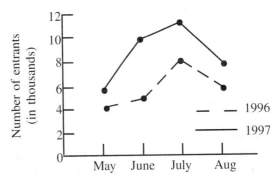

The double-line graph at the right shows the number of entrants (in thousands) to Sunset Crater National Monument during four months in the summers of 1996 and 1997. Use this graph in Exercises 11–18.

11. How many monument entrants were there in June of 1996?
12. How many monument entrants were there in June of 1997?
13. How many monument entrants were there in the four-month period in 1996?
14. How many monument entrants were there in the four-month period in 1997?
15. To the nearest percent, during the four-month period what was the percent increase in monument entrants from 1996 to 1997?
16. What was the ratio of monument entrants in June 1997 to June 1996?
17. What was the ratio of monument entrants in July 1996 to June 1996?
18. Between which two consecutive months in 1997 did the number of monument entrants increase the most?

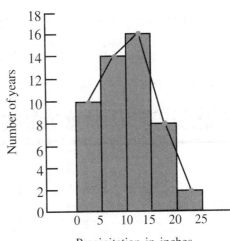

During a past period of years, the weather service has recorded the annual precipitation received by Morgan, Colorado, and the results are given in the histogram at the right. Use this information in Exercises 19–28. Assume that 5 inches is in the class interval 5 inches–10 inches, not in 0 inches–5 inches, similarly for 10 inches, 15 inches, and 20 inches.

19. In how many years was the precipitation total less than 5 inches?
20. In how many years was the precipitation total at least 10 inches and less than 15 inches?
21. In how many years did Morgan receive 10 inches or more of precipitation?
22. In how many years did Morgan receive less than 15 inches of precipitation?
23. What was the total number of years in the recording period?

24. What is the ratio of the number of years of 15 to 20 inches of precipitation to the number of years of 20 to 25 inches?

25. In what percent of the total number of years did Morgan receive 20 inches or more of precipitation?

26. What is the ratio of the number of years of less than 5 inches of precipitation to the number of years of 10 inches or more of precipitation?

27. What values would be used as the class midpoints of the class intervals to construct the frequency polygon for this data?

28. Draw the frequency polygon in the figure above.

CRITICAL THINKING

Refer to the line graphs and table given in Exercises 29-32 to answer the following questions.

29. What was the average value of each of the leveraged buy-outs in 1987?
30. What was the average value of each of the divestitures in 1993?
31. What was the ratio of the value of divestitures to the value of leveraged buy-outs in 1989?

32. What percent of the number of the divestitures was the number of the leveraged buy-outs in 1985?

GROUP PROJECT

Study the use of broken line graphs and histograms and compare these with graphs studied previously. Collect data or obtain data from tables and construct a graph that will help explain the data or its relationship to other data. For example, consider the table below. Construct line graphs that will allow you to compare fuel consumption with fuel production in the United States. Discuss the data and the graphs. What other graphs might be helpful?

Energy Supply and Disposition, by Type of Fuel: 1970 to 1993
[In quadrillion British thermal units (Btu).]

TYPE OF FUEL	1970	1973	1975	1980	1985	1986	1987	1988	1989	1990	1991	1992	1993
Production	62.1	62.1	59.9	64.8	64.9	64.4	65.0	66.1	66.1	67.9	67.5	66.9	65.81
Crude oil	20.4	19.5	17.7	18.3	19.0	18.4	17.7	17.3	16.1	15.6	15.7	15.2	14.48
Natural gas liquids	2.5	2.6	2.4	2.3	2.2	2.2	2.2	2.3	2.3	2.3	2.3	2.4	2.4
Netural gas[3]	21.7	22.2	19.6	19.9	17.0	16.5	17.1	17.6	17.9	18.4	18.2	18.4	18.98
Coal	14.6	14.0	15.0	18.6	19.3	19.5	20.1	20.7	21.4	22.5	21.6	21.6	20.49
Nuclear electric power	2.6	2.9	3.2	2.9	3.0	3.1	2.6	2.3	2.8	2.9	2.9	2.5	2.76
Hydroelectric power	0.2	0.9	1.9	2.7	4.2	4.5	4.9	5.7	5.7	6.2	6.6	6.6	6.52
Geothermal and other	(Z)	(Z)	0.1	0.1	0.2	0.2	0.2	0.2	0.2	0.2	0.2	0.2	0.18
Net trade[4]	−5.7	−12.7	−11.7	−12.3	−7.9	−10.3	−11.9	−13.2	−14.2	−14.1	−13.4	−14.6	−16.9
Exports	2.7	2.1	2.4	3.7	4.2	4.1	3.9	4.4	4.8	4.9	5.2	5.0	4.31
Coal	1.9	1.4	1.8	2.4	2.4	2.3	2.1	2.5	2.6	2.8	2.9	2.7	1.95
Imports	8.4	14.7	14.1	16.0	12.1	14.4	15.8	17.6	19.0	19.0	18.6	19.7	21.19
Crude oil	2.8	6.9	8.7	11.2	6.8	9.0	10.1	11.0	12.6	12.8	12.6	13.3	14.63
Consumption	66.4	74.3	70.6	76.0	74.0	74.3	76.9	80.2	81.3	81.3	81.1	82.1	83.96
Petroleum products	29.5	34.8	32.7	34.2	30.9	32.2	32.9	34.2	34.2	33.6	32.9	33.5	33.77
Natural gas[3]	21.8	22.5	20.0	20.4	17.8	16.7	17.7	18.6	19.4	19.3	19.6	20.1	20.79
Coal	12.3	13.0	12.7	15.4	17.5	17.3	18.0	18.9	18.9	19.1	18.8	18.9	19.63
Nuclear power	0.2	0.9	1.9	2.7	4.2	4.5	4.9	5.7	5.7	6.2	6.6	6.6	6.52
Hydroelectric power[6]	2.7	3.0	3.2	3.1	3.4	3.5	3.1	2.7	2.9	3.0	3.1	2.8	3.06
Geothermal and other	(Z)	(Z)	0.1	0.1	0.2	0.2	0.3	0.3	0.3	0.2	0.2	0.2	0.2

Z Less then 50 trillion.   [1]Represents peak year for U.S. energy production.   [2]Includes lease condensate.   [3]Dry marketed gas.
[4]Exports minus imports.   [5]Represents peak year for U.S. energy consumption.   [6]Includes industrial generation of hydropower and net electricity imports.

7.3 MEAN, MEDIAN, AND MODE

STUDENT GUIDEPOSTS
1. DETERMINING THE MEAN (AVERAGE)
2. WORKING WITH THE MEDIAN
3. WORKING WITH MODE

1 MEAN (AVERAGE)

In Sections 7.1 and 7.2 numerical data were presented using circle graphs, bar graphs, pictographs, broken-line graphs, and histograms. Often it is necessary to look for one number or statistic to characterize a whole collection of numbers. For example, suppose Jenny has scores of 69, 79, and 98 on three chemistry tests. To find out how she is doing in the course, Jenny might calculate the *mean* or *average* of her scores.

MEAN (AVERAGE)

The **mean** or **average** of several values is the ratio of the sum of the values to the number of values.

$$\text{mean (average)} = \frac{\text{sum of values}}{\text{number of values}}$$

To find the mean of 69, 79, and 98, add these three scores and divide by 3 (the number of scores).

$$\text{mean} = \frac{69 + 79 + 98}{3} \quad \leftarrow \textbf{Sum of the scores} \\ \leftarrow \textbf{Number of scores}$$

$$= \frac{246}{3} = 82$$

Making 69, 79, and 98 on three tests is the same as making

$$82, \quad 82, \quad \text{and} \quad 82$$

on three tests. The mean or average gives Jenny a better idea of how well she is doing in chemistry. Her instructor may use the average to compute her course grade.

EXAMPLE 1   FINDING A MEAN IN A BUSINESS

The daily sales at George's Pie Place were $285.85, $192.50, $222.82, $315.16, $427.45, and $396.80 for a six-day week. To get a better idea of how well his business is doing, George would like to know the average daily sales for the week. What is the average?   Add the sales for the 6 days and divide by 6.

$$\begin{array}{r} \$285.85 \\ 192.50 \\ 222.82 \\ 315.16 \\ 427.45 \\ 396.80 \\ \hline \$1840.58 \end{array}$$

$$\frac{\$1840.58}{6} \approx \$306.76 \qquad \text{To the nearest cent}$$

George's shop is averaging about $306.76 per day in sales.

In Example 1, if George had known that the total sales for the 6-day week were $1840.58, he would only have had to divide by 6. The next example illustrates this type of problem.

FINDING A MEAN IN INDUSTRY   EXAMPLE 2

Suppose tests by General Motors show that one of its cars will go 420 miles on a tank of gasoline. What is the average miles per gallon (mpg) of the car if the tank holds 12.5 gal?

In this problem the total miles traveled on the 12.5 gal is given. Thus, all that is needed to find the average is to divide 420 mi by 12.5 gal.

$$\frac{420 \text{ mi}}{12.5 \text{ gal}} = 33.6 \frac{\text{mi}}{\text{gal}} = 33.6 \text{ mpg}$$

2   MEDIAN

The mean of a collection of numbers can often be influenced by one very large or very small number (compared to the others). As a result, a mean is often a poor measure of the characteristics of a set of data. For example, the mean of the numbers

$$1, \quad 2, \quad 3, \quad 4, \quad 90$$

is

$$\frac{1+2+3+4+90}{5} = \frac{100}{5} = 20.$$

Since four of the five numbers are very small compared to the fifth number, to use 20 to describe this set of data might be somewhat misleading. Actually, a number closer to 1, 2, 3, or 4 than 20 would provide a better description. Another way to describe a set of data is to look at the value in the middle after the numbers are arranged by size. For example, consider the following:

$$1, \quad 2, \quad \mathbf{3,} \quad 4, \quad 90.$$
$$\uparrow$$
Middle

The value in the middle is 3, and certainly 3 gives a better description of the data set than the mean 20. The middle value of a collection of numbers that is arranged in order of size is the *median* of the data.

Suppose Russell made scores of 72, 65, and 88 on his first three tests. To find the middle score, or median score, arrange them in order of increasing value.

$$65, \quad \mathbf{72,} \quad 88$$
$$\uparrow$$
Middle

The median score is 72.

But what about the middle score if Russell had four test scores, 72, 65, 88, and 95? Once again arrange them in order.

$$65, \quad 72, \quad 88, \quad 95$$
$$\uparrow$$
Middle

In this case, there is no middle score. To approximate a middle score, average the *two* scores in the middle.

$$\text{median} = \frac{72+88}{2} = 80$$

MEDIAN

The middle value of several values is called the **median.** To find the median:

1. Arrange the values in increasing order from left to right.
2. If there is an odd number of values, the median is the middle one.
3. If there is an even number of values, the median is the average of the *two* values in the middle.

E X A M P L E 3   **FINDING A MEDIAN**

Find the median of the given numbers.

(a) 5, 12, 2, 14, 8, 7, 9

First arrange the numbers in order.

2,   5,   7,   **8,**   9,   12,   14

There are seven numbers, and the middle one is the fourth from the left. The median is 8.

(b) 125, 105, 216, 205, 110, 175

Arrange the numbers in order.

105,   110,   **125,   175,**   205,   216

The two numbers in the middle are 125 and 175. Find their average.

$$\frac{125+175}{2} = 150$$

Thus, 150 is the median of the numbers.

E X A M P L E 4   **AN APPLICATION OF MEAN AND MEDIAN**

In Greenborough, the number of traffic accidents per day is recorded. The following are the numbers for one week.

12,   18,   22,   10,   8,   15,   27

Find the average number of accidents per day and the median number per day.

First find the average.

$$\frac{12+18+22+10+8+15+27}{7} = \frac{112}{7} = 16$$

To find the median, arrange the numbers in order.

8,   10,   12,   **15,**   18,   22,   27

The median is 15 which is close to the mean of 16.

PRACTICE EXERCISE 3

Find the median of the given numbers.

(a) 9, 20, 2, 18, 27

(b) 206, 140, 180, 375

Answers: (a) 18 (b) 193

PRACTICE EXERCISE 4

Jeanine made scores of 22, 24, 15, 27, 19, and 30 on six quizzes in geology lab. Find the average score and the median score on these quizzes.

Answer: average score: 22.8, median score: 23

NOTE Remember to arrange the numbers by size before selecting the middle one as the median. For example, the median of

5, 1, 2, 3, 8

is 3, not 2. This is easy to see after rewriting the numbers as 1, 2, 3, 5, 8.

PRACTICE EXERCISE 5

Use the table in Example 5 to find each mean and median.

The next example solves the applied problem given in the chapter introduction.

MEAN AND MEDIAN OF PRESIDENTIAL VETOES   **EXAMPLE 5**

Use the table below to find each mean and median requested.

Congressional Bills Vetoed: 1961 to 1993

[See also *Historical Statistics, Colonial Times to 1970.* series Y 199-203]

PERIOD	President	Total vetoes	Regular vetoes	Pocket vetoes	Vetoes sustained	Bills passed over veto
1961-63	Kennedy	21	12	9	21	-
1963-69	Johnson	30	16	14	30	-
1969-74	Nixon	43	26	17	36	7
1974-77	Ford	66	48	18	54	12
1977-81	Carter	31	13	18	29	2
1981-89	Reagan	78	39	39	69	9
1989-93	Bush	44	29	15	43	1

- Represents zero.

Source: U.S. Congress, Senate Library, *Presidential Vetoes ... 1789-1968*; U.S. Congress. *Calendars of the U.S. House of Representatives and History of Legislation,* annual.

(a) Find the mean of the number of vetoes of the republican presidents in the list. (Nixon, Ford, Reagan, Bush)

(a) Find the mean number of vetoes for all presidents from Kennedy to Bush.

There were seven presidents during this time. We must add the number of vetos and divide by 7.

$$\frac{21+30+43+66+31+78+44}{7} = \frac{313}{7} \approx 45$$

Thus, these presidents used the veto an average of 45 times during their career.

(b) What was the median number of vetoes by republican presidents?

(b) What was the median number of vetoes of these presidents?

First we arrange the numbers in increasing order.

21, 30, 31, **43**, 44, 66, 78

Since there are 7 numbers, the middle one is the fourth number, 43. Thus, the median number of vetoes is 43.

Answers: (a) 58 (b) 55

| EXAMPLE 6 | FINDING THE MEAN AND MEDIAN USING A TABLE |

The Lopez Construction Company has thirty employees. Six of them earn $18,500 per year, five earn $19,200 per year, two earn $22,800 per year, ten earn $24,500 per year, four earn $32,800 per year, two earn $38,000 per year, and one earns $52,400 per year. What is the mean or average salary of the thirty employees? What is the median salary?

A good way to find the sum of the salaries is to set up a table.

Salary	Number of Employees	Salary Times Number of Employees
18,500	6	111,000
19,200	5	96,000
22,800	2	45,600
24,500	10	245,000
32,800	4	131,200
38,000	2	76,000
52,400	1	52,400
Totals	30	$757,200

When each salary is multiplied by the number of employees making that salary and the results are added, the total is $757,200. This is divided by 30, the total number of employees, to get the mean or average salary.

$$\frac{\$757,200}{30} = \$25,240$$

Since there are 30 employees, the median salary is the average of the middle two salaries once the salaries are arranged by size. This will be the average of the 15th and 16th salaries in the arrangement. Without actually listing all the salaries, we can find the 15th and 16th ones by looking at the table. Use the column for the number of employees and count down 15. Since the 15th and 16th positions are included in the 10 employees in the fourth row from the top, the 15th and 16th salary values are both $24,500, making the average of the two also $24,500. Thus, the median salary is $24,500.

A new car dealer has 40 cars in stock. Five are valued at $18,000, 12 at $15,000, 10 at $12,000, 7 at $9000, and 6 at $8000. What is the mean or average value of a car on his lot? What is the median value?

| 3 | MODE |

The final measure used to describe a set of data is called the *mode*. Consider the numbers   1,   5,   101,   101.

The mean is

$$\frac{1+5+101+101}{4} = \frac{208}{4} = 52,$$

and the median is

$$\frac{5+101}{2} = \frac{106}{2} = 53.$$

But does 52 or 53 give an accurate reflection of the data set? Since two of the four numbers are 101, much greater than 52 or 53, it might be better to describe this data set using 101, the number that occurs most frequently in the set.

MODE

The value that occurs most frequently in a set of values is the **mode** of the data. If there are two values that occur more frequently than all the others, the data has two modes and is called **bimodal.** If no value occurs more than once in the set, the data has **no mode.**

**EXPLORATION
GUIDE**

Collect a set of data that relates to you personally (some test scores, your annual income over several years, or other such data). Find the mean, median and mode of these data and decide which number gives the best information. Are all meaningful for your set of data?

| PRACTICE EXERCISE 7 | EXAMPLE 7 | FINDING A MODE |

Find the mode of the given numbers.

Find the mode of the given numbers.

(a) 1, 1, 1, 5, 2, 2, 9, 8

(a) 5, 8, 1, 8, 7, 9, 8, 5

Since 8 occurs three times, 5 occurs twice, and all the rest of the numbers occur only once, the mode is 8.

(b) 6, 6, 2, 1, 5, 2, 9, 10

(b) 2, 7, 3, 7, 8, 8, 1, 5

Since 7 and 8 both occur twice and all other numbers occur only once, the set of numbers has two modes, 7 and 8. It is a bimodal set.

(c) 2, 8, 5, 12, 9, 7

Answers: (a) 1 (b) 6 and 2 (bimodal) (c) no mode

(c) 3, 9, 7, 5, 2, 1, 11

Since every number occurs exactly one time, there is no mode.

7.3 EXERCISES

Answers to these exercises are given on page 654.

In Exercises 1–6 find the mean of the given numbers. Give answers to the nearest tenth when appropriate.

1. 7, 19, 13

2. 7, 9, 8, 12

3. 12, 22, 18, 25, 9

4. 102, 95, 116, 118, 125, 106

5. 7.2, 6.1, 8.6, 9.2, 5.5, 7.2, 8.8

6. 42, 43, 58, 55, 61, 41, 48, 48

In Exercises 7–12 find the median.

7. 7, 19, 13

8. 7, 9, 8, 12

9. 12, 22, 25, 18, 9

10. 102, 95, 116, 118, 125, 106

11. 7.2, 6.1, 8.6, 9.2, 5.5, 7.2, 8.8

12. 42, 43, 58, 55, 61, 41, 48, 48

In Exercises 13–18 find the mode.

13. 5, 6, 1, 6, 3, 2

14. 2, 3, 9, 2, 9, 7, 9, 11

15. 8, 3, 8, 5, 7, 3, 2

16. 2, 11, 17, 9, 6, 41

17. 4.3, 2.7, 4.3, 12.8, 15.1

18. 149, 150, 211, 150, 435, 147

Solve each applied problem in Exercises 19–23.

19. **GAS MILEAGE** A new domestic economy car will travel 552.9 miles on a tank of gasoline. If the tank holds 9.5 gallons, what is the average miles per gallon (mpg)?

20. **ENVIRONMENT** In a 30-day month 23,550 fish passed a counting station on a river. What was the average number of fish per day passing the station?

21. **SALES** During a six-day week, the sales at Joseph's Shop for Men were $482.16, $316.58, $299.81, $686.47, $819.72, and $992.16. What were the average daily sales?

22. **SPORTS** The heights of the starting five players on the Upstate University basketball team are 78 inches, 82 inches, 72 inches, 84 inches, and 73 inches. What is the average height? What is the median height?

23. **SALARY** The table at the right gives information on the yearly salaries of the employees at one plant of Mutter Manufacturing. Find the average salary. Find the median salary. What is the mode of the salaries?

Salary	Number of Employees	Salary Times Number of Employees
16,200	8	
20,800	10	
28,600	7	
32,000	2	
46,000	1	
	Totals	

    CRITICAL THINKING

24. **EDUCATION** Suppose Marni made scores of 65, 72, and 88 on the first three tests in math. What score did she make on the fourth test if the average score on the four was 80?

25. **EDUCATION** Suppose Burford made scores of 32, 38, 51, and 82 on four of five exams. If the median score of the five exams is 51, could the score on Burford's fifth test have been 35?

Which of the mean, median, or mode do you think is the best measure to describe each set of numbers in Exercises 26–29?

26. 1, 1, 1, 1, 20, 100

27. 1, 1, 99, 99

28. 1, 2, 3, 1000

29. 1, 2, 3, 4, 5

30. Do your teachers use the mean? Discuss how the mean could be used in education.

Use the table below in Exercises 31–32. Give answers to the nearest unit.

**Scholastic Assessment Test (SAT) Scores and Characteristics
of College-Bound Seniors: 1967 to 1994
[For school year ending in year shown.**
Data are for the SAT I: Reasoning Tests. Prior to 1994. named Scholastic Aptitude Test]

TYPE OF TEST AND CHARACTERISTIC	Unit	1967	1970	1975	1980	1985	1990	1991	1992	1993	1994
TEST SCORES[1]											
Verbal, total	Point	466	460	434	424	431	424	422	423	424	423
Male	Point	463	459	437	426	437	429	426	428	428	425
Female	Point	468	461	431	420	425	419	418	419	420	421
Math, total	Point	492	488	472	466	475	476	474	476	478	479
Male	Point	514	509	495	491	499	499	497	499	502	501
Female	Point	467	465	449	443	452	455	453	456	457	460

Source: College Entrance Examination Board, New York, NY, *National College-Bound Senior,* annual (copyright).

31. Determine the mean and median of the total verbal for the ten years reported. Discuss the meaning of these numbers and give any other observations that you have in regard to this data.

32. Determine the mean and median of the total math for the ten years reported. Discuss the meaning of these numbers and give any other observations that you have in regard to this data.

REVIEW OR PREVIEW

The profit (in millions of dollars) made by the ABC Corporation over a six-year interval is shown in the broken-line graph below. Use this graph in Exercises 33–39.

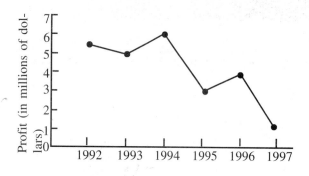

33. What profit was made in 1993?

34. What profit was made in 1992?

35. What was the total profit made in 1994 and 1995?

36. What was the total profit made during the six-year interval?

37. What was the ratio of the profit in 1994 to that in 1995?

38. What percent (to the nearest tenth) of the total profit in the six-year interval was made in 1993?

39. What percent (to the nearest tenth) of the total profit in the six-year interval was made in the years 1992 and 1993?

The number of years of teaching experience by the faculty at CSU is shown in the histogram below. Use this graph in Exercises 40–46.

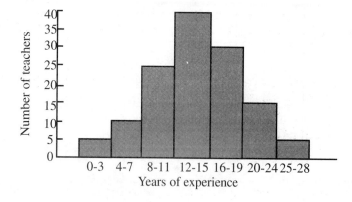

40. How many teachers have 0–3 years of experience?

41. How many teachers have 8–15 years of experience?

42. How many teachers have 12 or more years of experience?

43. How many teachers have 7 or less years of experience?

44. How many total teachers are represented by this data?

45. What percent (to the nearest tenth) of the total number of teachers have 16 or more years of experience?

46. What is the ratio of the number of teachers with 16–19 years of experience to those with 7 or less years of experience?

7.3 PARALLEL EXERCISES

Answers to these exercises are not given in the text.

In Exercises 1–6 find the mean of the given numbers. Give answers to the nearest tenth when appropriate.

1. 11, 21, 19

2. 8, 12, 14, 22

3. 14, 35, 16, 19, 43

4. 130, 87, 102, 96, 145, 110

5. 6.3, 4.7, 8.2, 9.6, 7.1, 8.3, 2.5

6. 51, 57, 62, 65, 71, 83, 90, 97

In Exercises 7–12, find the median.

7. 5, 12, 37

8. 6, 9, 10, 14

9. 5, 21, 27, 17, 19

10. 107, 93, 110, 84, 87, 130

11. 6.3, 4.7, 8.2, 9.6, 7.1, 8.3, 2.5

12. 51, 57, 62, 65, 90, 83, 71, 97

In Exercises 13–18, find the mode.

13. 11, 17, 5, 17, 6, 21, 17

14. 6, 3, 6, 8, 11, 3, 21, 3

15. 2, 12, 5, 2, 8, 5, 7, 1

16. 3, 9, 21, 8, 7, 26, 5

17. 4.8, 7.6, 8.1, 9.3, 7.6, 2.4

18. 159, 276, 423, 159, 342, 177

Solve each applied problem in Exercises 19–23.

19. **GAS MILEAGE** At a testing ground a pickup truck was driven 573.3 miles on 31.5 gallons of gasoline. What was the average miles per gallon (mpg)?

20. **ENVIRONMENT** In a study of a forest it was discovered that there were 4620 trees that had been killed by insects. If there are 1155 acres in the forest under study, what is the average number of trees per acre that had been killed?

21. **SALES** The number of TV sets sold per day by a dealer over a 12-day period is 2, 4, 6, 2, 10, 3, 6, 8, 12, 8, 22, and 12. What is the median number of sets sold per day? What is the average number of sets sold per day (to the nearest tenth)?

22. **EDUCATION** Maria scored 73, 85, 65, 92, 78, and 87 on six tests in math. What is her average score? What is her median score?

23. **MEDICAL** The Mutter Manufacturing record of sick-leave days available to employees is recorded below. What is the average number of days available? What is the median number? What is the mode?

Number of Days Sick Leave Available	Number of Employees	Number of Days Times Number of Employees
14	4	
21	12	
28	8	
35	4	
Totals		

CRITICAL THINKING

24. **EDUCATION** Walter had scores of 89, 79, and 93 on three tests but could not remember the score on his first test. If his average on the four tests was 84, what was his first score?

25. **EDUCATION** Burford knew he had scores of 35 and 45 on two tests and thought that he had made 70 on test three. If his average on the three tests was 40, can you tell him why a score of 70 was not possible?

Which of the mean, median, or mode do you think is the best measure to describe each set of numbers in Exercises 26–29?

26. 5, 5, 5, 60

27. 2, 4, 6, 8, 10, 12

28. 4, 8, 10, 2000

29. 100, 100, 100, 100, 200

30. Do your teachers use median and mode? Discuss how the median could be used in education.

Use the table given above Exercises 31–32 to determine the following. Give answers to the nearest unit.

31. Determine the mean and median of the verbal scores for females over the ten years reported. Discuss the meaning of these numbers and give any other observations that you have in regard to this data.

32. Determine the mean and median of the math scores for males over the ten years reported. Discuss the meaning of these numbers and give any other observations that you have in regard to this data.

GROUP PROJECT

Means (averages) and medians are used frequently in graphs in magazines and newspapers, such as the graphs related to education that appeared in the January 30, 1995 edition of Time. Look for additional examples of these measures, along with modes, in other articles. Which measure seems to be used most frequently, and which is used the least? Discuss what your research has found. Select certain articles to study in detail.

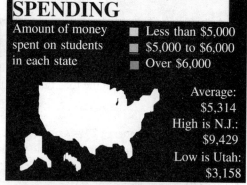

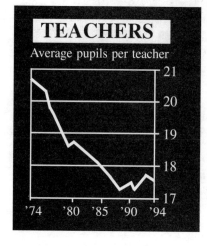

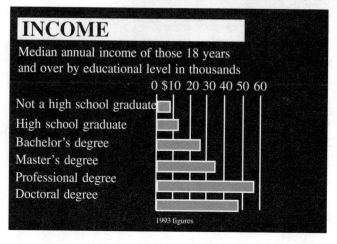

CHAPTER 7 REVIEW

KEY WORDS

 7.1

- **Statistics** is a branch of mathematics that deals with collecting, organizing, and summarizing numerical data in order to describe or interpret it.
- A **circle graph** uses pie-shaped sectors of a circle to represent different parts of a quantity.
- A **bar graph** is used to compare various parts of a data set.
- A **pictograph** uses appropriate pictures to compare data.

 7.2

- A **broken-line graph** can be used to show trends in data collected over a period of time.

- A **histogram** is a special type of bar graph used to display data that is divided into groups called **class intervals**. The **class frequency** of an interval is represented by the length or height of each bar.

7.3

- The **mean** or **average** of several values is the sum of the values divided by the number of values.
- The **median** of a data set is the middle value or the average of the two middle values when the values are arranged in order of size.
- The **mode** of a set of values is the value that occurs most frequently in the set.

KEY CONCEPTS

 7.1

1. Numerical data can be displayed or pictured using a circle graph, a bar graph, or pictograph.

 7.2

2. A histogram is often used when a large number of data items can best be described by dividing the data into groups.

7.3

1. Before finding the median of a collection of numbers, be sure to arrange the numbers in order of size.
2. If there is an even number of values, the median is the mean (average) of the two middle values.
3. A bimodal set of data has two values with the greatest frequency of occurrence. If all numbers in a collection occur exactly once, the data set has no mode.

CHAPTER 7 REVIEW EXERCISES

PART I

Answers to these exercises are given on page 654.

 7.1

Exercises 1–4 refer to the circle graph to the right which shows preference in vacation locations of 300 adults surveyed in a random poll. Give answers rounded to the nearest tenth.

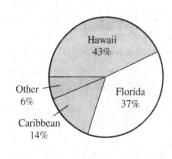

1. How many of those surveyed preferred Hawaii?

2. How many of those surveyed preferred the Caribbean?

3. What is the ratio of those preferring Hawaii to those preferring Florida?

4. How many of those surveyed preferred a vacation location other than Hawaii?

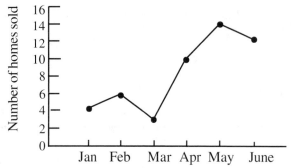 **7.2**

Exercises 5–10 refer to the broken-line graph below which shows the number of new homes sold in a subdivision over a six-month period.

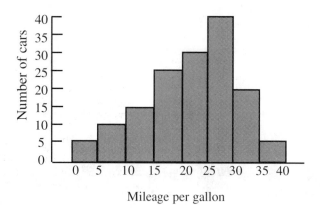

5. How many homes were sold in April?

6. How many homes were sold in May and June together?

7. Between which two consecutive months did sales of new homes show the greatest increase?

8. How many homes were sold in the six-month period?

9. What was the ratio of homes sold in April to those sold in March?

10. What percent (to the nearest tenth) of the homes sold in the six-month period were sold in January?

Exercises 11–16 refer to the histogram at the right which relates the number of cars to miles per gallon in an EPA survey. Assume that a car making 5 mpg, for example, is included in the range 5–10 mpg and not 0–5 mpg, similarly for 10 mpg, 15 mpg, and so forth.

11. How many cars got at least 5 mpg and less than 10 mpg?

12. How many cars got 30 mpg or better?

13. How many cars got less than 20 mpg?

14. How many cars were represented in the survey?

15. What percent of the total number of cars got 35 mpg or better?

16. What is the ratio of cars that got 30 mpg or better to those that got less than 5 mpg?

7.3

Find the mean and median. Give answers to the nearest tenth.

17. 16, 12, 19, 22, 8

18. 375, 206, 311, 222, 320, 312

19. **BUSINESS** A large department store is open from 10 A.M. to 10 P.M. If during these hours on Friday there were 3300 customers in the store, what was the average number of customers per hour?

In Exercises 20–21, find the mode.

20. 6, 5, 1, 3, 5, 7, 12, 5

21. 2, 9, 3, 2, 7, 3, 4, 12

22. **SALES** The Thai Villa Restaurant had sales of $1020, $926, $820, $772, $1428, and $1362 over a six-day period. What were the average daily sales to the nearest dollar? What was the median?

23. **SALARY** The following table gives information of the monthly salaries of the employees of Lloyd's Shoppe. Find the average salary. Find the median salary. What is the mode of the salaries?

Salary	Number of Employees	Salary Times Number of Employees
$ 820	4	
$ 860	8	
$ 920	5	
$ 980	2	
$1620	1	
Totals		

PART II

Exercises 24–27 refer to the bar graph below, which gives the number of adults choosing a particular sport as their favorite to view on television.

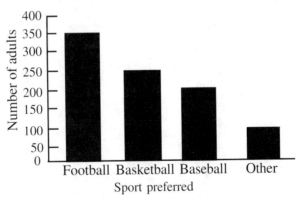

24. How many adults were in the survey?

25. What is the ratio of those preferring basketball to the total number surveyed?

26. What percent of those surveyed preferred basketball (to the nearest tenth of a percent)?

27. What is the ratio of those who prefer football to those who prefer baseball?

Find the mean, median, and mode in Exercises 28–31.

28. 12, 3, 9, 5, 5

29. 6.1, 2.5, 3.8, 9.2, 100.7

30. 18, 12, 17, 29, 40, 12

31. 4, 7, 4, 9, 7, 6, 8, 10

Exercises 32–40 refer to the double-bar graph below which compares the number of students enrolled in four math courses at State University in 1996 and 1997.

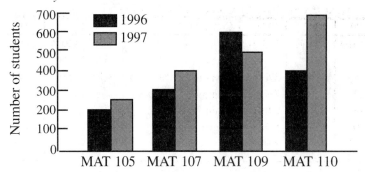

32. How many students were in MAT 107 in 1997?

33. How many students were in MAT 109 in 1996?

34. How many students were in these four math courses in 1996?

35. How many students were in these four math courses in 1997?

36. What was the ratio of students in MAT 110 in 1997 to those in MAT 110 in 1996?

37. What percent of students in all four classes in 1996 were in MAT 109?

38. During which year were there more students in MAT 109?

39. What was the percent increase in students taking MAT 110 from 1996 to 1997?

40. How many total students took MAT 105 in these two years?

Exercises 41–45 refer to the pictograph below which gives the number of doors sold by a company in the indicated year.

	Number of doors sold	⊞ = 1000 doors
1994	⊞ ⊞ ⊞	
1995	⊞ ⊞ ⊞ ⊞ ⊞	
1996	⊞ ⊞ ⊞ ⊞	
1997	⊞ ⊞ ⊞ ⊞ ⊞ ⊞	

41. What is the total number of doors sold in the four years?

42. What is the ratio of the least number sold in a year to the greatest number sold?

43. The number of doors sold in 1996 was what percent of the number sold in 1995?

44. To the nearest tenth of a percent, what percent of the total number sold in the four years were sold in 1997?

45. What is the ratio of the total sold the first two years to the total sold the last two years?

In Exercises 46–50 use the table below. Give answers to the nearest unit.

Meat Production, by Country: 1990 to 1993

COUNTRY	1990	1992	1993	COUNTRY	1990	1992	1993
World	178,169	184,323	185,917	Italy	3,950	3,988	3,936
				Japan	3,503	3,398	3,378
Argentina	3,383	3,540	3,617	Mexico	3,478	3,563	3,628
Brazil	6,439	7,343	7,545	Soviet Union (former)	19,996	16,297	15,566
France	5,765	6,188	6,085	Spain	3,466	3,681	3,701
Germany	7,292	6,204	5,947	United Kingdom	3,357	3,365	2,340
India	3,723	3,899	3,992	United States	28,632	30,780	31,350

Source: Food and Agriculture Organization of the United Nations. Rome, Italy, FAO AGRISTAT database.

46. What was the average production in the United States over the three year period given?

47. What was the average of the world production over the three years?

48. What was the median production of all countries in 1993?

49. What was the average of the top five producers in 1993?

50. What was the average of the bottom five producers in 1993?

CHAPTER 7 TEST

Answers to this test are given on page 655.

Problems 1–3 refer to the circle graph below which shows the distribution of responses from 1000 adults about television viewing preference.

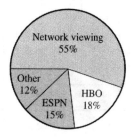

1. How many of those polled preferred HBO?

2. How many of those polled preferred ESPN?

3. What is the ratio of those who preferred network viewing to ESPN?

1. _____

2. _____

3. _____

Problems 4–8 refer to the bar graph below which shows the preferences of 150 adults in type of restaurant food.

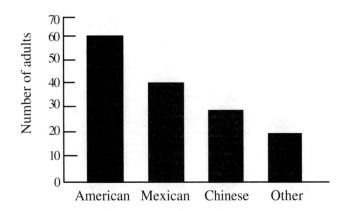

4. How many of those questioned preferred Mexican food?

5. How many of those questioned preferred food other than American food?

6. What is the ratio of those preferring American food to those preferring Chinese food?

7. What percent of those interviewed preferred Mexican food?

8. What percent of those interviewed preferred some kind of food besides American?

4. _____

5. _____

6. _____

7. _____

8. _____

CHAPTER 7 TEST

The weights of all the members of a football team are presented in the histogram below. Use this information in problems 9–12. Assume that 175 pounds is in the class 175–200 pounds, not in 150–175 pounds, similarly for 200 pounds, 225 pounds, and 250 pounds.

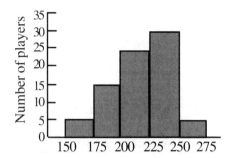

9. How many players weigh at least 200 and less than 225 pounds?

10. How many players are on the team?

11. What is the ratio of players weighing 225 pounds or more to the total number of players on the team?

12. What percent of the players weigh less than 200 pounds?

13. Find the mean of the given numbers.

$$11, 22, 32, 17, 18$$

14. Find the median of the given numbers.

$$11, 22, 32, 17, 18$$

15. Find the mode of the given numbers.

$$14, 8, 9, 17, 8, 17, 23, 8, 5$$

16. The weights of the starting four defensive linemen for PSU are 246 pounds, 253 pounds, 257 pounds, and 262 pounds. (a) What is the average weight? (b) What is the median weight? (c) What is the mode of the weights?

Answer true or false.

17. A histogram is a particular type of bar graph.

18. A frequency polygon is a particular type of broken-line graph.

19. The mean and the median are the same if there are only two data points.

20. Every set of data has a mode.

9. _____

10. _____

11. _____

12. _____

13. _____

14. _____

15. _____

16.   (a) _____

       (b) _____

       (c) _____

17. _____

18. _____

19. _____

20. _____

CUMULATIVE REVIEW: CHAPTERS 1–7

Answers to these exercises are given on page 655.

Change each fraction in Exercises 1–3 to a percent.

1. $\dfrac{3}{10}$

2. $\dfrac{9}{4}$

3. $\dfrac{25}{200}$

Find the mean of the numbers in Exercises 4–6.

4. $25, 35, 45, 55$

5. $106, 94, 88, 111, 75$

6. $8.6, 9.5, 6.2, 8.3, 9.9, 10.3$

Solve each applied problem in Exercises 7–10.

7. **RECREATION** Tickets for a rock concert, each selling for $8, went on sale at 9:00 A.M. At 1:00 the tickets were all sold. There were 3200 tickets sold the first hour, 2950 the second, 2400 the third, and 1500 the fourth.
   (a) How many tickets were sold?
   (b) What were the total receipts?

8. **BUSINESS** A nursery has a stock consisting of 42 willows, 70 crabapples, 38 black pines, and 18 weeping birches. How many trees are in the inventory?

9. **SALARY** Patrick received a raise of 14%. What is his new salary if his former salary was $36,000?

10. **BUSINESS** A retailer bought a lamp for $35.00 and marked up the price 60%. What was the markup and what was the selling price?

Complete each statement in Exercises 11–13.

11. $0.86\,\text{m} = $ _____ ft

12. $20\dfrac{1}{4}\,\text{gal} = $ _____ L

13. $1650\,\text{g} = $ _____ lb

Solve each proportion in Exercises 14–16.

14. $\dfrac{a}{10} = \dfrac{3}{2}$

15. $\dfrac{6}{a} = \dfrac{10}{4}$

16. $\dfrac{8}{42} = \dfrac{a}{3}$

Perform the indicated operations in Exercises 17–25.

17. $1478 + 296 + 3075$

18. $828 - 493$

19. $1111 + 3269 + 5432 + 107$

20. $\dfrac{15}{4} - \dfrac{8}{3}$

21. $2\dfrac{3}{8} - 1\dfrac{3}{10}$

22. $\dfrac{1}{2} \div 2$

23. $4.20603 + 8.1084$

24. $83.005 - 62.078$

25. $0.001 \div 0.000002$

CHAPTER 1 WHOLE NUMBERS

1.1 EXERCISES

1. natural or counting numbers   2. using a number line   3. 7 is greater than 2   4. 999   5. 10   6. 9   7. yes

8. no   9. 0   10. There is no largest whole number.   11. 2   12. 5   13. 10   14. 13   15. <   16. >   17. <

18. <   19. >   20. <   21. $2000 + 400 + 70 + 9$ 22. $500 + 3$ 23. $200,000 + 7000 + 500 + 10 + 9$

24. $4,000,000 + 100,000 + 20,000 + 7000 + 900 + 80 + 2$ 25. $5,000,000 + 40$

26. $6,000,000,000 + 20,000,000 + 300,000 + 20 + 7$ 27. 523   28. 10,621   29. 305   30. 439,721

31. 6,004,025   32. 20,500,008   33. four thousand, two hundred nineteen   34. one hundred seven thousand,

five hundred eighty-six   35. ninety-three thousand, one hundred seventeen   36. thirteen million, two hundred

nineteen thousand, four hundred seventy-five   37. 6705   38. 24,159   39. 3,427,193,200   40. 825,000,001

41. 5 thousands   42. 5 ten millions   43. 5 ones   44. 5 billions   45. 3   46. 7   47. 6   48. 9

49. 1,584,000,000   50. $3,625,150,000,000   51. five trillion, eight hundred seventy-nine billion, one hundred

ninety-five million   52. one hundred thirty-nine million, seven hundred ten thousand   53. yes   54. yes

55. yes   56. a and b represent the same number   57. answers vary   58. answers vary

1.2 EXERCISES

1. $1 + 5 = 6$ 2. $5 + 0 = 5$ 3. 17   4. 2   5. 10   6. 6   7. 6   8. 8   9. 0   10. 7   11. 14   12. 10

13. 9   14. 11   15. 15   16. 7   17. 3   18. 9   19. 14   20. 4   21. 4   22. 12   23. 9   24. 7   25. 4

26. 15   27. 11   28. 13   29. 8   30. 16   31. 3   32. 13   33. 11   34. 12   35. 4   36. 14   37. 18

38. 10   39. 9   40. 10   41. 8   42. 9   43. 10   44. 8   45. 7   46. 5   47. 7   48. 13   49. 7   50. 9

51. 11   52. $x + z = 47$

53.

54.

55. 7 tons   56. 13 tons   57. 15 tons   58. the blue truck and the white truck   59. 47   60. 87   61. 55

62. 84   63. 135   64. 122   65. 577   66. 431   67. 800   68. 1012   69. 7560   70. 11,110   71. 7011

72. 4113   73. 16   74. 17   75. 149   76. 184   77. 1541   78. 44   79. 125   80. 100   81. 2129

82. 10,000   83. 23,812   84. 61   85. 602 mi   86. 1297   87. $697; $1062   88. $7 + 2$ 89. 0   90. $(9 + 5)$

91. commutative law of addition   92. b 93. associative law of addition   94. 11 ft 6 in   95. 12 ft 5 in

96. answers vary   97. The numbers to be added are 498 and 268 and the sum is 766.   98. answers vary

99. answers vary   100. answers vary   101. 8,225,500,000,486   102. $60,000 + 3000 + 200 + 40 + 7$

103. eight million, two hundred seventy-five thousand, one hundred eleven   104. (a) 5   (b) 2   (c) 8   (d) 6

105. (a) $2 < a$ (b) $6 > b$ (c) $a > 5$ (d) $b < a$

1.3 EXERCISES

1. 30   2. 70   3. 20   4. 630   5. 200   6. 300   7. 400   8. 100   9. 8600   10. 5000   11. 1000

12. 9000   13. 10,000   14. 23,000   15. 127,000   16. 170   17. 210   18. 1670   19. 12,670   20. 1900

1.4 EXERCISES

1. $9 - 8 = 1$ 2. $11 - 4 = 7$ 3. 2   4. 4   5. 1   6. 3   7. 3   8. 7   9. 7   10. 5   11. 6   12. 6

13.   3 14. 1   15. 4   16. 1   17. 3   18. 0   19. 3   20. 4   21. 4   22. 6   23. 8   24. 7   25. 8

26. 8   27. 6   28. 7   29. 9   30. 8   31. 4   32. 9   33. 7   34. 7   35. 9   36. 8   37. 3   38. 8   39. 5

40. 5   41. 5   42. 6   43. 2   44. 8   45. 4   46. 7   47. 8   48. 3   49. 9 50. 5   51. 9   52. $a - v = 21$

53. 5 kittens   54. $8   55. 42   56. 21   57. 618   58. 115   59. 32   60. 222 61. 85 62. 140   63. 2648

64. 1381   65. 1766   66. 14,001   67. correct   68. correct   69. incorrect (should be 46)   70. correct

71. incorrect (should be 3709)   72. 318   73. 432   74. 224   75. 4405   76. 4015 n   77. estimated increase: $200; actual increase: $216   78. estimated difference: 3000 brochures; exact difference: 2895 brochures

79. (a) 977   (b) 229   80. (a) 1236 mi   (b) 35,061 mi   81. 14   82. 4   83. 7   84. 3   85. n can be any whole number   86. there is no whole number n that makes this true   87. 1   88. 4   89. 6   90. 3

91. answers vary   92. (a) 13,430   (b) 13,400   (c) 13,000   93. Rounded to the nearest ten, the estimated sum is 200; given sum appears incorrect.   94. Rounded to the nearest hundred, the estimated sum is 2000; given sum appears correct.   95. Rounded to the nearest hundred, the estimated sum is 3500; given sum appears correct.

1.5 EXERCISES

1. multiplier or factor   2. multiplicand or factor   3. product   4. 3   5. 0   6. 7   7. 8   8. 0   9. 21

10. 0   11. 72   12. 20   13. 24   14. 18   15. 10   16. 18   17. 9   18. 2   19. 0   20. 5   21. 42

22. 24   23. 8   24. 35   25. 48   26. 14   27. 63   28. 15   29. 40   30. 18   31. 54   32. 0   33. 6

34. 7   35. 28   36. 42   37. 0   38. 32   39. 56   40. 0   41. 1   42. 36   43. 0   44. 12   45. 9

46. 0   47. 0   48. 45   49. 36   50. 6   51. 15   52. 8   53. 16   54. 72   55. 28   56. $9a$ 57. da

58. $2w$ 59. 7   60. 1   61. 4   62. 5   63. 9   64. 3   65. 50   66. 66   67. 72   68. 159   69. 279

70. 1509   71. 1581   72. 2296   73. 2100   74. 15,009   75. 37,300   76. 516   77. 726   78. 3285

79. 1480   80. 6400   81. 25,326   82. 35,238   83. 482,603   84. 810,000   85. 920 calories   86. 1825 days   87. (a) 1920 gallons   (b) 48,080 gallons   88. 1,200,000   89. 24,052,024   90. 35,000,000

91. answers vary   92. answers vary   93. 68,328,000 miles   94. 8   95. 10   96. 6   97. 16   98. 16

99. $2 \times (5 + 3) = 16$ and $(2 \times 5) + (2 \times 3) = 16$.

1.6 EXERCISES

1. commutative law   2. that number   3. $3 \times (5 \times 7)$ 4. $(4 \times 5) + (4 \times 7)$ 5. (a) 77   (b) 77   (c) because of the distributive law   6. (a) 135   (b) 135   (c) because of the associative law   7. (a) 88   (b) 88   (c) because of the commutative law   8. 0   9. 893   10. 5957   11. 75,755   12. 90   13. 420   14. 3870   15. 700   16. 7700

17. 42,700   18. 5000   19. 42,000   20. 78,000   21. 529,000   22. 4200   23. 320,000 24. 14,000

25. 180,000   26. 3,500,000   27. $20 \times 80 = 1600$; appears to be correct   28. $40 \times 400 = 16,000$; appears to be correct   29. $500 \times 800 = 400,000$; appears to be incorrect (correct product is 399,183)   30. $5x + 15$ 31. $4y + 28$

32. $36 + 9z$ 33. $6a + 2$ 34. $35z + 49$ 35. $18 + 12m$ 36. $30 \times 1000 = 30,000$ pages   37. $100 \times 300 = \$30,000$

38. $100 \times 40 = 4000$ fish   39. $10 \times 100 = 1000$ revolutions   40. $(ab)c$ 41. bc 42. $ab + ac$ 43. a; 0

44. 1993   45. yes; fairly close; about 1500 (using 800+700)   46. $100,000; $98,010   47. $70,000; $68,508

48. answers vary   49. answers vary   50. answers vary   51. 10,373   52. 70,173   53. 190,755

1.7 EXERCISES

1. (a) dividend   (b) divisor   (c) quotient   2. dividend   3. a 4. 0   5. 9   6. 7   7. 5   8. 4   9. 2

10. 5   11. 1   12. 3   13. 3   14. 9   15. 9   16. 3   17. 2   18. 1   19. 0   20. 2   21. 1   22. 4

23. 7   24. 6   25. 1   26. 2   27. 8   28. 9   29. 8   30. 5   31. 6   32. 8   33. 0   34. 9   35. 6

36. 8   37. 8   38. 9   39. 4   40. 0   41. 6   42. 9   43. 0   44. 1   45. 3   46. 2   47. 6   48. 7

49. 7   50. 3   51. $7 \div y$ or $\frac{7}{y}$ or $y\overline{)7}$ 52. $p \div 8$ or $\frac{p}{8}$ or $8\overline{)p}$ 53. $v \div 9$ or $\frac{v}{9}$ or $9\overline{)v}$ 54. $a \div 5 = 7$ or $\frac{a}{5} = 7$ or $5\overline{)a}^{\,7}$

55. 23   56. 223   57. 102   58. 29   59. 18   60. 146   61. 75   62. 91   63. 181   64. 109   65. 1019

66. 3027   67. 709   68. 21   69. 47   70. Q: 9; R: 4 [$(9 \times 7) + 4 = 63 + 4 = 67$]   71. Q: 119; R: 0

[$(119 \times 6) + 0 = 714 + 0 = 714$]   72. Q: 17; R: 23 [$(17 \times 42) + 23 = 714 + 23 = 737$]

73. Q: 23; R: 18 [$(23 \times 466) + 18 = 10{,}718 + 18 = 10{,}736$]   74. approximate cost: $180 (using $1800 \div 10$); exact cost:

$198 (using $1782 \div 9$)   75. approximate number: 200 calories (using $4000 \div 20$); exact number: 191 calories

(using $4011 \div 21$)   76. 30   77. 3   78. 35   79. 7   80. 1   81. 0   82. no   83. division is not commutative

84. answers vary   85. answers vary   86. answers vary   87. 15,000   88. 540,000   89. 80,000

90. $90 \times 20 = 1800$; appears to be correct   91. $700 \times 100 = 70{,}000$; appears to be incorrect (correct product is 75,786)

1.8 EXERCISES

1. 7471   2. 1201   3. 54 ft   4. 132 in   5. 570   6. 39 shots   7. Castle Rock to Gunsight Butte is greater by

1 mi.   8. 26 mi   9. 73 points   10. 20 fouls   11. 2507 ft   12. 2576 mi   13. $564   14. $26   15. The

route through Butte is 251 mi shorter than through Reno and Portland.   16. 40 mi   17. 643 gallons

18. Thursday: $940; Saturday: $2030   19. 348 mi   20. $445   21. (a) 1825 days   (b) 8760 hours   (c) 43,800

hours   22. (a) 364 sq m   (b) 80 m   23. (a) 3150 tickets   (b) $22,050   24. $916   25. $120   26. $990

27. $441   28. (a) $270   (b) $140   (c) $440   (d) $60   (e) $20   (f) $56   (g) $986   29. (a) 360 pay-

ments (b) $187,200   30. (a) 18,250 seats   (b) $91,250   31. 256 minutes   32. 23 mpg   33. 57 mixers; $3 left

34. The 12-lb bag at 31¢ per lb is a better buy than the 9-lb bag at 32¢ per lb.   35. 22   36. 106   37. 1764 ft

38. 87 gallons   39. $50   40. 17 samples; 1 cubic centimeter   41. 11 cans (8 ounces will be left over)   42. 480

miles; 8 inches   43. $n = 256$ 44. $n = 3$ 45. answers vary   46. answers vary   47. Q:235; R:0   48. Q:209;

R:17   49. Q:416; R:0   50. 2, 4, 6, 8, 10, 12, 14   51. 3, 6, 9, 12, 15, 18

1.9 EXERCISES

1. true   2. false (prime number)   3. true   4. 1, 2, 3, 6, 9, 18   5. 1, 2, 4, 7, 14, 28   6. 1, 2, 4, 7, 8, 14, 28, 56

7. 0, 4, 8, 12, 16, 20, 24, 28, 32, 36   8. 0, 7, 14, 21, 28, 35, 42, 49, 56, 63   9. 0, 100, 200, 300, 400, 500, 600,

700, 800, 900   10. $55 = 5 \cdot 11$ 11. $65 = 5 \cdot 13$ 12. $78 = 2 \cdot 3 \cdot 13$ 13. $169 = 13 \cdot 13$ 14. $294 = 2 \cdot 3 \cdot 7 \cdot 7$

15. $429 = 3 \cdot 11 \cdot 13$ 16. $693 = 3 \cdot 3 \cdot 7 \cdot 11$ 17. $1300 = 2 \cdot 2 \cdot 5 \cdot 5 \cdot 13$ 18. $5100 = 2 \cdot 2 \cdot 3 \cdot 5 \cdot 5 \cdot 17$ 19. prime

20. composite   21. prime   22. composite   23. composite   24. prime   25. 120, 126, 240, 130, 104, 70, 72,

110, 88   26. 120, 126, 240, 147, 135, 72, 4125   27. 120, 240, 130, 70, 135, 110, 4125   28. 120, 240, 130, 70,

110   29. (a) exponent   (b) base   (c) fourth   30. the square of the number   31. multiplication   32. 256

33. 10,000   34. 512   35. 3^4 36. 9^5 37. 4^6 38. $2^2 \cdot 3^2 \cdot 7$ 39. $2 \cdot 3^3 \cdot 7^2$ 40. $2^4 \cdot 5^2 \cdot 11$ 41. 594

42. 11,025   43. 63,375   44. 7   45. 10   46. 11   47. 2401   48. 10,000   49. 14,641   50. 4   51. 1

52. 13   53. 7   54. 1   55. 1   56. 9   57. 0   58. 9   59. 1 60. 18   61. 13   62. 0   63. 29   64. 5

65. 25   66. 1   67. 10   68. 9   69. 14   70. 0   71. 441   72. 147   73. 441   74. 100   75. 58   76. 200

77. $2 \cdot 3 \cdot 5 \cdot 5 \cdot 7 \cdot 13$ 78. 9   79. answers vary   80. answers vary   81. answers vary   82. answers vary

83. answers vary   84. Burford should have divided before subtracting and then adding. The correct answer is 12.

85. 107 mi   86. $47 per month   87. $ 2080   88. (a) 144   (b) $28,800   89. 35 miles per inch   90. 7 bills

with $14 in change   91. 1020   92. (a) $1080   (b) $675   (c) $1755   93. 2680 pounds

CHAPTER 1 REVIEW EXERCISES

1. numeral   2. 1, 2, 3, 4, 5   3. 0, 1, 2, 3, 4   4. 0, 1, 2, 3, 4, 5, 6, 7, 8, 9   5. because the value of each digit is

determined by its place or position in the numeral   6. 3   7. 9   8. <   9. >   10. <   11. <

12. $10,000,000 + 3,000,000 + 200,000 + 40,000 + 7000 + 100 + 60 + 5$ 13. 403,405   14. twenty-seven million, four

hundred five thousand, thirty-six   15. 5   16. 0   17. 3   18. 8   19. (a) addends   (b) sum   (c) plus sign

20. $4 + 5$ 21. the given number   22. 625   23. 14,443   24. 10,013   25. $9 + x$ 26. $y + 20$ 27. because *two*

numbers are added at a time   28. associative law of addition   29. 70   30. 290   31. 4180   32. 500   33. 100

34. 2600   35. 7000   36. 1000   37. 13,000   38. 4850   39. 4800   40. estimated total: $770,000; exact total:

$771,510   41. (a) minuend   (b) subtrahend   (c) difference   (d) minus sign   42. 267   43. 265   44. 4129

45. $7 - z$ 46. 11   47. (a) multiplier (or factor)   (b) multiplicand (or factor)   (c) product 48. 4   49. 30,786

50. 22,413   51. 300,812   52. 2,847,495   53. 19,479,000   54. $6m$ 55. 10   56. commutative law

57. $6w + 21$ 58. $90 \cdot 30 = 2700$; appears to be correct   59. $300 \cdot 500 = 150,000$; appears to be incorrect (correct

product is 157,491)   60. (a) dividend   (b) divisor   (c) quotient   61. $4 \times 3 = 12$ 62. 1   63. 5   64. 0   65. undefined

66. Q:933; R:0   67. Q:26; R:30   68. $y \div 5 \text{ or } \frac{y}{5} \text{ or } 5)\overline{y}$ 69. $3 \div w \text{ or } \frac{3}{w} \text{ or } w)\overline{3}$ 70. $46,261   71. $457   72. $1164

73. $7245   74. $180   75. $112   76. 1835m   77. $1116   78. The 13-oz box for 78¢ is a better buy at 6¢ per

ounce than the 12-oz box for 84¢ at 7¢ per ounce.   79. (a) $11,515   (b) $11,560   c) $23,075   80. prime   81. compos-

ite   82. 1   83. even   84. one (only the number 2)   85. 1, 3, 5, 7, 15, 21, 35, 105   86. 0, 13, 26, 39, 52

87. $112 = 2 \cdot 2 \cdot 2 \cdot 2 \cdot 7$ 88. $1089 = 3 \cdot 3 \cdot 11 \cdot 11$ 89. $2730 = 2 \cdot 3 \cdot 5 \cdot 7 \cdot 13$ 90. 140, 150   91. 273, 105, 150

92. 140, 105, 150   93. 140, 150   94. no   95. 81   96. 3   97. $6 \cdot 6 \cdot 6 = 216$ 98. 5^6 99. 968

100. $2^3 \cdot 5^3 \cdot 11$ 101. 9   102. 12   103. 4   104. 3   105. 2   106. 9   107. 400   108. 80   109. 94

110. 35   111. 29   112. 100   113. approximate number: 20 groups; exact number: 19 groups   114. estimated

number: 110,000 people; exact number: 120,890 people   115. 498   116. 1046   117. Q:28; R:0   118. 27,705   119. 28

120. 0   121. 1   122. 7   123. 5   124. 9   125. 72   126. 1296   127. 256   128. 4   129. yes   130. $2 \cdot 3 \cdot 7 \cdot 7 \cdot 11$

131. commutative law of addition   132. additive identity   133. (a) 4350   (b) 4400   (c) 4000   134. 4500

135. $9 \div n \text{ or } \frac{9}{n} \text{ or } n)\overline{9}$ 136. $8 + x$ 137. $11 - w$ 138. $2y$ 139. 765 m²; 124 m   140. 2   141. >   142. 2000

143. $90 \cdot 50 = 4500$; appears to be correct   144. 350,000   145. (a) $449   (b) $2426   146. (a) 4865 kilowatt-

hours   (b) 3585 kilowatt-hours   147. estimated increase: $200; actual increase: $198   148. estimated total: 90

points; actual total: 91 points   149. 1745 seniors   150. 812 cartons

CHAPTER 1 TEST

1. false   2. associative law   3. <   4. 380,407   5. ten thousands   6. 8   7. 515   8. 9247   9. $30 + w$ 10. 8900

11. $500   12. 349   13. 207   14. $5 - m$ 15. 1300 gallons   16. 1316   17. 843,733   18. 5   19. 89,500 20.

$550,000   21. Q:236; R:0   22. Q:154; R:14   23. 2   24. $5   25. 1   26. 0   27. a 28. undefined   29. when the sum

of its digits is divisible by 3   30. $2 \cdot 5 \cdot 5 \cdot 7$ or $2 \cdot 5^2 \cdot 7$ 31. 5   32. 625   33. 9   34. 8   35. 216   36. 54

37. $622   38. $600   39. 8 inches   40. 1674 ft   41. no

CHAPTER 2 MULTIPLYING AND DIVIDING FRACTIONS

2.1 EXERCISES

1. numerator: 5; denominator: 7   2. numerator: 11; denominator: 4   3. numerator: 0; denominator: 8

4. numerator: 12; denominator: 12   5. $\frac{1}{4}$ 6. $\frac{1}{3}$ 7. $\frac{2}{5}$ 8. $\frac{2}{4}$ 9. $\frac{3}{8}$ 10. $\frac{3}{3}$ 11. $\frac{1}{2}$ 12. $\frac{3}{12}$

13. $\frac{5}{16}$ 14. $\frac{5}{4}$ 15. $\frac{9}{6}$ 16. $\frac{11}{8}$ 17. $\frac{5}{3}$ 18. 4   19. (a) $\frac{47}{50}$ (b) $\frac{3}{50}$ 20. $\frac{4}{9}$ 21. (a) $\frac{7}{6}$ (b) $\frac{5}{6}$

22. (a) $\frac{30}{300}$ (b) $\frac{75}{300}$ (c) $\frac{40}{300}$ (d) $\frac{155}{300}$ 23. 4   24. 0   25. 1   26. 2   27. proper   28. improper

29. improper   30. answer vary   31. $\frac{1}{2}$ 32. $\frac{1}{2}$ 33. $\frac{1}{3}$ 34. $\frac{5}{2}$

2.2 EXERCISES

1. $\frac{1}{4} = \frac{2}{8} = \frac{4}{16}$ 2. $\frac{2}{3} = \frac{4}{6} = \frac{6}{9}$ 3. $9 \cdot 4 = 12 \cdot 3$, so $\frac{9}{12} = \frac{3}{4}$ 4. $2 \cdot 7 \neq 5 \cdot 3$; so $\frac{2}{5} \neq \frac{3}{7}$ 5. $6 \cdot 8 = 16 \cdot 3$; so

$\frac{6}{16} = \frac{3}{8}$ 6. $6 \cdot 2 \neq 8 \cdot 3$; so $\frac{6}{8} \neq \frac{3}{2}$ 7. $12 \cdot 11 \neq 32 \cdot 4$; so $\frac{12}{32} \neq \frac{4}{11}$ 8. $8 \cdot 108 = 9 \cdot 96$; so $\frac{8}{9} = \frac{96}{108}$ 9. 9

10. 9   11. 11   12. 10   13. 3   14. 1   15. 10   16. 2   17. 1   18. 14   19. 27   20. 15   21. 5

22. 6   23. 7   24. $\frac{2}{5}$ 25. $\frac{3}{2}$ 26. $\frac{1}{3}$ 27. $\frac{2}{1}$ or 2   28. $\frac{3}{4}$ 29. $\frac{2}{5}$ 30. $\frac{11}{2}$ 31. $\frac{2}{1}$ or 2   32. $\frac{7}{3}$

33. Each lake had $\frac{2}{27}$ of the samples showing toxins.   34. $\frac{21}{77}$ and $\frac{18}{66}$ are the same fractional parts (both equal $\frac{3}{11}$

reduced to lowest terms).   35. $\frac{5}{4}$ 36. $\frac{1}{2}$ 37. $\frac{64}{189}$ 38. 12   39. $\frac{1}{3a^4}$ 40. $\frac{a}{2b^2}$ 41. answers vary

42. The rule for building fractions excludes 0, and $\frac{0}{0}$ is not defined.   43. $\frac{4}{6}$ (or $\frac{2}{3}$ reduced)   44. $\frac{4}{8}$ (or $\frac{1}{2}$

reduced)   45. 1   46. 0   47. 20   48. 7

2.3 EXERCISES

1. true   2. true   3. true   4. false (associative law)   5. false (multiplicative identity)   6. true   7. $\frac{2}{27}$

8. $\frac{2}{5}$ 9. $\frac{2}{9}$ 10. 4   11. $\frac{2}{3}$ 12. 24   13. 1   14. $\frac{2}{5}$ 15. $\frac{2}{7}$ 16. 2   17. 0   18. 14   19. $\frac{1}{10}$

20. $\frac{2}{7}$ 21. $\frac{5}{12}$ 22. $\frac{8}{9}$ 23. 7   24. 8   25. $\frac{9}{16}$ 26. $\frac{1}{81}$ 27. $\frac{49}{9}$ 28. $\frac{3}{4}$ 29. $\frac{1}{7}$ 30. $\frac{12}{5}$ 31. $\frac{1}{2}$

sq km   32. 36 mi   33. $135   34. $529   35. $\frac{a}{4}$ 36. $\frac{6a}{5b^2}$ 37. $\frac{a^5}{9b^2}$ 38. 380 pounds   39. The top

sections are each $\frac{1}{4}$ with 60 hours. The bottom sections are each $\frac{1}{6}$ with 40 hours.   40. $4 \cdot 6 \neq 5 \cdot 5$; so $\frac{4}{5} \neq \frac{5}{6}$

41. $4 \cdot 12 = 16 \cdot 3$; so $\frac{4}{16} = \frac{3}{12}$ 42. $9 \cdot 4 \neq 5 \cdot 7$; so $\frac{9}{5} \neq \frac{7}{4}$ 43. $\frac{2}{3}$ 44. $\frac{5}{7}$ 45. $\frac{3}{2}$ 46. 8   47. 2   48. 3

2.4 EXERCISES

1. $\frac{3}{2}$ 2. $\frac{5}{4}$ 3. 7   4. $\frac{1}{3}$ 5. 0 has no reciprocal   6. $\frac{2}{5}$ 7. 6   8. $\frac{3}{2}$ 9. $\frac{4}{3}$ 10. $\frac{3}{2}$ 11. $\frac{5}{2}$

12. $\frac{10}{3}$ 13. $\frac{2}{11}$ 14. $\frac{1}{9}$ 15. 1   16. $\frac{1}{77}$ 17. $\frac{16}{21}$ 18. 48   19. 6   20. 15   21. 14   22. $\frac{45}{2}$

23. $\frac{16}{9}$ 24. 55   25. 7   26. $\frac{12}{5}$ 27. 15 pieces   28. 48 pillows   29. 10 samples   30. 420 miles

31. $\frac{a}{77}$ 32. $\frac{16x}{21y^2}$ 33. $20b^2$ 34. You need only show one example of the law failing. $1 \div 2 \neq 2 \div 1$ and

$(4 \div 2) \div 2 = 1 \neq 4 = 4 \div (2 \div 2)$ 35. $\frac{11}{8}$ 36. $\frac{7}{13}$ 37. 6   38. $\frac{4}{11}$ 39. $\frac{19}{12}$ 40. $\frac{15}{8}$ 41. $16,000

42. $1500 in bonds; $5000 in the mutual fund   43. 48 points   44. $\frac{1}{6}$ gallon

2.5 EXERCISES

1. $1\frac{2}{5}$　　2. $5\frac{2}{3}$　　3. $2\frac{7}{8}$　　4. $7\frac{1}{2}$　　5. $7\frac{1}{10}$　　6. $9\frac{1}{2}$　　7. $33\frac{3}{4}$　　8. $28\frac{5}{9}$　　9. $12\frac{10}{11}$　　10. $\frac{10}{3}$　　11. $\frac{23}{5}$

12. $\frac{57}{8}$　　13. $\frac{43}{4}$　　14. $\frac{106}{11}$　　15. $\frac{65}{3}$　　16. $\frac{47}{8}$　　17. $\frac{327}{10}$　　18. $\frac{200}{3}$　　19. $14\frac{14}{15}$　　20. 12　　21. $51\frac{1}{3}$

22. $74\frac{4}{5}$　　23. $12\frac{1}{4}$　　24. $5\frac{19}{25}$　　25. $10\frac{1}{2}$　　26. 195　　27. $17\frac{1}{4}$　　28. $1\frac{4}{15}$　　29. $2\frac{11}{74}$　　30. $\frac{5}{13}$　　31.

$2\frac{1}{16}$　　32. $\frac{1}{6}$　　33. 34　　34. $5\frac{4}{7}$　　35. $\frac{5}{48}$　　36. $18\frac{2}{3}$　　37. 1842 pounds　　38. $378\frac{1}{5}$ gallons　　39. $32\frac{13}{16}$ mp

40. 8 uniforms　　41. $208\frac{1}{3}$ lb　42. 56 square yards　　43. $\frac{2a+1}{2}$　　44. $2a+1$　　45. The distributive law shows

four products.　46. $\frac{1}{3}$　　47. $\frac{1}{26}$　　48. 4　　49. 896 gallons　　50. 40 steaks　　51. 32 pieces　　52. 39 mi

✳ 2.6 EXERCISES

1. 360 gallons　　2. 160 gallons　　3. Huntsville: 2500; Lufkin: 1000　　4. $\frac{22}{35}$　　5. $46\frac{2}{5}$ miles　　6. $1\frac{2}{3}$ cups

7. $2\frac{1}{2}$ cups, $\frac{5}{12}$ cup　　8. 30 runs　　9. 7560 sq yd of turf at a cost of $113,400　　10. food: $3600; housing: $4500;

clothing: $1800; taxes: $6750　11. $3\frac{1}{3}$ minutes　　12. 210 gallons　　13. $7\frac{13}{90}$ minutes　　14. 220 revolutions

15. $\frac{3}{4}a = \frac{1}{12}$　　16. $ab = c$　　17. $\frac{a}{5}{6} = \frac{3}{25}$　　18. $\frac{a}{b} = c$　　19. Write the related division equation $x = \frac{b}{a}$.　　20. $7\frac{3}{5}$

21. $1\frac{18}{77}$　　22. $44\frac{4}{9}$　　23. 72　　24. $\frac{24}{25}$　　25. $2\frac{2}{11}$

CHAPTER 2 REVIEW EXERCISES

1. 9　　2. improper　　3. improper　　4. 0　　5. $\frac{2}{4}$ or $\frac{1}{2}$　　6. $\frac{1}{3}$　　7. $\frac{4}{9}$　　8. $\frac{3}{2}$　　9. $\frac{11}{14}$　　10. 1

11. undefined　　12. 0　　13. $\frac{8}{11} \neq \frac{5}{7}$　　14. $\frac{3}{12} = \frac{5}{20}$　　15. 15　　16. 3　　17. 1　　18. $\frac{2}{3}$　　19. $\frac{5}{4}$　　20. $\frac{3}{2}$

21. multiplication　　22. commutative law　　23. $\frac{12}{7}$ or $1\frac{5}{7}$　　24. $\frac{3}{5}$　　25. $\frac{2}{7}$　　26. $\frac{49}{36}$　　27. $\frac{11}{5}$　　28. 117

29. $\frac{7}{13}$　　30. 0　　31. $\frac{3}{2}$　　32. 16　　33. $\frac{1}{9}$　　34. 35　　35. $\frac{18}{25}$　　36. 780 gallons　　37. mixed number

38. addition　　39. $31\frac{3}{4}$　　40. $22\frac{1}{11}$　　41. $48\frac{1}{2}$　　42. $\frac{48}{13}$　　43. $\frac{106}{5}$　　44. $\frac{50}{3}$　　45. $14\frac{3}{32}$　　46. $1\frac{2}{3}$

47. $34\frac{1}{2}$　　48. 391　　49. $1\frac{14}{31}$　　50. $1\frac{1}{2}$　　51. 837　　52. 40 minutes　　53. 56 mi　　54. $124\frac{5}{16}$ dollars

55. 279 gallons　　56. 62 gallons　　57. $31\frac{1}{2}$ revolutions　　58. $34\frac{10}{11}$ mpg　　59. 16　　60. $\frac{5}{3}$　　61. $\frac{4}{49}$　　62. 6

63. $\frac{1}{6}$　　64. 20　　65. $56\frac{2}{3}$　　66. $2\frac{5}{6}$　　67. 15　　68. 5　　69. $22\frac{1}{2}$ mpg　　70. $287\frac{1}{2}$ mi　　71. 1　　72. 0

73. $\frac{5}{30} = \frac{2}{12}$　　74. $\frac{11}{9} \neq \frac{21}{18}$　　75. $\frac{45}{64}$　　76. $\frac{8}{3}$　　77. $\frac{1}{2}$　　78. $\frac{2}{3}$　　79. $\frac{1}{4}$　　80. $\frac{5}{2}$

CHAPTER 2 TEST

1. proper　　2. associative law　　3. $\frac{1}{6}$　　4. $\frac{9}{2} = \frac{36}{8}$　　5. 21　　6. 33　　7. $\frac{7}{3}$　　8. $\frac{12}{13}$　　9. $\frac{1}{28}$　　10. $\frac{3}{11}$

11. 15　　12. $\frac{9}{64}$　　13. $\frac{37}{12}$　　14. $\frac{55}{2}$ or $27\frac{1}{2}$　　15. $2\frac{2}{5}$　　16. $\frac{79}{11}$　　17. $22\frac{1}{10}$　　18. $\frac{66}{83}$　　19. 315　　20. $2\frac{1}{7}$

21. $20\frac{1}{4}$ gallons　22. 207 miles　　23. proper　　24. $3 \div 2 = \frac{3}{2} \neq \frac{2}{3} = 2 \div 3$　　25. Neither. It is undefined.

Cumulative Review: Chapters 1–2

1. 45　　2. 2　　3. 24　　4. incorrect (should be 127)　　5. correct　　6. correct　　7. $40,000 + 1000 + 70 + 5$

8. 10,016,205　　9. $\frac{4}{5}$　　10. $\frac{5}{7}$　　11. $\frac{36}{31}$　　12. yes　　13. 12,550　　14. At 2¢ per oz, the 78-oz box is a better buy

than the 43-oz box at 3¢ per oz.　　15. 2　　16. 0　　17. $\frac{52}{9}$　　18. 1257　　19. 109　　20. 837　　21. 3　　22. $\frac{7}{24}$

23. 2　　24. $34\frac{8}{13}$ mpg　25. $a - 17$　　26. $30 - a$　　27. 21　　28. $\frac{1}{3}$

CHAPTER 3 ADDING AND SUBTRACTING FRACTIONS

3.1 EXERCISES

1. $\frac{5}{7}$ 2. $\frac{3}{2}$ 3. $\frac{7}{6}$ 4. 1   5. 6   6. $\frac{5}{4}$ 7. $\frac{15}{8}$ 8. $\frac{9}{7}$ 9. 2   10. $\frac{1}{3}$ 11. $\frac{6}{11}$ 12. $\frac{1}{3}$ 13. $\frac{3}{5}$

14. $\frac{2}{7}$ 15. $\frac{7}{9}$ 16. $\frac{6}{13}$ 17. $\frac{2}{5}$ 18. $\frac{1}{2}$ 19. 7   20. $\frac{9}{10}$ 21. 0   22. $1\frac{4}{15}$ mi   23. $\frac{2}{5}$ of the field

24. $\frac{4}{3}$ gallons   25. $\frac{3}{12} = \frac{1}{4}$ gallon of white; $\frac{21}{12} = \frac{7}{4}$ gallons of yellow; and $\frac{24}{12} = 2$ gallons of red add up to $\frac{48}{12} = 4$

gallons of paint.   26. $\frac{27}{a}$ 27. $\frac{5}{a}$ 28. He should not add denominators. The actual sum is 1, not $\frac{1}{2}$.   29. $4\frac{3}{5}$

30. $1\frac{1}{2}$ 31. $3\frac{2}{3}$ 32. 10   33. $6\frac{2}{5}$ 34. $\frac{1}{3}$

3.2 EXERCISES

1. 72   2. 45   3. 60   4. 12   5. 60   6. 72   7. 180   8. 420   9. 117   10. 70   11. 242   12. 36

13. 1716   14. 360   15. 1210   16. 180   17. 252   18. 150   19. 270   20. 84   21. 900

22. LCM=24; $\frac{1}{8} = \frac{3}{24}$; $\frac{7}{12} = \frac{14}{24}$ 23. LCM=6; $\frac{2}{3} = \frac{4}{6}$; $\frac{5}{6} = \frac{5}{6}$ 24. LCM=84; $\frac{5}{28} = \frac{15}{84}$; $\frac{11}{42} = \frac{22}{84}$ 25. LCM=75;

$\frac{18}{25} = \frac{54}{75}$; $\frac{1}{15} = \frac{5}{75}$; $\frac{1}{3} = \frac{25}{75}$ 26. LCM=72; $\frac{3}{8} = \frac{27}{72}$; $\frac{2}{9} = \frac{16}{72}$; $\frac{5}{12} = \frac{30}{72}$ 27. LCM=1000; $\frac{3}{10} = \frac{300}{1000}$; $\frac{7}{100} = \frac{70}{1000}$; $\frac{19}{1000} = \frac{19}{1000}$

28. 84 months   29. 504 in   30. n 31. mn 32. mn 33. answers vary   34. $\frac{3}{4}$ 35. $\frac{7}{11}$ 36. 1   37. $\frac{2}{3}$

38. $\frac{2}{5}$ 39. 1   40. (a) up $\frac{19}{32}$ (b) $\frac{53}{32}$

3.3 EXERCISES

1. $\frac{7}{6}$ 2. $\frac{7}{4}$ 3. $\frac{43}{60}$ 4. $\frac{41}{30}$ 5. $\frac{23}{36}$ 6. $\frac{61}{105}$ 7. $\frac{41}{140}$ 8. $\frac{24}{5}$ 9. $\frac{31}{8}$ 10. $\frac{7}{6}$ 11. $\frac{23}{30}$ 12. $\frac{47}{75}$

13. $\frac{1}{8}$ 14. $\frac{1}{12}$ 15. $\frac{27}{77}$ 16. $\frac{2}{21}$ 17. $\frac{16}{5}$ 18. $\frac{1}{9}$ 19. $\frac{1}{12}$ 20. $\frac{41}{48}$ 21. $\frac{4}{15}$ 22. $\frac{1}{2}$ 23. $\frac{23}{60}$

24. $\frac{5}{12}$ 25. $\frac{19}{12}$ 26. $\frac{49}{30}$ 27. $\frac{1}{5}$ 28. $\frac{19}{40}$ 29. $\frac{11}{30}$ 30. $\frac{10}{21}$ 31. $\frac{257}{120}$ gallons   32. $\frac{17}{120}$ of a gallon

33. $\frac{3b+2a}{ab}$ 34. $\frac{5-2a}{ab}$ 35. $a + b = b + a$ 36. answers very   37. 945   38. 90   39. 84   40. $22\frac{1}{3}$

41. $\frac{22}{35}$ 42. $1\frac{3}{11}$

3.4 EXERCISES

1. $7\frac{7}{8}$ 2. $11\frac{11}{30}$ 3. $8\frac{7}{30}$ 4. $6\frac{11}{21}$ 5. $5\frac{43}{120}$ 6. $19\frac{7}{8}$ 7. $981\frac{28}{33}$ 8. $134\frac{17}{48}$ 9. $6\frac{2}{15}$ 10. $\frac{5}{8}$

11. $1\frac{7}{45}$ 12. $4\frac{7}{12}$ 13. $9\frac{6}{11}$ 14. $10\frac{7}{16}$ 15. $169\frac{1}{2}$ 16. $9\frac{61}{66}$ 17. 22   18. $11\frac{14}{15}$ 19. $15\frac{2}{3}$ 20. $9\frac{23}{36}$

21. $9\frac{1}{2}$ m   22. $31\frac{1}{20}$ ft   23. $47\frac{9}{14}$ cm   24. $672\frac{1}{6}$ in   25. $21\frac{23}{24}$ mi   26. $5\frac{11}{24}$ days   27. $371\frac{1}{12}$ acres

28. $15\frac{5}{8}$ gallons   29. 1   30. $3\frac{1}{2}$ 31. $8\frac{1}{8}$ 32. $17\frac{1}{10}$ 33. $115\frac{1}{2}$ 34. $83\frac{11}{14}$ 35. answers very   36. $1\frac{1}{10}$

37. $\frac{41}{42}$ 38. $\frac{2}{75}$ 39. $\frac{5}{42}$ 40. >   41. <   42. <   43. >

3.5 EXERCISES

1. $\frac{11}{15}$ 2. $\frac{4}{5}$ 3. $\frac{5}{6}$ 4. $1\frac{1}{2}$ 5. $\frac{9}{16}$ 6. $\frac{3}{32}$ 7. $\frac{7}{16}$ 8. $\frac{2}{5}$ 9. 0   10. 4   11. $\frac{7}{10}$ 12. $\frac{1}{2}$

13. $\frac{4}{15} > \frac{1}{4}$ 14. $\frac{29}{21} < \frac{25}{18}$ 15. $\frac{4}{6} > \frac{27}{42}$ 16. $\frac{35}{11} > \frac{41}{13}$ 17. $\frac{17}{30} > \frac{21}{40}$ 18. $\frac{19}{8} > \frac{81}{36}$ 19. true   20. false

21. true   22. false   23. false   24. false   25. 77°   26. $\frac{1}{6}$ of an inch more in May   27. 1988   28. 1975

29. 1985   30. cargo   31. $\frac{19}{60}$ 32. $7\frac{1}{14}$ 33. $a < c$ 34. $b > a$ 35. yes   36. answers vary   37. $5\frac{5}{6}$

38. $\frac{13}{14}$ 39. $617\frac{7}{9}$ 40. $16\frac{1}{2}$ 41. $12\frac{5}{8}$ 42. $\frac{1}{2}$ 43. $508\frac{37}{40}$ 44. $16\frac{1}{12}$

3.6 EXERCISES

1. $\frac{4}{15}$ of the accounts   2. $2\frac{29}{30}$ miles   3. $21\frac{19}{24}$ tons   4. $8\frac{5}{24}$ tons   5. 180 cm   6. $\frac{13}{48}$ inches more in June

7. $11\frac{11}{20}$ miles   8. $99\frac{3}{20}$ ft   9. $35\frac{13}{40}$ days   10. $1413   11. $\frac{11}{120}$ mi farther on Saturday   12. $122\frac{7}{8}$

13. $\frac{3}{20}$ or $\frac{7}{50}$ (two possibl estimates)   14. $\frac{7}{33}$ 15. $\frac{10}{9}$ 16. $\frac{17}{14}$ 17. $7\frac{1}{6}$ a units   18. $3\frac{7}{20}$ a units

19. answers vary   20. $\frac{1}{3}$ 21. $\frac{11}{16}$ 22. $\frac{2}{3}$ 23. false   24. true   25. true

REVIEW EXERCISES

1. $\frac{6}{11}$ 2. $\frac{8}{9}$ 3. $\frac{1}{5}$ 4. $\frac{1}{7}$ 5. $\frac{3}{2}$ or $1\frac{1}{2}$ 6. 0   7. 40   8. 60   9. 105   10. 90   11. 840   12. 252

13. $\frac{7}{12}$ 14. $\frac{34}{9}$ or $3\frac{7}{9}$ 15. $\frac{17}{42}$ 16. $\frac{5}{3}$ or $1\frac{2}{3}$ 17. $\frac{19}{15}$ or $1\frac{4}{15}$ 18. $\frac{20}{21}$ 19. $9\frac{7}{8}$ 20. $1\frac{13}{21}$ 21. $15\frac{11}{40}$

22. $4\frac{25}{42}$ 23. $590\frac{19}{44}$ 24. $205\frac{7}{8}$ 25. $\frac{1}{5}$ 26. $\frac{7}{9}$ 27. 0   28. $\frac{2}{3}$ 29. $\frac{1}{72}$ 30. $\frac{13}{50}$ 31. $\frac{1}{4}$ is larger

32. $\frac{8}{11}$ is larger   33. $\frac{47}{11}$ is larger   34. false   35. true   36. true   37. 18 ft   38. $22\frac{5}{8}$ inches

39. $1\frac{1}{3}$ weeks   40. $\frac{1}{3}$ mi more the first week   41. 176   42. 315   43. 168   44. >   45. <   46. <

47. $11\frac{1}{6}$ 48. $3\frac{1}{6}$ 49. $28\frac{13}{30}$ 50. $\frac{10}{11}$ 51. $\frac{65}{66}$ 52. $\frac{9}{16}$ 53. $\frac{2}{11}$ 54. $\frac{3}{22}$ 55. $\frac{23}{88}$ 56. $\frac{4}{1}$

CHAPTER 3 TEST

1. 210   2. 120   3. $\frac{1}{3}$ 4. $\frac{2}{3}$ 5. $\frac{23}{24}$ 6. $\frac{17}{60}$ 7. $\frac{9}{7}$ or $1\frac{2}{7}$ 8. $\frac{7}{24}$ 9. $9\frac{8}{9}$ 10. $8\frac{13}{15}$ 11. $17\frac{2}{3}$

12. $8\frac{5}{8}$ 13. $8\frac{1}{6}$ 14. $\frac{1}{90}$ 15. true   16. false   17. $80\frac{11}{40}$ lb   18. $3\frac{11}{12}$ hours   19. $\frac{1}{2}$ 20. $\frac{0}{1}$

21. No. $4\frac{1}{2}$ means $4+\frac{1}{2}$.   22. $\left(\frac{1}{2}-\frac{1}{2}\right)\cdot\frac{1}{4}+\frac{1}{3}$

CUMULATIVE REVIEW: CHAPTERS 1–3

1. 2   2. $\frac{1}{5}$ 3. $\frac{3}{8}$ 4. 1406   5. 409   6. 11,450   7. $2\frac{2}{3}$ 8. $\frac{2}{3}$ 9. $4\frac{1}{6}$ 10. 4   11. $\frac{5}{6}$ 12. $\frac{7}{16}$

13. 96 milliliters   14. The 8-lb bag at 38¢ per lb is a better buy than the 5-lb bag at 40¢ per lb.   15. correct

16. incorrect (should be 733)   17. 1, 2, 4, 5, 8, 10, 16, 20, 40, 80   18. $3\cdot5\cdot5\cdot5\cdot13$ 19. true   20. true

21. false   22. true   23. false   24. true   25. 640 gal

CHAPTER 4 DECIMALS

4.1   EXERCISES

1. decimal fractions or decimals   2. decimal point   3. seven tenths   4. two and five hundredths   5. forty-

three and twenty-nine hundredths   6. one hundred twenty-seven and five hundred sixty-two thousandths

7. three hundred two and eight thousandths   8. nine ten thousandths   9. 0.04   10. 228.9   11. 23.748

12. 801.108   13. 3.0001   14. 497.6043   15. $40+1+\frac{8}{10}$ 16. $30+\frac{7}{100}$ 17. $2000+50+\frac{7}{10}+\frac{3}{1000}$

18. $40+\frac{1}{10}+\frac{5}{10,000}$ 19. one dollar and forty-seven cents   20. twenty-three dollars and four cents

21. one hundred sixty-two dollars [and zero (or no) cents]   22. ten dollars and forty cents   23. Four hundred

twenty-seven and $\frac{68}{100}$ dollars   24. Twenty and $\frac{00}{100}$ dollars   25. Three and $\frac{02}{100}$ dollars   26. three and one

thousand four hundred sixteen ten thousandths   27. Thirty-two thousand five hundred twenty-nine and $\frac{75}{100}$ dollars

28. answers vary   29. $2\frac{1}{4}$ 30. $3\frac{9}{11}$ 31. $1\frac{3}{100}$ 32. $\frac{11}{5}$ 33. $\frac{57}{10}$ 34. $\frac{723}{100}$

4.2   EXERCISES

1. $1\frac{2}{5}$ or $\frac{7}{5}$ 2. $3\frac{1}{4}$ or $\frac{13}{4}$ 3. $21\frac{9}{10}$ or $\frac{219}{10}$ 4. $4\frac{1}{20}$ or $\frac{81}{20}$ 5. $3\frac{1}{500}$ or $\frac{1501}{500}$ 6. $\frac{3}{200}$ 7. $\frac{651}{5000}$ 8.

$493\frac{18}{25}$ or $\frac{12,343}{25}$ 9. $\frac{3}{10}$ 10. $\frac{11}{20}$ 11. $2\frac{7}{10}$ or $\frac{27}{10}$ 12. $\frac{61}{200}$ 13. $1\frac{29}{100}$ or $\frac{129}{100}$ 14. $2\frac{1}{200}$ or $\frac{401}{200}$ 15. 0.75

16. $0.8\overline{3}$ (Place the bar over 3 only; 8 does not repeat.)   17. $0.\overline{4}$ 18. $0.\overline{63}$ 19. 0.0625   20. $2.\overline{3}$ 21. 2.75

22. 1.1875   23. $\frac{1}{3}$ 24. $\frac{3}{8}$ 25. $\frac{1}{8}$ 26. $\frac{3}{2}$ 27. $\frac{2}{3}$ 28. $\frac{7}{8}$ 29. $\frac{1}{5}$ 30. $\frac{5}{8}$ 31. $\frac{1}{9}$ 32. $\frac{1}{4}$ 33. $\frac{1}{10}$

34. $\frac{5}{4}$ 35. $\frac{1}{2}$ 36. $\frac{3}{4}$ 37. $\frac{4}{3}$ 38. $236\frac{21}{40}$ 39. $1000\frac{1}{1000}$; one thousand and one thousandth

40. $0.\overline{142857}$ 41. $0.\overline{538461}$ 42. $\frac{1}{3}$ 43. $\frac{17}{99}$ 44. $\frac{41}{333}$ 45. four hundred one and three thousandths

46. 23.107 47. (a) Thirty-four and $\frac{85}{100}$ dollars (b) thirty four dollars and eighty-five cents 48. (a) 1370 (b) 1400

(c) 1000 49. (a) 12,500 (b) 12,500 (c) 13,000 50. (a) 7490 (b) 7500 (c) 7000

4.3   EXERCISES

1. 1 2. 2 3. 3 4. 4 5. 0 or none 6. 2 7. 3 8. 4 9. 3.2 10. 4.7 11. 3.3 12. 5.4 13. 32.8

14. 152.0 15. 7.32 16. 3.49 17. 4.32 18. 5.42 19. 34.01 20. 34.10 21. 3.458 22. 7.257

23. 3.491 24. 5.425 25. 45.009 26. 9.031 27. 24 28. 64 29. 5 30. 9 31. 20 32. 39

33. (a) 0.4 (b) 0.44 (c) 0.444 34. (a) 0.4 (b) 0.35 (c) 0.354 35. (a) 0.1 (b) 0.12 (c) 0.123 36. (a) 0.8 (b) 0.78

(c) 0.778 37. (a) 0.9 (b) 0.94 (c) 0.939 38. (a) 0.5 (b) 0.46 (c) 0.455 39. $4.24 40. $6.24 41. $7.23

42. $8.11 43. $37 44. $13 45. $29 46. $17 47. $800 48. $40 [using $100 \times 40 = 4000$¢]

49. (a) 0.3 (b) 0.29 (c) 0.286 50. $60,000 (using $20 \times \$3000$) 51. $120 (using $\$6000 \div 50$) 52. $6000

(using $\$20 \times 300$) 53. $1620 (using $9 \times 6 \times [5 + 25]$) 54. 29.1 mph 55. $7\frac{2}{25}$ 56. $2\frac{2}{125}$ 57. $0.\overline{8}$

58. $0.\overline{15}$ ## 4.4   EXERCISES

1. 75.1 2. 6.46 3. 247.53 4. 137.21 5. 117.025 6. 50.691 7. 32.062 8. 447.157 9. 4339.2573

10. $185.39 11. $4371.56 12. $8.17 13. $25.75 14. 8.85 mi 15. 8.65 mi 16. $730.79 17. $2138.57

18. 10.312 19. 11,640.7179; eleven thousand six hundred forty and seven thousand one hundred seventy-nine ten

thousandths 20. 18.8 21. 1.83 22. 34.5 23. 100.287 24. 0.25 25. 9.047 26. 53.786 27. 24.95

28. 5.991 29. $26,501.15 30. 2.17 grams 31. (a) $25.50 (b) $299.90 (c) $165.35 (d) $134.55 (e) $225.00

(f) $359.55 32. 0.46 units 33. $3415.95 34. yes 35. 1680.623; one thousand six hundred eighty and six

hundred twenty-three thousandths 36. (a) 12.9 milligrams (b) 17.6 milligrams 37. $x = 9.35$ ft; $y = 7.9$ ft

38. above the average by 0.5 inches 39. 278.0 lb 40. 5.05 cm 41. answers vary 42. Burford tried to subtract in

the wrong order. The correct answer is $6.21 - 4.35 = 1.86$. 43. 1.5 years 44. 26.3 years 45. 9.7 years 46. 5.5

47. 2.5 48. 6.4 49. Canada 50. 2 51. 3 52. 4 53. 0 54. (a) 3.2 (b) 3.16 (c) 3.159 55. $420

[using $280 + 140$]; $423.21 56. $140 [using $280 - 140$]; $143.45 57. 4 [using $600 \div 150$] 58. $1500

[using 5×300]

4.5   EXERCISES

1. 7.015 2. 7.896 3. 27.715 4. 5.1068 5. 42.8988 6. 10.42808 7. 67.0194 8. 159.64 9. (c)

10. (c) 11. (a) 12. (b) 13. 152.37 14. 1523.7 15. 152.370 16. 1.5237 17. 0.15237 18. 0.015237

19. 545¢ 20. 2198¢ 21. 79¢ 22. $2.50 23. $79.36 24. $0.04 25. $23.52 26. $274.37 27. 423 mi

28. 30,650 pounds 29. $23.50 30. 179.05 square meters 31. $838.82 32. $812.47 33. $78.20

34. $320 [using 40×8]; $322.67 35. $160 [using 4×40]; $155.00 36. $859.01 37. $851.70 38. answers

vary 39. Burford moved the decimal point 2 places left instead of right. The correct answer is 24,156.7 40. 5.2

41. 19.8 42. 12.18 43. $22.77 44. 23.7 yd 45. (a) 442.1 mi (b) 442 mi (c) 443 mi (d) Since answers differ,

it is better not to round until the last step (unless you are estimating an answer). 46. $800 [using $600 + 200$];

$775.59 47. $400 [using $600 - 200$]; $418.95 48. 5 [using $3000 \div 600$] [using $3000 \div 600$] 49. $1200

[using 6×200]

4.6 EXERCISES

1. 0.9   2. 2.3   3. 3.6   4. 6.86   5. 0.8   6. 0.08   7. 1.4   8. 7.2   9. 2.14   10. 6.3   11. 35   12. 2.76

13. 1.2   14. 6.6   15. 3.1   16. 1.24   17. 6.56   18. 3.12   19. (b)   20. (a)   21. (b)   22. (d)

23. 3.271   24. 0.4138   25. 0.0005329   26. 0.0062143   27. 0.008319   28. 0.327   29. 426,500   30. 6.27

31. 439.8   32. $11.\overline{7}$ 33. $2.0\overline{3}$ 34. $7.\overline{16}$ 35. 14 months   36. 41.2¢ or $0.412   37. $2601.36

38. $418.05   39. GPA=2.13   40. 13 apples at 17¢ each is better than 9 apples at 18¢ each   41. 21.4 mpg

42. answers vary   43. answers vary   44. Burford moved the decimal point 2 places right instead of left. The correct

answer is 2.41567.   45. 6.2   46. 6   47. 7.2   48. 1.51   49. 8.856   50. 14.09211   51. 69,135   52.

69.135   53. 6.9135   54. 1245¢   55. $0.17   56. $102.13   57. $210.70   58. $799.24   59. $15.37 (He

earned $799.24 for 52 hours of work, so divide $799.24 by 52.)   60. 54.78 sq yd   61. $21.11   62. <   63. >

64. <   65. 3   66. $\frac{1}{2}$ 67. 1

4.7 EXERCISES

1. $2\frac{17}{20}$ 2. $2\frac{7}{8}$ 3. $12\frac{19}{35}$ 4. $1\frac{1}{6}$ 5. $4\frac{23}{25}$ 6. $8\frac{2}{3}$ 7. 2.85   8. 2.87   9. 12.54   10. 1.17

11. 4.94   12. 8.68   13. 218.75 miles   14. $14.63   15. 99 samples   16. 0.375 or $\frac{3}{8}$ mile   17. 10.4

18. 35.24   19. 2.7   20. 32.44   21. 22.65   22. $4.46\overline{1}$ 23. $12.0\overline{6}$ 24. 219.165   25. 0.085, 0.85, 8.05, 8.5

26. 0.04, 0.047, 0.048, 0.08   27. 0.15, $\frac{7}{16}$, $\frac{1}{2}$, 0.51, 5.1   28. 0.65, $\frac{2}{3}$, $\frac{7}{10}$, 6.05, 6.5   29. $3.88 per pound

30. 5.4¢ per ounce   31. Brand A is $0.106 per ounce; Brand B is $0.104 per ounce; Brand C is $0.101 per ounce.

Thus, Brand C is the best buy.   32. Western is 0.235¢ per tissue; Eastern is 0.224¢ per tissue; Southern is 0.233¢

per tissue. Thus, Eastern is the best buy.   33. 98.6 (representing 98,600 more)   34. $8866   35. $35.03

36. answers vary   37. answers vary   38. answers vary   39. 2.9 or $2\frac{9}{10}$ 40. 3.25 or $3\frac{1}{4}$ 41. 2.31 or $2\frac{31}{100}$

42. $\frac{1}{3}$ or $0.\overline{3}$ 43. GPA=2.88   44. 466.8 ft   45. 21.4 mpg   46. $104.10

4.8 EXERCISES

(Some answers are rounded.)   1. $10+35=45$ 2. $62-31=31$ 3. $38\times24=912$ 4. $55\div11=5$

5. $2.3+1.4=3.7$ 6. $4.7+0.9=5.6$ 7. $6.12\times5.3=32.436$ 8. $1.3\div4.5=0.28$ 9. $62.34\div42.357=1.4717756$

10. $1.5+3.62+54.7+80=139.82$ 11. $(1.6)^2=2.56$ 12. $\sqrt{25.37}=5.0368641$ 13. $(11)^4=14,641$

14. $6\div(2+1)=2$ 15. $6\div2+1=4$ 16. $\sqrt{25}+3^2=14$ 17. 16.23   18. 408.96   19. 604.464   20. 9.4

21. 661.77   22. 482.489   23. 91.14   24. 293.7627   25. 47,447.883   26. 2.5625   27. 0.0753

28. 5.2050868   29. 0.2   30. 7.3125   31. $0.\overline{3}$ 32. 2.9   33. $11.48\overline{3}$ 34. $10.\overline{6}$ 35. 48.7204

36. 2.0712315   37. 115,927.41   38. 3.2   39. 3.45   40. 46.70678   41. 2603.4683   42. $522.80

43. $1855.32   44. 339.09 square meters   45. $278.84   46. 11.46 yd   47. $3070.35; $614.07   48. 8.33 cm

49. $3312.06   50. answers vary   51. Burford didn't understand that the display was giving the answer in

scientific notation. The correct answer is 4,225,000,000.   52. 0.013, $\frac{3}{10}$, 0.31, $\frac{1}{3}$, 3.1   53. 3.75 ¢ per ounce

54. $107.63   55. $40.37   56. $79.55

CHAPTER 4 REVIEW EXERCISES

(Some answers are rounded.)   1. decimal fractions or decimals   2. twenty-three and four tenths   3. seven and

five ten thousandths   4. 4.07   5. 233.0302   6. Twenty-seven and $\frac{16}{100}$ dollars   7. $\frac{63}{100}$ 8. $2\frac{7}{10}$ 9. $5\frac{1}{8}$

10. $0.\overline{1}$ 11. $1.\overline{6}$ 12. 0.1875   13. 3   14. 3   15. 5   16. 3.26   17. 6.491   18. 26.1   19. $38   20. 0.8

21. 0.85   22. 0.848   23. $0.43   24. $12.00 [using 2.00×6.00]   25. $200 [using $8000 \div 40$]   26. 72.8711

27. $2217.08   28. $2908.28   29. $29,298.90   30. 39.52   31. 25.64   32. 0.997   33. 11.72 liters   34. $12.29

35. 35.262   36. 6.408248   37. 0.52013   38. 275 mi   39. $411.59   40. (c)   41. approximate range; 360 mi

[using 30×12]; exact range: 352.6 mi; yes   42. 1200 pounds [using 3×400]; 1203.93   43. 10,785   44. 1.0785

45. 0.10785   46. 2.13   47. 5.3   48. 41.6   49. 3.8   50. 51.91   51. 21.4 mpg   52. GPA=2.33   53. $2

[$20 \div 10$]; $2.05   54. $20; $20.50   55. (b) 10.15   56. 0.4389   57. 0.001497   58. 28.61   59. 7.92

60. 14.64   61. 3.95   62. 136.45 pounds   63. 5.9¢   64. $56.88   65. 0.074, 0.74, 7.04, 7.4, 70.4   66. Brand

X is $0.427; Brand Y is $0.428; Brand Z is $0.415. Thus, Brand Z is the best buy.   67. 17.4   68. 6.5725

69. $8.7 \div 12 = 0.725$ 70. $21.6 - 4.37 = 17.23$ 71. $1.009 \times 3.5 = 3.5315$ 72. $6 + 2.5 - 4 = 4.5$

73. $2.3 \times 6 + 8.9 = 22.7$ 74. $9 \times 9 \times 9 = 729$ 75. $(4.2)^2 = 17.64$ 76. $\sqrt{3.27} = 1.8083141$

77. $(1.5)^6 = 11.390625$ 78. $6 \div (2 + 3) - 1 = 0.2$ 79. $600.85   80. $21.66   81. 9.43805   82. 27.384

83. 104.734   84. 115.96   85. 0.011596   86. 0.11596   87. 1159.6   88. 2.14   89. 13.4   90. 6.23

91. 3.47   92. 30.42   93. (a) 6.49 (b) 6.5 (c) 6   94. $3.\overline{6}$ 95. $\frac{17}{20}$ 96. One hundred two and $\frac{38}{100}$ dollars

97. 240.000 [using 6000×40]   98. $614.18   99. $1135.82   100. $13.15   101. The 24-ounce bottle at 5¢ an

ounce is better than the 38-ounce bottle at 6¢ an ounce.   102. 23.6 mpg   103. approximate cost: $200; actual cost:

$198   104. (b)   105. 25,008.874   106. 60.949425   107. 6.8   108. 1340.0957   109. 1.905

110. 8.8690473   111. 2.2   112. 13.6   113. 6.93   114. 9   115. 7.35 or $7\frac{7}{20}$ 116. 0.64 or $\frac{16}{25}$

CHAPTER 4 TEST

1. seventy-three and five thousandths   2. 92.06   3. $\frac{4}{25}$ 4. 0.4375   5. 6.36   6. 45.1   7. 0.75   8. 110.02

9. 5.997   10. $24.60   11. 50¢; 48¢   12. 127.89   13. 10.08   14. 635.7   15. 0.6357   16. 0.006357

17. 63.57   18. $155.92   19. 26.2 mpg   20. $36.00 [using $400 \times 9¢$]; $38.60   21. 14.1

22. $8.03 \div 2.5 = 3.212$ 23. 0.06, 0.0635, 0.075   24. 0.0115 inches   25. moved 5 places to the left

CUMULATIVE REVIEW: CHAPTERS 1–4

1. $\frac{9}{16}$ 2. $\frac{5}{4}$ 3. $\frac{10}{9}$ 4. 46.49   5. 0.4649   6. 8.273   7. $8\frac{1}{3}$ 8. 3   9. $\frac{1}{18}$ 10. $\frac{5}{4}$ 11. $2\frac{7}{8}$

12. 6.05   13. true   14. true   15. false   16. 12 gallons   17. 18 gallons   18. 58 players   19. $182

20. no   21. yes   22. yes   23. 3.75   24. 0.50   25. 92.74   26. (a) $316.39 (b) $316 (c) $317 (d) Since

answers vary, never round until the last step (unless you are estimating an answer).

CHAPTER 5 RATIO, PROPORTION, AND MEASUREMENT

5.1 EXERCISES

1. $\frac{1}{8}$ 2. $\frac{2}{7}$ 3. $\frac{6}{4}$ or $\frac{3}{2}$ 4. $\frac{12}{3}$ or $\frac{4}{1}$ 5. $\frac{6}{1}$ 6. $\frac{4}{4}$ or $\frac{1}{1}$ 7. 1 to 4   8. 3 to 5   9. 5 to 2   10. 13 to 6

11. 6 to 13   12. 9 to 9 or 1 to 1   13. 2   14. 3   15. 16   16. $\frac{7}{4}$ 17. 1   18. 3   19. 5   20. $\frac{1}{2}$

21. 646 people   22. 6500 votes   23. 132 pounds   24. 130 miles   25. 1764 miles   26. about 240 antelope

27. 3   28. 805 pounds   29. $\frac{9}{14}$ (using 42,000 for 1993)   30. $\frac{11}{9}$ (using 33,000 for 1991)   31. 0.41

32. 0.68   33. 34.7 gallons

34. Burford set up the proportion incorrectly since the ratio on the right side should have been $\frac{15}{a}$. Burford should have realized that his answer is incorrect since a 15-foot section could not possibly weigh less than a 10-foot section. The correct answer is 36 pounds.   35. answers vary   36. answers vary   37. 46 ¢ per pound   38. 36 ¢ per pound   39. 24.4   40. 27.42

5.2 EXERCISES

1. $\frac{22 \text{ feet}}{3 \text{ seconds}}$ 2. $\frac{9 \text{ children}}{4 \text{ families}}$ 3. $\frac{18 \text{ gallons}}{5 \text{ seconds}}$ 4. $\frac{\$20}{3 \text{ boards}}$ 5. $7\frac{1}{3}$ ft/sec or $7.\overline{3}$ ft/sec   6. 2.25 children per family   7. 3.6 gal/sec   8. $6.67 per board   9. 21.4 mpg   10. 70 trees per acre   11. $2 per pound   12. 8 ounces per glass   13. 1.5 television sets per household   14. 2.5 cups of flour per cake   15. 225 words per page   16. $450 per week   17. $8.75/yd   18. 22.2¢/oz   19. 550 mph   20. 2.1 cents per ounce   21. Kleen is the better buy at 0.445¢ per tissue than WipeOff at 0.464¢ per tissue.   22. The 32-oz jar is a better buy at 9.0¢ per oz than the 14-oz jar at 9.2¢ per oz.   23. 1100 ft/sec   24. answers vary   25. answers vary   26. $\frac{7}{8}$ 27. 12 to 11 or 12:11   28. 4   29. $\frac{1}{7}$ 30. 20 pounds   31. 13,125 square feet   32. 1.8 cartridges   33. $1166.\overline{6}$ pages

5.3 EXERCISES

1. 60   2. 6   3. 2   4. 3   5. 4   6. 1.5   7. 4.5   8. 2.25   9. 42   10. 15,840   11. 4.5   12. $1\frac{1}{3}$ 13. 3600   14. 1.5   15. $2\frac{2}{3}$ 16. 252   17. 96,000   18. 3   19. 126,720   20. 30,240   21. $\frac{1}{12}$ 22. 22   23. 60   24. 1.80   25. $\frac{2}{15}$ 26. 0.7   27. $\frac{1}{30}$ 28. $9.51   29. yes; $5\frac{\text{mi}}{\text{hr}}$ 30. $30\frac{\text{gal}}{\text{hr}}$ 31. $3168   32. 17.4   33. 80.7   34. 0.4   35. 3.8   36. 15,000 ft·lb   37. 604,800 ft·lb   38. answers vary   39. $15\frac{5}{6}$ 40. $25\frac{13}{20}$ 41. $44\frac{17}{36}$ 42. $23\frac{1}{14}$ 43. $10\frac{8}{15}$ 44. $86\frac{19}{30}$

5.4 EXERCISES

1. 1 hr 23 min   2. 4 hr 32 min   3. 7 yd 2 ft   4. 12 gal 1 qt   5. 18 lb 9 oz   6. 6 yd 2 ft 11 in   7. 12 lb 13 oz   8. 19 hr 33 min   9. 8 gal 1 qt   10. 14 yd 1 ft 8 in   11. 4 yd 1 ft   12. 6 hr 4 min   13. 3 gal 2 qt   14. 20 hr 28 min   15. 6 yd 2 ft 5 in   16. 15 hr 48 min   17. 23 gal 3 qt   18. 11 yd 2 ft 8 in   19. 13 hr 49 min 24 sec   20. 36 sq in   21. 84 sq yd   22. 2 lb 14 oz   23. 2 hr 31 min   24. 6   25. 5 caps   26. 10 gal 1 qt   27. 3 gal 2 qt   28. 12 lb 4 oz   29. 194.3 sq ft   30. 14 oz   31. 7.20   32. Burford is trying to add unlike units. He should either change miles to feet then add, or change feet to miles, then add.   33. answers vary   34. answers vary   35. 102   36. 3.5   37. 7.75   38. 32.000   39. 30   40. 6

5.5 EXERCISES

1. true   2. false (about 2 m)   3. true   4. true   5. false (about one kilogram)   6. true   7. 1000   8. 100   9. 10   10. 10   11. 0.001   12. 1000   13. 0.062   14. 0.032   15. 160   16. 0.00103   17. 0.721   18. 0.063   19. 1.7   20. 162.5   21. 21.2   22. 9.26   23. 4.728   24. 5000   25. 520   26. 700   27. 0.32   28. 953   29. 420   30. 72,000   31. 1080   32. 1.4   33. 6,000.000   34. 10.02 m   35. 406.4 ml   36. 259 kg   37. 46.65 cm   38. 81.5 m   39. 81.5 m² (m × m = m²)   40. 32 samples   41. $3.60   42. $1000\frac{\text{m}}{\text{min}}$ 43. $4000   44. 3   45. He moved the decimal point the wrong direction. The correct answer is 0.0005438 hg.   46. answers vary   47. answers vary   48. answers vary   49. 10 ft 2 in   50. 4 lb 13 oz   51. 5 gal 3 qt   52. 39 yd 2 ft 2 in   53. 2 hr 20 min   54. 6

5.6 EXERCISES

(Some answers are rounded.)   1. 1 mile   2. 3 cm   3. 1 L   4. 3 lb   5. 9.9   6. 206   7. 102.4   8. 183

9. 9837   10. 97.5   11. 50   12. 32   13. 18.9   14. 10.6   15. 110   16. 2270   17. 8.8   18. 284

19. 104   20. 10   21. 392   22. $93\frac{1}{3}$ 23. 51.8 liters   24. $62\frac{mi}{hr}$ 25. 117 kg   26. No

($95°$ C $= 203°$ F)   27. 8.35   28. 122.48   29. 163.68   30. Explain to them that since conversion units are

only approximations, slight differences such as they obtained can be expected. They should not be concerned, both are

correct!   31. 72   32. 450   33. 2100   34. 3.25   35. 2.45   36. 0.8   37. $\frac{3}{10}$ 38. $\frac{7}{50}$ 39. $5\frac{3}{5}$

40. 0.57

CHAPTER 5 REVIEW EXERCISES

(Some answers are rounded.)   1. $\frac{8}{5}$ 2. 1:8 or 1 to 8   3. 4   4. 18   5. 11.836   6. 220 miles

7. $\frac{91\ miles}{2\ hours}$ 8. 45.5 mph   9. $150 per disk   10. 3.5 hours per cord   11. 20.4¢ per ounce   12. 84

13. 2.5   14. 3   15. 1.5   16. 6000   17. 2.25   18. 17 ft 5 in   19. 3 ft 1 in   20. 24 hr 18 min   21. 12

hr 26 min   22. 19 yd 1 ft 10 in   23. 5 yd 2 ft 6 in   24. 17 gal 2 qt 1 pt   25. 24 ft²   26. 2 lb 15 oz   27. 6

28. 0.86   29. 58.2   30. 4.83   31. 0.0483   32. 3.5   33. 560   34. 90.5 m   35. 414.7 L   36. 299.6 g

37. 7.452   38. 10.668   39. 80.5   40. 20.8   41. 4.77   42. 7264   43. no (it would feel hot: $65°$ C $= 149°$ F)

44. 14.31 gal   45. 1.13   46. 237.7   47. 46   48. 0.0635   49. 0.099   50. 0.08   51. 3600   52. 0.1

53. 15   54. $129,837.50   55. $90   56. 11 lb 4 oz   57. 800 miles   58. $\frac{14\ gallons}{5\ seconds}$ 59. 2.8 gallons per

second   60. metric system   61. 0.90   62. 1.14   63. 1.06   64. 0.31

CHAPTER 5 TEST

1. $\frac{13}{7}$ 2. 13 to 5 or 13:5   3. 3   4. 279 pounds   5. 5 pages per minute   6. 306 ft   7. 325 mi   8. 2.5

9. 0.028   10. 14.3   11. 149   12. 28.38   13. 724.5   14. 8 yd 2 ft 7 in   15. $41.34   16. all of them

17. false; kilometer   18. true   19. true   20. true

CUMULATIVE REVIEW: CHAPTERS 1–5

1. 180   2. 70   3. 240   4. 12   5. 3.5   6. 20   7. 6   8. $\frac{27}{31}$ 9. $\frac{50}{21}$ 10. $5\frac{1}{4}$ 11. $33\frac{1}{3}$

12. $2\frac{2}{7}$ 13. 18 ft 6 in   14. 8 ft 11 in   15. 1252.55   16. $\frac{1}{4}$ 17. $\frac{1}{8}$ 18. $\frac{2}{23}$ 19. 60 mi/hr

20. 2300   21. 9080   22. 50   23. $55   24. 2928 mi

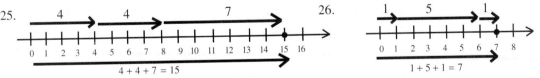

25. 4 + 4 + 7 = 15   26. 1 + 5 + 1 = 7

CHAPTER 6 PERCENT

6.1 EXERCISES

1. hundred   2. $\frac{1}{100}$ 3. left   4. $\frac{87}{100}$ 5. $\frac{4}{25}$ 6. $\frac{5}{4}$ 7. 10   8. $\frac{1}{400}$ 9. $\frac{7}{1000}$ 10. $\frac{1}{6}$ 11. $\frac{1}{2000}$

12. 0.92   13. 0.01   14. 1.45   15. 0.001   16. 0.3735   17. 0.0025   18. 43.925   19. 0.0675   20. (a) $\frac{76}{100}$

(or $\frac{19}{25}$, reduced to lowest terms)   (b) 76%   (c) 0.76   21. (a) $\frac{45}{100}$ (or $\frac{9}{20}$, reduced to lowest terms)   (b) 45%

(c) 0.45   22. 0.008   23. 7%   24. 37.5%   25. 375%   26. 3750%   27. 37,500%   28. 0.9%   29. 0.09%

30. 3.2%   31. 130%   32. 175%   33. $166\frac{2}{3}$%   34. 14%   35. 0.1%   36. $3333\frac{1}{3}$% 37. 350%   38. 53%

39. 57.1%   40. 22.2%   41. 115.4%   42. 0.3; 30%   43. $\frac{3}{5}$; 60%   44. $\frac{5}{8}$; 0.625   45. 1.0; 100%

46. $\frac{7}{8}$; 87.5%   47. $\frac{2}{3}$; $0.\overline{6}$ 48. 0.05; 5%   49. $\frac{1}{3}$; $33\frac{1}{3}$%   50. $\frac{5}{6}$; $0.8\overline{3}$ 51. 0.5; 50%   52. $\frac{1}{6}$; $16\frac{2}{3}$%

53. $\frac{1}{8}$; 0.125   54. $\frac{42}{50}$ or $\frac{21}{25}$ (reduced); 0.84; 84%   55. $\frac{8}{50}$ or $\frac{4}{25}$ (reduced); 0.16; 16%   56. $\frac{12}{25}$; 0.48; 48%

57. $\frac{13}{25}$; 0.52; 52%   58. 56.10%   59. 6.93%   60. 25.79%   61. 259.27%   62. (a) $\frac{7}{20}$ (b) $\frac{13}{20}$ (c) 65%

63. 0.0525; $\frac{21}{400}$ 64. Write the numerator followed by the % symbol.   65. answers vary   66. answers vary

67. 450   68. 1200 miles   69. 440   70. 17.5 hours

6.2 EXERCISES

1. 30   2. 28   3. 420   4. 50   5. 500   6. 3   7. 20%   8. 500%   9. $33\frac{1}{3}$%   10. 24.5   11. 25%

12. 0.25   13. 1870   14. 80 in   15. 17,171   16. 29%   17. 4931 votes   18. 73%   19. 32.64

20. 428.57   21. 146.99%   22. $33,836.89   23. 54.0%   24. 18.4%   25. 80.0%   26. If $P = 80$, then

$P\% = 80\% = 80(0.01) = 0.8$.   27. answers vary   28. answers vary   29. $\frac{7}{20}$ 30. 0.135   31. 0.0875

32. 17%   33. 0.5%   34. 5%   35. 50%   36. 37.5%   37. $77.\overline{7}$%   38. (a) $\frac{71}{112}$ (b) 0.634   (c) 63.4%

(d) 36.6%   39. (a) $\frac{54}{91}$ (b) 0.593   (c) 59.3%   (d) 40.7%

6.3 EXERCISES

1. $10.95; $193.45   2. $82.50; $1582.50   3. $0.38; $15.58   4. 2%   5. $126.00   6. 5%   7. $250

8. $307.24; $7134.74   9. $979.60   10. $5449.80 (she only paid tax on the first $87,900)   11. $4037.50

12. $2132.50; $1289.60   13. 1.9%; 27.7%   14. 3.2%   15. $326.00   16. The tax was 90¢, not 9¢, so the total

came to $15.90, and Burford did not have enough cash in his pocket.   17. answers vary   18. 44.1   19. 65

20. 130%   21. 350   22. 86%   23. 4784   24. 67.5%

6.4 EXERCISES

(Answers may vary slightly due to round-off differences.)   1. $258.00   2. $580.82   3. 15%   4. $5326

5. $6232.80   6. $1058.40   7. 2.3% (to the nearest $\frac{1}{10}$%)   8. $32.15; $96.45   9. $129.60; $590.40

10. 30%   11. $35.00   12. $202.80   13. 20%   14. $85.68   15. 40%   16. $39.27   17. 247.43, 68.5%

18. Burford did not understand that the 20% discount was to be taken on the discounted (10%) price.   19. answers

vary   20. $0.36; $9.30   21. 5%   22. $1215.20   23. $2361.45

6.5 EXERCISES

1. $840.00   2. 6.5%   3. $654   4. 10%   5. $636.68   6. $6798.30   7. $283.26   8. $83.59   9. $900;

$116.67   10. $2862.25   11. $744.98   12. $7717.50: $7726.70   13. $1816.70   14. $9083.48

15. $18,166.97   16. $10,140.87   17. Burford did not divide the annual interest rate, 10%, by 2, the number of

compounding periods. The correct amount is $110.250   18. answers vary   19. $1443.70   20. $190.95

21. $1236.50   22. $104.89

6.6 EXERCISES

1. $45,262.50   2. $39,462.50   3. $115,276   4. 22,440   5. 17.5%   6. 297%   7. 28.8%   8. $12,160

9. 139: 17.3%   10. $8518.52   11. 28 mpg   12. 6 mpg   13. 44.1 mpg   14. 40 mpg   15. 18.2%

16. 36.6 mpg   17. 2.8%   18. 6.5%   19. 34.1%   20. 115.7%   21. $6667.74   22. The +1.5% and +2.7%

mean percent increases and the –0.1% is a percent decrease.   23. answers vary   24. $45.17   25. $1754.79

26. $42.98   27. The account with 11% simple interest will return more interest ($660) than the other account

($646.22).

6.7 EXERCISES

1. $80.75   2. $2152; 80%   3. $8.75; $12.25   4. 150%   5. 48¢   6. 25%   7. $115.50   8. 22%   9. 90¢;

54¢   10. $144; $122.40   11. $2.40; 2%   12. $4.50; 2.5%   13. $173.25   14. markup; percent markup

15. Use a markdown of $33.\overline{3}\%$.   16. 11.2%   17. $18,200   18. 26.1mpg   19. 11%

CHAPTER 6 REVIEW EXERCISES

1. hundred   2. $\frac{23}{100}$ 3. $\frac{81}{25}$ 4. $\frac{3}{500}$ 5. $\frac{1}{16}$ 6. 0.84   7. 2.67   8. 0.0075   9. 0.003   10. 63%

11. 3.2%   12. 320%   13. 60%   14. 186   15. 1200   16. 12.5%   17. 258   18. 86.4%   19. 40

20. $1.05; $18.55   21. 5.5%   22. $1075.70   23. $8,562.50   24. 18%   25. $1025   26. $151.20

27. 35%   28. $274.46   29. $4094.50   30. 22,064   31. 7.2%   32. 20%   33. 30%   34. 26.6mpg

35. No. The markup is 24%.   36. $21,400.80   37. $49.17   38. $573.70   39. $64.50   40. 4% (loss)

41. $464.38   42. 12%   43. $0.75   44. 0.25; 25%   45. $\frac{21}{50}$; 42%   46. $\frac{7}{20}$; 0.35   47. $\frac{13}{10}$; 130%

48. $1.\overline{3}$; $133.\overline{3}\%$ or $133\frac{1}{3}\%$ 49. $\frac{1}{200}$; 0.005   50. 30%   51. 4.44   52. 95   53. 7.2%   54. 3.8%

55. 49.7%   56. 98.9%   57. 563%   58. 85%   59. answers vary

CHAPTER 6 TEST

1. $\frac{19}{20}$ 2. 0.008   3. 506%   4. 180%   5. 45.5%   6. 20%   7. 21.6   8. 40   9. $20.65   10. $610.20

11. $1703.76   12. 18.3%   13. 2% profit   14. $1.60; $2.00   15. $20.93   16. $648.96   17. $A = P\% \cdot B$

18. 7.3%   19. true   20. true

CUMULATIVE REVIEW CHAPTERS 1–6

1. 6   2. 8000   3. 3.5   4. $\frac{22}{7}$ 5. $\frac{98}{9}$ 6. $\frac{33}{5}$ 7. $288   8. 20%   9. $22,000   10. 15%   11. 2.0272

12. 0.18   13. 5940.48   14. 7.83   15. 1.02   16. 10   17. $\frac{1}{10}$ 18. $4\frac{1}{12}$ 19. 9   20. $\frac{5}{16}$ 21. $\frac{1}{2}$ 22. $19\frac{1}{2}$

23. 12   24. 24   25. 56.

CHAPTER 7 INTRODUCTION TO STATISTICS

7.1 EXERCISES

1. $12,000   2. labor   3. $\frac{2}{1}$ or 2 to 1   4. $\frac{2}{3}$ or 2 to 3   5. $\frac{3}{1}$ or 3 to 1   6. 25%   7. 50%   8. $8.\overline{3}\%$ or

$8\frac{1}{3}\%$ 9. grades $K-8$ 10. university students   11. 22,950   12. 9350   13. 5950   14. 4250

15. 32,300   16. 10,200   17. $\frac{11}{5}$ or 11 to 5   18. $\frac{27}{11}$ or 27 to 11   19. $\frac{11}{12}$ or 11 to 12   20. 10,200   21. 1300

22. $\frac{3}{13}$ or 3 to 13   23. 23.1%   24. $\frac{4}{13}$ or 4 to 13   25. 30.8%   26. 53.8%   27. $\frac{8}{5}$ or 8 to 5   28. $\frac{1}{2}$ or 1 to 2

29. 15.4%   30. 450   31. 34.6%   32. $\frac{7}{4}$ or 7 to 4   33. 1994   34. 1996   35. 1994   36. 1997

37. $\frac{4}{3}$ or 4 to 3   38. $\frac{5}{3}$ or 5 to 3   39. 1997   40. Yes; the number of males and females seemed to decline over the period.   41. $16,000   42. $4000   43. 40.6%   44. $\frac{3}{13}$ 45. 25%   46. $\frac{7}{40}$ 47. $\frac{19}{120}$ 48. $\frac{23}{120}$

49. approximately 35%   50. 1100; 1093; This is well within the ability to read the graph.

7.2 EXERCISES

1. 15   2. weeks 1 and 6   3. 90   4. $\frac{6}{1}$ or 6 to 1   5. week 5   6. week 3   7. between weeks 3 and 4

8. between weeks 5 and 6   9. 33.$\overline{3}$% or 33$\frac{1}{3}$%   10. 11.$\overline{1}$% or 11$\frac{1}{9}$%   11. 15   12. 20   13. 90   14. 120

15. 33% increase   16. $\frac{3}{4}$ or 3 to 4   17. $\frac{3}{2}$ or 3 to 2   18. August and September   19. 5   20. 18   21. 36

22. 33   23. 51   24. $\frac{6}{17}$ or 6 to 17   25. 35.3%   26. $\frac{5}{6}$ or 5 to 6   27. $4, $6, $8, $10, $12

28.

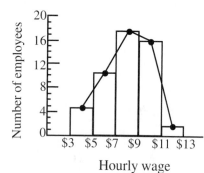

29. approximately 75,000,000   30. approximately 25,000,000   31. approximately 5.3   32. approximately 30%

33. $1300   34. $750   35. $250   36. $\frac{15}{26}$ or 15 to 26   37. 100   38. 725   39. 27.6%   40. $\frac{10}{1}$ or 10 to 1

41-46. answers vary

7.3 EXERCISES

1. 13   2. 9   3. 17.2   4. 110.3   5. 7.5   6. 49.5   7. 13   8. 8.5   9. 18   10. 111   11. 7.2   12. 48

13. 6   14. 9   15. 8 and 3 (bimodal)   16. no mode   17. 4.3   18. 150   19. 58.2 mpg   20. 785   21. $599.48

22. 77.8; 78   23. $23,135.71; $20,800; $20,800   24. 95   25. No. If it had been 35, the median would have been

38 not 51.   26. mode   27. mode (bimodal)   28. median   29. mean or median   30. answers vary   31. 433;

424; answers vary   32. 478; 476; answers vary   33. 5 million dollars   34. 5.5 million dollars   35. 9 million

dollars   36. 24.5 million dollars   37. $\frac{2}{1}$ or 2 to 1   38. 20.4%   39. 42.9%   40. 5   41. 65   42. 90

43. 15   44. 130   45. 38.5%   46. $\frac{2}{1}$ or 2 to 1

CHAPTER 7 REVIEW EXERCISES

1. 129   2. 42   3. $\frac{43}{37}$ or 43 to 37   4. 171 5. 10   6. 26   7. between March and April   8. 49   9. $\frac{10}{3}$ or

10 to 3   10. 8.2%   11. 10   12. 25   13. 55   14. 150   15. 3.$\overline{3}$% or 3$\frac{1}{3}$%   16. $\frac{5}{1}$ or 5 to 1

17. 15.4; 16   18. 291; 311.5   19. 275   20. 5   21. 2 and 3 (bimodal)   22. $1055; $973   23. $917; $860;

$860   24. 900   25. $\frac{5}{18}$ or 5 to 18   26. 27.8%   27. $\frac{7}{4}$ or 7 to 4   28. 6.8; 5; 5   29. 24.46; 6.1; no mode

30. 21.$\overline{3}$; 17.5; 12   31. 6.875; 7; 4 and 7   32. 400   33. 600   34. 1500   35. 1850   36. $\frac{7}{4}$ or 7 to 4

37. 40%   38. 1996   39. 75%   40. 450   41. 18,000   42. $\frac{1}{2}$ or 1 to 2   43. 80%   44. 33.3%

45. $\frac{4}{5}$ or 4 to 5   46. 30,254   47. 183,803   48. 3964   49. 13,299   50. 3333

CHAPTER 7 TEST

1. 180   2. 150   3. $\frac{11}{3}$ or 11 to 3   4. 40   5. 90   6. $\frac{2}{1}$ or 2 to 1   7. 26.$\overline{6}$%   8. 60%   9. 25   10. 80

11. $\frac{7}{16}$ or 7 to 16   12. 25%   13. 20   14. 18   15. 8   16. (a) 254.5 pounds (b) 255 pounds (c) no mode

17. true   18. true   19. true   20. false

CUMULATIVE REVIEW: CHAPTERS 1–7

1. 30%   2. 225%   3. 12.5%   4. 40   5. 94.8   6. 8.8   7. (a) 10,050 tickets (b) $80,400   8. 168

9. $41,040   10. $21.00; $56.00   11. 2.82   12. 76.6   13. 3.63   14. 15   15. 2.4   16. $\frac{4}{7}$ 17. 4849

18. 335   19. 9919   20. $\frac{13}{12}$ 21. $1\frac{3}{40}$ 22. $\frac{1}{4}$ 23. 12.31443   24. 20.927   25. 500

APPLICATIONS INDEX

Numbers give the pages where applications are found. If a number is in parentheses, it is an exercise number on the indicated page.

AERONAUTICS, 34 (**35**)

AGRICULTURE, 92 (**3**), 114 (**76**), 179 (**23**), 181 (**23**), 200 (**25**), 209, 211 (**3,4**), 324 (**30**), 525, 527 (**16**), 629 (**47**)

AVERAGES, 251 (**39**), 254 (**39**), 272, 320, 636 (**17**)

AVIATION, 549

BAKING, 332 (**28, 30**), 333 (**30**), 352 (**56**), 522

BANKING, 24 (**87**), 31, 41, 80, 89 (**13**), 92 (**13**), 94 (**37**), 113 (**72**), 128 (**22**), 245, 248, 250 (**31**), 253 (**31**), 296 (**28**), 548, 558 (**31**), 561, 569, 580 (**54**), 581 (**93**), 583 (**16**), 630

BIOLOGY, 626 (**27**)

BUSINESS, 14 (**52**), 45 (**80**), 63 (**37**), 65 (**37**), 77 (**74**), 79 (**74**), 84, 86, 87 (**2**), 89 (**18, 20, 24**), 90 (**28, 33**), 93 (**17, 20, 23**), 94 (**28, 33**), 113 (**70**), 114 (**79**), 119 (**20**), 128 (**22**), 136 (**34**), 137 (**33**), 160 (**38**), 168 (**52**), 198 (**26**), 208 (**26**), 212 (**1, 11**), 124 (**47**), 243 (**47**), 261 (**25**), 263 (**25**), 274 (**56**), 292 (**47**), 296 (**27**), 299 (**99**), 316 (**32, 33**), 355 (**23**), 366 (**67, 22**), 377 (**15**), 389-390, 390 (**8-10**), 391(**11-17**), 392 (**8-16, 18**), 399 (**20**), 405 (**7**), 407 (**4, 6, 7**), 410-413, 413 (**1-12**), 414 (**13, 1-12**), 415 (**13**), 417 (**26, 27**), 418 (**31-33, 35, 40**), 420 (**13-15**), 421 (**7**), 445, 457 (**19**), 462 (**8, 10**), 551 (**26**), 553 (**26**), 559 (**31**), 564 (**37**), 575 (**58**), 577 (**55, 58**), 581 (**92**), 623, 626 (**38**), 630, 633 (**66**), 634 (**79**), 637 (**19**), 638 (**16**)

CHEMISTRY, 27 (**85**), 91 (**40**), 160 (**41**), 163 (**11**), 165 (**6**), 219 (**13**), 332 (**26**), 339 (**40**), 340 (**40**), 365 (**56, 57**), 375, 377 (**16**), 379 (**16**)

COMMISSION, 387-390, 390 (**1-7**), 391 (**1-6**), 392 (**7, 17**), 399 (**19, 21**), 417 (**24, 25**), 418 (**38**)

COMMUNICATIONS, 54 (**93**)

CONSTRUCTION, 65 (**38**), 88 (**3**), 94 (**31**), 151 (**27**), 152 (**30**), 160 (**40**), 161, 180 (**24,25**), 181 (**24,25**), 183, 186 (**29**), 187 (**29**), 192 (**31, 32**), 209, 212 (**3, 4, 5**), 215 (**37, 39**), 243 (**52**), 261 (**36**), 263 (**31**), 273 (**36**), 275 (**36**), 292 (**44**), 294 (**44**), 298 (**62**), 309 (**23**), 333 (**29**), 484 (**22**), 504 (**21**), 507 (**7**), 508 (**21, 29**), 511, 516, 518 (**31, 32**), 519 (**40**), 520 (**29, 31, 32**), 525, 527 (**15, 16**), 532 (**31**), 533 (**52, 54**), 629 (**31**), 633 (**67**)

CONSUMER, 14 (**50, 51**), 32 (**35**), 43 (**54**), 45 (**79**), 86, 89 (**14**), 90 (**25, 26, 27, 34**), 91 (**44**), 92 (**12**), 93 (**14, 25, 26**), 94 (**27, 34**), 106 (**87, 90, 92**), 113 (**71**), 114 (**77, 78**), 116 (**146**), 119 (**24, 37, 38**), 123, 125, 126 (**21, 22**), 128 (**21**), 145 (**38**), 151 (**28, 41**), 159 (**38, 50**), 160 (**42**), 162, 163 (**4, 6, 7**), 165 (**9**), 168 (**54**), 173 (**14**), 175, 205, 219 (**14**), 240, 241 (**48, 50**), 243 (**48, 50**), 250 (**34**), 252 (**55-58**), 253 (**34**), 254 (**38**), 259, 261 (**31, 33, 35**), 262 (**46-49**), 264 (**33, 35, 36**), 273 (**40**), 274 (**57**), 386 (**40**), 282 (**29,**

30), 286 (**46, 15**), 284 (**30**), 292 (**45**), 293 (**53, 55, 56**), 294 (**45**), 296 (**24**), 297 (**34**), 298 (**53, 54, 63, 64, 66**), 299 (**100, 101, 103**), 300 (**10, 11, 18**), 301 (**20**), 310 (**37, 38**), 314, 315 (**17, 19-22**), 316 (**17, 19-21**), 317 (**22**), 323, 332 (**25**), 333 (**25**), 339 (**41**), 340 (**41, 43**), 347 (**23**), 348 (**23**), 351 (**11**), 352 (**44**), 354 (**15**), 391 (**18**), 398 (**3, 4, 5**), 399 (**22, 3-5**), 402-403, 405 (**6, 10**), 407 (**21, 3, 8**), 408 (**21**), 420 (**9, 10**), 494, 503 (**7, 8**), 504 (**22**), 505 (**30, 53**), 507 (**8**), 508 (**22, 30**), 533 (**51, 55**), 537 (**6**), 563, 584 (**10, 12**), 626 (**41**), 630

COOKING, 191, 333 (**28**)

DATA PROCESSING, 65 (**39**)

DEMOGRAPHY, 129 (**29**)

DIET, 77 (**75**), 91 (**41**)

ECONOMICS, 12 (**50**), 32 (**33**), 34 (**32, 33**), 44 (**77**), 127 (**29**), 622

EDUCATION, 3 (**36**), 26 (**84**), 32 (**34**), 53, 56 (**86, 93**), 91 (**35**), 92 (**1, 5**), 94 (**35**), 95 (**44**), 117 (**149**), 126 (**19**), 134, 151 (**43**), 164 (**3**), 168 (**28**), 200 (**26**), 211 (**2**), 241 (**52**), 273 (**39**), 275 (**39**), 282 (**43**), 297 (**52**), 364 (**21**), 365 (**54, 55**), 366 (**21**), 367 (**56, 57**), 377 (**18**), 379 (**17**), 386 (**22**), 401, 405 (**4**), 417 (**17**), 418 (**30**), 451 (**24, 25**), 453 (**22**), 454 (**24, 25**), 485 (**9**), 626 (**33, 34, 40**), 629 (**32, 34, 38**), 633 (**72, 78**), 635 (**14**)

ELECTRICITY, 325 (**31**), 333 (**31**), 352 (**55**)

ELECTRONICS, 211 (**5**)

ENGINEERING, 151 (**44**), 152 (**28**), 159 (**49, 51**), 163 (**1, 2, 12**), 164 (**1, 2**), 165 (**12, 14**), 168 (**55, 56**), 181 (**22**), 302 (**16, 17**), 499, 628 (**24**)

ENTERTAINMENT, 164 (**4**), 165 (**7**), 178, 212 (**8**)

ENVIRONMENT, 32 (**32**), 45 (**78**), 63 (**38**), 136 (**33**), 165 (**5**), 199 (**28**), 200 (**28**), 309 (**28**), 311 (**28**), 377 (**13**), 407 (**5**), 450 (**20**), 453 (**20**)

EXERCISE SCIENCE, 79 (**75**)

FARMING, 117 (**150**), 141, 527 (**22**), 626 (**48**), 628 (**26**)

FINANCE, 3 (**38**), 4 (**39, 40**), 62, 94 (**36**), 143 (**34**), 145 (**33**), 163 (**10**), 165 (**10**), 186 (**40**), 241 (**51**), 243 (**51**), 245, 250 (**33**), 253 (**33**), 273 (**38**), 292 (**43**), 294 (**43**), 376, 570

FOOD, 76, 218 (**17**)

FORESTRY, 527 (**13**)

GAME MANAGEMENT, 367 (**26**), 370 (**26**)

GARDENING, 299 (**80**), 316 (**30, 31**), 332 (**29**), 482 (**22**), 537 (**8**), 584 (**11**), 624, 637 (**20**)

GAS MILEAGE, 87, 90 (**32**), 91(**38**), 94 (**32, 38**), 118 (**11**), 245, 283 (**45**), 297 (**38, 51**), 299 (**102**), 301 (**19**), 323, 404, 405 (**11-16**), 408 (**11-16**), 414 (**16, 18**), 418 (**34**), 420 (**12**), 446, 450 (**19**), 453 (**19**)

GAS STORAGE, 118 (**15**), 526 (**16**)

GEOGRAPHY, 12 (**22**), 86, 91 (**37**), 539, 556, 624

GEOMETRY, 85, 88 (**4**), 89 (**22**), 92 (**4**), 93 (**22**), 119 (**40**), 143 (**31**), 145 (**31**), 159 (**42**), 211 (**8**), 250 (**37**), 254 (**37**), 261 (**30**), 262 (**44**), 263 (**30**), 274 (**60**), 282 (**44**), 292 (**46, 48**), 294 (**46, 48**), 304, 311 (**23**), 584 (**7, 8**), 624, 625 (**24**), 626 (**25, 43-47**), 628 (**30**), 629 (**43-46, 48**), 633 (**69, 70**), 634 (**77, 82**)

HAULING, 23 (**55- 58**)

HEALTH, 54 (**85**), 405 (**9**), 422 (**10**), 423, 553 (**27**), 585, 621

HOME MORTGAGE PAYMENTS, 90 (**29**), 94 (**29**), 106 (**88**)

HYDROLOGY, 54 (**87**), 275 (**41**), 325 (**30**), 340 (**42**), 379 (**13**), 505 (**29**), 518 (**30**), 520 (**30**), 533 (**53**)

INCOME TAX, 166 (**145**), 247, 383-384, 385 (**11, 12**), 386 (**11,12**), 391 (**23**), 417 (**23**)

INVESTMENT, 34 (**34**), 91 (**36**), 113 (**73**), 151 (**42**), 211 (**12**), 212 (**12**), 283 (**14**), 293 (**49**), 294 (**49**), 367 (**63**), 378 (**31**), 407 (**25, 27, 10**), 418 (**29, 42**), 421 (**16**), 422 (**8**), 575 (**57**), 577 (**57**), 626 (**29, 39, 42**)

LABOR, 211 (**9, 10**), 212 (**9, 10**)

LIBRARY SCIENCE, 63 (**36**)

LOANS, 393, 397, 398 (**1, 6, 9, 11**), 399 (**1, 6, 9, 11, 12**), 500 (**17**), 418 (**28, 37**)

MANUFACTURING, 56 (**87**), 159 (**37**)

MAP READING, 22, 81, 112, 119 (**39**), 142, 245, 247, 309 (**24**), 311 (**24**), 351 (**6**), 354 (**7**)

MARKETING, 162

MECHANICS, 301 (**24**), 505 (**31-33**), 508 (**31-33**)

MEDICINE, 250 (**32, 36**), 253 (**32**), 325 (**28**), 352 (**54**), 366 (**20**), 453 (**23**), 564 (**37**), 575 (**55**)

METEOROLOGY, 250 (**38**), 377 (**14**), 379 (**14**), 551 (**27**), 559 (**32**)

MILITARY, 407 (**9**), 558 (**32**)

MINING, 89 (**11**), 152 (**29**), 253 (**30**), 518 (**29**)

MONEY, 302 (**19**)

MONTHLY PAYMENTS, 83, 91 (**39**), 94 (**39**), 106 (**86**), 273 (**35**), 275 (**35**), 296 (**25**), 395, 398 (**7, 8**), 399 (**7, 8**), 407 (**24, 26**), 421 (**18**)

NUMBER-AGE, 618-619, 625 (**21-23**), 626 (**26, 28, 30-32**), 628 (**21-23, 25, 27-29**), 633 (**65, 68, 71**)

NUTRITION, 95 (**41**)

PAINTING, 509 (**53**), 523, 526 (**14, 15**), 527 (**23**)

PHYSICS, 12 (**51**), 260, 261 (**28**), 263 (**28**), 315 (**23**), 317 (**23**), 324 (**36, 37**) 326 (**36, 37**)

POLITICS, 27 (**86**), 56 (**85**), 92 (**6**), 128 (**19**), 137 (**34**), 163 (**3**), 193 (**31, 32**), 303, 305, 308, 309 (**22**), 311 (**22**), 351 (**5**), 364 (**20**), 377 (**17**), 378 (**38**), 379 (**15**), 417 (**19**), 448

POLLING, 386 (**21**)

POPULATION, 115 (**114**), 172 (**23**), 405 (**5**), 629 (**39**), 637 (**18**)

PRODUCTION, 163 (**8**), 165 (**8**), 168 (**51**), 210, 264 (**34**), 515

PUBLISHING, 44 (**78**)

RANCHING, 296 (**29**), 324 (**31**), 339 (**43**), 479, 482 (**23**), 483 (**23**), 519 (**39**)

RATE-MOTION, 322

REAL ESTATE, 199 (**27**)

RECREATION, 42 (**53**), 44 (**54**), 63 (**39**), 87 (**1**), 88 (**5**), 89 (**23**), 91 (**43**), 92 (**11**), 93 (**15, 16**), 95 (**40**), 106 (**85, 91**), 107 (**93**), 112 (**40**), 113 (**74**), 157, 159 (**52**), 160 (**37**), 162, 163 (**5, 13, 14**), 165 (**13**), 168 (**57**), 173 (**13**), 179 (**22**), 198 (**25**), 211 (**2, 7, 11**), 212 (**6, 7**), 215 (**40**), 221, 252 (**14, 15**), 262 (**43**), 273 (**41**), 274 (**61**), 275 (**38**), 280, 281 (**16**), 302 (**26**), 324 (**28**), 332 (**27, 31**), 333 (**26, 27**), 377 (**22**), 378 (**39**), 379 (**18**), 462 (**7**), 463, 537 (**7**), 564 (**38**), 656 (**38**), 575 (**56**), 577 (**56**), 626 (**35**), 629 (**35, 41**)

RETAIL, 144 (**38**), 365 (**62**), 366 (**69**)

SALARY, 93 (**18**), 145 (**34**), 261 (**32, 34**), 263 (**26, 32**), 274 (**58**), 281 (**14**), 284 (**35**), 293 (**54**), 297 (**39**), 405 (**1-3, 8**), 407 (**1, 2**), 408 (**22**), 414 (**17, 19**), 418 (**36, 41**), 422 (**9**), 449, 451 (**23**), 457 (**23**), 462 (**9**), 626 (**37**), 629 (**37, 42**), 638 (**15**)

SALES, 24 (**84**), 44 (**79**), 65 (**36**), 93 (**24**), 95 (**43**), 211 (**1**), 261 (**29**), 263 (**29**), 309 (**21**), 311 (**21**), 367 (**54, 55**), 450 (**21**), 453 (**21**), 459 (**22**), 537 (**5**), 626 (**36**), 629 (**33, 40**)

SALES TAX, 380-384, 385 (**1-8, 15, 16**), 386 (**1-8, 15**), 391 (**20, 21**), 417 (**20, 21**), 418 (**39, 43**)

SAVINGS, 394, 398 (**2, 10, 12, 16, 17**), 399 (**2, 10, 16**)

SCIENCE, 12 (**49**), 14 (**49**), 151 (**29**), 159 (**41**), 250 (**30**), 281 (**15**), 297 (**33**)

SEARCH AND RESCUE, 115 (**113**)

SEWING, 157, 159 (**40**), 197, 277, 283 (**13**)

SHIPPING, 44 (**53**), 297 (**42**)

SOCIAL SECURITY, 117 (**147**), 382-383, 35 (**9, 10**), 386 (**9, 10, 16**), 391 (**22**), 417 (**22**), 420 (**11**)

SPACE, 5, 82, 186 (**28**), 187 (**28**)

SPORTS, 2 (**14**), 3 (**37**), 24 (**86**), 80, 88 (**6, 9, 10**), 90 (**30**), 92 (**2, 9, 10**), 94 (**30**), 113 (**75**), 117 (**148**), 121, 126 (**20**), 128 (**20**), 134, 163 (**9**), 167 (**9**), 254 (**36**), 302 (**18**), 309 (**27**), 311 (**27**), 347 (**25**), 349 (**25**), 364 (**22**), 376, 417 (**18**), 450 (**22**), 581 (**88**), 634 (**80**)

STATISTICS, 386 (**23**)

STORAGE, 26 (**55- 58**)

TAX, 250 (**29**), 253 (**29**), 261 (**37**), 263 (**37**), 273 (**37**), 275 (**37**), 292 (**42**), 294 (**42**), 299 (**79, 98**), 357, 365 (**63**), 367 (**62**), 379 (**22**), 381, 385 (**13, 14**), 386 (**13, 14**)

TEMPERATURE, 206 (**25**), 208 (**25**), 346, 347 (**26**), 349 (**26**), 352 (**43**), 583 (**17**)

TIME MEASUREMENT, 54 (**86**), 89 (**21**), 93 (**21**)

TRANSPORTATION, 89 (**17**), 526 (**13**)

TRAVEL, 24 (**85**), 27 (**87**), 44 (**80**), 45 (**77**), 88 (**7, 8**), 89 (**12, 15, 16, 19**), 91 (**42**), 92 (**7, 8**), 93 (**19**), 95 (**42**), 106 (**89**), 143 (**32**), 145 (**32**), 150, 151 (**30**), 152 (**27**), 159 (**39**), 160 (**39**), 165 (**11**), 168 (**53, 58**), 169 (**69, 70**), 172 (**22**), 173 (**24**), 200 (**27**), 249 (**14, 15**), 261 (**27**), 262 (**45**), 263 (**27**), 281 (**13**), 282 (**35**), 283 (**16, 29**), 294 (**47**), 297 (**41**), 306, 311 (**25**), 315 (**25**), 316 (**18**), 324 (**18**), 325 (**29**), 325 (**29**), 339 (**42**), 347 (**24**), 348 (**24**), 352 (**57**), 355 (**24**), 366 (**68**), 368, 638 (**13**)

WAGES, 143 (**33**), 259, 261 (**26**), 274 (**59**), 401, 629 (**36**)

WEATHER, 206 (**26**), 211 (**6**), 215 (**38**)
WEIGHT, 197, 354 (**4**), 514
WORD PROCESSING, 90 (**31**)
WORK, 179, 210, 218 (**18**), 366 (**70**), 386 (**24**), 535
  (**20**)

INDEX

Absolute value, 541, 542, 568
Acre, 502
Acute angle, 467, 474
Addends, 15
Addition
  associative law of, 21, 572
  basic facts, 15, 16, 544, 545
  on the calculator, 285
  carrying, 18
  checking, 21, 30, 31
  commutative law of, 20, 572
  of decimals, 244-246, 276, 277
  estimating sums, 30, 31
  of fractions, 176, 177, 187-191,
    194, 195, 276, 277
  horizontal display, 15
  of integers, 544-550
  of measurement numbers, 328
  of mixed numbers, 194, 195
  plus sign, 15
  of rational numbers, 568
  -subtraction rule, 599-601
  sum, 15, 16
  table, 16
  vertical display, 15
  of whole numbers, 15-22
  of zero, 17, 572
Additive check of subtraction, 40,
  41
Additive identity, 20, 572
Algebraic expression, 590
  and the distributive law, 572
  evaluation of, 599
  simplifying, 592-594
Algorithm, 75
Angles, 466-470
  acute, 467, 474
  alternate interior, 469
  central, 486
  classifying, 467
  complementary, 467
  congruent, 467
  corresponding, 469
  exterior, 469
  inscribed, 487
  interior, 469
  measuring, 467
  obtuse, 467, 474
  right, 467, 474
  straight, 467

  supplementary, 467
  vertical, 467
Applications
  of addition, 22, 80-82, 85, 178,
    191, 197, 244, 245, 546, 569
  of division, 83, 87, 148, 150,
    271, 272
  of fractions, 134, 157, 161-163,
    204, 205, 209, 210
  of geometry, 84, 85, 304, 623,
    624
  of mean (average) and median,
    445-449
  method for solving, 80-83
  of multiplication, 53, 62, 84, 85,
    142, 259, 260
  of percent, 368-376, 621, 622
  of ratio and proportion, 304-308
  of statistics, 424-428, 435-437
  of subtraction, 39, 83, 179, 197,
    247, 248
Approximately equal, 238
Arcs, 486
Area, 141, 493
  of a circle, 498, 499
  of a parallelogram, 495
  of a rectangle, 84, 141, 494
  special units, 502, 503
  of a square, 494
  of a trapezoid, 497
  of a triangle, 496
  units in the English system, 502
  units in the metric system, 503
Associative law
  of addition, 21, 572
  of multiplication, 59, 140, 572
Average, 445, 446

Bar graph, 426, 427
Base, 369
  of an exponential expression,
    100, 587
Binary operation, 20
Borrowing, 38-40, 196
Broken-line graph, 435, 436

Calculator, 285-291
  special functions on, 288-291
Carrying, 18
Celsius temperature, 345, 346

  converting, 346
Checking
  addition, 21, 30, 31
  division, 75, 76
  multiplication, 58, 61
  subtraction, 40, 41
Chords, 487
Circle, 485-489
  area of, 498, 499
  center of, 485
  circumference of, 485, 486
  diameter of, 485
  graph, 424, 425
  radius of, 485
  sector, 498
Circumference of a circle, 485,
  486
Class frequency, 437
Class interval, 437
Class midpoint, 438
Clearing parentheses, 593, 594
Clear key, 285
Coefficient, 591
Commission, 387-390
  rate, 387
Common multiple, 181
Commutative law
  of addition, 20, 572
  of multiplication, 57, 140, 572
Complementary angle, 467
Composite number, 97
  prime factorization of, 98, 101
Contradiction, 599, 613
Converting
  cubic units, 512, 513
  decimal notation to fractional
    notation, 228-230
  decimals to percent, 360
  English units, 318-323
  fractional notation to decimal
    notation, 230-234
  fractions to percent, 362
  to improper fractions, 155
  to like fractions, 187-191
  between the metric system and
    the English system, 341-346
  metric units, 334-338
  to mixed numbers, 153-155
  percent to decimals, 359
  percent to fractions, 358

square units, 500, 501
table for decimals and fractions, 228, 363
table for percent, 363
temperature units, 345, 346
units of measure, 318, 341
Counting numbers, 6
Cross products, 130
Cube, 510
  surface area of, 516, 517
  volume of, 510, 512
Cube of number, 100, 588
Cylinder, 521-524
  surface area of, 522, 523
  volume, 521, 522

Decimal
  adding, 244-246, 276, 277
  comparing, 279, 330
  converting, 228-234, 359, 360
  dividing, 265-272
  expanded notation, 224
  fractional form, 276
  multiplying, 255-260
  repeating, 232, 233
  rounding, 237-240
  subtracting, 246-248
  table for, 222, 228, 363
  terminating, 232, 233
  word names for, 222-225
Decimal fraction, 222, 228, 229
Decimal notation, 222-225
Decimal places, 238
Decimal point, 222
  in differences, 246
  estimating placement of, 240, 257, 269
  in products, 255-260
  in quotients, 230, 231, 270-272
  in sums, 244
Decrease, percent, 400-404, 621
Denominator, 122
Diameter of a circle, 485
Difference, 35
Digit, 7, 223
Discount, 389-390
  rate, 389
Display, 285
Distributive law, 59, 572, 591, 592, 612
  and factoring, 591, 592
Dividend, 66, 153
Dividing out (canceling) factors, 133-135

Divisibility, 97, 99-100
Division
  on the calculator, 286
  checking, 75,76
  of decimals, 230, 271, 265-272
  of fractions, 146-150, 156
  of integers, 562,
  of measurement numbers, 330
  of mixed numbers, 156
  of a number by itself, 69
  by one, 69
  of rational numbers, 570
  with remainders, 72, 75
  by repeated subtraction, 66, 70, 71
  symbols used, 66
  by trial and error, 75
  of whole numbers, 66-76
  by zero, 70
Divisor, 66, 95, 96
Double-negative, 549

Endpoints, 464
English system of measures, 318-323
  arithmetic of measurement numbers, 326-331
  changing units, 318-323, 500, 503
  converting to the metric system, 341-346
  cubic units, 510
  square units, 493
  table of household units, 321
  table of units of measure, 318, 321, 341
  unit fractions, 318
Equality and the number line, 540
Equation, 36, 598
  conditional, 599
  contradiction, 599
  equivalent, 599
  identity, 599
  linear, 599
  solution of, 599
  solving, 599-601, 609-614
  verbal statement into, 617, 618
Equivalent equations, 599
Eratosthenes, 97
Estimating, 28, 30
  products, 61, 240, 257
  quotients, 83, 269
  by rounding, 28, 61, 240
  sums, 28, 30-31

Euclid, 463
Evaluating with parentheses, 103
Even numbers, 99
Expanded notation, 8, 17, 18, 49
  for decimals, 224, 225
Exponent, 100, 587
Exponential notation, 100, 587

Factor tree, 98
Factoring, 98, 591
Factorization, prime, 97-99, 101, 182, 183
Factors, 46, 96, 97-100, 587, 588
  common, 592
Fahrenheit temperature, 345
  converting, 345, 346
Fermat, Pierre, 175
Fibonacci, Leonard, 5
Fractions, 120-125
  addition of, 176, 177, 187-191, 194, 195, 276
  building up, 130, 131
  comparing size of, 203, 204
  converting, 153-155, 188, 228-234, 358-359, 362, 363
  and decimals, 228-234
  denominator of, 122
  dividing out (canceling) factors, 133-135
  division of, 146-150, 156
  equivalent, 129, 130, 234
  improper, 124, 125, 233
  like, 176-179
  meaning of, 122-124
  multiplication of, 138-141, 155
  numerator of, 122
  powers of, 141
  proper, 123
  reciprocal, 146
  reducing, 131-133
  reduction to lowest terms, 132-133
  roots, 141, 142
  subtraction of, 177, 178, 187-191, 195, 196
  table for, , 228, 363
  types, summary, 125
  unlike, 176, 187-191
  for whole numbers, 124, 125
  for zero, 125
Frequency polygons, 438

Geometry, 463-530
  angles, 466-470

area, 141, 493
circles, 485-489
endpoints, 464
lines, 464, 465
parallelograms, 478
perimeter, 85, 475-476
point, 464
Pythagorean theorem, 572, 573
quadrilaterals, 478-480
rays, 464
rectangles, 478, 479
squares, 478, 479
transversal, 469
trapezoids, 480
triangles, 474-478, 572, 573
Golden ratio, 306
Golden rectangle, 306
Gram, 335
Graph
  bar, 426, 427
  broken-line, 435, 436
  circle, 424, 425
  histogram, 437, 438
  pictographs, 427, 428
Greater than, 7, 540, 568
Grouping symbols, 102, 103, 612, 613

Half, 222
Hectare, 503
Histogram, 437, 438
Hypotenuse, 572

Identity
  additive, 20, 572
  multiplicative, 58, 140, 572
Identity equation, 599, 613
Improper fraction, 124, 125
  converting, 153, 154, 194, 195
Income tax, 383
Increase, percent, 400-404
Inequality symbols, 7
Integers, 540
  absolute value of, 541, 542
  addition of, 545-550
  division of, 562
  multiplication of, 560-561
  subtraction of, 554-557
Interest, 393-397
  compound, 396-397
  rate of, 393
  simple, 393-394
Irrational numbers, 571, 572

Keyboard, 285
Kronecker, Leopold, 121

Least common denominator, 187
Least common multiple, 181-185
  of denominators, 185
  listing method, 182
  prime factorization, 182, 183
  special algorithm, 184-185
Legs, of triangle, 572
Less than, 7, 540, 568
Like terms, 592, 593, 610
Linear equations, 599
Lines, 464, 465
  coinciding, 465
  intersecting, 465
  parallel, 465, 469
  perpendicular, 468
Liter, 334
Loan payments, 393, 394

Major arc, 486
Markdown, 409-413
Markup, 409-413
Mean (average), 445, 446
Median, 446
Meter, 334
Metric system of measures, 334-338
  converting, 336-338, 501, 503, 513
  to the English system, 341-346
  prefixes, 335
  table of units of measure, 335, 336, 341
  units of area, 503
Minor arc, 486
Minuend, 35
Minus sign, 35, 540
Mixed number, 153-157, 194-197
  operations with, 155-157, 194-197
Mode, 449, 450
Multiples, 48-49, 60, 96, 181
Multiplicand, 46
Multiplication
  associative law of, 59, 140, 572
  on the calculator, 286
  checking, 58, 61
  commutative law of, 57, 140, 572
  of decimals, 255-260, 276
  distributive law of, 59, 591, 592
  -division rule, 604

estimating products, 61
factors, 46, 96, 587, 588
  of fractions, 138-141, 155
  horizontal display, 47
  of integers, 560-561
  of measurement numbers, 329, 330
  of mixed numbers, 155, 156
  by multiples of 10, 100, and 1000, 60, 61, 257
  by one, 58, 140
  product, 46
  of rational numbers, 569, 570
  reverse-order check, 58
  symbols used, 46, 47
  table, 48
  vertical display, 47
  of whole numbers, 46-53
  by zero, 58
Multiplicative identity, 58, 140, 572
Multiplier, 46

Natural number, 6
Negative, 540, 572
Negative integers, 540
Nonnegative integers, 540
Number keys, 285
Number line, 6-7, 540-542
  and addition, 15-17, 545, 546
  and equality, 540
  and negative numbers, 540
  and rounding, 28
  and subtraction, 36
Numbers
  composite, 97
  counting, 6
  even, 99
  irrational, 571, 572
  mixed, 153-157
  natural, 6, 586
  odd, 99
  prime, 96, 182
  rational, 567-570
  real, 571-572
  rounded, 28
  whole, 5, 6
Numerals, 6
Numerator, 122
Numerical data, 424

Obtuse angle, 467, 474
Odd numbers, 99
Operation keys, 285

Order
  of decimals, 276
  of rational numbers, 568
  of whole numbers, 6, 7
Order of operations, 102, 201-
    205, 276

Parallelogram, 478
  area of, 495
  perimeter of, 478
Pascal, Blaise, 285
Percent, 358
  converting, 358-363
  decrease, 400-404, 621
  equation, basic, 368, 369, 380
  increase, 400-404, 621
  markdown, 409-413
  markup, 409-413
  problems, 368-376
  symbol, 358
  table for, 363
Perfect square, 101
Perimeter, 85, 475-476
  of a parallelogram, 478
  of a rectangle, 85, 478, 479
  of a square, 479
  of a trapezoid, 480
  of a triangle, 475
Perpendicular lines, 468
pi, 486, 571, 572
Pictographs, 427, 428
Place-holder, 8, 73
Place-value system, 7, 8, 222, 223
Plane, 465
Plus sign, 15
Point, 464
Positive integers, 540
Powers, 100, 141, 288, 587
Prime number, 96, 182
Principal, 393
Product, 46
Proper fractions, 123
Proportion, 306
  percent, 372, 373
  solving, 306, 307
Pythagoras, 572
Pythagorean theorem, 572, 573

Quadrilaterals, 478-480
Quotient, 66, 153

Radical, 102
Radius of a circle, 485
Rate, 313

Ratio, 304-305
Rational numbers, 567-570
  absolute value of, 568
  addition of, 568
  associative law, 572
  commutative law, 572
  distributive law, 572
  division of, 570
  identity for addition, 572
  identity for multiplication, 572
  multiplication of, 569
  negative, 572
  order of, 567
  reciprocal, 572
  subtraction of, 568
Ray, 464
Real numbers, 571-572
Reciprocal, 146, 572
Rectangle, 478, 479
  area of, 84, 494
  perimeter of, 85, 479
Rectangular solid, 511
  surface area, 514-516
  volume of, 511
Register, 285
Related addition equation, 36, 37,
    600
Related division equation, 67, 149
Related multiplication equation,
    67
Related subtraction equation, 36,
    600
Remainder, 72, 75, 153
Repeating decimal, 232, 233
Reverse-order check
  of addition, 21
  of multiplication, 58
Right angle, 467, 474
Rounding, 28-34
  and addition, 31
  decimals, 237-240

Sales tax, 380-384
  rate, 380-384
Secant, 488
Segments, 464
Semicircles, 488
Similar (like) terms, 591
Social Security tax, 382
Solving equations, 599-601
  addition-subtraction rule, 599,
    600
  multiplication-division rule, 604,
    605

summary of rules, 613
  with parentheses, 612, 613
Solving word problems, 618, 619
  age, 619
  ATTACK strategy, 620
  average, 620
  geometry, 623
  techniques, 617-621
Speed, 313, 343
Sphere, 523, 524
  surface area of, 524
  volume of, 523
Square, 478, 479
  area of, 493
  perimeter of, 479
Square of number, 100, 288
Square root, 101, 289
  table of, 102
Standard notation, 8, 9
Statistics, 424
  using ratio in, 424, 425
Straight angle, 467
Subtraction
  basic facts, 35-36, 554, 555
  on the calculator, 286
  checking, 40, 41
  of decimals, 246-248
  difference, 35
  of fractions, 177, 178, 187-191,
    195, 196
  horizontal display, 35
  of integers, 554-557
  of measurement numbers, 328
  of mixed numbers, 195, 196
  of rational numbers, 568
  symbols used, 35
  take-away method, 35
  vertical display, 35
  of whole numbers, 35-41
Subtrahend, 35
Sum, 15
Supplementary angles, 467
Surface area, 514-517
  of a cube, 516, 517
  of a cylinder, 522, 523
  of a rectangular solid, 514-516
  of a sphere, 525
Symbols
  addition, 15
  approximately equal to, 238
  division, 66
  greater than, 7
  grouping, 102, 103
  of inequality, 7

less than, 7
minus, 35
multiplication, 46, 47
percent, 358
pi, 486
plus, 15
radical, 102
repeating digits bar, 232, 270
subtraction, 35
translating words into, 586, 587

Tables
  addition, 16
  decimals and fractions, 228, 363
  of household units, 321
  multiplication, 48
  percent, 363
  units of measure in the English
    system, 318, 321, 341
  units of measure in the metric
    system, 335, 336, 341
Take-away method, 35
Tangent, 488
Tax
  income, 383
  sales, 380-384
    rate, 380-384
  Social Security, 382
Temperature, 345, 346
Terminating decimals, 232, 233
Terms, 591
Times sign, 46, 47
Total value (price), 84, 381
Transversal, 469
Trapezoid, 480
  area, 497
Triangle, 474-478, 572
  area, 496
  classifying, 474, 475
  congruent, 476, 477
  similar, 477, 478

Unit fraction, 318, 319
Unit price, 87, 279, 314
Unit rate, 313
Units of measure, 318-323, 334-
    338, 341
  compound, 322, 323
  converting, 500-503
  square, 493
  table, 318, 321, 335, 336, 341

Variable, 6, 586, 587
Vertex, 466

Vertical angles, 467
Volume, 593-597
  of a cube, 510
  of a cylinder, 521, 522
  of a rectangular solid, 511
  of a sphere, 524
  units, 510
    converting, 512, 513

Whole numbers, 5, 6
  addition of, 15-22
  division of, 66-76
  fractions, 124, 125
  multiplication of, 46-53
  order of, 6, 7
  quotients of two, 562
  subtraction of, 35-41
  word names for, 9-11
Word names
  for decimals, 222-225
  for whole numbers, 9-11
Word problems. *See* Application.

Zero
  in addition, 20, 572
  in division, 70
  in multiplication, 58
  as place-holder, 8, 73
  properties, 572
  in subtraction, 38, 40